BASIC GRAPHICS

WARREN J. LUZADDER PROFESSOR OF ENGINEERING GRAPHICS, PURDUE UNIVERSITY

PRENTICE-HALL, INC. ENGLEWOOD CLIFFS, NEW JERSEY

M	T	W	Th.	F	S
{ M	151 CE	M	~~CE~~	M	
9 141 Mech	153 CE	Mech	~~Mech~~	Mech	
10	Phys		Phys		Phys
11					
12					
1	151 CE	Cal	M		
2					
3					
4					

BASIC GRAPHICS FOR ENGINEERS AND TECHNICAL STUDENTS

Second printing......September, 1962

OTHER BOOKS BY THE AUTHOR:

Fundamentals of Engineering Drawing, 4th ed, Prentice-Hall, 1959.
Graphics for Engineers, Prentice-Hall, 1957.
Technical Drafting Essentials, 2nd ed., Prentice-Hall, 1956.
Problems in Engineering Drawing, 4th ed., Prentice-Hall, 1959.
Problems for Engineering Graphics, Prentice-Hall, 1958.
Problems in Drafting Fundamentals, Prentice-Hall, 1956.
Purdue University Engineering Drawing Films, with J. Rising, *et al.*

PREFACE

BASIC GRAPHICS is intended to fulfill the present day needs of engineering and technical education —the education of a new era in which decisive changes in curriculums have been forced upon us by the phenomenal advances that have been made in scientific knowledge since the early years of World War II. In this new era, engineers now find themselves working closely with theoretical scientists for the purpose of bringing to the people of the world the benefits of new scientific discoveries. As a person oriented strongly towards the sciences, the efforts of the professional engineer are now largely directed towards research and to the creation and development of new devices and structures for which there is a need.

All around the world industrial competition has been keen and will continue to be so as countries and industrial organizations within their borders strive for economic supremacy. Under these conditions, the survival of an industrial organization often depends upon technological improvement in products and production methods. Realizing this fact, administrators are depending upon their engineers to use their creative ability and scientific knowledge to the utmost to develop new ideas for useful mechanisms and to improve existing ones. This new role, which has been assigned to the engineer, has made it necessary that, as a group, engineers be relieved of much of the design and routine testing and development work that they have done in the past. These tasks, as they have been relinquished, have been taken on by the other members of the engineering team—the engineering technician and engineering technologist who work under the direct supervision of an engineer or an engineering administrator.

The Report on Evaluation of Engineering Education prepared by the Committee on Evaluation of Engineering Education of the ASEE in 1955 states, concerning engineering graphics:

Graphical expression is both a form of communication and a means for analysis and synthesis. The extent to which it is successful for these purposes is a measure of its professional usefulness. Its value as a skill alone does not justify its inclusion in a curriculum. The emphasis should be on spatial visualization, experience in creative thinking, and the ability to convey ideas, especially by freehand sketching, which is the normal mode of expression in the initial stages of creative work. Though the engineer may only supervise the preparation of the drawings required to execute his designs, he can hardly be expected to do this effectively unless he himself is thoroughly familiar with graphical communication.

In our more progressive schools of engineering, the art of making engineering drawings has been almost ignored in graphics courses for some time and increased attention has been given to developing the ability to visualize spatial conditions, to solve problems by graphical methods, and to use graphical forms of representation, prepared by freehand sketching, as a means of communication. Of particular importance to teachers of courses in engineering graphics is the fact that the engineering profession is now more aware of the importance of both freehand pictorial sketching and the usefulness of graphics in solving problems that arise in engineering. It is for this reason that full coverage has been given to the methods and aids that can be used for preparing satisfactory pictorial representations. Some of these aids can be abandoned as the sketcher becomes proficient, for it must be remembered that sketching must be done rapidly in creative work, when a first sketch is apt to be followed quickly by others as ideas are conceived and either developed or discarded. The written material and related illustrations for vector geometry, graphical calculus, empirical equations, and alignment charts should prove to be within the comprehension of those students who have had a high school physics course. Problems that would require an understanding of one or more of the engineering sciences have been avoided in general.

The various chapters covering multiview drawing (orthographic projection) will be found to cover fully all of the fundamentals of projection. With a full knowledge of these basic principles, the student should be able to understand completely the graphical methods of representing shapes and to solve problems by using projection. Descriptive geometry is presented along with multiview projection, of which it is logically a part. The material as presented will satisfy the needs of most design engineers and technologists. Aeronautical engineers and others who plan to enter specialized fields of design should expect to take a formal course in descriptive geometry.

The coverage given to screw threads and fasteners, the practices of dimensioning, and working (shop) drawings is intended to be complete enough to meet the needs of the draftsman and designer while serving as a source of general information for the engineer. An instructor should find that sufficient material has been provided for two semesters of communication drawing and one semester of graphical calculations and descriptive geometry. The subject matter has been selected and presented so as to permit the instructor wide latitude in the preparation of graphics courses for engineering and technical students. To offer some experience in creative thinking, a few problems of a new type are given at the end of the chapter covering pictorial sketching. Additional problems may be created by requiring the redesign of some existing part of a mechanism as given in the problem sections of other chapters of the text.

Since the justification for new editions of texts has at times been questioned by many sincere persons, the principal reasons for the preparation of this revised edition are listed here; they are:
   1) to bring existing material up-to-date, 2) to improve both written and graphic presentations that have not met expectations, and 3) to add new material for which a need has been shown.

The extensive use of the first edition has permitted a thorough check of all of the instructional material and most of the problems by teachers at many institutions. The varied suggestions of these teachers, when listed, provided a skeleton outline for this revision. Some of the comments have strengthened the author's belief in the original aim which was to create a nearly self-teaching book with written presentations and illustrations so clear and easily understood that the student would enjoy, at least to some extent, what he cannot avoid, that is, the reading and studying of text material.

In general, this edition may be thought of as being divided into three divisions, namely: 1) communication drawing, 2) descriptive geometry, and 3) graphical calculation. Even though an engineer may be interested mainly in those phases of the graphic science that enable him to solve graphically many of the problems that arise in research and development, he must also have a working knowledge of the communication drawing if he is to be able to detect errors and omissions on drawings and decide whether or not the design of a mechanism or structure as shown and the procedures specified are the best and most economical. Legally and ethically the engineer usually must assume full responsibility for the final mechanism or structure that he has conceived. In assuming such responsibility the experienced person realizes that full and complete communication without error is as important in engineering as in law and medicine.

This edition has been revised extensively and two new chapters have been added—GRAPHICAL ARITHMETIC AND ALGEBRA and EMPIRICAL EQUATIONS. The chapters of the former edition on MULTIVIEW DRAWING and CONVENTIONAL PRACTICES have been rewritten and combined for more effective use. The chapter on DESCRIPTIVE GEOMETRY has been expanded so as to present sufficient material for use over a full semester and a considerable amount of new material has· been added to the chapters on ENGINEERING GEOMETRY and GRAPHICAL CALCULUS. In addition, the expansion of material covering alignment charts made desirable the creation of a new chapter—NOMOGRAPHY. For over-all improvement, new illustrations and problems have been added to almost every chapter and it is thought that the new shaded pictorial drawings that have been added to line drawing illustrations will lead to clearer understanding of the written material by the student and at the same time assist the instructor in making needed explanations.

The author is particularly grateful to Professor Clarence J. Rogers for his many valuable suggestions and for volunteering to read the manuscript and check the new problems. Also, acknowledgement must be made here for the assistance of Professor M. H. Bolds in preparing some of the layouts and to Mr. Joseph deMartino for securing several of the drawings from industry that have been used in the text.

Finally, it is fitting for the author to call attention to his continued indebtedness to Professors R. C. Carpenter, J. H. Porsch, and C. J. Rogers, all of Purdue University, for their advice and assistance in the past. Not to be forgotten are Professor F. J. Burns of the Newark College of Engineering, and Major R. H. Hammond of the United States Military Academy, for their helpful criticisms and sound suggestions so unselfishly given while the first edition was in preparation.   W. J. L.

CONTENTS

1

INTRODUCTION

An engineer of professional caliber must be dedicated to creating structures and products for the benefit of his fellow men. This requires that he bring together knowledge of the arts of production and an understanding of the sciences, and that he add his own original thinking. For most improvements in the design and operation of machines and structures are produced by imaginations sparked with desire to change and improve existing ways of producing something for which there is a need. The imagination, freely exercised, can ultimately create entirely new products.

The rapid advance of scientific knowledge and the shortage of professionally trained men has brought about changes in the place and the work expected of the engineer in an industrial organization. He has become a decidedly more creative person, who must be able to visualize and strengthen the space relationship and movement of dim images of ideas.

Since an engineer may frequently have to prepare preliminary design drawings and to direct the making of the working (shop) drawings which follow, he should have a complete understanding of the principles of orthographic projection and a knowledge of conventional practices and dimensioning. Without this knowledge he is in no position to assume the professional responsibilities that may be placed upon him by his superiors and by the laws of his state.

For a full and complete exchange of ideas with others, the engineer must be proficient in the three means of communication that are at his disposal: (1) English; both written and oral, (2) symbols; as used in the basic sciences, and (3) engineering graphics.

In past years emphasis has been placed upon the communication forms of graphics, such as working drawings for the fabrication and erection of structures and graphical representations for conveying semitechnical information to associates. The engineers of today and of the future must all be given more training in the art of sketching so they will be fully capable of "thinking with a pencil."

At first, ideas may be presented with sketches in either orthographic or pictorial form. Orthographic and pictorial sketches follow one after another as problems are encountered and possible solutions are considered. Sketch-making continues into the preliminary design stages, for the engineer usually must serve as both planner and director. In so doing, he uses sketches to exchange ideas around the conference table and to present instructions to others. One need not have an artist's training to produce satisfactory engineering sketches, for the technical sketcher need only be able to draw fairly straight lines and judge proportions reasonably well.

Proficiency in applying the principles of orthographic projection leads to easy graphical methods of solving space problems such as the determination of the clearance distance between members of a structure, the distance from a point to a plane, or the true angle between plane surfaces.

Since there are many problems arising in engineering design where a graphical method for solution is faster and much less laborious than its mathematical counterpart, engineering students as well as professional men should have some knowledge of both vector geometry and graphical calculus. Noncoplanar or three-dimensional force problems are solved by applying the principles of orthographic drawing. Graphical integration and differentiation are particularly desirable for problems where only empirical data are available or where values are shown by mechanically produced curves.

A study of engineering graphics offers an insight into the engineer's methods of attacking his problems. Its lessons teach the importance of accuracy, exactness, and positiveness both in representation and in the solution of problems. Finally, it tends to develop ability to visualize space conditions as they arise in the creation of nonexisting structures and to analyze situations and recognize relationships when solving problems.

2

FREEHAND TECHNICAL LETTERING

2.1. Introduction. To impart to the men in the shops all the necessary information for the complete construction of a machine or structure, the shape description, which is conveyed graphically by the views, must be accompanied by size descriptions and instructive specifications in the form of figured dimensions and notes (Fig. 2.1).

All dimensions and notes should be lettered freehand in a plain, legible style that can be rapidly executed. Poor lettering detracts from the appearance of a drawing, and often impairs its usefulness, regardless of the quality of the line work.

2.2. Single-stroke letters (Reinhardt). Single-stroke letters are now used universally for technical drawings. This style is suitable for most purposes because it possesses the qualifications necessary for legibility and speed. On commercial drawings it appears in slightly modified forms, however, as each person finally develops a style that reflects his own individuality.

The expression "single-stroke" means that the width of the straight and curved lines that form the letters are the same width as the stroke of the pen or pencil.

2.3. The general proportions of letters. Although there is no fixed standard for the proportions of the letters, certain definite rules in their design must be observed if one wishes to have his lettering appear neat and pleasing. The recognized characteristics of each letter should be carefully studied, and then thoroughly learned through practice.

It is advisable for the beginner, instead of relying on his untrained eye for proportions, to follow the fixed proportions given

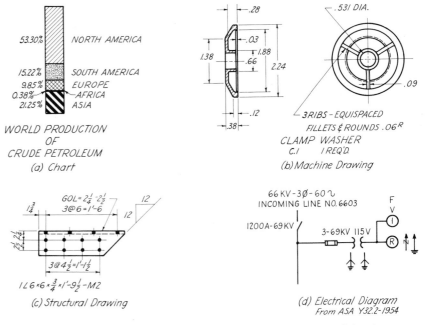

Fig. 2.1. Technical drawings.

in this chapter. Otherwise, his lettering most likely will be displeasing to the trained eye of the professional man. Later, after he has thoroughly mastered the art of lettering, his individuality will be revealed naturally by slight variations in the shapes and proportions of some of the letters.

It is often desirable to increase or decrease the width of letters in order to make a word or group of words fill a certain space. Letters narrower than normal letters of the same height are called *compressed letters;* those that are wider are called *extended letters* (Fig. 2.2).

2.4. Lettering pencils and pens. Pencil lettering is usually done with a medium-soft pencil. Since the degree of hardness of the lead required to produce a dark opaque line will vary with the type of paper used, a pencil should be selected only after drawing a few trial lines. In order to obtain satisfactory lines, the pencil should be sharpened to a long conical point and then rounded slightly on a piece of scratch paper. To keep the point symmetrical while lettering, the pencil should be rotated a partial revolution before each new letter is started.

The choice of a type of pen point for lettering depends largely upon the personal preference and characteristics of the individual. The beginner can learn only from experience which of the many types available are best suited to him.

A pen that makes a heavy stroke should be used for bold letters in titles and so forth, while a light-stroke pen is required for the lighter letters in figures and notes.

A very flexible point never should be used for lettering. Such a point is apt to shade the downward stem strokes as well as the downward portions of curved strokes. A good point has enough resistance to normal pressure to permit the drawing of curved and stem strokes of uniform width.

Four of the many special pens designed for single-stroke letters are illustrated in Fig. 2.3. The *Barch-Payzant* pen (*a*) is available

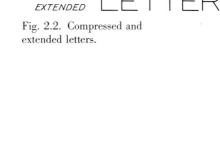

Fig. 2.2. Compressed and extended letters.

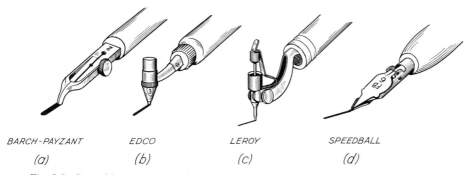

BARCH-PAYZANT　　EDCO　　LEROY　　SPEEDBALL

(*a*)　　(*b*)　　(*c*)　　(*d*)

Fig. 2.3. Special lettering pens.

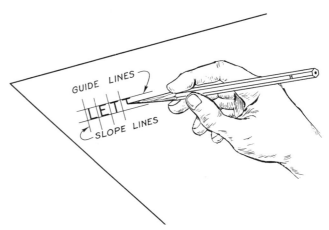

Fig. 2.4. Guide lines and slope lines.

in graded sizes from No. 000 (very coarse) to No. 8 (very fine). The very fine size is suitable for lettering ⅛ in. to 3/16 in. high on technical drawings. The *Edco* (*b*) has a patented holder into which any one of a graded set of lettering nibs (ranging in sizes from No. 0 to No. 6) may be screwed. The tubular construction of the point makes it possible to draw uniform lines regardless of the direction of the stroke. Also of tubular construction is the *Leroy* (*c*). The *Speedball* (*d*) may be obtained in many graded sizes.

2.5. Devices for drawing guide lines and slope lines. Devices for drawing guide lines (Fig. 2.4) are available in a variety of forms. The two most popular are the *Braddock lettering triangle* (Fig. 2.5), and the *Ames lettering instrument* (Fig. 2.6).

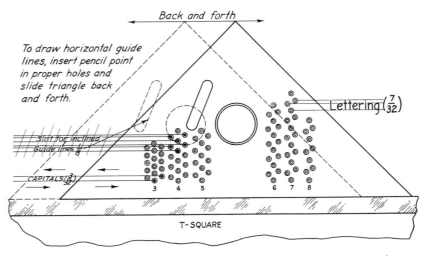

Fig. 2.5. Braddock lettering triangle.

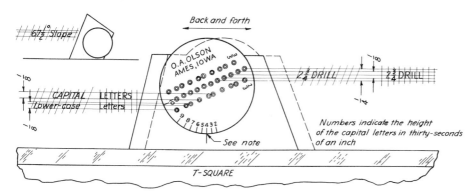

Fig. 2.6. Ames lettering instrument.

The Braddock lettering triangle is provided with sets of grouped countersunk holes that may be used to draw guide lines by inserting a sharp-pointed pencil (4H or 6H) into the holes and sliding the triangle back and forth along the guiding edge of a T-square or a triangle supported by a T-square. The holes are grouped to give guide lines for capitals and lower-case letters. The numbers below each set indicate the height of the capitals in thirty-seconds of an inch. For example, the No. 3 set is for capitals $\frac{3}{32}$ in. high, the No. 4 set is for capitals $\frac{1}{8}$ in. high, the No. 5 is for capitals $\frac{5}{32}$ in. high, and so on.

2.6. Uniformity in lettering. Uniformity in height, inclination, spacing, and strength of line is essential for good lettering (Fig. 2.7). Professional appearance depends as much upon uniformity as upon the correctness of the proportion and shape of the individual letters. Uniformity in height and inclination is assured by the use of guide lines and slope lines; uniformity in weight and color, by the skillful use of the pencil and proper control of the pressure of its point on the paper. The ability to space letters correctly becomes easy after continued thoughtful practice.

2.7. Composition. In combining letters into words, the spaces for the various combinations of letters are arranged so that the areas appear to be equal (Fig. 2.8). For standard lettering, this area should be about equal to one-half the area of the letter M. If the adjacent sides be stems, this area is obtained by making the distance

UNIFORMITY IN HEIGHT, INCLINATION, AND STRENGTH OF LINE IS ESSENTIAL FOR GOOD LETTERING.

Fig. 2.7. Uniformity in lettering.

Fig. 2.8. Letter areas.

between the letters slightly greater than one-half the height of a letter, and a smaller amount depending on the contours, for other combinations. Examples of good and poor composition are shown in Fig. 2.8.

The space between words should be equal to or greater than the height of a letter, but not more than twice the height. The space between sentences should be somewhat greater. The distance between lines of lettering may vary from one-half the height of the capitals to 1½ times their height.

2.8. Stability. If the areas of the upper and lower portions of certain letters are made equal, an optical illusion will cause them to appear to be unstable and top heavy. To overcome this effect, the upper portions of the letters B, E, F, H, K, S, X, and Z and the figures 2, 3, and 8 must be reduced slightly in size.

An associated form of illusion is the phenomenon that a horizontal line drawn across a rectangle at the vertical center will appear to be below the center. Since the letters B, E, F, and H are particularly subject to this illusion, their central horizontal strokes must be drawn slightly above the vertical center in order to give them a more balanced and pleasing appearance.

The letters K, S, X, Z and the figures 2, 3, and 8 are stabilized by making the width of the upper portion less than the width of the lower portion.

2.9. The technique of freehand lettering. Any prospective engineer can learn to letter if he practices intelligently and is persistent in his desire to improve. The necessary muscular control, which must accompany the knowledge of lettering, can be developed only through constant repetition.

Pencil letters should be formed with strokes that are dark and sharp; never with strokes that are gray and indistinct. Beginners should avoid the tendency to form letters by sketching, as strokes made in this manner vary in color and width.

When lettering with ink, the results obtained depend largely upon the manner in which the pen is used. Many beginners complain that the execution of good freehand lettering is impossible with an ordinary pen point although their own incorrect habits may have resulted in the inability to make strokes of uniform width. This lack of uniformity may be due to one of four causes: (1) excessive pressure on the pen point; (2) an accumulation of lint, dirt, or dried ink on the point; (3) tilting the point while forming a stroke; or (4) fresh ink on the point. The latter cause requires some explanation, since very few persons know the proper method of "inking" the pen. The pen should be wiped thoroughly clean, and the ink should be deposited on the under side over the slot, well above the point. When the pen is filled in this manner, the ink feeds down the slit in an even flow, making possible the drawing of uniform curved and straight lines. If ink is placed on the point or allowed to run to the point, an excessive amount of ink will be deposited on the first letters made, and the width of the strokes will be somewhat wider than the strokes of, say, the sixth or seventh letter (Fig. 2.9).

When lettering, the pen is held as shown in Fig. 2.10. It should rest so loosely between the fingers that it can be slid up and down with the other hand.

The thin film of oil on a new point must be removed by wiping before the point is used.

INK ON POINT
Fig. 2.9

Fig. 2.10. Holding the pen.

2.10. Inclined and vertical capital letters. The letters shown in Figs. 2.11 and 2.12 have been arranged in related groups. In laying out the characters, the number of widths has been reduced to the smallest number consistent with good appearance; similarities of shape have been emphasized and minute differences have been eliminated. Each letter is drawn to a large size on a cross-section grid that is two units wider, to facilitate the study of its characteristic shape and proportions. Arrows with numbers indicate the order and direction of the strokes. The curves of the inclined capital letters are portions of ellipses while the curves of the vertical letters are parts of circles.

The I, T, L, E, and F. The letter I is the basic or stem stroke. The horizontal stroke of the T is drawn first, and the stem starts at the exact center of the bar. The L is 5 units wide, but it is often desirable to reduce this width when an L is used in combination with such letters as A and T. It should be observed that the letter L consists of the first two strokes of the E. The middle bar of the E is 3½ units long and is placed slightly above the center for stability. The top bar is one-half unit shorter than the bottom bar. The letter F is the E with the bottom bar omitted.

The H and N. Stroke 3 of the H should be slightly above the center, for stability. The outside parallel strokes of the N are drawn first to permit an accurate estimate of its width. The inclined stroke should intersect these accurately at their extremities.

The Z and X. The top of the Z should be one unit narrower

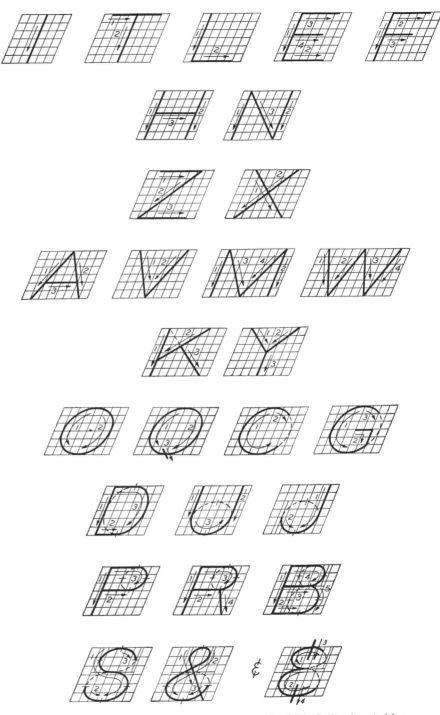

Fig. 2.11. Inclined capital letters.

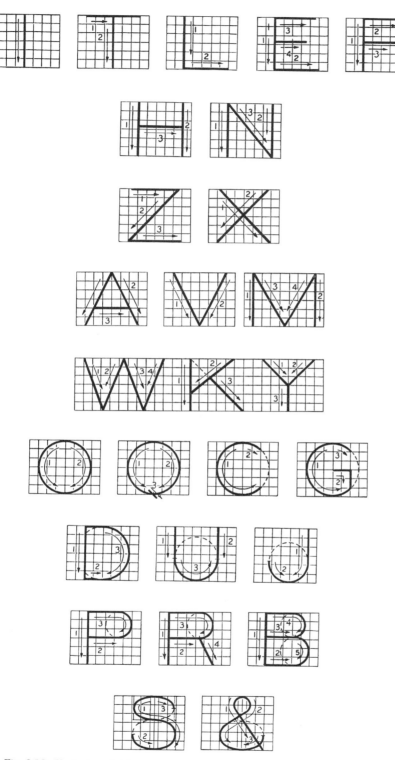

Fig. 2.12. Vertical capital letters.

than the bottom, for stability. In the smaller sizes, this letter may be formed without lifting the pen. The X is similar to the Z in that the top is made one unit narrower than the bottom. The inclined strokes cross slightly above center.

The A, V, M, and W. The horizontal bar of the A is located up from the bottom a distance equal to one-third of the height of the letter. The V is the letter A inverted without the crossbar, and is the same width. The letters M and W are the widest letters of the alphabet. The outside strokes of the M are drawn first, so that its width may be judged accurately. The inside strokes of this letter meet at the center of the base. The W is formed by two modified V's. Alternate strokes are parallel.

The K and Y. The top of the letter K should be made one unit narrower than the bottom, for stability. Stroke 2 intersects the stem one-third up from the bottom. Stroke 3 is approximately perpendicular to stroke 2, and, if extended, would touch the stem at the top. The strokes of the Y meet at the center of the enclosing parallelogram or square.

The O, Q, C, and G. Stroke 1 of the letter O starts just to the right of the top and continues to the left around the side to a point beyond the bottom. Thus stroke 1 forms more than half of the ellipse or circle. The Q is the letter O with the added kern, which is a straight line located near the bottom tangent point. The C is based on the O, but since it is not a complete ellipse or circle, it is narrower than either the O or Q. The top extends one unit down and the bottom one unit up on the right side. G is similar to C. The horizontal portion of stroke 2 starts at the center.

The D, U, and J. The first two strokes of the D form an incomplete letter L. Stroke 3 starts as a horizontal line. The bottom third of the U is one-half of an ellipse or circle. J is similar to the letter U.

The P, R, and B. The middle horizontal bar of the P is located at the center of stroke 1. The curved portion of stroke 3 is one-half of a perfect ellipse or circle. The R is constructed similarly to the P. The tail joins at the point of tangency of the curve and middle bar. To stabilize the letter B, the top is made one-half unit narrower than the bottom and the middle bar is placed slightly above the center. The curves are halves of ellipses or circles.

The S and &. The upper and lower portions of the S are perfect ellipses with one-quarter removed. The top ellipse should be made one-half unit narrower than the lower one, for stability. In the smaller sizes this letter may be made with one or two strokes, depending upon its size. The true ampersand is made with three strokes. Professional men, however, usually represent an ampersand with a character formed by using portions of the upper and lower ellipses of the numeral 8 with the addition of two short bars.

Although many favor the inclined letters, recent surveys indicate that vertical letters are used more generally.

2.11. Inclined and vertical numerals. The numerals shown in Figs. 2.13 and 2.14 have been arranged in related groups in accordance with the common characteristics that can be recognized in their construction.

The 1, 7, and 4. The stem stroke of the 4 is located one unit in from the right side. The bar is 1½ units above the base. The stem of the 7 terminates at the center of the base.

The 0, 6, and 9. The cipher, which is one unit narrower than the letter O, is the basic form for this group. In the figure 6, the right side of the large ellipse ends one unit down from the top, and the left side ends at the center of the base. The small loop is slightly more than three-fourths of an ellipse. The 9 is the 6 inverted.

The 8, 3, and 2. Each of these figures is related to the letter S, and the same rule of stability should be observed in their construction. The top portion of the figure 8 is shorter and one-half unit narrower than the lower portion. Each loop is a perfect ellipse. The figure 3 is the 8 with the lower left quarter of the upper loop and the upper left quarter of the lower loop omitted. The 2 is simply three-quarters of the upper loop of the 8 and the upper left quarter of the lower loop of the 8 with straight lines added.

The 5. This figure is a modification of the related groups previously described. The top is one-half unit narrower than the bottom,

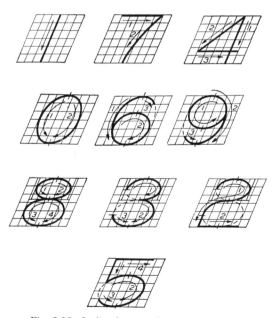

Fig. 2.13. Inclined numerals.

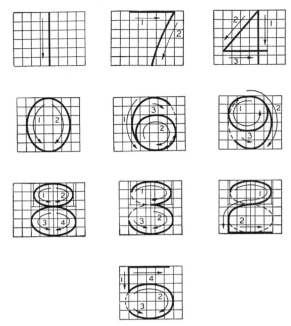

Fig. 2.14. Vertical numerals.

for stability. The curve is a segment of a perfect ellipse, ending one unit up from the bottom.

2.12. Single-stroke lower-case letters. Single-stroke lower-case letters, either vertical or inclined, are commonly used on map drawings, topographic drawings, structural drawings, and in survey field books. They are particularly suitable for long notes and statements because, first, they can be executed much faster than capitals and, second, words and statements formed with them can be read more easily.

The construction of inclined lower-case letters is based upon the straight line and the ellipse (Fig. 2.15). This basic principle of forming letters is followed more closely for lower-case letters than for capitals. The body portions are two-thirds the height of the related capitals. As shown in Fig. 2.16, ascenders extend to the cap line, and descenders descend to the drop line. For lower-case letters based on a capital letter six units high, the waistline is two units down from the top and the drop line two units below the base line.

The order of stroke, direction of stroke, and formation of the letters follow the same principles as for the capitals. The letters are presented in family groups having related characteristics, to enable the beginner to understand their construction. The vertical lower-case letters, illustrated in Fig. 2.17, are constructed in the same manner as inclined letters.

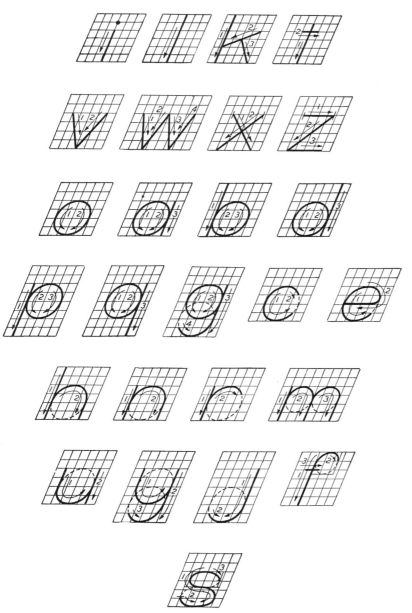

Fig. 2.15. Inclined lower-case letters.

The i, l, k, and t. All letters of this group are formed by straight lines of standard slope. The i is drawn four units high, and the dot is placed halfway between the waistline and cap line. Stroke 2 of the k starts at the waistline and intersects stroke 1 two units above the base. Stroke 3, extended, should intersect stroke 1 at the top. The t is five units high, and the crossbar is on the waistline.

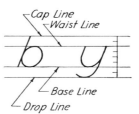

Fig. 2.16

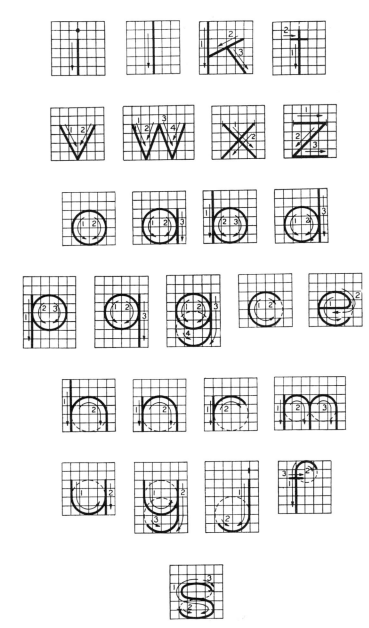

Fig. 2.17. Vertical lower-case letters.

The v, w, x, and z. All of these letters are similar to the capitals. Alternate strokes of the w are parallel. The width of the top of both the x and the z is made one-half unit less than the width across the bottom, for stability.

The o, a, b, d, p, and q. The bodies of the letters in this group are formed by the letter o, and they differ only in the position and length of the stem stroke. The o is made with two strokes, and the first stroke should form more than half of the character.

The g. The g is related to the letters o and y. Stroke 3 starts at the waistline and ends slightly beyond the point of tangency of the curve with the drop line.

The c and e. The c is a modified letter o. It is not a complete form, and therefore, its width is less than its height. Stroke 1 ends one unit up on the right side, stroke 2 one unit down. The e is similarly constructed, except for the fact that stroke 2 continues as a curve and finishes as a horizontal line that terminates at the middle of the back.

The h, n, r, and m. The curve of the h is the upper portion of the letter o. Stroke 2 starts two units above the bottom of the stem and finishes parallel to stroke 1. The n differs from the h in that the stem stroke extends only from the waistline to the base line. The r is a portion of the letter n, stroke 2 ending one unit down from the top. The m consists of two modified letter n's. The straight portions of strokes 2 and 3 are parallel to stroke 1.

The u and y. The letter u is an inverted n, and the curve is a portion of the letter o. It should be noted that stroke 2 extends to the base line. The y is a partial combination of the letters u and g.

The j and f. The portion of the j above the base line is the letter i. The curve is the same as that which forms the tail of the g. The curved portion of the f is 2½ units wide, stroke 1 starting slightly to the right of the point of tangency with the cap line.

The s. The lower-case s is almost identical to the capital S.

2.13. Fractions. The height of the figures in the numerator and denominator is equal to three-fourths the height of the whole number, and the total height of the fraction is twice the height of the whole number. The division bar should be horizontal and centered between the fraction numerals as shown in Fig. 2.18. It should be noted that the sloping center line of the fraction bisects both the numerator and denominator and is parallel to the sloping center line of the whole number.

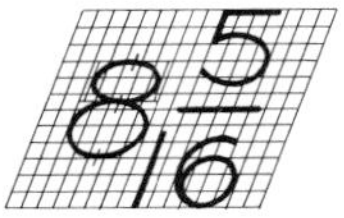

Fig. 2.18

2.14. Large caps and small caps in combination. Many commercial draftsmen use a combination of large caps and small caps in forming words, as illustrated in Fig. 2.19. When this style is used, the height of the small caps should be approximately four-fifths the height of the first capital letter of the word.

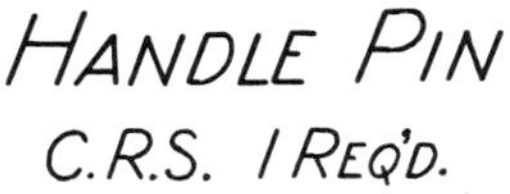

2.15. Titles. Every drawing, sketch, graph, chart, or diagram has some form of descriptive title to impart certain necessary information and to identify it. On machine drawings, where speed and legibility are prime requirements, titles are usually single-stroke.

HANDLE PIN
C.R.S. I REQ'D.

Fig. 2.19. Use of large and small caps.

APPROVED BY CUSTOMER	*ROSS-SHOER CO.*
ADAMS MFG. CO.	
AURORA, ILL.	

ASSEMBLY
STANDARD DUTY
FLANGE UNIT

SCALE *FULL SIZE*	DATE *JAN. 3, 1959*
DRAWN BY *CARL KING*	CHECKED BY *J.B. JONES*
TRACED BY *K. BODINE*	APPROVED BY *W.L. KOE*
ORDER NO. *M-L-24631*	DRG. *5-19-9612*

Fig. 2.20. A machine-drawing title block.

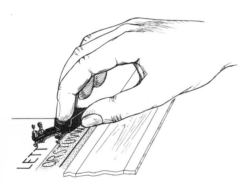

Fig. 2.21. Leroy lettering device.

On display drawings, maps, and so on, which call for an artistic effect, the titles are usually composed of "built-up" ornate letters.

Figure 2.20 shows a title block that might be used on a machine drawing. It should be noted that the important items are made more prominent by the use of larger letters formed with heavier lines. Less important data, such as the scale, date, drafting information, and so on, are given less prominence.

To be pleasing in appearance, a title should be symmetrical about a vertical center line and should have some simple geometric form.

An easy way to insure the symmetry of a title is first to count the letter and word spaces, then, working to the left and right from the middle space or letter on the vertical center line, to sketch the title lightly in pencil, before lettering it in finished form. An alternate method is to letter a trial line along the edge of a piece of scrap paper and place it in a balanced position just above the location of the line to be lettered.

2.16. Mechanical lettering devices and templates. Although mechanical lettering devices produce letters that may appear stiff to an expert, they are used in many drafting rooms for the simple reason that they enable even the unskilled to do satisfactory lettering with ink. The average draftsman rightly prefers stiff uniformity to wavy lines and irregular shapes. One of the oldest instruments of this sort on the market is the *Wrico* outfit. With a satisfactory set of Wrico pens and templates, letters ranging in size from ³⁄₃₂ in. to ½ in. in height may be executed. The letters are formed by a stylographic pen that is guided around the sides of openings in a template made of transparent pyralin.

The *Leroy* device, shown in Fig. 2.21, is possibly even more efficient than the Wrico, for it does not require the sliding of a template to complete a letter.

EXERCISES

It should be noted that while these exercises are offered to give the student practice in letter forms and word composition, they also contain statements of important principles of drawing, shop notes, and titles with which every engineer should be familiar. Each lettering exercise should be submitted to the instructor for severe criticism before the student proceeds to the next. Section 2.3 should be reread before starting the first exercise.

1. Letter the statement given in Fig. 2.22 in ⁵⁄₃₂ in. capital letters using an appropriate pencil that is suited to the type of paper being used and one that will produce uniform opaque lines. The necessary guide lines should be drawn with a hard pencil.

2-3. Letter the statements given in Figs. 2.23–2.24 in ⅛ in. capital letters using an appropriate pencil that is suited to the type of paper being used and one that will produce uniform opaque lines. The necessary guide lines should be drawn with a hard pencil.

4. Letter the statement given in Fig. 2.25 in 5/32 in. capital letters using an appropriate pencil that is suited to the type of paper being used and one that will produce uniform opaque lines. The necessary guide lines should be drawn with a hard pencil.

5-6. Letter the statements given in Figs. 2.26–2.27 in ⅛ in. capital letters using an appropriate pencil that is suited to the type of paper being used and one that will produce uniform opaque lines. The necessary guide lines should be drawn with a hard pencil.

7-16. Letter the following statements in ⅛ in. capital letters using an appropriate pencil that is suited to the type of paper being used and one that will produce uniform opaque lines. The necessary guide lines should be drawn with a hard pencil.

POOR LETTERING DETRACTS FROM THE APPEARANCE OF A DRAWING

Fig. 2.22

IN LEARNING TO LETTER, CERTAIN DEFINITE RULES OF FORM & DESIGN MUST BE OBSERVED

Fig. 2.23

WHEN LETTERING WITH INK, THE INK SHOULD BE WELL ABOVE THE TIP OF THE POINT

Fig. 2.24

#26 (.1470) DRILL AND REAM FOR #1×1 TAPER PIN WITH PC #41 IN POSITION

Fig. 2.25

S.A.E. 1020 - COLD DRAWN STEEL BAR
1-12 UNF-2B   1-8 UNC-2A   1-5 SQUARE
BREAK ALL SHARP CORNERS UNLESS OTHERWISE SPECIFIED

Fig. 2.26

$\frac{5}{16}$ DRILL - $\frac{3}{8}$-16 UNC-2A $\frac{21}{32}$ DRILL - C'BORE $\frac{29}{32}$ D × $\frac{7}{8}$ DEEP -2 HOLES

Fig. 2.27

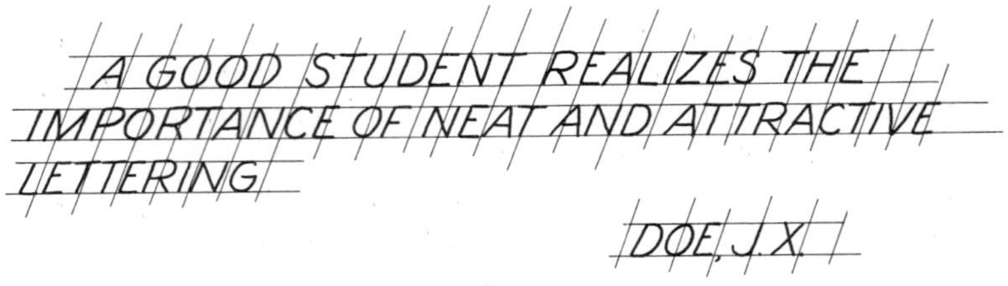

A GOOD STUDENT REALIZES THE
IMPORTANCE OF NEAT AND ATTRACTIVE
LETTERING

DOE, J. X

Fig. 2.28

7. A GOOD STUDENT REALIZES THE IMPORTANCE OF NEAT AND ATTRACTIVE LETTERING.

8. THE CIRCUMFERENCE OF A CIRCLE MAY BE DIVIDED INTO TWENTY-FOUR EQUAL ARCS USING ONLY A T-SQUARE IN COMBINATION WITH THE 30°–60° AND 45° TRIANGLES.

9. A TRUE ELLIPSE MAY BE CONSTRUCTED BY THE TRAMMEL METHOD.

10. THE POSITION OF THE VIEWS OF AN ORTHOGRAPHIC DRAWING MUST BE IN STRICT ACCORDANCE WITH THE UNIVERSALLY RECOGNIZED ARRANGEMENT ILLUSTRATED IN FIG. 6.6.

11. THE VIEWS OF AN ORTHOGRAPHIC DRAWING SHOULD SHOW THE THREE DIMENSIONS, WIDTH, DEPTH, AND HEIGHT.

12. AN INVISIBLE LINE SHOULD START WITH A SPACE WHEN IT FORMS AN EXTENSION OF A SOLID LINE.

13. THE FRONT VIEW OF AN ORTHOGRAPHIC DRAWING SHOULD BE THE VIEW THAT SHOWS THE CHARACTER-ISTIC SHAPE OF THE OBJECT.

14. AN AUXILIARY VIEW SHOWS THE TRUE SIZE AND SHAPE OF AN INCLINED SURFACE.

15. A SECTIONAL VIEW SHOWS THE INTERIOR CONSTRUC-TION OF AN OBJECT.

16. #404 WOODRUFF KEY.
DRILL AND REAM FOR #2 TAPER PIN WITH PC#10 IN POSITION.

17-21. Using a hard pencil, draw two or more sets of horizontal and inclined guide lines for 5/32 in. letters, then execute directly with India ink the following exercises in lower-case letters:

17. The front and top views are always in line vertically.

18. The front and side views are in line horizontally.

19. The depth of the top view is the same as the depth of the side view.

20. If a line is perpendicular to a plane of projection, its projection will be a point.

21. If a line is parallel to a plane of projection, its projection on the plane is exactly the same length as the true length of the line.

22-26. Draw two or more sets of both horizontal and inclined guide lines, and letter the following series of words, whole numbers, and fractions, once in pencil and once in India ink.

22. $1\frac{1}{2}$, $3\frac{3}{4}$, $2\frac{7}{8}$, $1\frac{9}{16}$, $9\frac{17}{32}$, $4\frac{5}{8}$, $9\frac{13}{32}$, $7\frac{13}{64}$, $8\frac{1}{2}$, $\frac{11}{16}$, $5\frac{3}{8}$.

23. $\frac{1}{2}''$ × $2\frac{3}{4}''$ HEX. HD. CAP SCREW, $\frac{3}{8}$ × $1\frac{1}{4}$ UNC HEX. HD. BOLT & HEX. NUT.

24. $\frac{3}{16}$ DRILL—$\frac{3}{8}$ DEEP, $\frac{1}{4}$ DRILL—4 HOLES, $\frac{1}{8}$ × 45° CHAMFER.

25. $\frac{1}{8}$ AM. STD. PIPE TAP, $\frac{1}{2}$—13 UNC—2B.

26. 2$\angle$s $2\frac{1}{2}$ × $2\frac{1}{2}$ × $\frac{1}{4}$ × 8′-4″, 10″ I 30#, 24″ W⊤74#.

27. Draw horizontal and inclined guide lines and letter the following detail titles. Use $\frac{5}{32}$ in. capitals for the part names and $\frac{1}{8}$ in. capitals for the remainder of the titles.

BASE	BUSHING	SPINDLE
C.I. 1 REQ'D	BRO. 1 REQ'D	C.R.S. 1 REQ'D

3

DRAWING EQUIPMENT AND USE OF INSTRUMENTS

3.1. Introduction. The instruments and materials needed for making ordinary engineering drawings are shown in Fig. 3.1. The instruments in the plush-lined case should be particularly well made, for with inferior ones, it is often difficult to produce accurate drawings of professional quality.

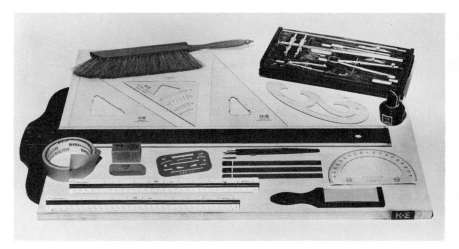

Fig. 3.1. Essential drafting equipment.

3.2. List of equipment and materials. The following list is a practical selection of equipment and materials necessary for making pencil drawings and ink tracings.

1. Case of drawing instruments.
2. Drawing board.
3. T-square.
*4. 45° triangle.
5. 10″ 30°–60° triangle.
6. French curve.
7. Scales (see Sec. 3.15).
8. Drawing pencils.
9. Pencil pointer (file or sandpaper pad).
10. Thumb tacks, brad machine, or Scotch tape.
11. Pencil eraser.
12. Cleaning eraser.
13. Erasing shield.
14. Dusting brush.
15. Bottle of black waterproof drawing ink.
16. Pen wiper.
17. Penholder.
18. Lettering pens.
19. Protractor.
20. Pad of sketching paper (plain or ruled).
21. Drawing paper.
22. Tracing paper.
23. Tracing cloth.

To these may be added the following useful items:

24. Piece of soapstone.
25. Ink-bottle holder.
26. Tack lifter.
27. Slide rule.

3.3. The set of instruments. A standard set of drawing instruments in a velvet-lined case and a large-bow set, which is capable of fulfilling the needs of most engineers and draftsmen, are shown in Figs. 3.2 and 3.3 respectively.

Large-bow sets are preferred by many persons, especially in the aircraft and automotive fields. A complete set might include the following: large bow (compass), beam compass with an extension

---

* A 6″ 45° Braddock lettering triangle, which may be used as either a triangle or a lettering instrument, may be substituted for this item.

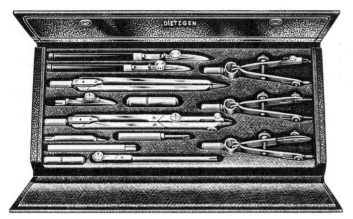

Fig. 3.2. A standard set of drawing instruments.

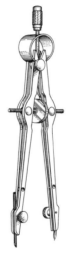

bar for drawing very large circles, dividers, small bow, and a slip-handle ruling pen. Since the large bow (Fig. 3.4) is particularly suited for drawing circles of very small size up to ten inches in diameter, its range covers that of both the bow instruments and the compass (without the extension bar) of the standard set (Fig. 3.2).

The large bow is preferred by its advocates because its sturdy construction permits the draftsman to exert the pressure necessary to secure black, opaque lines on pencil drawings that are to be used for making prints.

Fig. 3.4. Large bow (Vemco).

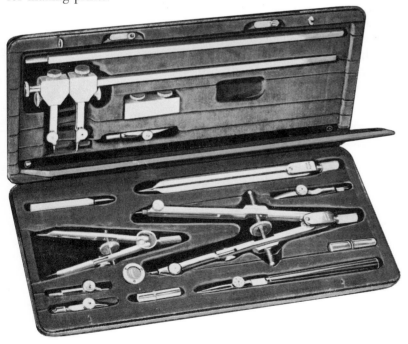

Fig. 3.3. The Purdue Riefler set.

3.4. Pencils. The student and professional man should be equipped with a selection of good, well-sharpened pencils with leads of various degrees of hardness such as: 9H, 8H, 7H, and 6H (hard); 5H and 4H (medium hard); 3H and 2H (medium); and H and F (medium soft).

The grade of pencil to be used for various purposes depends upon the type of line desired, the kind of paper employed, and the humidity, which affects the surface of the paper. Standards for line quality usually will govern the selection. As a minimum, however, the student should have available a 6H pencil for the light construction lines in layout work where accuracy is required, a 4H for repenciling light finished lines (dimension lines, center lines and invisible object lines), a 2H for visible object lines, and an F or H for all lettering and freehand work.

3.5. Pointing the pencil. Many persons prefer the conical point for general use (Fig. 3.5), while others find the wedge point more suitable for straight-line work, as it requires less sharpening and makes a denser line (Fig. 3.6).

When sharpening a pencil, the wood should be cut away (on the unlettered end) with a knife or a pencil sharpener equipped with draftsman's cutters. About ⅜ in. of the lead should be exposed and should form a cut, including the wood, about 1½ in. long. The lead then should be shaped to a conical point on the pointer (file or sandpaper pad). This is done by holding the file stationary in the left hand and drawing the lead toward the handle while rotating the pencil against the movement (Fig. 3.5). All strokes should be made in the same manner, a new grip being taken each time so that each stroke starts with the pencil in the same rotated position as at the end of the preceding stroke.

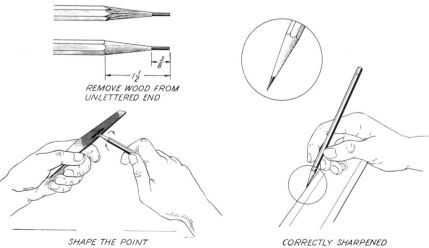

REMOVE WOOD FROM
UNLETTERED END

SHAPE THE POINT

CORRECTLY SHARPENED

Fig. 3.5. Conical point.

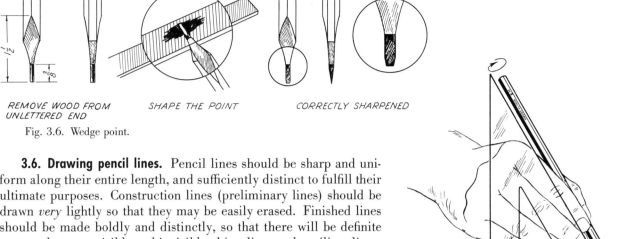

REMOVE WOOD FROM UNLETTERED END   SHAPE THE POINT   CORRECTLY SHARPENED

Fig. 3.6. Wedge point.

3.6. Drawing pencil lines. Pencil lines should be sharp and uniform along their entire length, and sufficiently distinct to fulfill their ultimate purposes. Construction lines (preliminary lines) should be drawn *very* lightly so that they may be easily erased. Finished lines should be made boldly and distinctly, so that there will be definite contrast between visible and invisible object lines and auxiliary lines, such as dimension lines, center lines, and section lines. To give this contrast, which is necessary for clearness and ease in reading, object lines should be of medium width and very black, invisible lines black and not so wide, and auxiliary lines dark and thin.

When drawing a line, the pencil should be inclined slightly (about 60°) in the direction in which the line is being drawn (Fig. 3.7). The pencil should be "pulled" (never pushed) at the same inclination for the full length of the line. If it is rotated (twirled) slowly between the fingers as the line is drawn, a symmetrical point will be maintained and a straight uniform line will be insured.

3.7. Placing and fastening the paper. For accuracy and ease in manipulating the T-square, the drawing paper should be located well up on the board and near the left-hand edge. The lower edge of the sheet (if plain) or the lower border line (if printed) should be aligned along the working edge of the T-square before the sheet is fastened down at all four corners with thumb tacks, Scotch tape, or staples.

3.8. The T-square. The T-square is used primarily for drawing horizontal lines and for guiding the triangles when drawing vertical and inclined lines. It is manipulated by sliding the working edge (inner face) of the head along the left edge of the board [Fig. 3.8(*a*)] until the blade is in the required position. The left hand then should be shifted to a position near the center of the blade to hold it in place and to prevent its deflection while drawing the line. Experienced draftsmen hold the T-square, as shown in Fig. 3.8(*b*), with the fingers pressing on the blade and the thumb on the paper. Small adjustments may be made with the hand in this position by sliding the blade with the fingers.

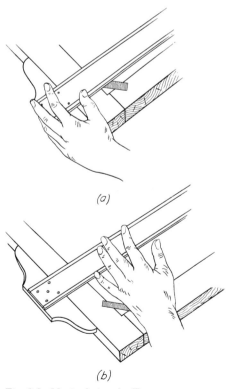

Fig. 3.7. Using the pencil.

(*a*)

(*b*)

Fig. 3.8. Manipulating the T-square.

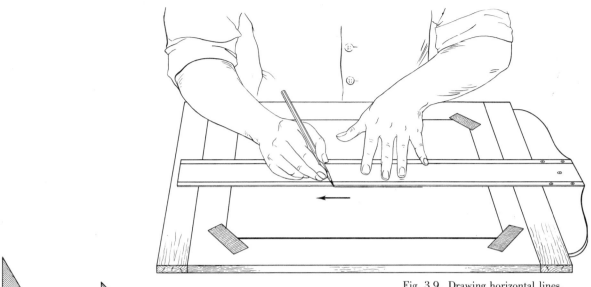

Fig. 3.9. Drawing horizontal lines.

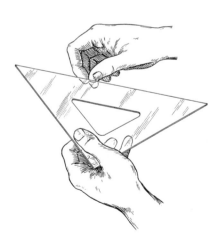

Fig. 3.10. Triangles.

Horizontal lines are drawn from left to right along the upper edge of the T-square (Fig. 3.9). (*Exception:* left-handed persons should use the T-square head at the right side of the board and draw from right to left.) While drawing the line, the ruling hand should slide along the blade on the little finger.

3.9. The triangles. The 45° and the 30° × 60° triangles are the ones commonly used for ordinary work (Fig. 3.10). A triangle may be checked for nicks by sliding the thumbnail along the ruling edges as shown in Fig. 3.11.

3.10. Vertical lines. Vertical lines are drawn upward along the vertical leg of a triangle whose other (horizontal) leg is supported and guided by the T-square blade. The blade is held in position with the palm and thumb of the left hand, and the triangle is adjusted and held by the fingers as shown in Fig. 3.12. In the case of a right-handed person, the triangle should be to the right of the line to be drawn.

Either the 30° × 60° or the 45° triangle may be used since both triangles have a right angle. However, the 30° × 60° is generally preferred because it usually has a longer perpendicular leg.

3.11. Inclined lines. Triangles also are used for drawing inclined lines. Lines that make angles of 30°, 45°, or 60° with the horizontal may be drawn with the 30° × 60° or the 45° triangle in combination with the T-square, as shown in Fig. 3.13. If the two triangles are combined, lines that make 15° or a multiple of 15°

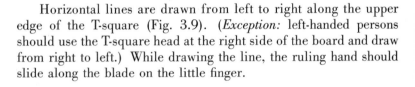

Fig. 3.11. Testing a triangle for nicks.

may be drawn with the horizontal. Several possible arrangements and the angles that result are shown in Fig. 3.14.

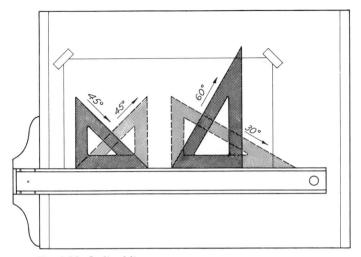

Fig. 3.13. Inclined lines.

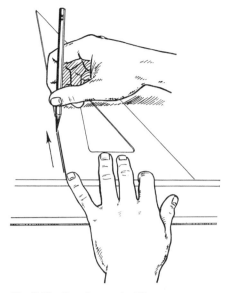

Fig. 3.12. Drawing vertical lines.

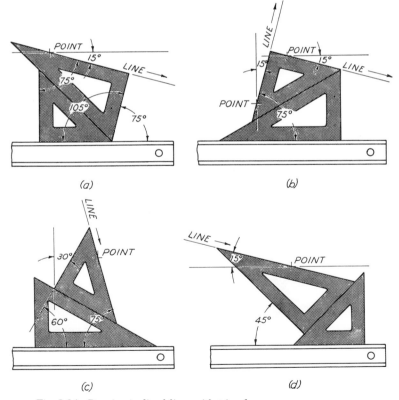

Fig. 3.14. Drawing inclined lines with triangles.

The triangles used singly or in combination offer a useful method for dividing a circle into four, six, eight, twelve, or twenty-four equal parts (Fig. 3.15). For angles other than those divisible by 15, a protractor must be used.

3.12. Parallel lines. The triangles are used in combination to draw a line parallel to a given line. To draw such a line, place a ruling edge of a triangle, supported by a T-square or another triangle, along the given line; then slip the triangle, as shown in Fig. 3.16, to the required position and draw the parallel line along the same ruling edge that previously coincided with the given line.

3.13. Perpendicular lines. Either the sliding triangle method [Fig. 3.17(a)] or the revolved triangle method [Fig. 3.17(b)] may be used to draw a line perpendicular to a given line. When using the sliding triangle method, adjust to the given line a side of a triangle that is adjacent to the right angle. Guide the side opposite the right angle with a second triangle as shown in Fig. 3.17(a); then slide the first triangle along the guiding triangle until it is in the required position for drawing the perpendicular along the other edge adjacent to the right angle.

Although the revolved triangle method is not so quickly done, it is widely used [Fig. 3.17(b)]. To draw a perpendicular using this method, align along the given line the hypotenuse of a triangle, one leg of which is guided by the T-square or another triangle; then hold the guiding member in position and revolve the triangle about the

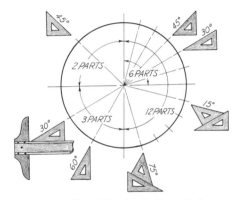

Fig. 3.15. To divide a circle into four, six, eight, twelve, or twenty-four equal parts.

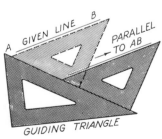

Fig. 3.16. To draw a line parallel to a given line.

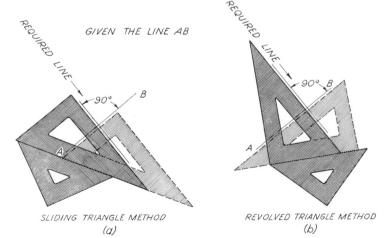

GIVEN THE LINE AB

SLIDING TRIANGLE METHOD
(a)

REVOLVED TRIANGLE METHOD
(b)

Fig. 3.17. To draw a line perpendicular to another line.

right angle until the other leg is against the guiding edge. The new position of the hypotenuse will be perpendicular to its previous location along the given line and, when moved to the required position, may be used as a ruling edge for the desired perpendicular.

3.14. Inclined lines making 15°, 30°, 45°, 60°, or 75° with an oblique line. A line making an angle with an oblique line equal to any angle of a triangle may be drawn with the triangles. The two methods previously discussed for drawing perpendicular lines are applicable with slight modifications. To draw an oblique line using the revolved triangle method [Fig. 3.18(a)], adjust along the given line the edge that is opposite the required angle, then revolve the triangle about the required angle, slide it into position, and draw the required line along the side opposite the required angle.

To use the sliding triangle method [Fig. 3.18(b)], adjust to the given line one of the edges adjacent to the required angle, and guide the side opposite the required angle with a straight edge; then slide the triangle into position and draw the required line along the other adjacent side.

To draw a line making 75° with a given line, place the triangles together so that the sum of a pair of adjacent angles equals 75°, and adjust one side of the angle thus formed to the given line; then slide the triangle, whose leg forms the other side of the angle, across the given line into position, and draw the required line, as shown in Fig. 3.19(a).

To draw a line making 15° with a given line, select any two angles whose difference is 15°. Adjust to the given line a side adjacent to one of these angles, and guide the side adjacent with a straight edge. Remove the first triangle and substitute the other so

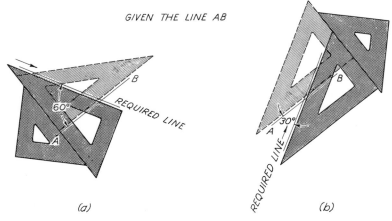

Fig. 3.18. To draw lines making 30°, 45°, or 60° with a given line.

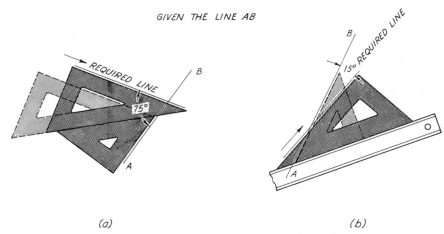

Fig. 3.19. To draw lines making 15° or 75° with a given line.

that one adjacent side of the angle to be subtracted is along the guiding edge, as shown in Fig. 3.19(*b*); then slide it into position and draw along the other adjacent side.

3.15. Scales. A number of kinds of scales are available for varied types of engineering design. For convenience, however, all scales may be classified according to their use as mechanical engineers' scales (both fractional and decimal), civil engineers' scales, architects' scales, or metric scales.

The mechanical engineers' scales are generally of the full-divided type, graduated proportionally to give reductions based on inches. On one form the principal units are divided into the common fractions of an inch; 4, 8, 16, 32 parts (Fig. 3.20). The scales are indicated on the stick as eighth size ($1\frac{1}{2}'' = 1'$), quarter size ($3'' = 1'$), half size ($6'' = 1'$), and full size.

Since the decimal system, employed in automotive design for more than twenty years and in aircraft design since World War II, has been rapidly spreading into other fields in recent years, decimals of an inch may soon replace the use of fractions in most of the divisions of American industry. In any case, the use of decimal scales has become so widespread that the American Standards Association found it desirable to establish the standard ASA Z75.1–1955 for markings on scales used with decimal-inch dimensioning. The full-size scale, which has the principal units (inches) divided into fiftieths, is particularly suited for use with the two place decimal system (Fig. 3.21). The half-size, three-eighths size, and quarter-size scales have the principal units divided into tenths (Fig. 3.24).

The civil engineers' (chain) scales are full-divided, and are graduated in decimal parts, usually 10, 20, 30, 40, 50, 60, 80, and 100 divisions to the inch (Fig. 3.22).

Architects' scales differ from mechanical engineers' scales in that the divisions represent a foot, and the end units are divided into inches, half inches, quarter inches, and so forth (6, 12, 24, 48, or 96 parts). The usual scales are ⅛″ = 1′, ¼″ = 1′, ⅜″ = 1′, ½″ = 1′, 1″ = 1′, 1½″ = 1′, and 3″ = 1′ (Fig. 3.23).

Fig. 3.20. Mechanical engineers' scale. Full divided.

Fig. 3.21. Engineers' decimal scale.

Fig. 3.22. Civil engineers' scale.

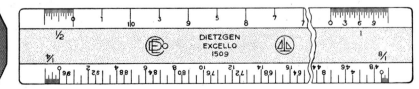

Fig. 3.23. Architects' scale. Open-divided.

The sole purpose of the scale is to reproduce the dimensions of an object full size on a drawing or to reduce or enlarge them to some regular proportion such as eighth size, quarter size, half size, or double size. The scales of reduction most frequently used are as follows:

FRACTIONAL

Mechanical engineers' scales

Full size	(1″ = 1″)
Half size	(½″ = 1″)
Quarter size	(¼″ = 1″)
Eighth size	(⅛″ = 1″)

Architects' or mechanical engineers' scales

Full size	(12″ = 1′)
Half size	(6″ = 1′)
Quarter size	(3″ = 1′)
Eighth size	(1½″ = 1′)
1″ = 1′	¼″ = 1′
¾″ = 1′	³⁄₁₆″ = 1′
½″ = 1′	⅛″ = 1′
⅜″ = 1′	³⁄₃₂″ = 1′

DECIMAL

Mechanical engineers' scales

Full size	(1.00″ = 1.00″)
Half size	(0.50″ = 1.00″)
Three-eighths size	(0.375″ = 1.00″)
Quarter size	(0.25″ = 1.00″)

Civil engineers' scales

10 scale: 1″ = 1′; 1″ = 10′; 1″ = 100′; 1″ = 1000′
20 scale: 1″ = 2′; 1″ = 20′; 1″ = 200′; 1″ = 2000′
30 scale: 1″ = 3′; 1″ = 30′; 1″ = 300′; 1″ = 3000′
40 scale: 1″ = 4′; 1″ = 40′; 1″ = 400′; 1″ = 4000′
50 scale: 1″ = 5′; 1″ = 50′; 1″ = 500′; 1″ = 5000′
60 scale: 1″ = 60′; etc.
80 scale: 1″ = 80′; etc.

The first four scales, full size, half size, quarter size, and eighth size, are the ones most frequently selected for drawing machine parts although other scales can be used. Since objects drawn by structural draftsmen and architects vary from small to very large, scales from full size to ³⁄₃₂″ = 1′ (¹⁄₁₂₈ size) are commonly encountered. For maps the civil engineers' decimal scales having 10, 20, 30, 40, 50, 60, and 80 divisions to the inch are used for representing 10′, 20′, 30′, and so forth, to the inch.

The decimal scales shown in Fig. 3.24 have been approved by the American Standards Association for making machine drawings when the decimal system is used.

It is essential that a draftsman always think and speak of each dimension as full size when scaling measurements, because the dimension figures given on the finished drawing indicate full-size measurements of the finished piece, regardless of the scale used.

The reading of an open-divided scale is illustrated in Fig. 3.25 with the eighth size (1½″ = 1′) scale shown. The dimension can be read directly as 21 in., the 9 in. being read in the divided division to the left of the cipher. Each long open division represents 12 in. (1 ft).

To lay off a measurement, using a scale starting at the left of the

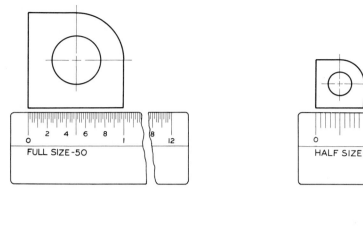

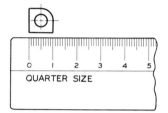

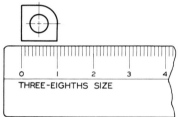

FULL SIZE-50

HALF SIZE

THREE-EIGHTHS SIZE

QUARTER SIZE

Fig. 3.24. Decimal scales.

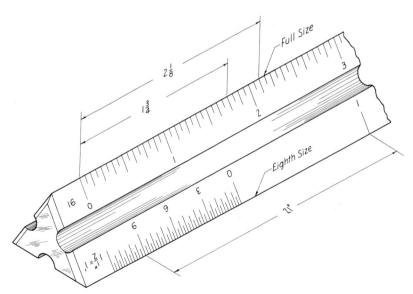

Fig. 3.25. Reading a scale.

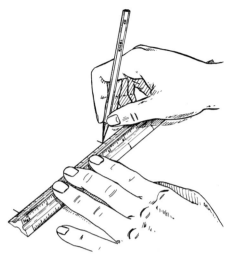

Fig. 3.26. To lay off a measurement.

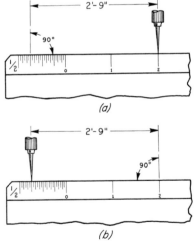

Fig. 3.27. To lay off a measurement.

stick, align the scale in the direction of the measurement with the zero of the scale being used toward the left. After it has been adjusted to the correct location, make short marks opposite the divisions on the scale that establish the desired distance (Fig. 3.26). For ordinary work most men use the same pencil used for the layout. When extreme accuracy is necessary, however, it is better practice to use a pricker and make slight indentations (not holes) at the required points. If a regular pricker is not available, the dividers may be opened to approximately 60° and the point of one leg used as a substitute.

To insure accuracy, place the eye directly over the division to be marked, hold the marking instrument perpendicularly to the paper directly in front of the scale division, and mark the point. Always check the location of the point before removing the scale. If a slight indentation is made, it will be covered by the finished line; if a short mark is made, and it is *very* light, it will be unnoticeable on the finished drawing.

To set off a measurement (say 2'-9") to half-scale, the scale indicated either as ½ (Fig. 3.27) or ½" = 1' should be used. If the measurement is to be made from left to right, place the 9-in. fractional division mark (counted toward the left from the cipher) on the given line, and make an indentation (or mark) opposite the 2-ft division point [Fig. 3.27(a)]. The distance from the line to the point represents 2'-9", although it is actually 1⅜ in. To set off the same measurement from right to left, place the 2-ft mark on the given line, and make an indentation opposite the 9-in. fractional division mark [Fig. 3.27(b)].

The procedure for setting off a distance to full size is illustrated in Fig. 3.28. The scale that is full divided into inches and sixteenths is best suited for this purpose.

To set off a measurement (say 1⁹⁄₁₆ in.) from left to right, place the initial mark at the start of the scale on the given line, and make an indentation opposite the 1⁹⁄₁₆-in. mark [Fig. 3.28(a)]. To set off the same measurement from right to left, place the 1⁹⁄₁₆-in. mark on the given line, and make an indentation opposite the initial division mark at the start of the scale [Fig. 3.28(b)].

The use of the decimal scale is illustrated in Fig. 3.29.

3.16. The compass or large bow. The compass or large bow is used for drawing circles and circle arcs. For drawing pencil circles, the style of point illustrated in Fig. 3.30(c) should be used because it gives more accurate results and is easier to maintain than most other styles. This style of point is formed by first sharpening the outside of the lead on a file or sandpad to a long flat bevel approximately ¼ in. long [Fig. 3.30(a)], and then finishing it [Fig. 3.30(b)] with a slight rocking motion to reduce the width of the point.

Although a hard lead (4H to 6H) will maintain a point longer without resharpening, it gives a finished object line that is too light in color. Soft lead (F or H) gives a darker line but quickly loses its edge and, on larger circles, gives a thicker line at the end than at the beginning. Some draftsmen have found that a medium grade (2H–3H) lead is a satisfactory compromise for ordinary working drawings. For design drawings, layout work, and graphical solutions, however, a harder lead will give better results.

The needle point should have the shouldered end out, and should be adjusted approximately ⅜ of an inch beyond the end of the split sleeve (Fig. 3.31).

3.17. Using the compass or large bow. To draw a circle, it is first necessary to draw two intersecting center lines at right angles and mark off the radius. The pivot point should be guided accurately into position at the center. After the pencil point has been adjusted to the radius mark, the circle is drawn in a clockwise direction as shown in Fig. 3.32. While drawing the circle, the instrument should be inclined slightly forward. If the pencil line is not dark enough, it may be drawn around again.

When using a compass for a radius larger than 2 in., the legs should be bent at the knee joints to stand approximately perpendicular to the paper (Fig. 3.33). It is particularly important that this adjustment be made when drawing ink circles, otherwise both nibs will not touch the paper. For circles whose radii exceed 5 in., the lengthening bar should be used to increase the capacity.

The beam compass is manipulated by steadying the instrument at the pivot leg with one hand while rotating the marking leg with the other (Fig. 3.34).

3.18. The dividers. The dividers are used principally for dividing curved and straight lines into any number of equal parts, and for

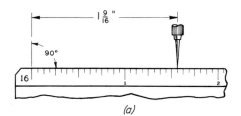

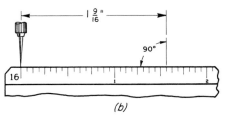

Fig. 3.28. To lay off a measurement (full size).

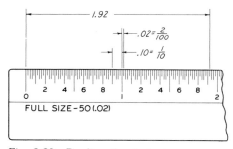

Fig. 3.29. Reading the decimal scale.

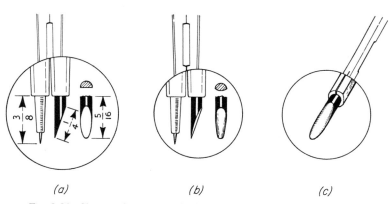

Fig. 3.30. Shaping the compass lead.

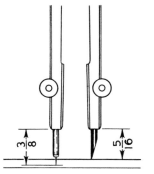

Fig. 3.31. The adjustment of the needle point.

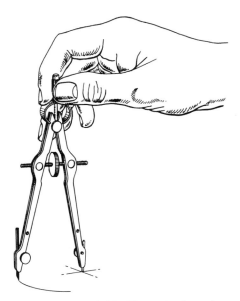

Fig. 3.32. Using the large bow (Vemco).

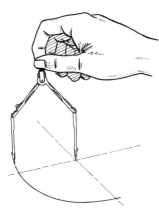

Fig. 3.33. Using the compass (legs bent).

transferring measurements. If the instrument is held with one leg between the forefinger and second finger, and the other leg between the thumb and third finger, as illustrated in Fig. 3.35, an adjustment may be made quickly and easily with one hand. The second and third fingers are used to "open out" the legs, and the thumb and forefinger to close them. This method of adjusting may seem awkward to the beginner at first, but with practice absolute control can be developed.

3.19. Use of the dividers. The trial method is used to divide a line into a given number of equal parts (Fig. 3.36). To divide a line into a desired number of equal parts, open the dividers until the distance between the points is estimated to be equal to the length of a division, and step off the line *lightly*. If the last prick mark misses the end point, increase or decrease the setting by an amount estimated to be equal to the error divided by the number of divisions, before lifting the dividers from the paper. Step off the line again. Repeat this procedure until the dividers are correctly set, then space the line again and indent the division points. When stepping off a line, the dividers are rotated alternately in an opposite direction on either side of the line, each half revolution, as shown in Fig. 3.36.

Although the dividers are used to transfer a distance on a drawing, they should never be used to transfer a measurement from the scale, as the method is slow and inaccurate and results in serious damage to the graduation marks. Care should be taken to avoid pricking large unsightly holes with the divider points. It is the common practice of many expert draftsmen to draw a small freehand circle around a very light indentation to establish its location.

3.20. Use of the bow instruments. The bow pen and bow pencil are convenient for drawing circles having a radius of 1 in. or less (Fig. 3.37). The needle points should be adjusted slightly longer than the marking points, as in the case of the compass.

Small adjustments are made by the fingers of the hand holding the instrument, with the pivot point in position at the center of the required circle or arc.

3.21. Use of the French curve. A French curve is used for drawing irregular curves that are not circle arcs. After sufficient points have been located, the French curve is applied so that a portion of its ruling edge passes through at least three points, as shown in Fig. 3.38. It should be so placed that the increasing curvature of the section of the ruling edge being used follows the direction of that part of the curve that is changing most rapidly. To insure that the finished curve will be free of humps and sharp breaks, the first

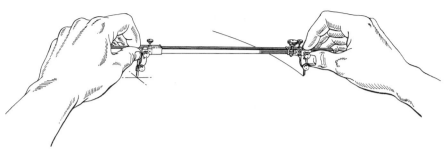

Fig. 3.34. Drawing large circles (Vemco beam compass).

line drawn should start and stop short of the first and last points to
which the French curve has been fitted. Then the curve is adjusted
in a new position with the ruling edge coinciding with a section of
the line previously drawn. Each successive segment should stop
short of the last point matched by the curve. In Fig. 3.38, the curve
fits the three points, A, 1, and 2. A line is drawn from between point
A and point 1 to between point 1 and point 2. Then, the curve is
shifted, as shown, to again fit points 1 and 2 with an additional point
3, and the line is extended to between point 2 and point 3.

Fig. 3.35. To adjust the large
dividers.

Some people sketch a smooth continuous curve through the
points in pencil before drawing the mechanical line. This procedure
makes the task of drawing the curve less difficult, since it is easier
to adjust the ruling edge to segments of the freehand curve than to
the points.

3.22. Use of the erasing shield and eraser. An erasure is made on
a drawing by placing an opening in the erasing shield over the work
to be erased and rubbing with a pencil eraser (never an ink eraser)
until it is removed (Fig. 3.39). Excessive pressure should not be

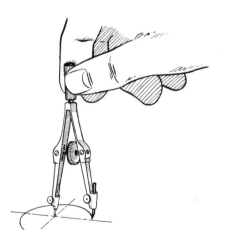

Fig. 3.37. Use of the bow pencil.

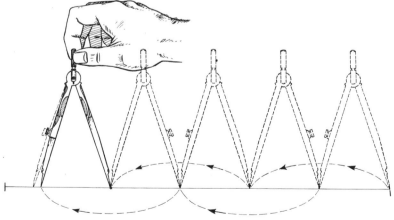

Fig. 3.36. Use of the dividers.

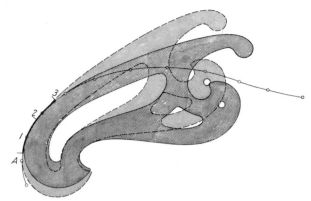

Fig. 3.38.   Using the irregular curve.

Fig. 3.39. Using the erasing shield.

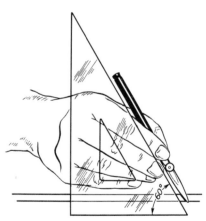

Fig. 3.40. Holding the pen.

applied to the eraser, because, although the lines will disappear more quickly, the surface of the paper is likely to be permanently damaged. The fingers holding the erasing shield should rest partly on the drawing paper to prevent the shield from slipping.

3.23. Use of the ruling pen. The ruling pen is used to ink mechanical lines. It is always guided by the working edge of a T-square, triangle, or French curve, and is never used freehand.

When ruling a line, the pen should be in a vertical plane and inclined slightly (approximately 60°) in the direction of the movement. It is held by the thumb and forefinger, as illustrated in Fig. 3.40, with the blade against the second finger and the adjusting screw on the outside away from the ruling edge. The third and fourth fingers slide along the T-square blade and help control the pen. Short lines are drawn with a hand movement; long lines with a free arm movement that finishes with a finger movement. While drawing, the angle of inclination and speed must remain constant to obtain a line of uniform width and straightness. Particular attention should be given to the position of the pen, as practically all faulty lines are due to incorrect inclination or to leaning the pen so that the point is too close to the straightedge or too far away from it. The correct position of the pen for drawing a satisfactory line is illustrated in Fig. 3.40.

If the pen is held so that it leans outward, as shown in Fig. 3.41(*a*), the point will be against the straightedge, and ink will run under and cause a blot; or, if it leans inward, as in Fig. 3.41(*b*), the outer nib will not touch the paper and the line will be ragged.

Unnecessary pressure against the straightedge changes the distance between the nibs, which in turn may either reduce the width of the line along its entire length or cause its width to vary as in Fig. 3.41(*d*).

It will not take any beginner long to discover that care must be taken when removing a T-square or triangle away from a wet ink line [Fig. 3.41(c)].

The ruling pen is filled by inserting the quill or dropper device of the stopper between the nibs. Care must be taken, while filling, to see that there is enough ink to finish the line and that none of the ink from the filler gets on the outside of the blades. No more than ¼ in. should ever be put in; there is a danger of blotting if the pen is used with a greater amount.

The width of a line is determined by the distance between the nibs, which is regulated by the adjusting screw. When setting the pen, a series of test lines should be drawn with a straightedge on a small piece of the same kind of paper or cloth to establish the setting for the desired width of the line. The draftsman's line gauge, shown in Fig. 3.42, is convenient for testing the widths of trial lines as illustrated. If the first trial line is not of the desired width, another and another should be drawn until the final one agrees with the selected width as given on the gauge.

If the ink refuses to flow when the pen is touched to the paper, either the ink has thickened or the opening between the nibs has become clogged. To start it flowing, draftsmen often touch the point to the back of a finger or pinch the blades together. Whenever this

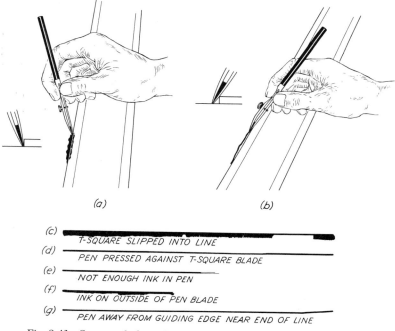

(a) (b)

(c) T-SQUARE SLIPPED INTO LINE
(d) PEN PRESSED AGAINST T-SQUARE BLADE
(e) NOT ENOUGH INK IN PEN
(f) INK ON OUTSIDE OF PEN BLADE
(g) PEN AWAY FROM GUIDING EDGE NEAR END OF LINE

Fig. 3.41. Common faults in handling a ruling pen.

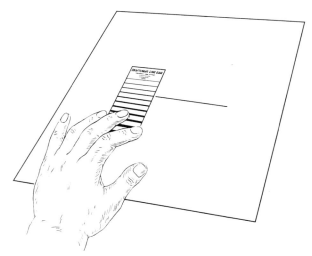
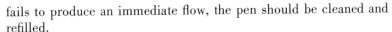

Fig. 3.42. Testing a trial line on a "try sheet."

Fig. 3.43. Cleaning the ruling pen.

fails to produce an immediate flow, the pen should be cleaned and refilled.

A dirty pen in which the ink has been allowed to thicken will not draw any better than a dull one. To avoid changing the setting of the pen when cleaning it, fold the pen wiper twice at 90° and draw the corner of the fold between the ends of the blades (Fig. 3.43).

3.24. Tracing. Often, when it is necessary to make duplicate copies (blueprints) of important drawings for a machine or structure, the original pencil drawings are traced in ink on a tracing medium, usually tracing cloth. Contrary to the practice of old-time draftsmen and the intention of the early manufacturers of this medium, the dull side is now almost universally used for the inking surface instead of the slick side because it produces less light glare, will take both pencil and ink lines better, and will withstand more erasing. The fact that the dull side will take pencil lines is important because, on some occasions, in order to save time, drawings are made directly on the cloth and then traced. Upon completion of the tracing, all pencil lines including the guide lines and slope lines for the lettering may be removed by wiping the surface of the cloth with a rag moistened with a small amount of gasoline, benzine, or cleaning fluid.

When the tracing cloth has been fastened down over the drawing, a small quantity of tracing cloth powder may be sprinkled over the surface to make it take the ink evenly and smoothly. After it has been well rubbed in, the excess must be thoroughly removed by wiping with a clean cloth, for even a small amount of loose powder left on the surface can cause clogging of the pen. Powder is also used by some persons over a spot where an erasure has been made; but a better practice is to use a piece of soapstone, which will put a smooth, slick finish over the damaged area. In applying the soapstone, rub the spot and then wipe a finger over it a few times. Following this treatment, the erased area will take ink almost as well as the original surface.

Since ink lines are made much wider than pencil lines, in order to get a good contrast on a blueprint, they should be carefully centered over the pencil lines when tracing. The center of an ink line should fall directly on the pencil line as shown correctly in Fig. 3.44. For ink work it might be said that ink lines are tangent when their center lines touch. In this same illustration, note the poor junctures obtained when ink lines are not centered so that their center lines are tangent.

Figure 3.45(a) shows the filled-in corner effect that frequently appears to the disgust of the draftsman, when an ink line is drawn from or to another previously drawn line that is still wet.

When a working drawing is traced in ink on either paper or cloth, the lines should be "inked" in a definite order. Otherwise, the necessity of waiting for the ink to dry after every few lines not only wastes time, but often results in a line here and there being left out. Furthermore, hit-and-miss inking may produce lines of unequal width. It is therefore recommended that the student make a conscientious attempt to follow the order of inking suggested in this chapter.

After the paper or cloth has been fastened down over the drawing, and before the inking is begun, each tangent point should be marked and all centers should be indented.

ORDER OF INKING

I. Curved lines:
  1. Circles and circle arcs (small circles first) in the order of (a), (b), and (c).
    (a) Visible.
    (b) Invisible.
    (c) Circular center lines and dimension lines.
  2. Irregular curves.
    (a) Visible.
    (b) Invisible.

II. Straight lines:
  1. Visible.
    (a) Horizontal, from the top of the sheet down.
    (b) Vertical, from the left side of the sheet to the right.
    (c) Inclined, from the left to right.
  2. Invisible.
    (a) Horizontal.
    (b) Vertical.
    (c) Inclined.

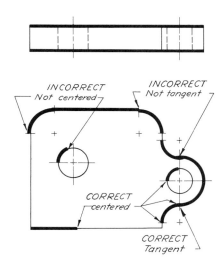

Fig. 3.44. Inking over pencil lines.

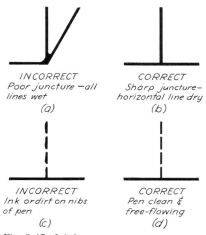

Fig. 3.45. Ink lines.

3. Auxiliary (center, extension, dimension lines, etc.).
  (a) Horizontal.
  (b) Vertical.
  (c) Inclined.
  (d) Section lines.
III. Arrowheads and dimension figures.
IV. Notes and titles.
V. Border.

3.25. Conventional line symbols. Symbolic lines of various weights are used in making technical drawings. The recommendations of the American Standards Association as given in ASA Y14.2–1957 are:

Three widths of lines—thick, medium, and thin—are recommended for use on drawings (Fig. 3.46). Pencil lines in general should be in proportion to the ink lines except that the thicker pencil lines will be necessarily thinner than the corresponding ink lines, but as thick as practicable for pencil work. Exact thicknesses may vary according to the size and type of drawing. For example, where lines are close together, the lines may be slightly thinner.

Pencil lines may be further simplified, if desired, to two widths of lines—*medium-thick* for visible, hidden, cutting-plane, and short-break lines; and *thin* for section, center, extension, dimension, long-break, and phantom lines.

The lines illustrated in Fig. 3.46 are shown full-size. When symbolic lines are used on a pencil drawing they should not vary in color. For example, center lines, extension lines, dimension lines, and section lines should differ from object lines only in width. The resulting contrast makes a drawing easier to read. All lines, except construction lines, should be very dark and bright to give the drawing the "snap" that is needed for good appearance. If the drawing is on tracing paper the lead must be "packed on" so that a satisfactory print can be obtained. Construction lines should be drawn *very* fine so as to be unnoticeable on the finished drawing. The lengths of the dashes and spaces, shown in Figs. 6.32 and 9.22, are recommended for the hidden lines, center lines, and cutting plane lines on average-size drawings.

3.26. The protractor. The protractor is used for measuring and laying off angles (Fig. 3.47).

3.27. Special instruments and templates. A few of the many special instruments and templates that are convenient for drawing are shown in Figs. 3.48 to 3.53.

The flexible curves shown in Fig. 3.48, because of their limitless variations, are extremely convenient. The type shown in (a) is a

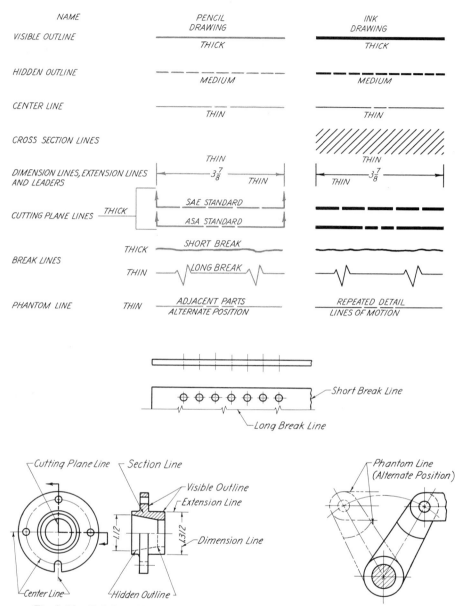

Fig. 3.46. Alphabet of lines (finished weight).

lead bar enclosed in rubber. The more desirable one shown in (b) has a steel ruling edge attached to a spring with a lead core.

Although it is not widely used, the protractor angle (Fig. 3.49) is a useful device. It is hinged in such a manner that it may be substituted for a protractor and a set of triangles.

One of several types of special triangles that may be used for drawing the end views of standard bolt heads is shown in Fig. 3.50.

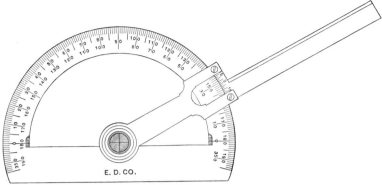

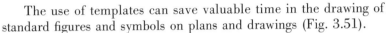

Fig. 3.47. Protractor.

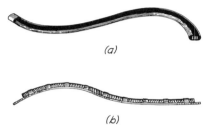

(a)

(b)

Fig. 3.48. Flexible curves.

The use of templates can save valuable time in the drawing of standard figures and symbols on plans and drawings (Fig. 3.51).

Proportional dividers are used to reproduce distances to a reduced or an enlarged scale (Fig. 3.52).

The drafting machine (Fig. 3.53) is designed to combine the functions of the T-square, triangles, scale, and protractor. Drafting machines are used extensively in commercial drafting rooms because it has been estimated that their use leads to a 25 to 50 per cent saving in time.

3.28. Tracing paper. White light-weight tracing paper, on which pencil drawings can be made and from which blueprints can be produced, is used in most commercial drafting rooms in order to keep labor costs at a minimum.

3.29. Tracing cloth. The two general types of cloth available are ink cloth and pencil cloth. The cloth used for ink is clear and transparent, dull on one side, and glossy on the other. Pencil cloth is a white cloth with a surface specially prepared to take pencil marks readily.

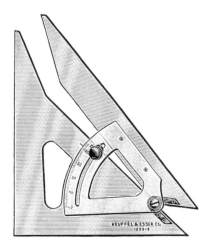

Fig. 3.49. Protractor angle.

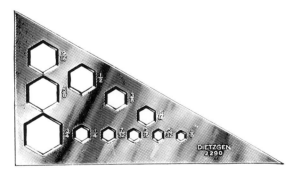

Fig. 3.50. Wrico triangle (*Courtesy Eugene Dietzgen Co.*).

ELECTRO SYMBOL TEMPLATE

CHEMISTRY TEMPLATE

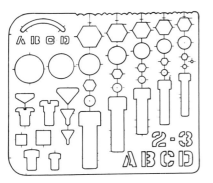

TOOLING TEMPLATE

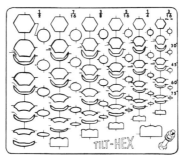

TILT-HEX DRAFTING TEMPLATE

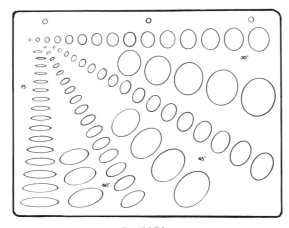

ELLIPSES

Fig. 3.51. Special templates (*Courtesy Frederick Post Co.*).

Fig. 3.52. Proportional dividers.

Fig. 3.53. Drafting machine (*Courtesy Keuffel & Esser Co.*).

Exercises in instrumental drawing

The following elementary exercises have been designed to offer experience in the use of the drafting instruments. The designs should be drawn *lightly* with a hard pencil. After making certain that all constructions shown on a drawing are correct, the lines forming the designs should be heavied with a medium-hard pencil. The light construction lines need not be erased if the drawing has been kept relatively clean. All dimensions and letters should be omitted except in Problem 5.

1. (Fig. 3.54.) On a sheet of drawing paper reproduce the line formations shown. If the principal border lines have not been printed on the sheet, they may be drawn first so that the large 5½″ × 8¼″ rectangle can be balanced horizontally and vertically within the border. To draw the inclined lines, first draw the indicated measuring lines through the lettered points at the correct angle, and mark off ¼″ distances. These division points establish the locations of the required lines of the formation. The six squares of the formation are equal in size.

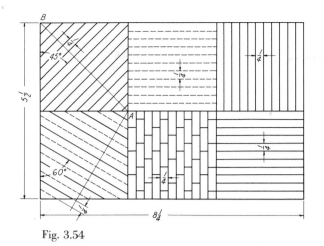

Fig. 3.54

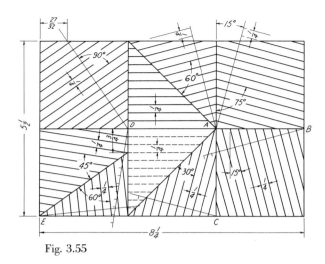

Fig. 3.55

2. (Fig. 3.55.) Reproduce the line formations shown, following the instructions given for Problem 1.

3. (Fig. 3.56.) This exercise is designed to give the student practice with the bow pencil and compass by drawing some simple geometric figures. The line work within each large circle may be reproduced with the knowledge only that the diameter is 3¼″. All circles and circle arcs are to be made finished weight when they are first drawn, since retracing often produces a double line. Do not "overrun" the straight lines or stop them too short.

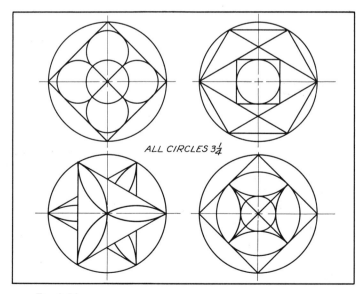

Fig. 3.56

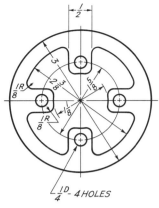

Fig. 3.57

4. (Fig. 3.57.) Reproduce the contour view of the stamping.

5. (Fig. 3.58.) Select a suitable scale and reproduce the design of the highway intersection shown. Using ³⁄₁₆″ capital letters, letter the words HIGHWAY INTERSECTION. Using ⅛″ letters and numerals, letter the dimensions. Draw the arrows indicating the direction of traffic flow.

6-9. (Figs. 3.59–3.62.) Reproduce the geometric shapes.

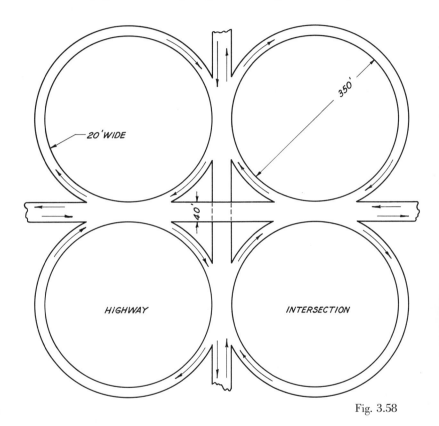

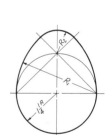

Fig. 3.59. Oval.

Fig. 3.58

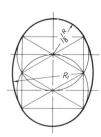

Fig. 3.60. Ellipse (approximate).

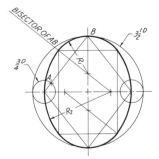

Fig. 3.61. Ellipse (approximate).

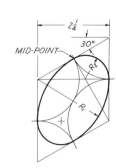

Fig. 3.62. Ellipse (pictorial).

ENGINEERING GEOMETRY

4.1. Introduction. The simplified geometrical constructions presented in this chapter are those with which an engineer should be familiar, for they frequently occur in engineering drawing. The methods are applications of the principles found in textbooks on plane geometry. The constructions have been modified to take advantage of time-saving methods made possible by the use of drawing instruments.

Since a study of the subject of plane geometry should be a prerequisite for a course in engineering drawing, the mathematical proofs have been omitted intentionally. Geometric terms applying to lines, surfaces, and solids, however, are given in Figs. 4.62 and 4.63 for the purpose of review.

4.2. To bisect a straight line (Fig. 4.1).

(*a*) With *A* and *B* as centers, strike the intersecting arcs as shown using any radius greater than one-half of *AB*. A straight line through points *C* and *D* bisects *AB*.

(*b*) Draw either 60° or 45° lines through *E* and *F*. Through their intersection draw the perpendicular *GH* that will bisect *EF*.

The use of the dividers to divide or bisect a line by the trial method is explained in Sec. 3.19.

4.3. To trisect a straight line (Fig. 4.2).
Given the line *AB*. Draw the lines *AO* and *OB* making 30° with *AB*. Similarly, draw *CO* and *OD* making 60° with *AB*. *AC* equals *CD* equals *DB*.

4.4. To bisect an angle (Fig. 4.3).

(*a*) Given the angle *BAC*. Use any radius with the vertex *A* as a center, and strike an arc that intersects the sides of the angle at *D* and *E*. With *D* and *E* as centers and a radius larger than one-half of *DE*, draw intersecting arcs. Draw *AF*. Angle *BAF* equals angle *FAC*.

(*b*) Given an angle formed by the lines *KL* and *MN* having an inaccessible point of intersection. Draw *BA* parallel to *KL* and *CA* parallel to *MN* at the same distance from *MN* as *BA* is from *KL*. Bisect angle *BAC* using the method explained in (*a*). The bisector *FA* of angle *BAC* bisects the angle between the lines *KL* and *MN*.

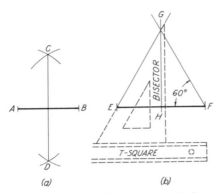

(*a*)   (*b*)

Fig. 4.1. To bisect a straight line.

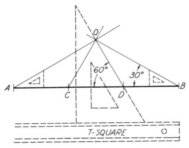

Fig. 4.2. To trisect a straight line.

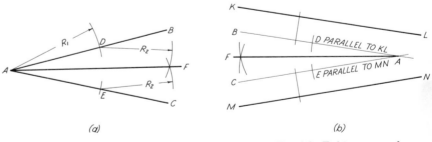

(*a*)   (*b*)

Fig. 4.3. To bisect an angle.

4.5. To draw parallel curved lines about a curved center line (Fig. 4.4). Draw a series of arcs having centers located at random along the given center line *AB*. Using the French curve, draw the required curved lines tangent to these arcs.

4.6. To trisect an angle (Fig. 4.5). Given the angle *BAC*. Lay off along *AB* any convenient distance *AD*. Draw *DE* perpendicular to *AC* and *DF* parallel to *AC*. Place the scale so that it passes through *A* with a distance equal to twice *AD* intercepted between the lines *DE* and *DF*. Angle *HAC* equals one-third of the angle *BAC*.

4.7. To divide a straight line into a given number of equal parts (Fig. 4.6). Given the line *LM* which is to be divided into five equal parts.

(*a*) Step off, with the dividers, five equal divisions along a line making any convenient angle with *LM*. Connect the last point *P* with *M*, and through the remaining points draw lines parallel to *MP* intersecting the given line. These lines divide *LM* into five equal parts.

(*b*) Some commercial draftsmen prefer a modification of this construction known as the scale method. For the first step, draw a vertical *PM* through point *M*. Place the scale so that the first mark of five equal divisions is at *L* and the last mark falls on *PM*. Locate the four intervening division points, and through these draw verticals intersecting the given line. The verticals will divide *LM* into five equal parts.

4.8. To divide a line proportionally (Fig. 4.7). Given the line *AB*. Draw *BC* perpendicular to *AB*. Place the scale across *A* and *BC* so that the number of divisions intercepted is equal to the sum of the numbers representing the proportions. Mark off these proportions

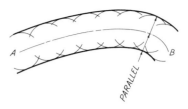

Fig. 4.4. To draw parallel curved lines.

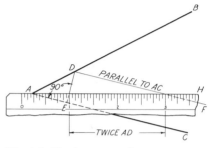

Fig. 4.5. To trisect an angle.

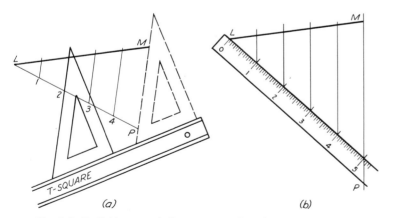

Fig. 4.6. To divide a straight line into a number of equal parts.

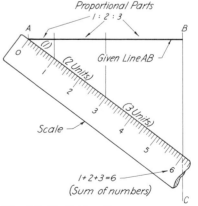

Fig. 4.7. To divide a line proportionally.

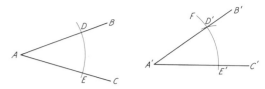

Fig. 4.8. To construct an angle equal to a given angle.

and draw lines parallel to BC to divide AB as required. The proportions in Fig. 4.7 are $1:2:3$.

4.9. To construct an angle equal to a given angle (Fig. 4.8). Given the angle BAC and the line $A'C'$ that forms one side of the transferred angle. Use any convenient radius with the vertex A as a center, and strike the arc that intersects the sides of the angle at D and E. With A' as a center, strike the arc intersecting $A'C'$ at E'. With E' as a center and the chord distance DE as a radius, strike a short intersecting arc to locate D'. $A'B'$ drawn through D' makes angle $B'A'C'$ equal angle BAC.

4.10. To draw a line through a given point and the inaccessible intersection of two given lines (Fig. 4.9). Given the lines KL and MN, and the point P. Construct any triangle such as PQR having its vertices falling on the given lines and the given point. At some convenient location construct triangle STU similar to PQR, by drawing SU parallel to PR, TU parallel to QR, and ST parallel to PQ. PS is the required line.

4.11. To construct an angle, tangent method (Fig. 4.10). Draftsmen often find it necessary to draw long lines having an angle between them that is not equal to an angle of a triangle. Such an angle may be laid off with a protractor, but it should be remembered that as the lines are extended any error is multiplied. To avoid this situation, the tangent method may be used. The tangent method involves trigonometry but, since it is frequently used, a discussion of it here is pertinent. (See Table 27 of the Appendix.)

In this method, a distance D_1 is laid off along a line that is to form one side of the angle, and a distance D_2, equal to D_1 times the natural tangent of the angle, is marked off along a perpendicular through point P. A line through point X is the required line, and angle A is the required angle. In laying off the distance D_1, unnecessary multiplication will be eliminated if the distance is arbitrarily made 10 in. When the use of 10 in. for D_1 makes P fall off the drawing, a temporary auxiliary sheet will furnish space needed to carry out the construction.

This method is also used for angles formed by short lines whenever a protractor is not available.

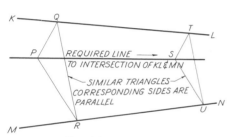

Fig. 4.9. To draw a line through a given point and the inaccessible intersection of two given lines.

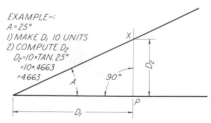

Fig. 4.10. To construct an angle, tangent method.

4.12. To construct an angle, chord method (Fig. 4.11). Engineers and draftsmen frequently select the chordal method for constructing an angle accurately. This method, as applied in laying out a given angle, involves the use of an easily determined chord length for a selected length of radius laid off in units. Given the angle (say 29°) the procedure is as follows: First, lay off any convenient distance, usually 10 in., along a line that is to form one side of the angle and strike an arc of indefinite length using this distance as a radius; Second, obtain the unit chord value for the given angle from Table 29 of the Appendix (29° = .5008) and multiply this value by 10. With the compass or dividers lay off the chord length (.5008 × 10 = 5.008) along the arc from the starting line and complete the angle.

When a table of chords is not available, the chord length for a 1-in. radius may be calculated for a given angle by taking the sine of one-half the angle and multiplying by 2. For example, one-half of 29° = 14° 30′. The sine of 14° 30′ multiplied by 2 is .2504 × 2 = .5008.

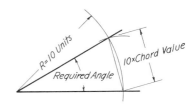

Fig. 4.11. To construct an angle, chord method.

4.13. To construct a triangle having its three sides given (Fig. 4.12). Given the three sides AB, AC, and BC. Draw the side AB in its correct location. Using its end points A and B as centers and radii equal to AC and BC, respectively, strike the two intersecting arcs locating point C. ABC is the required triangle. This construction is particularly useful for developing the surface of a transition piece by triangulation.

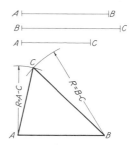

Fig. 4.12. To construct a triangle with three sides given.

4.14. To construct an equilateral triangle (Fig. 4.13). Given the side AB.

(*a*) Using the end-points A and B as centers and a radius equal to the length of AB, strike two intersecting arcs to locate C. Draw lines from A to C and C to B to complete the required equilateral triangle.

(*b*) Using a 30°–60° triangle, draw through A and B lines that make 60° with the given line. If the line AB is inclined, the 60° lines should be drawn as shown in Fig. 3.18.

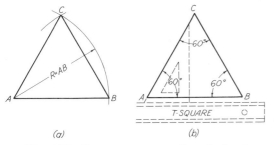

Fig. 4.13. To construct an equilateral triangle.

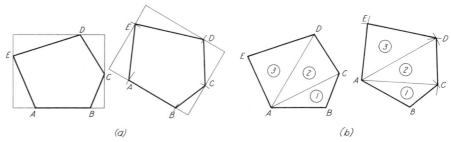

Fig. 4.14. To transfer a polygon.

4.15. To transfer a polygon (Fig. 4.14).   Given the polygon *ABCDE*.

(*a*) Enclose the polygon in a rectangle. Draw the "enclosing rectangle" in the new position and locate points *A, B, C, D*, and *E* along the sides by measuring from the corners of the rectangle. A compass may be used for transferring the necessary measurements.

(*b*) To transfer a polygon by the triangle method, divide the polygon into triangles and, using the construction explained in Sec. 4.13, reconstruct each triangle in its transferred position.

4.16. To construct a square (Fig. 4.15).

(*a*) Given the side *AB*. Using a T-square and a 45° triangle, draw perpendiculars to line *AB* through points *A* and *B*. Locate point *D* at the intersection of a 45° construction line through *A* and the perpendicular from *B*. Draw *CD* parallel to *AB* through *D* to complete the square. To eliminate unnecessary movements the lines should be drawn in the order indicated.

(*b*) Given the diagonal length *EF*. Using a T-square and a 45° triangle, construct the square by drawing lines through *E* and *F* at an angle of 45° with *EF* in the order indicated.

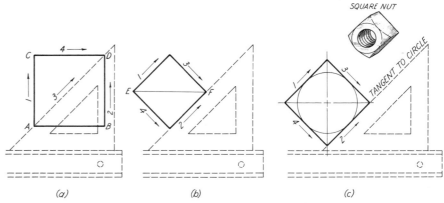

Fig. 4.15. To construct a square.

(*c*) The construction of an inscribed circle is the first step in one method for drawing a square when the location of the center and the length of one side are given.

Using a T-square and a 45° triangle, draw the sides of the square tangent to the circle. This construction is used in drawing square bolt heads and nuts.

4.17. To construct a regular pentagon (Fig. 4.16).

Given the circumscribing circle. Draw the perpendicular diameters *AB* and *CD*. Bisect *OB* and, with its mid-point *E* as a center and *EC* as a radius, draw the arc *CF*. Using *C* as a center and *CF* as a radius, draw the arc *FG*. The line *CG* is one of the equal sides of the required pentagon. Locate the remaining vertices by striking off this distance around the circumference.

If the length of one side of a pentagon is given, the construction described in Sec. 4.20 should be used.

4.18. To construct a regular hexagon (Fig. 4.17).

(*a*) Given the distance *AB* across corners. Draw a circle having *AB* as a diameter. Using the same radius and with points *A* and *B* as centers, strike arcs intersecting the circumference. Join these points to complete the construction.

(*b*) Given the distance *AB* across corners. Using a 30°–60° triangle and a T-square, draw the lines in the order indicated by the numbers on the figure.

(*c*) Given the distance across flats. Draw a circle whose diameter equals the distance across flats. Using a 30°–60° triangle and a T-square, as shown, draw the tangents that establish the sides and vertices of the required hexagon.

This construction is used in drawing hexagonal bolt heads and nuts.

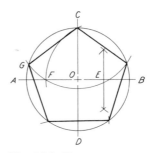

Fig. 4.16. To construct a regular pentagon.

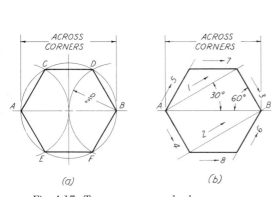

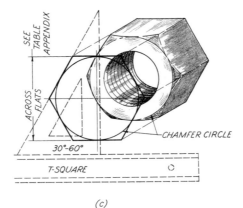

Fig. 4.17. To construct a regular hexagon.

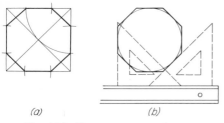

(a)   *(b)*

Fig. 4.18. To construct a regular octagon.

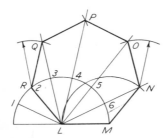

Fig. 4.19. To construct any regular polygon, having one side given.

4.19. To construct a regular octagon (Fig. 4.18).

(*a*) Given the distance across flats. Draw the circumscribed square and its diagonals. Using the corners as centers and one-half the diagonal as a radius, strike arcs across the sides of the square. Join these points to complete the required octagon.

(*b*) Given the distance across flats. Draw the inscribed circle; then, using a 45° triangle and T-square, draw the tangents that establish the sides and vertices of the required octagon.

4.20. To construct any regular polygon having one side given (Fig. 4.19).
Given the side *LM*. With *LM* as a radius, draw a semicircle and divide it into the same number of equal parts as the number of sides needed for the polygon. Suppose the polygon is to be seven-sided. Draw radial lines through points 2, 3, and so forth. Point 2 (the second division point) is always one of the vertices of the polygon, and line *L2* is a side. Using point *M* as a center and *LM* as a radius, strike an arc across the radial line *L6* to locate point *N*. Using the same radius with *N* as a center, strike another arc across *L5* to establish *O* on *L5*. Although this procedure may be continued with point *O* as the next center, more accurate results will be obtained if point *R* is used as a center for the arc to locate *Q*, and *Q* as a center for *P*.

4.21. To divide the area of a triangle or trapezoid into a given number of equal parts (Fig. 4.20).

(*a*) Given the triangle *ABC*. Divide the side *AC* into (say five) equal parts, and draw a semicircle having *AC* the diameter. Through the division points (1, 2, 3, and 4) draw perpendicular lines to points of intersection with the semicircle (5, 6, 7, and 8). Using *C* as a center, strike arcs through these points (5, 6, 7, and 8) that will cut *AC*. To complete the construction, draw lines parallel to *AB* through the points (9, 10, 11, and 12) at which the arcs intersect the side *AC*.

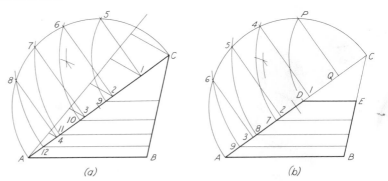

(a)   *(b)*

Fig. 4.20. To divide the area of a triangle (or trapezoid) into a given number of equal parts.

(*b*) Given the trapezoid *DEBA*. Extend the sides of the trapezoid to form the triangle *ABC* and draw a semicircle on *AC* with *AC* as a diameter. Using *C* as a center and *CD* as a radius, strike an arc cutting the semicircle at point *P*. Through *P* draw a perpendicular to *AC* to locate point *Q*. Divide *QA* into the same number of equal parts as the number of equal areas required (in this case four), and proceed using the construction explained in (*a*) for dividing the area of a triangle into a given number of equal parts.

4.22. To find the center for a circle through three given points not in a straight line (Fig. 4.21). Given the three points *A*, *B*, and *C*. Join the points with straight lines (which will be chords of the required circle), and draw the perpendicular bisectors. The point of intersection *O* of the bisectors is the center of the required circle, and *OA*, *OB*, or *OC* is its radius.

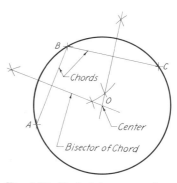

Fig. 4.21. To find the center of a circle through three points.

4.23. Tangent circles and arcs. Figure 4.22 illustrates the geometry of tangent circles. In (*a*) it can be noted that the locus of centers for circles of radius *R* tangent to *AB* is a line that is parallel to *AB* at a distance *R* from *AB*. The locus of centers for circles of the same radius tangent to *CD* is a line that is parallel to *CD* at *R* (radius) distance from *CD*. Since point *O* at which these lines intersect is *R* distance from both *AB* and *CD*, a circle of radius *R* with center at *O* must be tangent to both *AB* and *CD*.

In (*b*) the locus of centers for circles of radius R_3 that will be tangent to the circle with a center at *O* and having a radius R_1 is a circle that is concentric with the given circle at R_3 distance. The radius of the locus of centers will be $R_1 + R_3$. In the case of the circle with center at point *P*, the radius of the locus of centers will be $R_2 + R_3$. Points *Q* and Q_1 where these arcs intersect are points that are R_3 distance from both circles. Therefore, circles of R_3 radius that are centered at *Q* and Q_1 will be tangent to both circles with centers at *O* and *P*.

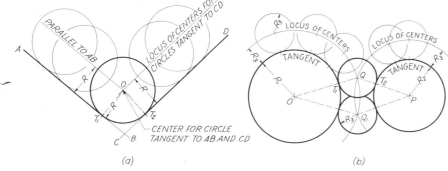

(*a*) (*b*)

Fig. 4.22. Tangent circles.

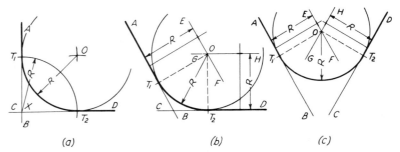

Fig. 4.23. To draw a circular arc tangent to two lines.

4.24. To draw a circular arc of radius *R* tangent to two lines (Fig. 4.23).

(*a*) Given the two lines *AB* and *CD* at right angles to each other, and the radius of the required arc *R*. Using their point of intersection *X* as a center and *R* as a radius, strike an arc cutting the given lines at T_1 and T_2 (tangent points). With T_1 and T_2 as centers and the same radius, strike the intersecting arcs locating the center *O* of the required arc.

(*b*), (*c*) Given the two lines *AB* and *CD*, not at right angles, and the radius *R*. Draw lines *EF* and *GH* parallel to the given lines at a distance *R*. Since the point of intersection of these lines is distance *R* from both given lines, it will be the center *O* of the required arc. Mark the tangent points T_1 and T_2 that lie along perpendiculars to the given lines through *O*.

These constructions are useful for drawing fillets and rounds on views of machine parts.

4.25. To draw a circular arc of radius R_1 tangent to a given circular arc and a given straight line (Fig. 4.24). Given the line *AB* and the circular arc with center *O*.

(*a*), (*b*) Let R_1 be the radius of the required arc. Draw line *CD* parallel to *AB* at a distance R_1. Using the center *O* of the given arc and a radius equal to its radius plus or minus the radius of the required arc (R_2 plus or minus R_1), swing a parallel arc intersect-

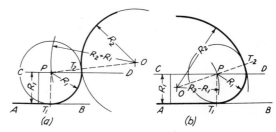

Fig. 4.24. To draw a circular arc tangent to a given circular arc and a line.

ing *CD*. Since the line *CD* and the intersecting arc will be the loci of centers for all circles of radius R_1, tangent respectively to the given line *AB* and the given arc, their point of intersection *P* will be the center of the required arc. Mark the points of tangency T_1 and T_2. T_1 lies along a perpendicular to *AB* through the center *P*, and T_2 along a line joining the centers of the two arcs.

This construction is also useful for drawing fillets and rounds on views of machine parts.

4.26. To draw a circular arc of a given radius R_1 tangent to two given circular arcs (Fig. 4.25). Given the circular arcs *AB* and *CD* with centers *O* and *P*, and radii R_2 and R_3, respectively. Let R_1 be the radius of the required arc.

(*a*), (*b*) Using *O* as a center and R_2 plus R_1 as a radius, strike an arc parallel to *AB*. Using *P* as a center and R_3 plus R_1 as a radius, strike an intersecting arc parallel to *CD*. Since each of these intersecting arcs is the locus of centers for all circular arcs of radius R_1 tangent to the given arc to which it is parallel, their point of intersection *S* will be the center for the required arc that is tangent to both. Mark the points of tangency T_1 and T_2 that lie on the lines of centers *PS* and *OS*.

(*c*) Using *O* as a center and R_2 plus R_1 as a radius, strike an arc parallel to *AB*. Using *P* as a center and R_3 minus R_1 as a radius, strike an intersecting arc parallel to *CD*. The point of intersection of these arcs is the center for the required arc.

4.27. To draw a reverse (ogee) curve (Fig. 4.26). Given the two parallel lines *AB* and *CD*. At points *B* and *C*, the termini and tangent points of the reverse curve, erect perpendiculars. Join *BC* with a straight line and assume a point *E* that will be the point at which the curves will be tangent to each other. Draw the perpendicular bisectors of *BE* and *EC*. Since an arc tangent to *AB* at *B* must have its center on the perpendicular *BP*, point of intersection *P* of the bisector and the perpendicular is the center for the required

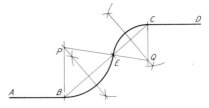

Fig. 4.26. To draw a reverse curve.

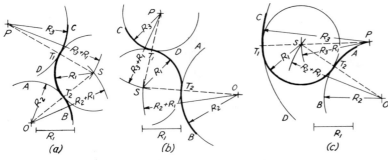

Fig. 4.25. To draw a circular arc tangent to two given arcs.

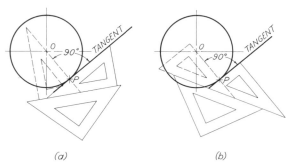

Fig. 4.27. To draw a line tangent to a circle at a point on the circumference.

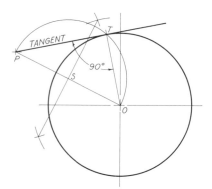

Fig. 4.28. To draw a line tangent to a circle through a given point outside.

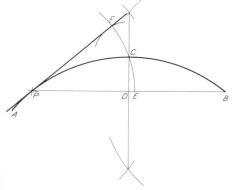

Fig. 4.29. To draw a tangent to a circular arc having an inaccessible center.

arc that is to be tangent to the line at B and the other required arc at point E. For the same reason, point Q is the center for the other required arc.

This construction is useful to engineers in laying out center lines for railroad tracks, pipe lines, and so forth.

4.28. To draw a line tangent to a circle at a given point on the circumference (Fig. 4.27). Given a circle with center O and point P on its circumference. Place a triangle supported by a T-square or another triangle in such a position that one side passes through the center O and point P. When using the method illustrated in (a), align the hypotenuse of one triangle to the center of the circle and the point of tangency; then, with a guiding triangle held in position, revolve the triangle about the 90° angle and slide into position for drawing the required tangent line.

Another procedure is shown in (b). To draw the tangent by this method, align one leg of a triangle, which is adjacent to the 90° angle, through the center of the circle and the point of tangency; then, slide it along the edge of a guiding triangle into position.

This construction satisfies the geometric requirement that a tangent must be perpendicular to a radial line drawn to the point of tangency.

4.29. To draw a line tangent to a circle through a given point outside the circle (Fig. 4.28). Given a circle with center O, and an external point P.

Join the point P and the center O with a straight line, and bisect it to locate point S. Using S as a center and SO (one-half PO) as a radius, strike an arc intersecting the circle at point T (point of tangency). Line PT is the required tangent.

4.30. To draw a tangent through a point P on a circular arc having an inaccessible center (Fig. 4.29). Draw the chord PB; then, erect a perpendicular bisector. With point P as a center swing an arc through point C where the perpendicular bisector cuts the given arc. With C as a center and a radius equal to the chord distance CE, draw an arc to establish the location of point F. A line drawn through points P and F is the required tangent.

4.31. To draw a line tangent to a circle through a given point outside the circle (Fig. 4.30).

Place a triangle supported by a T-square or another triangle in such a position that one leg passes through point P tangent to the circle, and draw the tangent. Slide the triangle along the guiding edge until the other leg coincides with the center O, and mark the point of tangency. Although this method is not as accurate as the geometric one explained in Sec. 4.29, it is frequently employed by commercial draftsmen.

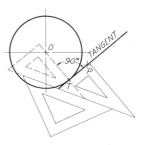

Fig. 4.30. To draw a line tangent to a circle through a given point outside.

4.32. To draw a line tangent to two given circles (Fig. 4.31).

Given two circles with centers O and P and radii R_1 and R.

(a) Open belt—Using P as a center and a radius equal to R minus R_1, draw an arc. Through O draw a tangent to this arc using the method explained in Sec. 4.29. With the location of tangent point T established, draw line PT and extend it to locate T_1. Draw OT_2 parallel to PT_1. The line from T_2 to T_1 is the required tangent to the given circles.

(b) Crossed belt—Using P as a center and a radius equal to R plus R_1, draw an arc. With the location of tangent point T determined through use of the method shown in Fig. 4.28, locate tangent point T_1 on line TP and draw OT_2 parallel to PT. The line T_1T_2, drawn parallel to OT, is the required tangent.

4.33. To approximate a curve with tangent circular arcs (Fig. 4.32).

Draftsmen often find it desirable to approximate a noncircular curve with a series of tangent arcs. If the curve consists of a number of points, a pleasing curve should be sketched lightly through points

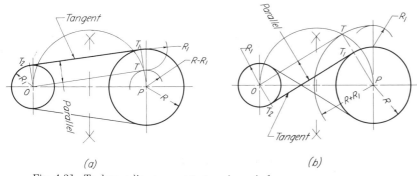

(a)   (b)

Fig. 4.31. To draw a line tangent to two given circles.

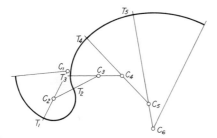

Fig. 4.32. To approximate a curve with tangent circular arcs.

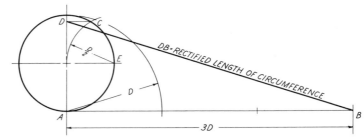

Fig. 4.33. To lay off the approximate length of the circumference of a circle.

before starting to draw the arcs. The centers and radii are selected by trial but it must be remembered after the first arc has been drawn as far as it coincides with the sketched curve that when arcs are tangent the centers are on a common normal through their point of tangency. Sometimes draftsmen use this method to draw curves in ink instead of using a French curve.

4.34. To lay off the approximate length of the circumference of a circle (Fig. 4.33). Draw a line through point A tangent to the circle and lay off along it a distance AB equal to three times the diameter ($3D$). Using point E on the circumference as a center and a radius equal to the radius of the circle strike an arc to establish the location of point C. Draw CD perpendicular to the vertical center line through point A. DB is the rectified length of the circumference; however, it is slightly longer than the true circumference by a negligible amount (approximate error $1/21,800$).

4.35. To lay off the approximate length of a circular arc on its tangent (Fig. 4.34). Given the arc AB.

(a) Draw the tangent through A, and extend the chord BA. Locate point C by laying off AC equal to one-half the length of the chord AB. With C as a center and a radius equal to CB, strike an

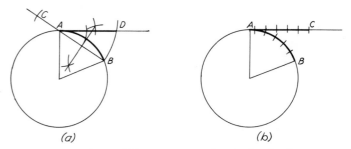

Fig. 4.34. To lay off the approximate length of a circular arc on its tangent.

arc intersecting the tangent at D. The length AD along the tangent is slightly shorter than the true length of the arc AB by an amount that may be disregarded, for, when the angle between the chord and the tangent is less than $60°$, the length of AD differs from the true length of the arc AB by less than 6 ft in one mile; when $30°$, the error is $4\frac{1}{2}$ in. in one mile.

(*b*) Draw the tangent through A. Using the small dividers, start at B and step off equal chord distances around the arc until the point nearest A is reached. From this point (without raising the dividers) step off along the tangent an equal number of distances to locate point C. If the point nearest A is indented into the tangent instead of the arc, the almost negligible error in the length of AC will be still less.

Since the small distances stepped off are in reality the chords of small arcs, the length AC will be slightly less than the true length of the arc. For most practical purposes the difference may be disregarded.

4.36. Conic sections (Fig. 4.35). When a right circular cone of revolution is cut by planes at different angles four curves of intersection are obtained that are called *conic sections.*

When the intersecting plane is perpendicular to the axis the resulting curve of intersection is a *circle.*

If the plane makes a greater angle with the axis than do the elements the intersection is an *ellipse.*

If the plane makes the same angle with the axis as the elements the resulting curve is a *parabola.*

Finally, if the plane makes a smaller angle with the axis than do the elements or is parallel to the axis the curve of intersection is a *hyperbola.*

The geometric methods for constructing the ellipse, parabola, and hyperbola are discussed in succeeding sections.

4.37. The ellipse. Mathematically the ellipse is a curve generated by a point moving so that at any position the sum of its distances

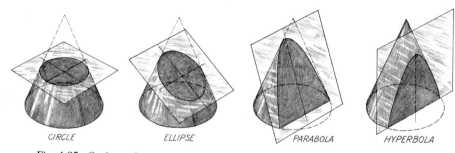

CIRCLE   ELLIPSE   PARABOLA   HYPERBOLA

Fig. 4.35. Conic sections.

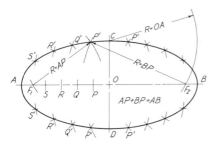

Fig. 4.36. To draw an ellipse, using the foci.

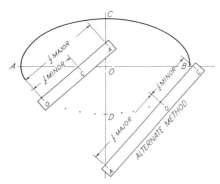

Fig. 4.37. To construct an ellipse, trammel method.

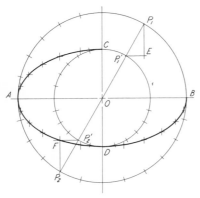

Fig. 4.38. To construct an ellipse, concentric circle method.

from two fixed points (foci) is a constant (equal to the major diameter). It is encountered very frequently in orthographic drawing when holes and circular forms are viewed obliquely. Ordinarily, the major and minor diameters are known.

4.38. Ellipse construction—foci method (Fig. 4.36). Draw the major and minor axes (AB, CD) and locate the foci F_1 and F_2 by striking arcs, centered at C, having a radius equal to OA (one-half of the major diameter). The construction is as follows: Determine the number of points needed along the circumference of each quadrant of the ellipse for a relatively accurate layout (say four) and mark off this number of division points (P, Q, R, and S) between O and F_1 on the major axis. In many cases, it may be desirable to use additional points spaced closer together nearer F_1 in order to form accurately the sharp curvature at the end of the ellipse. Next, with F_1 and F_2 as centers and the distances AP and BP as radii respectively, strike intersecting arcs to locate P' on the circumference of the ellipse. Distances AQ and BQ are radii for locating points Q'. Locate points R' and S' in a similar manner and complete the ellipse using a French curve.

This method is sometimes known as the definition method, since it is based upon the mathematical definition of the ellipse as given in Sec. 4.37.

4.39. To construct an ellipse, trammel method (Fig. 4.37). Given the major axis AB and the minor axis CD. Along the straight edge of a strip of paper or cardboard, locate the points O, C, and A, so that the distance OA is equal to one-half the length of the major axis and the distance OC is equal to one-half the length of the minor axis. Place the marked edge across the axes so that point A is on the minor axis and point C is on the major axis. *Point O will fall on the circumference of the ellipse.* Move the strip, keeping A on the minor axis and C on the major axis, and mark at least five other positions of O on the ellipse in each quadrant. Using a French curve, complete the ellipse by drawing a smooth curve through the points. The ellipsograph, which draws ellipses mechanically, is based on this same principle. The trammel method is an accurate method.

An alternate method for marking off the location of points A, O, and C is given in Fig. 4.37.

4.40. To construct an ellipse, concentric circle method (Fig. 4.38). Given the major axis AB and the minor axis CD. Using the center of the ellipse (point O) as a center, describe circles having the major and minor axes as diameters. Divide the circles into equal central angles and draw diametrical lines such as P_1P_2. From point P_1 on the circumference of the larger circle, draw a line parallel to CD, the minor axis, and from point P_1' at which the diameter P_1P_2 intersects the inner circle, draw a line parallel to AB, the major axis. The point of intersection of these lines, point E, is on the required ellipse. At points P_2 and P_2' repeat the same procedure and locate point F. Thus, two points are established by the line P_1P_2. Locate at least five points in each of the four quadrants. The ellipse is completed by drawing a smooth curve through the points.

This is one of the most accurate methods used to form ellipses.

4.41. To construct an ellipse, four-center method (Fig. 4.39). Given the major axis AB and the minor axis CD. Draw the line AC. Using the center of the ellipse O as a center and OC as a radius, strike an arc intersecting OA at point E. Using C as a center and EA as a radius, strike an arc intersecting the line AC at F. Draw the perpendicular bisector of the line AF. The points G and H, at which the perpendicular bisector intersects the axes AB and CD (extended) are the centers of two of the arcs forming the ellipse. Locate the other two centers, J and K, by laying off OJ equal to OH and OK equal to OG. To determine the junction points (tangent points), T, T_1, T_2, and T_3, for the arcs, draw lines through the centers of the tangent arcs. The figure thus formed by the four circle arcs approximates a true ellipse.

4.42. To construct an ellipse, parallelogram method (Fig. 4.40). Given the major axis AB and the minor axis CD. Construct the circumscribing parallelogram. Divide AO and AE into the same number of equal parts (say four) and number the division points from A. From C draw a line through point 3 on line AE, and from D draw a line through point 3 on line AO. The point of intersection of these lines is on the required ellipse. Similarly, the intersections of lines from C and D through points numbered 1 and 2 are on the ellipse. A similar construction will locate points in the other three quadrants of the ellipse. Use of a French curve will permit a smooth curve to be drawn through the points.

Had the circumscribing parallelogram not been a rectangle as in Fig. 4.40, the completed construction would appear as in Fig. 4.41, and AB and CD would be conjugate axes. To establish the major and minor axes, draw a semicircle on CD as a diameter, intersecting the ellipse at E. FG, running parallel to CE through the center of the ellipse, will be the required minor axis. HK, running through the center of the ellipse parallel to DE and perpendicular to FG, will be the major axis.

4.43. To draw a tangent to an ellipse at any given point (Fig. 4.42). Given any point, such as P, on the perimeter of the ellipse $ABCD$. Using C as a center and a radius equal to OA (one-half the

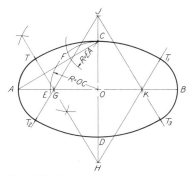

Fig. 4.39. To construct an ellipse, center method.

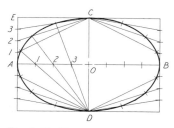

Fig. 4.40. To construct an ellipse, parallelogram method.

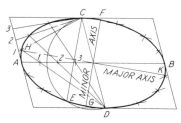

Fig. 4.41. To draw the major and minor axes of an ellipse, given the conjugate diameters.

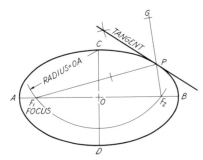

Fig. 4.42. To draw a tangent to an ellipse.

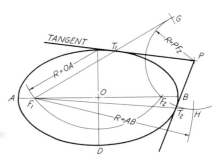

Fig. 4.43. To draw a tangent to an ellipse through a point outside of the ellipse.

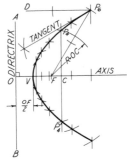

Fig. 4.44. To construct a parabola.

major diameter), strike arcs across the major axis at F_1 and F_2. From these points, which are foci of the ellipse, draw F_1P and F_2G. The bisector of the angle GPF_1 is the required tangent to the ellipse.

In practice it will often be convenient to use the chord method explained in Sec. 22.5 for constructing tangents. See Fig. 22.13.

4.44. To draw a tangent to an ellipse from a given point P outside of the ellipse (Fig. 4.43). With the end of the minor axis as a center and a radius R equal to one-half of the length of the major axis, strike an arc to find the foci F_1 and F_2. With point P as a center and the distance PF_2 as a radius, draw an arc. Using F_1 as a center and the length AB as a radius strike arcs cutting the arc with center of P at points G and H. Draw lines GF_1 and HF_1 to establish the location of the tangent points T_1 and T_2. Draw the required tangent.

4.45. The parabola. Mathematically the parabola is a curve generated by a point moving so that at any position its distance from a fixed point (the focus) is always exactly equal to its distance to a fixed line (the directrix). The construction shown in Fig. 4.44 is based on this definition.

In engineering design, the parabola is used for parabolic sound and light reflectors, for vertical curves on highways, and for bridge arches.

4.46. To construct a parabola (Fig. 4.44). Given the focus F and the directrix AB. Draw the axis of the parabola perpendicular to the directrix. Through any point on the axis, for example point C, draw a line parallel to the directrix AB. Using F as a center and the distance OC as a radius, strike arcs intersecting the line at points P_4 and P_4'. Repeat this procedure until a sufficient number of additional points have been located to determine a smooth curve. The vertex V is located at a point midway between O and F.

To construct a tangent to a parabola, say at point P_6, draw the line P_6D parallel to the axis; then, bisect the angle DP_6F. The bisector of the angle is the required tangent. Read Sec. 22.5 and study Fig. 22.13.

4.47. To construct a parabola, tangent method (Fig. 4.45). Given the points A and B and the distance CD from AB to the vertex. Extend the axis CD, and set off DE equal to CD. EA and EB are tangents to the parabola at A and B respectively.

Divide EA and EB into the same number of equal parts (say six), and number the division points as shown. Connect the corresponding points 1 and 1, 2 and 2, 3 and 3, and so forth. These lines,

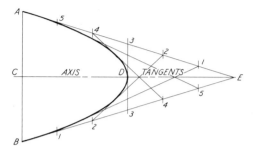

Fig. 4.45. To construct a parabola, tangent method.

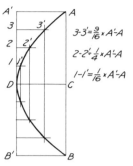

Fig. 4.46. To construct a parabola, offset method.

as tangents of the required parabola, form its envelope. Draw the tangent curve.

4.48. To construct a parabola, offset method (Fig. 4.46). Given the enclosing rectangle $A'ABB'$. Divide DA' into any number of equal parts (say four), and draw from the division points the perpendiculars parallel to DC, along which the offset distances are to be measured off. The offsets vary as the square of their distances from D. For example, since $D1$ is one-fourth of the distance from A' to D, $1-1'$ will be $(\frac{1}{4})^2$, or $\frac{1}{16}$ of $A'A$. Similarly, $2-2'$ will be $(\frac{1}{2})^2$, or $\frac{1}{4}$ of $A'A$; and $3-3'$ will be $\frac{9}{16}$ of $A'A$. To complete the parabola, lay off the computed offset values along the perpendiculars and form the figure with a French curve.

This method is preferred by civil engineers for laying out parabolic arches and computing vertical curves for highways.

4.49. To construct a curve of parabolic form through two given points (Fig. 4.47). Given the points A and B. Assume a point C. Draw the tangents CA and CB, and construct the parabolic curve using the tangent method shown in Fig. 4.45. This method is frequently used in machine design to draw curves that are more pleasing than circular arcs.

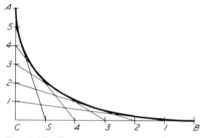

Fig. 4.47. To construct a curve of parabolic form.

4.50. To construct a parabola, parallelogram method. Since the dimensions for a parallelogram that will enclose a given parabola are generally known, a parabola may be constructed by the parallelogram method illustrated in Fig. 4.48. With the enclosing rectangle drawn to the given width and depth dimensions [see (a)] divide VA and AB into the same number of equal divisions (say five) and number the division points as shown. Draw light construction lines from point V to each of the division points along AB. Then, draw lines parallel to the axis from points 1, 2, 3, and 4 on VA. The intersection of the construction lines from points numbered 1 is on the parabola.

Likewise, the intersection of the lines from points numbered 2

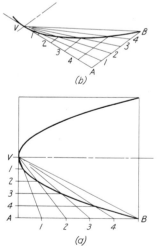

Fig. 4.48. To construct a parabola, parallelogram method.

is on the parabola. The complete parabolic outline passes through the additional points at the intersection of the lines from points numbered 3 and the lines from points numbered 4. The method as explained for a parabola enclosed in a rectangle may be applied to a nonrectangular shape as shown in (b).

4.51. To locate the directrix and focus of a given parabolic curve (Fig. 4.49). With the location of the axis known [see (a)] draw the tangent PY by locating point Y on the axis extended at a distance D_1 from the vertex V. Draw PX parallel to the axis and construct angle FPY equal to YPX. The point at which the line forming the newly constructed angle cuts the given axis is the focus F. The directrix through O is perpendicular to the axis at the same distance from the vertex V as the focus F.

When the position of the axis is not known the procedure illustrated in (b) will establish the location of the axis, focus, and directrix. As the initial step, draw two parallel chords at random and locate the mid-point of each, points R and S. Draw line RS to establish the direction of the axis that will be parallel to RS. Next, draw a chord perpendicular to RS at any location and through the mid-point M draw the axis of the parabola as required. The position of the vertex is now known and one might follow the procedure given in (a) to locate the focus and directrix. However, the position of the directrix may be found easily and quickly merely by drawing a tangent to the parabola at 45° with the axis. The directrix passes through O at the intersection of the tangent and the axis extended.

4.52. The hyperbola. Mathematically, the hyperbola can be described as a curve generated by a point moving so that at any position the difference of its distances from two fixed points (foci) is a constant (equal to the transverse axis of the hyperbola). This definition is the basis for the construction shown in Fig. 4.50.

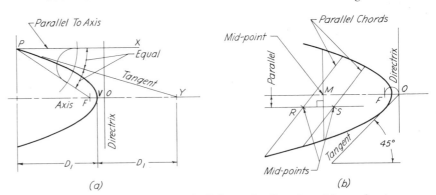

Fig. 4.49. To locate the directrix and focus of a given parabolic curve.

4.53. To construct a hyperbola (Fig. 4.50). Given the foci F_1 and F_2, and the transverse axis AB. Using F_1 and F_2 as centers and any radius R_1 greater than F_1B, strike arcs. With these same centers and a radius equal to $R_1 - AB$, strike arcs intersecting the first arcs at point P. Point P is on the required hyperbola. Repeat this procedure and locate as many additional points, such as P_1, P_2, and so forth, as are required to form the hyperbola accurately with a French curve.

The tangent to the hyperbola at any point, such as P, is the bisector of the angle between the focal radii F_1P and F_2P. Read Sec. 22.5 and study Fig. 22.13.

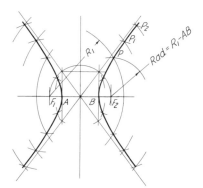

Fig. 4.50. To construct a hyperbola.

4.54. Brianchon's theorem. Brianchon's theorem can be stated as follows: *If the sides of a hexagon are tangent to a conic, the diagonals of the hexagon (three lines from opposite vertices) will meet at a point.* This point is sometimes called *Brianchon's point* (see Fig. 4.51). Brianchon's theorem is often used for constructing conic curves through the use of an envelope of tangents, for a specific conic can be definitely determined by five known conditions relating to tangents as follows: (1) five tangents to the conic, (2) four tangents and a point of tangency, and (3) three tangents and two points of tangency. By applying the theorem to any five known conditions, the sixth condition can be determined. In this discussion our interest will be centered entirely on the first condition where the conic is established by five known tangents.

In Fig. 4.51(a) a conic is to be constructed having the tangents 1 through 5 given. The position of the sixth tangent (shown by a broken line) is sought. For this particular hexagon opposite vertices are: A and D, B and E and C and F. As the first step, connect A and D with a light construction line. Through B draw a random line cutting the tangent DR at E. Points P and E, as determined by this line, will be Brianchon's point and the vertex opposite B respectively for the hexagon. A line from C through P extended to

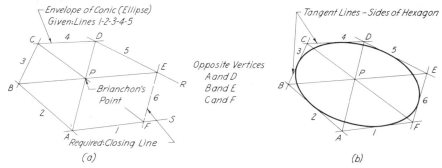

Fig. 4.51. Brianchon's theorem.

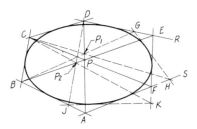

Fig. 4.52. Brianchon's point used to construct a conic as determined by five tangents.

tangent *AS* establishes the position of point *F*, the vertex opposite *C*. *EF* is the required sixth side of the hexagon for the position of *P* on *AD* as determined by the random line initially drawn from the vertex *B*. Figure 4.51(*b*) shows the inscribed conic drawn tangent to all six sides of the hexagon.

Additional tangents between *DR* and *AS* may be found by varying the position of *P* along the line *AD* as shown in Fig. 4.52. For example, point P_1 on *AD* produces tangent *GH* as a closing side of an enveloping hexagon which has the same five original sides. Whenever the enclosing hexagon has been once established, any one of the new sides may be used as one of five sides needed to establish a new hexagon enclosing the conic. Thus, a new point P_2 (Fig. 4.52) on line *BE* gives tangent *JK*. As many tangents should be drawn as are needed to obtain a smooth curve.

4.55. Pascal's theorem. This theorem states that the three pairs of opposite sides of a hexagon inscribed in a conic will intersect at three points that will lie on a straight line, commonly known as *Pascal's line*. This theorem is frequently applied to the construction of conic curves through five known points as located to meet special conditions of design. In practice, conic curves must be fitted to specific data in ship and aircraft lofting and in automobile body layout drawing. In Fig. 4.53(*a*), opposite sides 1–6 and 3–4 intersect at point *M*; 1–2 and 4–5 intersect at *N*; and 2–3 and 5–6 intersect at *O*. Points *M*, *N*, and *O* lie on a straight line. As a further check of the theorem an ellipse has been used as the conic in Fig. 4.53(*b*) instead of a circle as in (*a*).

The procedure to be followed to construct a conic through five given points is illustrated in Fig. 4.54. The arrangement of the points is shown in (*a*). The opposite sides for the hexagon are listed in (*b*) and may be seen clearly in (*c*). As the first step, draw lines 1–2 and 4–5 and extend them to intersect at point *P*. Through *P*

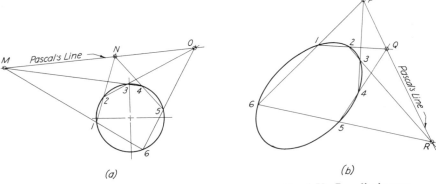

(*a*)   (*b*)

Fig. 4.53. Pascal's theorem.

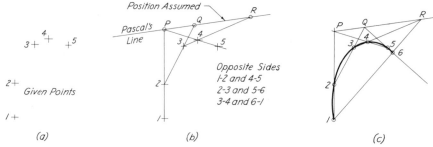

Fig. 4.54. To construct a conic determined by five points.

draw a random line in an assumed direction to serve as the Pascal line for the hexagon. Next, sides 2–3 and 3–4 of the hexagon must be extended to the Pascal line to locate points Q and R respectively. Since opposite sides 2–3 and 5–6 must intersect at Q, line $Q5$ extended contains point 6 [see (c)]. Likewise, since opposite sides 3–4 and 6–1 must meet at R, line $1R$ also contains point 6. Point 6, a point on the curve, lies at the intersection of lines $Q5$ and $1R$. Additional points as needed may be found by varying the position of the Pascal line through point P.

Since the graphic construction for both line conics and point conics are both based upon the hexagon, a generalized concept that recognizes the hexagon as a plane figure formed by joining the six points in any order must be accepted. The student should observe that the hexagon shown in Fig. 4.55 is not open as is the case in Fig. 4.54. The graphic construction for locating point 6 in Fig. 4.55 is as explained for the previous illustration. Point 6 lies at the intersection of line $1T$ extended and $5S$.

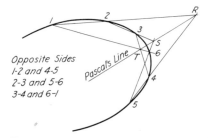

Fig. 4.55. Conic determined by five points.

4.56. An involute. The spiral curve traced by a point on a chord as it unwinds from around a circle or a polygon is an *involute curve*. Figure 4.56(a) shows an involute of a circle, while (b) shows that of a square. The involute of a polygon is obtained by extend-

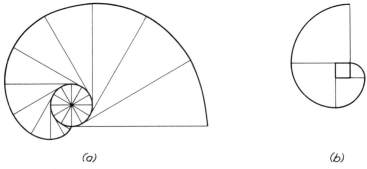

Fig. 4.56. The involute.

ing the sides and drawing arcs using the corners, in order, as centers. The circle in (a) may be considered to be a polygon having an infinite number of sides.

4.57. To draw an involute of a circle [Fig. 4.56(a)]. Divide the circumference into a number of equal parts. Draw tangents through the division points. Then, along each tangent, lay off the rectified length of the corresponding circular arc, from the starting point to the point of tangency. The involute curve is a smooth curve through these points. The involute of a circle is used in the development of tooth profiles in gearing.

4.58. To draw the involute of a polygon [Fig. 4.56(b)]. Extend the sides of the polygon as shown in (b). With the corners as centers, in order around the polygon, draw arcs terminating on the extended sides. The first radius is equal to the length of one side of the polygon. The radius of each successive arc is the distance from the center to the terminating point of the previous arc.

4.59. A cycloid. A cycloid is the curve generated by a point on the circumference of a moving circle when the circle rolls in a plane along a straight line, as shown in Fig. 4.57.

4.60. To draw a cycloid (Fig. 4.57). Draw the generating circle and the line AB tangent to it. The length AB should be made equal to the circumference of the circle. Divide the circle and the line AB into the same number of equal parts. With this much of the construction completed, the next step is to draw the line of centers CD through point O and project the division points along AB to CD by drawing perpendiculars. Using these points as centers for the various positions of the moving circle, draw circle arcs. For the purpose of illustration, assume the circle is moving to the left. When the circle has moved along CD to x, point P will have moved to point P_x. Similarly, when the center is at y, P will be at P_y. To locate positions of P along the cycloidal curve, project the division points of the

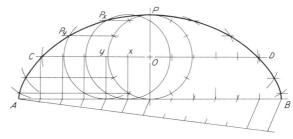

Fig. 4.57. A cycloid.

divided circle in their proper order, across to the position circles. A smooth curve through these points will be the required cycloid.

4.61. An epicycloid (Fig. 4.58). An epicycloid is the curve generated by a point on the circumference of a circle that rolls in a plane on the outside of another circle. The method used in drawing an epicycloid is similar to the one used in drawing the cycloid.

4.62. A hypocycloid (Fig. 4.59). A hypocycloid is the curve generated by a point on the circumference of a circle that rolls in a plane on the inside of another circle. The method used to draw a hypocycloid is similar to the method used to draw the cycloid.

Additional information on the use of cycloidal curves to form the outlines of cycloidal gear teeth may be found in the chapter on gears in the author's text, *Fundamentals of Engineering Drawing,* fourth edition.

4.63. Spiral of Archimedes. Archimedes' spiral is a plane curve generated by a point moving uniformly around and away from a fixed point. In order to define this curve more specifically, it can be said that it is generated by a point moving uniformly along a straight line while the line revolves with uniform angular velocity about a fixed point.

The definition of the Spiral of Archimedes is applied in drawing this curve as illustrated in Fig. 4.60. To find a sufficient number of points to allow the use of an irregular curve for drawing the spiral it is the practice to divide the given circle into a number of equal parts (say twelve) and draw radial lines to the division points. Next, divide a radial line into the same number of equal parts as the circle and number the division points on the circumference of the circle beginning with the radial line adjacent to the divided one. With the center of the circle as a center draw concentric arcs that in each case will start at a numbered division point on the divided radial line and will end at an intersection with the radial line that is numbered correspondingly. The arc starting at point 1 gives a point on the curve at its intersection with radial line 1; the arc starting at 2 gives an intersection point on radial line 2; etc. The spiral is a smooth curve drawn through these intersection points.

4.64. The helix (Fig. 4.61). The cylindrical helix is a space curve that is generated by a point moving uniformly on the surface of a cylinder. The point must travel parallel to the axis with uniform linear velocity while at the same time it is moving with uniform angular velocity around the axis. The curve can be thought of as being generated by a point moving uniformly along a straight line while the line is revolving with uniform angular velocity around the axis of the given cylinder. Study the pictorial drawing, Fig. 4.61.

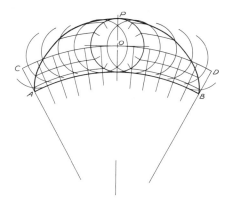

Fig. 4.58. An epicycloid.

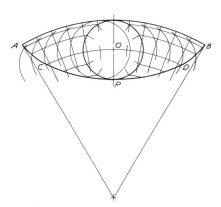

Fig. 4.59. A hypocycloid.

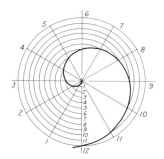

Fig. 4.60. Spiral of Archimedes.

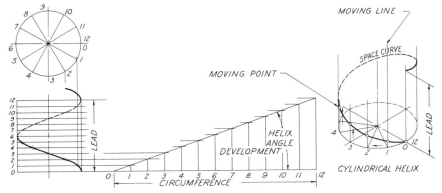

Fig. 4.61. The helix.

The first step in drawing a cylindrical helix is to lay out the two views of the cylinder. Next, the lead should be measured along a contour element and divided into a number of equal parts (say twelve). Divide the circular view of the cylinder into the same number of parts and number the division points.

The division lines of the lead represent the various positions of the moving point as it travels in a direction parallel to the axis of

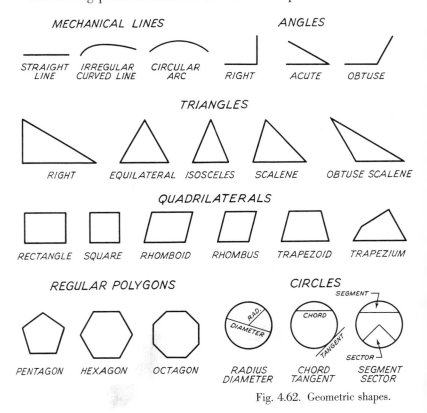

Fig. 4.62. Geometric shapes.

the cylinder along the moving line. The division points on the circular view are the related position of the moving line. For example, when the line has moved from the 0 to the 1 position, the point has traveled along the line a distance equal to one-twelfth of the lead; when the line is in the 2 position, the point has traveled one-sixth of the lead. (See pictorial drawing, Fig. 4.61.) In constructing the curve the necessary points are found by projecting from a numbered point on the circular view to the division line of the lead that is numbered similarly.

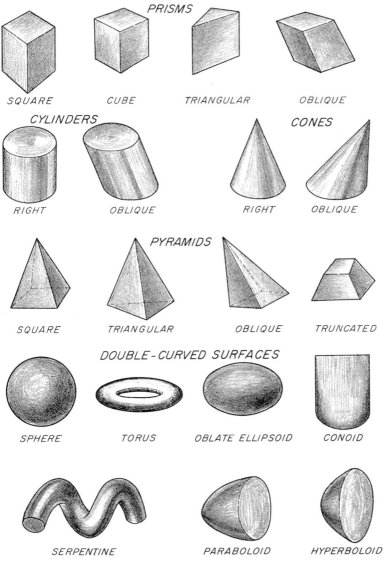

PRISMS

SQUARE CUBE TRIANGULAR OBLIQUE

CYLINDERS CONES

RIGHT OBLIQUE RIGHT OBLIQUE

PYRAMIDS

SQUARE TRIANGULAR OBLIQUE TRUNCATED

DOUBLE-CURVED SURFACES

SPHERE TORUS OBLATE ELLIPSOID CONOID

SERPENTINE PARABOLOID HYPERBOLOID

Fig. 4.63. Geometric shapes.

A helix may be either right-hand or left-hand. The one shown in Fig. 4.61 is a left-hand helix.

When the cylinder is developed, the helix becomes a straight line on the development as shown. It is inclined to the base line at an angle known as the "helix angle."

A screw thread is an example of a practical application of the cylindrical helix.

PROBLEMS

The following exercises not only require the student to study and use certain common geometric constructions, but also furnish additional practice in applying good line technique to the drawing of instrumental figures and practical designs. All work should be very accurately done. Tangent points should be indicated by a light, short dash across the line.

1. Draw a horizontal line 4⅜ in. long. Bisect it by the method shown in Fig. 4.1(*b*).

2. Draw a line 3¾ in. long, inclined at 30° to the horizontal. Divide it into five equal parts. Use the method illustrated in Fig. 4.6(*a*).

3. Draw a line 3¼ in. long. Divide it into three equal parts. Use the method shown in Fig. 4.2.

4. Draw a line 3⅛ in. long. Divide it proportionally in the ratio 1:2:3. Use the method shown in Fig. 4.7.

5. Using a line 3¼ in. long as the base line, construct a triangle having sides 2½ in., 3¼ in., and 3¾ in. long, respectively. Study the method that is illustrated in Fig. 4.12.

6. Construct a regular hexagon having a 2½ in. distance across flats. Select the most practical procedure.

7. Construct a regular hexagon having a 3¼ in. distance across corners. Select the most practical method.

8. Construct a regular pentagon having 1¼ in. sides. Use the method illustrated in Fig. 4.19.

9. Divide the area of the triangle in Problem 5 into four equal parts. Use the method shown in Fig. 4.20(*a*).

10. Trisect the angle between the 3¼ in. and 3¾ in. sides of the triangle in Problem 5. Use the method illustrated in Fig. 4.5.

11. Draw two horizontal lines 2 in. apart. Locate two points 3 in. apart horizontally, one on each line. Draw an ogee curve tangent to these lines. Study the procedure illustrated in Fig. 4.26.

12. Draw a 2½ in. circle. Select a point 2 in. from the center and draw a line tangent to it, using the method illustrated in Fig. 4.28.

13. Draw a 2¾ in. circle, and draw tangent to it a line that makes 15° with the horizontal. Draw a 1½ in. circle tangent to the line and the 2¾ in. circle. Use the method illustrated in Fig. 4.24.

14. Draw a 3 in. circle. Inside this circle, and tangent to it, draw a 1¾ in. circle. See that the centers of both circles are on the same vertical center line. Draw two 1 in. circles tangent to the 3 in. and the 1¾ in. circle. Use the method illustrated in Fig. 4.25.

15. Construct an ellipse having a major diameter of 4¼ in. and a minor diameter of 2¾ in. Use the trammel method illustrated in Fig. 4.37.

16. Construct an ellipse having a major diameter of 4 in. and a minor diameter of 2¾ in. Use the concentric circle method illustrated in Fig. 4.38. Find a sufficient number of points to obtain a smooth curve.

17. Construct the ellipse required in Problem 16, using the four-center method. Study Sec. 4.41 and Fig. 4.39.

18. Construct an ellipse having conjugate axes 3¾ in. and 2½ in. long, inclined one to the other at 75°. Determine the major and minor axes (Fig. 4.41).

19. Construct a parabola with vertical axis. Make the focus ¾ in. from the directrix. Select a point on the curve and draw a line tangent to the parabola. Study Sec. 4.46 and Fig. 4.44.

20. Construct a hyperbola having a transverse axis of 1 in. and foci 1⅝ in. apart. Study Sec. 4.53 and Fig. 4.50.

21. Construct the involute of an equilateral triangle with 1 in. sides. Study Sec. 4.58.

22. Construct the involute of a circle ⅞ in. in diameter. Study Sec. 4.57 and Fig. 4.56(a).

23. Construct the cycloid generated by a 1½ in. circle. Study Sec. 4.60 and Fig. 4.57.

24. Construct the epicycloid generated by a 1½ in. circle rolling on a 5 in. circle. Study Sec. 4.61 and Fig. 4.58.

25. Construct the hypocycloid generated by a 1½ in. circle rolling on a 4½ in. circle. Study Sec. 4.62 and Fig. 4.59.

26. Reconstruct the view of the gasket shown in Fig. 4.64 to full scale. Mark all of the tangent points with short lines. Study Fig. 4.25. Do not place dimensions on the finished drawing.

27. Reconstruct the view of the wrench shown in Fig. 4.65. Mark all tangent points with short lines.

28. Reconstruct the view of the gasket shown in Fig. 4.66. Mark all tangent points with short marks across tangent lines.

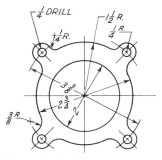

Fig. 4.64. Gasket.

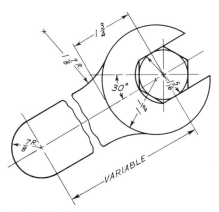

Fig. 4.65. Wrench.

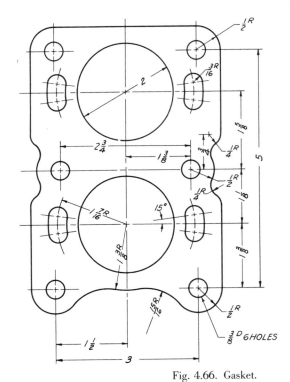

Fig. 4.66. Gasket.

29. Reconstruct the view of the guide plate (Fig. 4.67).

30. Reconstruct the view of the cam shown in Fig. 4.68. Mark all tangent points.

31. Construct the shape of the slotted guide shown in Fig. 4.69. Show all construction for locating centers and mark points of tangency.

32. Construct the adjustable Y-clamp shown in Fig. 4.70. Show all construction for locating centers and mark points of tangency.

33. Reconstruct the geometric design shown in Fig. 4.71. Mark all tangent points with short marks across tangent lines, as shown in the given view.

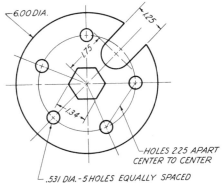

Fig. 4.67. Guide plate.

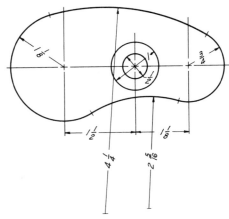

Fig. 4.68. Cam.

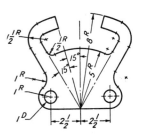

Fig. 4.69. Slotted guide.

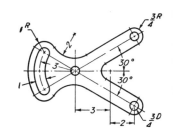

Fig. 4.70. Adjustable Y-clamp.

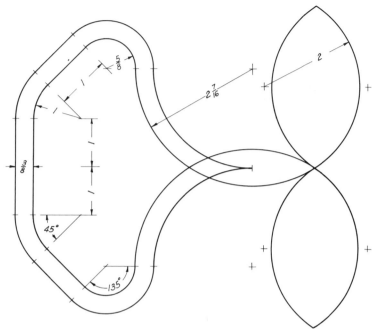

Fig. 4.71. Geometric design.

34. Reconstruct the view of the C-ring shown in Fig. 4.72.

35. (Fig. 4.73.) Using an eighth-size scale, make a one-view drawing of the housing gasket. Use approved geometric constructions and mark all tangent points with ⅛ in. dash across the line. Be prepared to explain to your instructor the procedure for determining

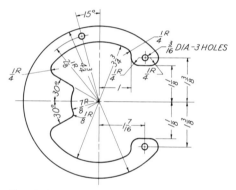

Fig. 4.72. C-ring.

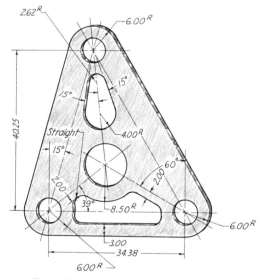

Fig. 4.73. Housing gasket.

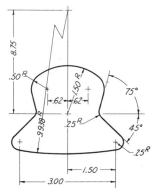

Fig. 4.74. End view—dolly block.

the locations for centers and tangent points and demonstrate the manipulation of the triangles for the 15° angles. Study Sec. 4.11. *Supplementary information:* (1) the three small circular holes are to be 6 in. in diameter, (2) the large hole in the center of the gasket must have a 10½ in. diameter, (3) all small radii are 2 in., (4) the gasket is to be cut from ¹⁄₁₆ in. fiber stock.

36. Reconstruct the end view of the dolly block shown in Fig. 4.74.

37. Reconstruct the view of the electrode shown in Fig. 4.75.

38. Reconstruct the plat of a land survey shown in Fig. 4.76. Use the tangent method, as explained in Sec. 4.11, to determine the direction of the center line of State Road 26. The triangles used in combination will produce the other angles.

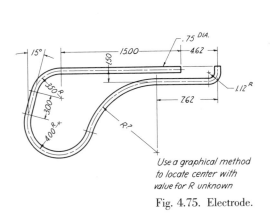

Use a graphical method
to locate center with
value for R unknown

Fig. 4.75. Electrode.

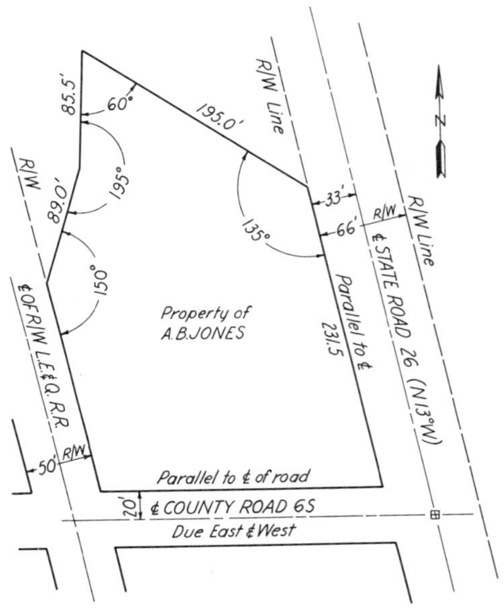

Fig. 4.76. A plat of a land survey.

39. (Fig. 4.77.) Part *A* is free to pivot about a shaft. If this part should be revolved in a counterclockwise direction as indicated by the arrows, it would contact surface *C*. Reproduce the drawing as given and show part *A* revolved until it is in contact with surface *C*. Use the symbolic line for showing an alternate position for part *A* in this new position. Show all geometric constructions clearly and do not erase construction lines.

40. (Fig. 4.78.) Part *A* revolves about shaft *B* in a clockwise direction from the position shown until surface *C* comes into contact with the cylindrical surface of the roller. Reproduce the drawing as given and show part *A* in its revolved position using the symbolic alternate position line for this new position. Show all geometric constructions clearly and do not erase construction lines.

41. (Fig. 4.79.) Draw the top of the arch through point *C*. Use an exact method. Scale and record the rise of the arch (one-half of the length of the minor axis). Locate the foci. Show all construction.

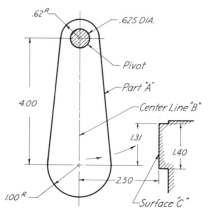

Fig. 4.77. Geometric construction.

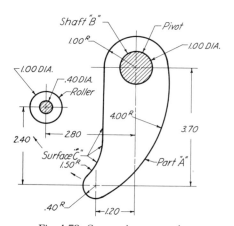

Fig. 4.78. Geometric construction.

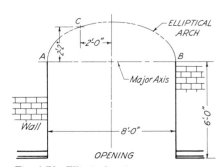

Fig. 4.79. Elliptical arch.

5

THE THEORY OF PROJECTION

5.1. Introduction. Since engineers are confronted with the task of recording the shapes and sizes of three-dimensional objects on the plane of a sheet of drawing paper, it is obvious that recognized procedures must be followed if their drawings and sketches are to be easily understood. Size description and shape description are equally important, but, in order to simplify the presentation of the fundamentals of making drawings and sketches, this chapter is concerned entirely with the methods commonly employed in describing shape. A later chapter will discuss size description.

Each of the different methods, axonometric, oblique, and orthographic, is based on some form of projection. The theory governing a method should be understood thoroughly before it is used.

5.2. Perspective (scenographic) projection. In perspective projection, the projecting lines (visual rays) converge to a point, as shown in Fig. 5.1. The representation upon the transparent picture plane may be considered the view that would be seen by one eye located at a definite point in space. The picture is established on the imaginary plane by the piercing points of the projecting lines from the eye to the object. The size of the view depends upon the distance from the observer to the plane and the distance from the plane to the object.

Perspective projection is not suitable for working drawings because a perspective view does not reveal exact size and shape. It is used to some extent by engineers in preparing preliminary sketches.

5.3. Orthographic projection (parallel projection). If the observer in Fig. 5.1 moves straight back from the picture plane until he is an infinite distance from it, the projecting lines (projectors) from the eye to the object become parallel to each other and perpendicular to the picture plane. The resulting projection (Fig. 5.2) will then be the same shape and size as the front surface of the object. From a practical viewpoint, the projection may be thought of as being formed by perpendicular projectors extended from the object to the plane. The view is called an *orthographic projection.*

Since the view shown in Fig. 5.2 does not reveal the thickness of the object, one or more additional projections (Fig. 5.3) are necessary to complete the description. Two projections are usually

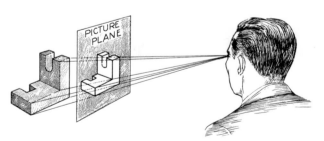

Fig. 5.1. Perspective projection.

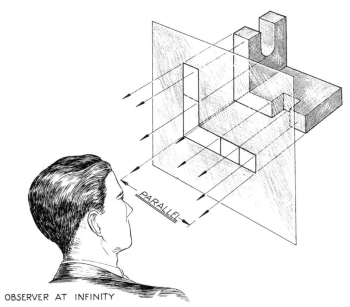

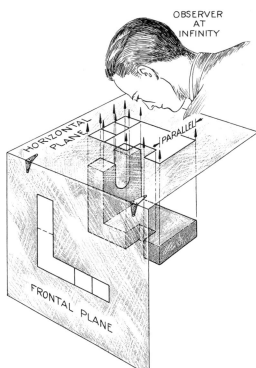

OBSERVER AT INFINITY

Fig. 5.2. Orthographic projection.

Fig. 5.3. Planes of projection.

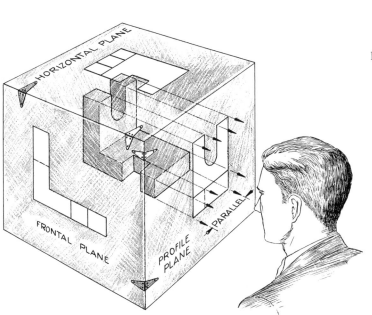

Fig. 5.4. Planes of projection.

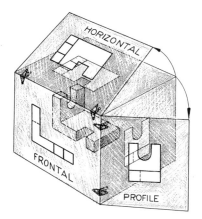

Fig. 5.5. The revolution of the planes of projection.

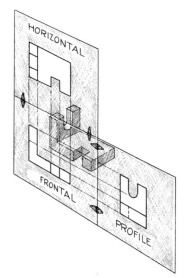

Fig. 5.6. The planes resolved into the plane of the paper.

sufficient to describe simple objects, but three or more are necessary for complicated ones.

The picture planes are customarily called the *principal* or *coordinate* planes of projection, and the perpendiculars, *projectors*. In engineering drawing, the planes are usually arranged as shown in Fig. 5.4. Since all three are mutually perpendicular, they are called the horizontal, frontal, and profile coordinate planes. To maintain this mutual relationship when laying out views, it is the usual practice to consider the frontal plane as lying in the plane of the paper and the horizontal and profile planes as being revolved into position (Fig. 5.6). Note in Fig. 5.5 the manner in which the planes are revolved. This theoretical treatment of the coordinate planes establishes an absolute relationship between the views. Visualizing an object would be considerably more difficult than it is, if it were not for this fixed relationship, for it would be impossible to determine quickly the direction of sight for a particular view.

5.4. One-plane projection. If the object is turned and then tilted so that three faces are inclined to the plane of projection, the resulting projection is a special type of orthographic projection known as *axonometric projection*. Figure 5.7 illustrates an axonometric projection of a cube. Note that the projectors from the object to the plane are perpendicular to the plane. The three recognized subdivisions of axonometric projection, namely, isometric, dimetric, and trimetric, are explained in Chapter 10.

Another form of one-plane projection is known as *oblique projection*. This form differs from orthographic projection in that,

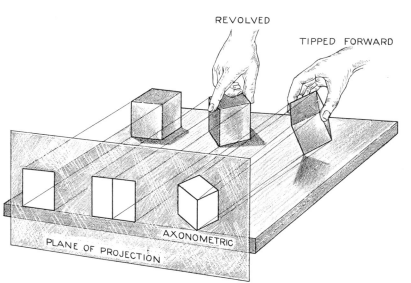

Fig. 5.7. Theory of axonometric projection.

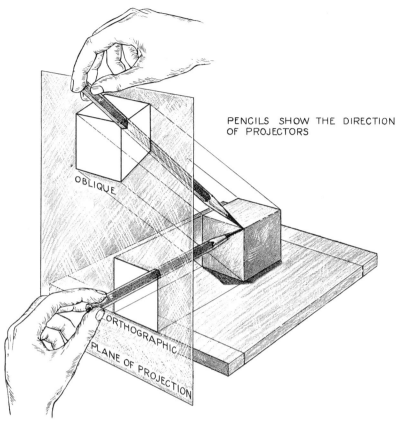

PENCILS SHOW THE DIRECTION OF PROJECTORS

OBLIQUE

ORTHOGRAPHIC

PLANE OF PROJECTION

Fig. 5.8. Oblique projection.

although one face is imagined to be parallel to the plane of projection, the projectors make an angle other than 90° with it (Fig. 5.8). Obviously an infinite number of different views are possible, depending upon the angle the parallel projectors make with the plane of projection (picture plane). The various subdivisions are cavalier projection, cabinet projection, and clinographic projection (Chapter 10).

Axonometric projection, oblique projection, and perspective projection may all be classed together as *one-plane pictorial projection.*

5.5. First- and third-angle projection. If the horizontal and frontal planes are assumed to extend indefinitely on one side of the profile plane, four dihedral angles are formed and are designated as the *first, second, third,* and *fourth* angles (Fig. 5.9). The lines of intersection of these planes are called coordinate axes. Their point of intersection is called the origin. In this discussion of first- and third-angle projection, it should be remembered that no matter in which angle the object is placed, the observer views it from in front

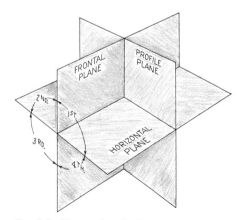

Fig. 5.9. Planes of projection.

of the frontal plane and from above the horizontal plane. To avoid misunderstandings, the directions for revolving the horizontal and profile planes into the frontal plane are illustrated in Fig. 5.10. Note that the first and third quadrants are "opened" and the second and fourth are "closed" in revolving the horizontal plane into the frontal plane.

If an object, such as the one shown in Fig. 5.10, is placed so that its main faces are parallel to the principal planes, the respective projection on each plane will show the true size and shape of all surfaces that are parallel to that principal plane. Theoretically, the object could have been shown in any one of the four quadrants. It has been placed in the third quadrant simply because engineering custom in the United States dictates the use of the third. This quadrant is used because the views, when revolved into the frontal plane, are in their natural positions. That is: the top view appears *above* the front view, as is expected, and the profile view, showing the *right side*, falls on the *right* of the front view.

In most foreign countries, "first-angle projection" is used for working drawings (study Fig. 5.11). Observe that the top view is projected upon the horizontal plane and the front view upon the frontal plane. For this reason, the top view falls below the front view when the coordinate planes are revolved.

In this country, the use of first-angle projection for working

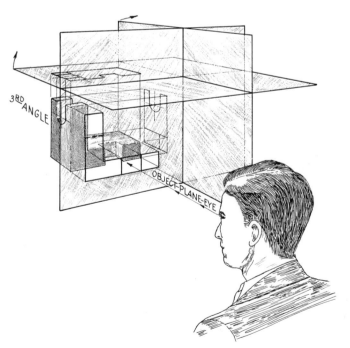

Fig. 5.10. Third-angle projection.

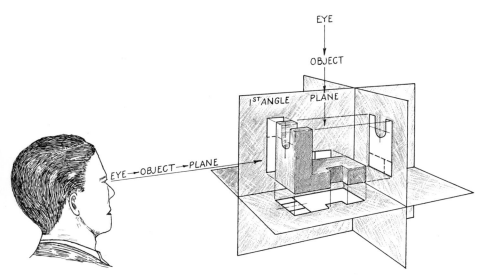

Fig. 5.11. First-angle projection.

drawings was abandoned by engineering draftsmen some fifty years ago, although it is still used by architects and structural designers.

5.6. Systems of projection. The different systems of projection may be conveniently classified as follows:

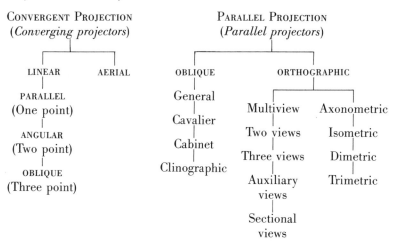

CONVERGENT PROJECTION
(*Converging projectors*)

LINEAR　　AERIAL

PARALLEL
(One point)

ANGULAR
(Two point)

OBLIQUE
(Three point)

PARALLEL PROJECTION
(*Parallel projectors*)

OBLIQUE

General

Cavalier

Cabinet

Clinographic

ORTHOGRAPHIC

Multiview

Two views

Three views

Auxiliary views

Sectional views

Axonometric

Isometric

Dimetric

Trimetric

6

MULTIVIEW REPRESENTATION AND CONVENTIONAL PRACTICES
A: MULTIVIEW DRAWING

6.1. Introduction. Engineers use the orthographic system of projection for describing the shape of machine parts and structures (Fig. 6.1). Practical application of this method of describing an object results in a drawing consisting of a number of systematically arranged

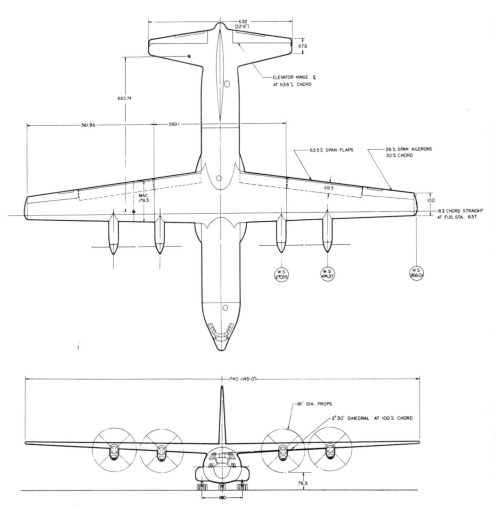

Fig. 6.1. A multiview drawing (*Courtesy of Lockheed, Georgia Division*).

views that reproduce the object's exact shape. It was explained in the preceding chapter, Sec. 5.3, that a set of views showing the object from different positions is always taken. The position of these views, in strict accordance with a universally recognized arrangement, must show the three dimensions, width, height, and depth. Although three views (Fig. 6.2) are usually required to describe an ordinary object, only two may be needed for a particularly simple one. A very complicated object may require four or more views. A view projected upon an auxiliary plane also may be desirable (see Figs. 8.1 and 8.2). Such a view often makes possible the elimination of one of the principal views. Therefore, it is up to the individual to

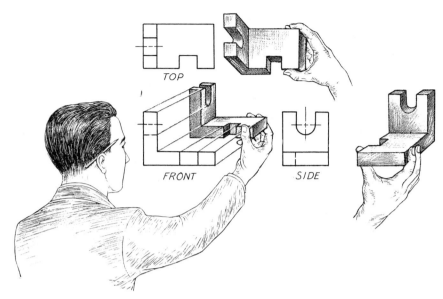

Fig. 6.2. Obtaining three views of an object.

determine the number and type of views needed to produce a satisfactory drawing. He will soon develop a knack for this, if he bears in mind that the number of views required depends entirely upon the complexity of the shape to be described.

6.2. Definition. Multiview (multiplaner) projection is a method by means of which the exact shape of an object can be represented by two or more separate views produced upon projection planes that are usually at right angles to each other.

6.3. Methods of obtaining the views. The views of an object may be obtained by either of two methods: (1) the natural method; (2) the "glass box" method.

Since the resulting views will be the same in either case, the beginner should adopt the method he finds the easiest to understand. Both methods are explained here in detail.

6.4. The natural method. In using this method, each of the necessary views is obtained looking directly at the particular side of the object the view is to represent.

Figure 6.2 shows three of the principal views of an object, the front, top, and side views. They were obtained by looking directly at the front, top, and right side, respectively. In the application of this method, some consider the position of the object as fixed and the position of the observer as shifted for each view; others find it

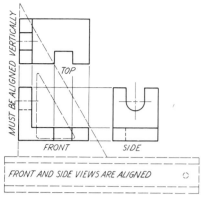

Fig. 6.3. Position of views.

easier to consider the observer's position as fixed and the position of the object as changed for each view (Fig. 6.2). Regardless of which procedure is followed, the top and side views must be arranged in their natural positions relative to the front view.

Figure 6.3 illustrates the natural relationship of views. Note that the top view is *vertically above* the front view, and the side view is *horizontally in line with* the front view. In both of these views the *front of the block is toward the front view.*

6.5. The "glass box" method. An imaginary "glass box" is used widely by instructors to explain the arrangement of orthographic views. An explanation of this scheme can be best made by reviewing the use of planes of projection (Chap. 5). It may be considered that planes of projection placed parallel to the six faces of an object form an enclosing "glass box" (see Fig. 6.4). The observer views the enclosed object from the outside. The views are obtained by running projectors from points on the object to the planes. This procedure is in accordance with the theory of orthographic projection explained in Sec. 5.3, as well as the definition in Sec. 6.2. The front, top, and right side of the box represent the H (horizontal), F (frontal), and P (profile) projection planes.

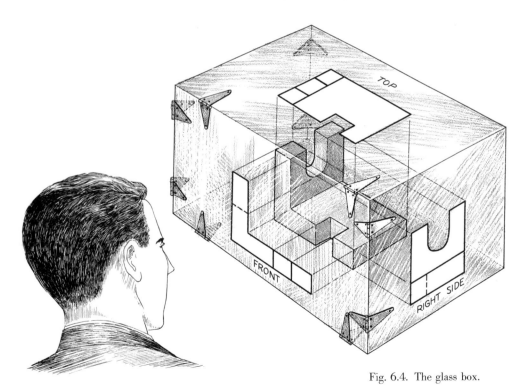

Fig. 6.4. The glass box.

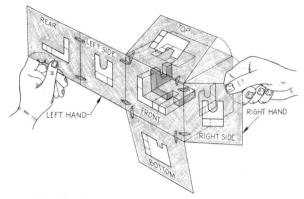

Fig. 6.5. Opening the glass box.

Since the projections on the sides of the three-dimensional transparent box are to appear on a sheet of drawing paper, it must be assumed that the box is hinged (see Fig. 6.5) so that, when it is opened outward into the plane of the paper, the planes assume the positions illustrated in Figs. 6.5 and 6.6. Note that all of the planes, except the back one, are hinged to the frontal plane. In accordance with this universally recognized assumption, the top projection must take a position directly above the front projection, and the right side projection must lie horizontally to the right of the front projection. To identify the separate projections, engineers call the one on the frontal plane the *front view* or *front elevation*, the one on the horizontal plane the *top view* or *plan*, and the one on the side or

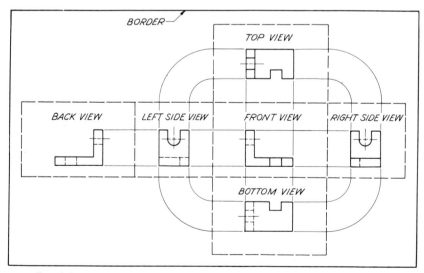

Fig. 6.6. Six views of an object on a sheet of drawing paper.

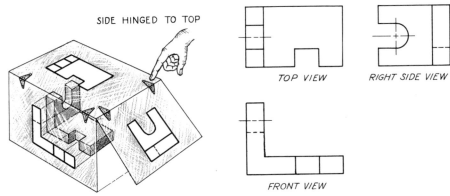

SIDE HINGED TO TOP

TOP VIEW   RIGHT SIDE VIEW

FRONT VIEW

Fig. 6.7. The "second position" for the side view.

profile plane the *side view, side elevation,* or *end view.* Figure 6.6 shows the six views of the same object as they would appear on a sheet of drawing paper. Ordinarily, only three of these views are necessary (front, top, and right side). A bottom or rear view will be required in comparatively few cases.

6.6. The "second position." Sometimes, especially in the case of a broad, flat object, it is desirable to hinge the sides of the box to the horizontal plane so that the side view will fall to the right of the top view, as illustrated in Fig. 6.7. This arrangement conserves space on the paper and gives the views better balance.

6.7. The principles of multiview drawing. The following principles should be studied carefully and understood thoroughly before any attempt is made to prepare an orthographic drawing:

1. The front and top views are *always* in line vertically (Fig. 6.3).
2. The front and side views are in line horizontally, except when the second position is used (Fig. 6.3).
3. The front of the object in the top view faces the front view (Fig. 6.5).
4. The front of the object in the side view faces the front view (Fig. 6.5).
5. The depth of the top view is the same as the depth of the side view (or views) (see Fig. 6.8).
6. The width of the top view is the same as the width of the front view (Fig. 6.8).
7. The height of the side view is the same as the height of the front view (Fig. 6.8).

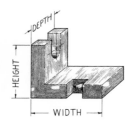

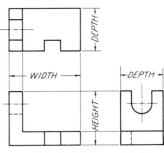

Fig. 6.8. View terminology.

8. A view taken from above is a top view and *must* be drawn above the front view (Fig. 6.6).

9. A view taken from the right, in relation to the selected front, is a right-side view and *must* be drawn to the right of the front view (Fig. 6.6).

10. A view taken from the left is a left-side view and *must* be drawn to the left of the front view (Fig. 6.6).

11. A view taken from below is a bottom view and *must* appear below the front view (Fig. 6.6).

6.8. Projection of lines.   A line may project either in true length, foreshortened, or as a point in a view depending upon its relationship to the projection plane upon which the view is projected (see Fig. 6.9). In the top view, the line projection $A^H b^H$ shows the true length of the edge AB (see pictorial) because AB is parallel to the horizontal plane of projection. Looking directly at the frontal plane, along the line, AB projects as a point ($a^F b^F$). Lines, such as CD, that are inclined to one of the planes of projection, will show a foreshortened projection in the view on the projection plane to which the line is inclined and true length in the view on the plane of projection to which the line is parallel. The curved line projection $e^F f^F$ shows the true length of the curved edge.

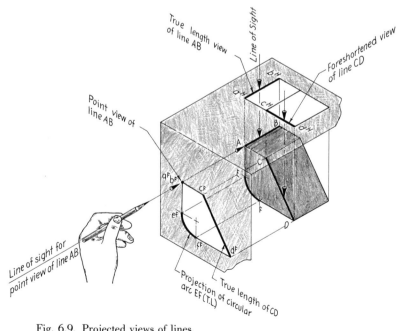

Fig. 6.9. Projected views of lines.

The student should study Fig. 6.10 and attempt to visualize the space position of each of the given lines. It is very necessary both in preparing and reading graphical representations to recognize the position of a point, line, or plane and to know whether the projection of a line is true length or foreshortened or whether the projection of a plane shows the true size and shape. The indicated reference lines may be thought of as representing the edges of the glass boxes shown. The projections of a line are identified as being on either a frontal, horizontal, or profile plane by the use of the letters F, H, or P with the lower-case letters that identify the end-points of the line. For example, in Fig. 6.10(a), $a^H b^H$ is the horizontal projection of line AB, $a^F b^F$ is the frontal projection, and $a^P b^P$ is the profile projection.

It is suggested that the student hold a pencil before him and move it into the following typical line positions to observe the conditions under which the pencil, representing a line, appears in true length.

1. *Vertical line.* The vertical line is perpendicular to the horizontal and will therefore appear as a point in the H (top) view. It will appear in true length in the F (frontal) view, in true length in the P (profile) view.

2. *Horizontal line* [Fig. 6.10(b)]. The horizontal line will appear in true length when viewed from above because it is parallel to the H-plane of projection and its end-points are theoretically equidistant from an observer looking downward.

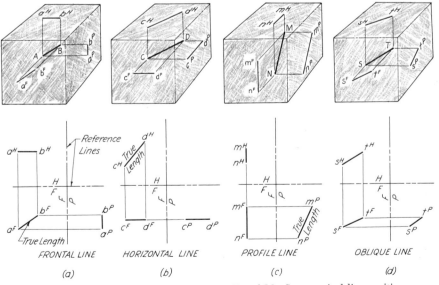

Fig. 6.10. Some typical line positions.

3. *Inclined line* [Fig. 6.10(c)]. The inclined line is any line not vertical or horizontal that is parallel to either the frontal plane or the profile plane of projection. An inclined line will show true length in the *F* (frontal) view or *P* (profile) view.

4. *Oblique line* [Fig. 6.10(d)]. The oblique line will not appear in true length in any of the principal views because it is inclined to all of the principal planes of projection. It should be apparent that in viewing the pencil alternately from the directions used to obtain the principal views, namely from the front, above, and side, that one end of the pencil is always farther away from the observer than the other. Only when looking directly at the pencil from such a position that the end-points are equidistant from the observer can the true length be seen. On a drawing, the true length projection of an oblique line will appear in a supplementary *A* (auxiliary) view projected on a plane that is parallel to the line (Sec. 12.11).

6.9. Meaning of lines. On a multiview drawing a visible or invisible line may represent either the intersection of two surfaces, the edge view of a surface, or it may be the limiting element of a surface. These three different meanings of a line are illustrated in Fig. 6.11. In the top view, the curved line is an edge view of surface *C* while a straight line is the edge view of surface *A*. The full circle in the front view may be considered as the edge view of the cylindrical surface of the hole. In the side view, the top line, representing the contour element of the cylindrical surface, indicates the limits for the surface and therefore can be thought of as being a surface limit line. The short vertical line in this same view represents the intersection of two surfaces. In reading a drawing,

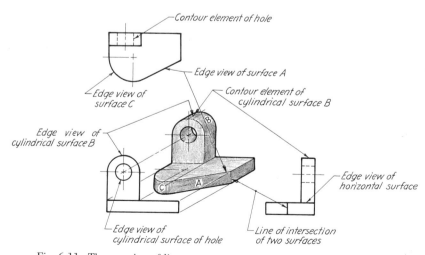

Fig. 6.11. The meaning of lines.

one can be sure of the meaning of a line on a view only after an analysis of the related view or views. All views must be studied carefully.

6.10. Projection of surfaces. The components of most machine parts are bounded by either plane or single-curved surfaces. Plane surfaces bound cubes, prisms, and pyramids, while single-curved surfaces, ruled by a moving straight line, bound cylinders and cones. The projected representations (lines or areas) of both plane and single curved surfaces are shown in Fig. 6.12. From this illustration the student should note that: (1) when a surface is parallel to a plane of projection, it will appear in true size in the view on the plane of projection to which it is parallel; (2) when it is perpendicular to the plane of projection, it will project as a line in the view; and (3) when it is positioned at an angle, it will appear foreshortened. A surface will always project either as a line or an area on a view. The area representing the surface may be either a full-size or foreshortened representation.

In Fig. 6.12, the cylindrical surface *A* appears as a line in the side (profile) view and as an area in the top and front views. Surface *B* shows true size in the top view and as a line in both the front and side views. Surface *C*, a vertical surface, will appear as a line when observed from above.

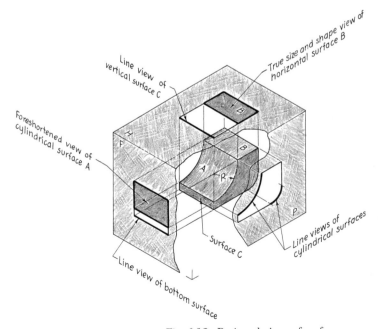

Fig. 6.12. Projected views of surfaces.

6.11. Analysis of surfaces, lines, and points in three principal views. An analysis of the representation of the surfaces of a mutilated block is given pictorially in Fig. 6.13. It can be noted that each of the surfaces *A, B,* and *C* appears in true size and shape in one view, and as a line in each of the other two related views. Surface *D,* which is inclined, appears with foreshortened length in the top and side views, and as an inclined line in the front view.

Three views of each of the visible points are shown on the multiview drawing. At the very beginning of an elementary course in drawing, a student will often find it helpful to number the corners of an object in all views.

6.12. The selection of views. Careful study should be given to the outline of an object before the views are selected (Fig. 6.14), otherwise there is no assurance that the object will be described completely from the reader's viewpoint (Fig. 6.15). Only those views that are necessary for a clear and complete description should be selected. Since the repetition of information only tends to confuse the reader, superfluous views should be avoided. In Fig. 6.6, note that three views (front, top, and right side) describe the object fully. The other three views are unnecessary.

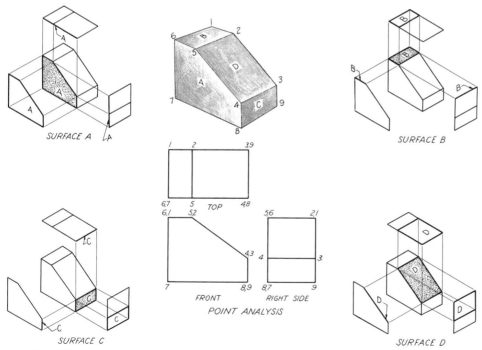

Fig. 6.13. Analysis of surfaces, lines, and points.

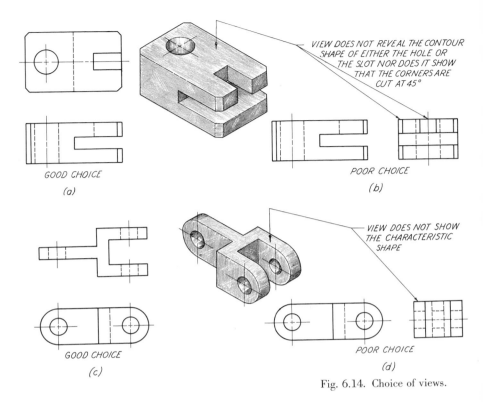

VIEW DOES NOT REVEAL THE CONTOUR
SHAPE OF EITHER THE HOLE OR
THE SLOT NOR DOES IT SHOW
THAT THE CORNERS ARE
CUT AT 45°

GOOD CHOICE
(a)

POOR CHOICE
(b)

VIEW DOES NOT SHOW
THE CHARACTERISTIC
SHAPE

GOOD CHOICE
(c)

POOR CHOICE
(d)

Fig. 6.14. Choice of views.

Although some objects, such as cylinders, bushings, bolts, and so forth, require only two views (front and side), more complicated pieces may require an auxiliary or sectional view in addition to the ordinary three views.

The space available for arranging the views often governs the choice between the use of a top or side view. The difference be-

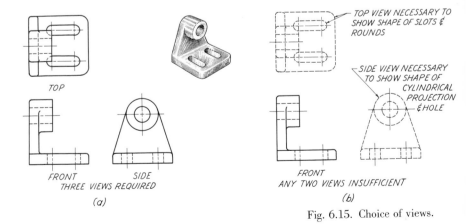

TOP

FRONT   SIDE
THREE VIEWS REQUIRED
(a)

TOP VIEW NECESSARY TO
SHOW SHAPE OF SLOTS &
ROUNDS

SIDE VIEW NECESSARY
TO SHOW SHAPE OF
CYLINDRICAL
PROJECTION
& HOLE

FRONT
ANY TWO VIEWS INSUFFICIENT
(b)

Fig. 6.15. Choice of views.

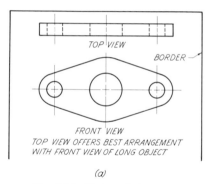 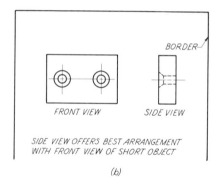

Fig. 6.16. Choice of views.

tween the descriptive values of the two frequently is not great. For example, a draftsman often finds that the views of a long object will have better balance if a top view is used [see Fig. 6.16(a)]; while, in the case of a short object [see (b)], the use of a side view may make possible a more pleasing arrangement. It should be remembered that the choice of views for many objects is definitely fixed by the contour alone, and no choice is offered as far as spacing is concerned. It is more important to have a set of views that describes an object clearly than one that is artistically balanced.

Often there is a choice between two equally important views, such as between a right-side and left-side view (Fig. 6.17) or between a top and bottom view (Fig. 6.18). In such cases, one should adhere to the following rule: *A right-side view should be used in preference to a left-side view, and a top view in preference to a bottom view.* When this rule is applied to irregular objects, the front (contour) view should be drawn so that the most irregular outline is toward the top and right side.

Another rule, one that must be considered in selecting the front view, is as follows: *Place the object so as to obtain the smallest number of hidden lines.*

6.13. The principal (front) view. The principal view is the one that shows the characteristic contour of the object [see Fig. 6.19(a) and (b)]. Good practice dictates that this be used as the front view on a drawing. It should be clearly understood that the view of the natural front of an object is not always the principal view, because frequently it fails to show the object's characteristic shape. Therefore, another rule to be followed is: *Ordinarily, select the view showing the characteristic contour shape as the front view, regardless of the normal or natural front of the object.*

When an object does have a definite normal position, however, the front view should be in agreement with it. In the case of most

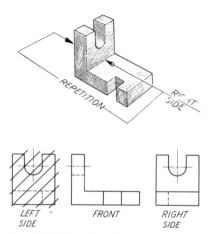

Fig. 6.17. The preferred side view.

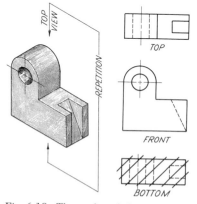

Fig. 6.18. The preferred choice of a top view.

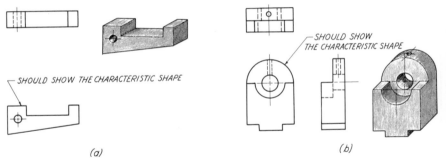

SHOULD SHOW THE CHARACTERISTIC SHAPE

SHOULD SHOW THE CHARACTERISTIC SHAPE

(a)

(b)

Fig. 6.19. The principal view of an object.

machine parts, the front view can assume any convenient position that is consistent with good balance.

6.14. Invisible lines. Dotted lines are used on an external view of an object to represent surfaces and intersections invisible at the point from which the view is taken. In Fig. 6.20(*a*), one invisible line represents a line of intersection or edge line while the other invisible line may be considered to represent either the surface or lines of intersection. On the side view in (*b*) there are invisible lines which represent the contour elements of the cylindrical holes.

6.15. Treatment of invisible lines. The short dashes that form an invisible line should be drawn carefully in accordance with the recommendations in Sec. 6.24. An invisible line always starts with a dash in contact with the object line from which it starts, unless it forms a continuation of a visible line. In the latter case, it should start with a space, in order to establish at a glance the exact location of the end-point of the visible line (see Fig. 6.21*C*). Note that the effect of definite corners is secured at points *A*, *B*, *E*, and *F*, where, in each case, the end dash touches the intersecting line. When the point of intersection of an invisible line and another object line does not represent an actual intersection on the object, the

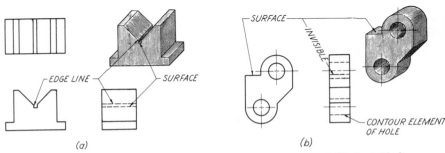

EDGE LINE   *SURFACE*

SURFACE   *INVISIBLE*

CONTOUR ELEMENT OF HOLE

(a)

(b)

Fig. 6.20. Invisible lines.

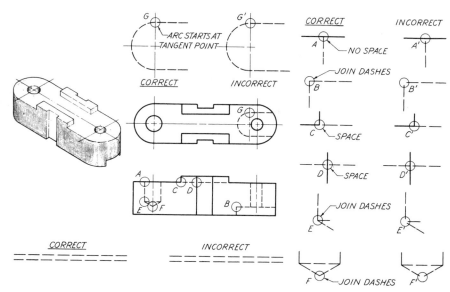

Fig. 6.21. Correct and incorrect junctures of invisible outlines.

intersection should be open as at points C and D. An open inter-section tends to make the lines appear to be at different distances from the observer.

Parallel invisible lines should have the breaks staggered.

The correct and incorrect treatment for starting invisible arcs is illustrated at G and G'. Note that an arc should start with a dash at the point of tangency. This treatment enables the reader to determine the exact end-points of the curvature.

6.16. Omission of invisible lines. Although it is common practice for commercial draftsmen to omit hidden lines when their use tends to further confuse an already overburdened view or when the shape description of a feature is sufficiently clear in another view, it is not advisable for a beginning student to do so. The beginner, until he has developed the discrimination that comes with experience, will be wise to show all hidden lines.

6.17. Precedence of lines. When one discovers in making a multiview drawing that two lines coincide, the question arises as to which line should be shown or, in other words, which line must have precedence if the drawing is to be read intelligently. For example, as revealed in Fig. 6.22, a solid line may have the same position as an invisible line representing the contour element of a hole, or an invisible line may occur at the same place as a center line for a hole. In these cases the decision rests on the relative importance

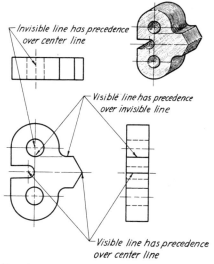

Fig. 6.22. Precedence of lines.

of each of the two lines that can be shown. The precedence of lines is:

> *Solid lines* (visible object lines) take precedence over all other lines.

> *Dashed lines* (invisible object lines) take precedence over center lines, although evidence of center lines may be indicated as shown in both the top and side views of Fig. 6.22.

> A *cutting plane line* takes precedence over a center line where it is necessary to indicate the position of a cutting plane.

6.18. Projection of angles. When an angle lies in a plane that is parallel to one of the planes of projection, the angle will show in true size in the view on that particular plane of projection to which the angle is parallel. In Fig. 6.23, those angles indicated as actual show in their true size. The 60° angle, that lies in a surface that is not parallel to the *H*-plane, appears at less than 60° in the top view. The 30° angle for the sloping line on the component portion that is inclined backwards projects at greater than 30° in the front view. It may be said that, except for a 90° angle having one leg as a normal line, angles lying on inclined planes will project either larger or smaller than true size, depending upon the position of the plane in which the angle lies. A 90° angle always projects in true size, even on an inclined plane, if the line forming one side of the angle is parallel to the plane of projection and a normal view of the line results. The normal view of a line is any view of a line that is obtained with the direction of sight perpendicular to the line.

What has been stated concerning angles on inclined surfaces can be easily verified by the student if he will observe what hap-

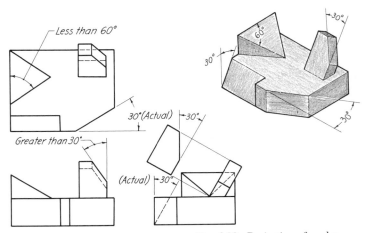

Fig. 6.23. Projection of angles.

pens to the angles of a 30° × 60° triangle resting on the long leg, as it is revolved from a vertical position downward onto the surface of his desk top.

6.19. Treatment of tangent surfaces. When a curved surface is tangent to a plane surface, as illustrated in several ways on the pictorial drawing in Fig. 6.24, no line should be shown as indicated at *A* and *B* in the top view and as noted for the front and side views. At *C* in the top view the line represents a small vertical surface that must be shown even though the upper and lower lines for this surface may be omitted in the front view, depending upon the decision of the draftsman. In the top view a line has been drawn to represent the intersection of the inclined and horizontal surfaces at the rear, even though they meet in a small round instead of a sharp edge. The presence of this line emphasizes the fact that there are two surfaces meeting here that are at a definite angle, one to the other. Several typical examples of tangencies and intersections have been illustrated in Fig. 6.25.

6.20. Parallel lines. When parallel surfaces are cut by a plane, the resulting lines of intersection will be parallel as shown by the pictorial drawing in Fig. 6.26, where the two near corners of the object have been removed by the oblique plane *ABC*. It can be observed from the multiview drawing that "when two lines are parallel in space their projections will be parallel in all of the views," even though at times both lines may appear as points in one view.

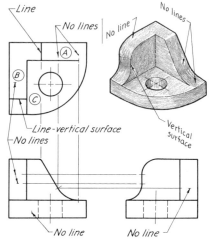

Fig. 6.24. Treatment of tangent surfaces.

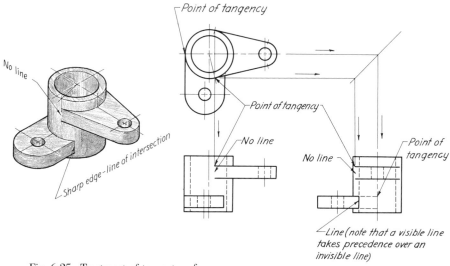

Fig. 6.25. Treatment of tangent surfaces.

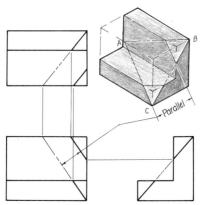

Fig. 6.26. Parallel lines.

6.21. Plotting an elliptical boundary. The actual intersection of a circular cylinder or cylindrical hole with a slanting surface (inclined plane) is an ellipse (see Fig. 6.27). The elliptical boundary in (a) appears as another ellipse in the top view, as a line in the front view, and as a semicircle in the side view. The ellipse was plotted in the top view by projecting selected points (such as points A and B) from the circle arc in the side view as shown. For example, point A was projected first to the inclined line in the front view and then to the top view. The mitre line shown was used to project the depth distance for A in the top view for illustrative purposes only. Ordinarily, dividers should be used to transfer measurements so as to secure great accuracy.

In (b) the intersection of the hole with the sloping surface is represented by an ellipse in the side view. Points selected around the circle in the top view (such as points C and D) projected to the side view as shown permit the draftsman to form the elliptical outline. It is recommended that a smooth curve be sketched freehand through the projected points before the French curve is applied to draw the finished ellipse, because it is easier to fit a curved ruling edge to a line than to scattered points.

6.22. Projecting a curved outline (space curve). When a boundary curve lies in an inclined plane, the projection of the curve may be found in another view by projecting points along the curve as illus-

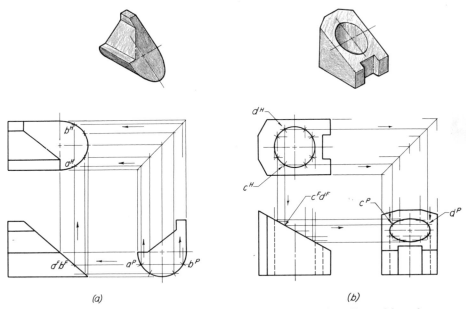

(a)   (b)

Fig. 6.27. Representation of an elliptical boundary.

trated in Fig. 6.28. In the example, points selected along the arcs forming the curve in the top view were first located in the side view using distances taken from the top view as shown by the X and Y measurements. Then, the front view positions of these points, through which the front view of the curve must pass, were established by projecting horizontally from the side view and downward from the top view.

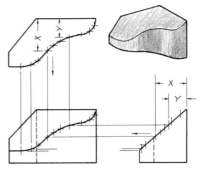

Fig. 6.28. Projecting a space curve.

6.23. Treatment of intersecting finished and unfinished surfaces. Figure 6.29 illustrates the removal of material when machining surfaces, cutting a slot, and drilling a hole in a small part. The italic f on a surface of a pictorial drawing indicates that the surface has been machined. The location of sharp and rounded corners as illustrated in (b) and (c) are noted on the multiview drawing. A discussion covering rounded internal and external corners is given in Sec. 6.34.

6.24. To make an orthographic drawing. The location of all views should be determined before a drawing is begun. This will insure balance in the appearance of the finished drawing. The contour view is usually started first. After the initial start, the draftsman should construct his views simultaneously by projecting back and forth from one to the other. It is poor practice to complete one view before starting the others, as much more time will be required to complete the drawing. Figure 6.30 shows the procedure for laying out a three-view drawing. The general outline of the views first should be drawn lightly with a hard pencil and then heavied with

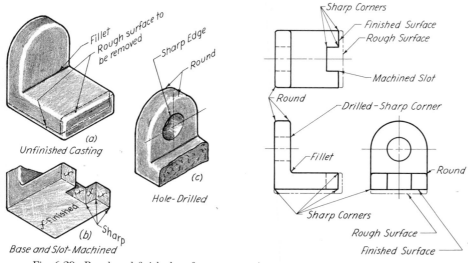

Fig. 6.29. Rough and finished surfaces on a casting.

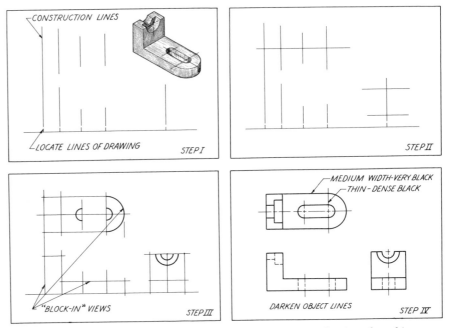

Fig. 6.30. Steps in making a three-view drawing of an object.

a medium grade pencil. Although experienced persons sometimes deviate from this procedure by drawing in the lines of known length and location in finished weight while constructing the views, it is not recommended that beginners do so (see Fig. 6.30, step III).

Although a 45° mitre line is sometimes used for transferring depth dimensions from the top view to the side view, or vice versa, as shown in Fig. 6.31(*b*), it is better practice to use dividers [see (*a*)]. Continuous lines need not be drawn between the views

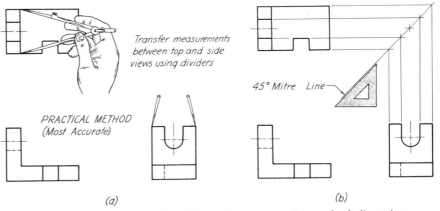

Fig. 6.31. Methods for transferring depth dimensions.

and the mitre line, as in the illustration, for one may project from short dashes across the mitre line. The location of the mitre line may be obtained by extending the construction lines representing the front edge of the top view and the front edge of the side view to an intersection.

When making an orthographic drawing in pencil, the beginner should endeavor to use the line weights recommended in Sec. 3.25. The object lines should be made very dark and bright, to give snap to the drawing as well as to create the contrast necessary to cause the shape of the object to stand out. Special care should be taken to gauge the dashes and spaces in invisible object lines. On ordinary drawings, ⅛ in. dashes and 1/32 in. spaces are recommended (Fig. 6.32).

Center lines consist of alternate long and short dashes. The long dashes are from ¾ in. to 1½ in. long, the short dashes ⅛ in., and the spaces 1/32 in. (Fig. 6.32). The following technique is recommended in drawing center lines:

1. Where center lines cross, the short dashes should intersect symmetrically (see Fig. 6.32). (In the case of very small circles the breaks may be omitted.)

2. The breaks should be so located that they will stand out and allow the center line to be recognized as such.

3. Center lines should extend approximately ⅛ in. beyond the outline of the part whose symmetry they indicate (Fig. 6.32).

4. Center lines should not end at object lines.

5. Center lines which are aligned with object lines should have not less than a 1/16 in. space between the end of the center line and the object line.

For a finished drawing to be pleasing in appearance, all lines of the same type must be uniform, and each type must have proper

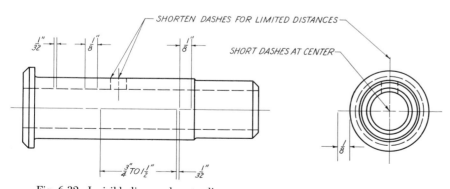

Fig. 6.32. Invisible lines and center lines.

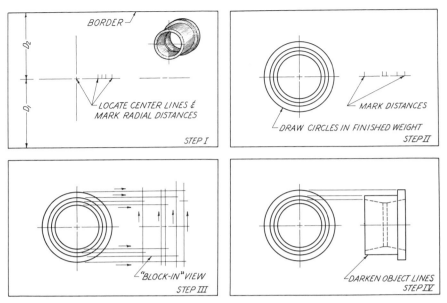

Fig. 6.33. Steps in making a two-view drawing of a circular object.

contrast with other symbolic types. The contrast between the types of pencil lines is similar to that of ink lines (Fig. 3.46), except that pencil lines are never as wide as ink lines (read Sec. 3.25). On commercial drawings, the usual practice is to "burn in" the object lines by applying heavy pressure.

If reasonable care is taken not to soil a drawing, it will not be necessary to clean any part of it with an eraser. Since the practice in most commercial drawing rooms is not to erase construction lines if they have been drawn lightly, the student, at the very beginning of his first course, should try to acquire habits that insure cleanliness.

When constructing a two-view drawing of a circular object, the pencil work must start with the drawing of the center lines, as shown in Fig. 6.33. This is necessarily the first step because the construction of the circular (contour) view is based upon a horizontal and a vertical center line. The horizontal object lines of the rectangular view are projected from the circles.

6.25. Visualizing an object from given views. Most students in elementary graphics courses find it difficult to visualize an object from two or more views. This trouble is largely due to the lack of systematic procedure for analyzing complex shapes.

The simplest method of determining shape is illustrated pictorially in Fig. 6.34. This method of "breaking down" may be applied to any object, since all objects may be thought of as consisting of

Fig. 6.34. "Breaking down" method.

elemental geometric forms, such as prisms, cylinders, cones, and so on. These imaginary component parts may be additions in the form of projections or subtractions in the form of cavities. Following such a detailed geometric analysis, a clear picture of an entire object can be obtained by mentally assembling a few easily visualized forms.

It should be realized, when analyzing component parts, that it is impossible ordinarily to determine whether a form is an addition or a subtraction by looking at one view. For example, the small circles in the top view in Fig. 6.34 indicate a cylindrical form, but they do not reveal whether the form is a hole or a projection. By consulting the front view, however, the form is shown to be a hole (subtracted cylinder).

The graphic language is similar to the written language in that neither can be read at a glance. A drawing must be read patiently by referring systematically back and forth from one view to another. At the same time the reader must imagine a three-dimensional object and not a two-dimensional flat projection.

A student usually will find that a pictorial sketch will clarify the shape of a part that is difficult to visualize. The method for preparing quick sketches in isometric is explained in Secs. 11.3 and 11.4.

6.26. Interpretation of adjacent areas of a view. To obtain a full understanding of the true geometric shape of a part, all of the areas on a given view must be carefully analyzed because each area represents a surface on the part. For example, in reading a drawing it must be determined whether or not a particular area in a top view represents a surface that is inclined or horizontal or whether the surface is higher or lower than adjacent ones. Five distinctly different objects are shown in Fig. 6.35, all having the same top view. In determining the actual shape of these objects, memory and previous experience can be a help, but one can easily be mislead if he

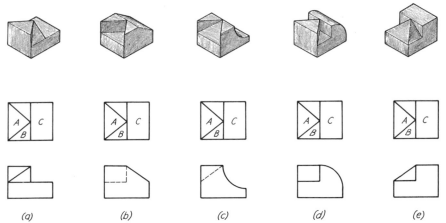

A third view may be necessary for the complete shape description of a particular object shown.

Fig. 6.35. Meaning of areas.

does not approach the analysis with an open mind, for it is only through trial and error effort and by referring back and forth from view to view that a drawing can be read. In considering area *A* in (*a*) it might be thought that the triangular surface could be high and horizontal, which would be correct because of the arrangement of lines in the front view. However, in considering the top view alone *A* could be either sloping as in (*c*) and (*e*) or low and horizontal as in (*b*). An analysis of the five parts reveals that the surface represented by area *B* can also be either sloping, high and horizontal, or low and horizontal. Area *C* offers even a wider variety of possibilities in that it may be either low and horizontal (*a*), sloping (*b*), cylindrical (*c*) and (*d*), or high and horizontal (*e*).

The student must realize at this point that since there are infinite possibilities for the shape, position, and arrangement of surfaces that form objects, he must learn to study tediously the views of any object with which he is not familiar until he is sure of the exact shape. Multiview drawings cannot be read with the ease of our written language which lists all of the components in a dictionary.

Figure 6.36 shows a pictorial drawing and a three-view orthographic drawing of a mutilated block. The accompanying table gives an orderly analysis of the reading of the three views of the object. A table similar to this one may be prepared by a student to facilitate study of a particular drawing.

All lines and surfaces are numbered at random on the orthographic drawing so that the student may take each surface designated on the pictorial drawing and identify it by a different number on each of the three views. For example, surface *I* on the pictorial view appears as a surface in the top view and is identified by the num-

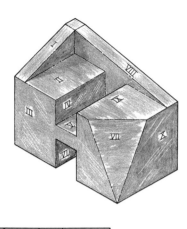

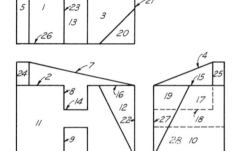

SURFACE NUMBER ON PICTORIAL	PROJECTS AS LINE OR SURFACE		
	NUMBER ON TOP VIEW	NUMBER ON FRONT VIEW	NUMBER ON END VIEW
I	5	24	4
II	1	2	15
III	26	11	27
IV	23	8	17
V	13	14	18
VI	23	9	28
VII	20	12	19
VIII	6	7	25
IX	3	16	15
X	21	22	10

Fig. 6.36. Lines and surfaces.

ber 5. The same surface appears as surface 24 in the front view, and as line 4 in the end view.

6.27. Representation of holes. In preparing drawings of parts of mechanisms, a draftsman finds it necessary to represent machined holes, that most often are either drilled, drilled and reamed, drilled and countersunk, drilled and counterbored, or drilled and spotfaced. Graphically, a hole is represented to conform with the finished form. The form may be completely specified by a note attached to the view showing the circular contour (see Fig. 6.37). The shop note, as prepared by the draftsman, usually specifies the several shop operations in the order that they are to be performed in the shop. For example, in (d) the hole, as specified, is drilled before it is counterbored. When depth has not been given in the note for a hole, it is understood to be a through hole, that is, the hole goes entirely through the piece [see (a), (c), (d), and (e)]. A hole that does not go through is known as "blind hole" [see (b)]. For such holes, depth is the length of the cylindrical portion (b). Drilled, bored,

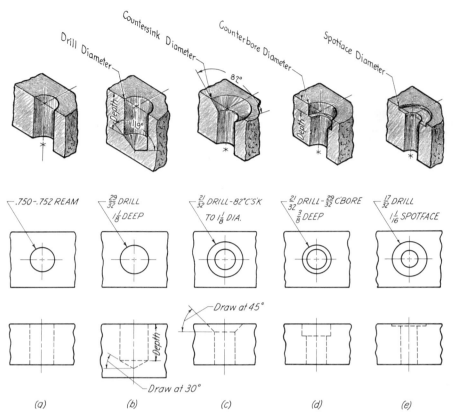

(For representations of threaded holes see chapter covering screw threads and fasteners)

Fig. 6.37. Representation of holes.

reamed, cored, or punched holes are always specified by giving their diameter—never their radius. Drill diameters for number- and letter-size drills are given in Table 25 in the Appendix.

In drawing the hole shown in (a), which must be drilled before it is reamed, the limits are ignored and the diameter is scaled to the nearest regular fractional or decimal size. In (b) the 30° × 60° triangle is used to draw the approximate representation of the conical hole formed by the drill point. In (c) a 45° triangle has been used to draw an approximate representation of the outline of the conical enlargement. The actual angle of 82° is ignored in order to save time in drawing. The spotface in (e) is most often cut to a depth of 1/16 in., however, the depth is usually not specified.

The beginner should now scan the several sections in the chapter on shop processes to obtain some general information on the production of holes. Complete information on the preparation of shop notes for holes may be found in Chapters 16 and 17.

6.28. Half views and partial views. When the space available is insufficient to allow a satisfactory scale to be used for the representation of a symmetrical piece, it is considered good practice to make one view either a half view or a partial view, as shown in Fig. 6.38. The half view, however, must be the top or side view and not the front view, which shows the characteristic contour. The half view should be the front half of the top or side view. In the case of the partial view shown in (*b*), a break line is used to limit the view.

B: CONVENTIONAL PRACTICES

6.29. To reduce the high cost of preparing engineering drawings and at the same time to convey specific and concise information without a great expenditure of effort, some generally recognized systems of symbolic representation and conventional practices have been adopted by American industry.

A standard symbol or conventional representation can express information that might not be understood from a true line representation unless accompanied by a lettered statement. In many cases, even though a true line representation would convey exact information, very little more would be gained from the standpoint of better interpretation. Some conventional practices have been adopted for added clearness. For instance, they can eliminate awkward conditions that arise from strict adherence to the rules of projection.

These idioms of drawing have slowly developed with the graphic language until at the present time they are universally recognized and observed, and appear in the various standards of the American Standards Association.

Professional men and skilled workmen have learned to accept and respect the use of the symbols and conventional practices, for they can interpret these representations accurately and realize that their use saves valuable time in both the drawing room and the shop.

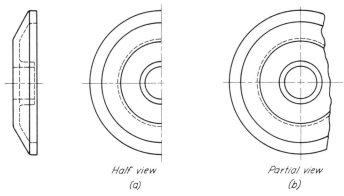

Half view   Partial view
(a)   (b)

Fig. 6.38. Half views and partial views.

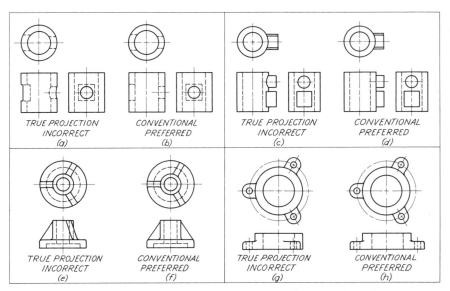

TRUE PROJECTION
INCORRECT
(a)

CONVENTIONAL
PREFERRED
(b)

TRUE PROJECTION
INCORRECT
(c)

CONVENTIONAL
PREFERRED
(d)

TRUE PROJECTION
INCORRECT
(e)

CONVENTIONAL
PREFERRED
(f)

TRUE PROJECTION
INCORRECT
(g)

CONVENTIONAL
PREFERRED
(h)

Fig. 6.39. Conventional practice of representing unimportant intersections, ribs, and lugs.

6.30. The treatment of unimportant intersections. The conventional methods of treating various unimportant intersections are shown in Fig. 6.39. To show the true line of intersection in each case would add little to the value of the drawing. Therefore, in the views designated as preferred, true projection has been ignored in the interest of simplicity. On the front views, in (*a*) and (*b*) for example, there is so little difference between the descriptive values of the true and approximate representations of the hole that the extra labor necessary to draw the true representation is unwarranted.

6.31. Aligned views. Pieces that have arms, ribs, lugs, or other parts at an angle are often shown aligned or "straightened out" in one view, as illustrated in Fig. 6.40. By this method, it is possible to show the true shape as well as the true position of such features.

6.32. Developed views. Bent pieces, similar to the piece shown in Fig. 6.41, are often drawn so that one view is a developed view of the blank from which the piece is to be formed, and the other is a true view showing the characteristic contour.

In laying out the developed view extra metal must be allowed for bends. The empirical formula used for computing the bend allowance (arc length) for a bend is shown in (*b*).

6.33. Conventional treatment of radially arranged features. Many objects that have radially arranged features may be shown more

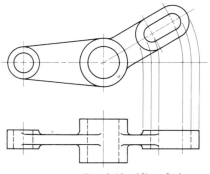

Fig. 6.40. Aligned views.

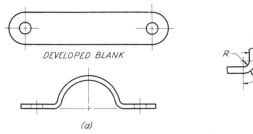

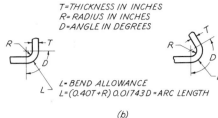

T=THICKNESS IN INCHES
R= RADIUS IN INCHES
D=ANGLE IN DEGREES

DEVELOPED BLANK

L=BEND ALLOWANCE
L=(0.40T+R) 0.01743D =ARC LENGTH

(a)   *(b)*

Fig. 6.41. Developed views.

clearly if true projection is violated as in Fig. 6.39(f) and (h). Violation of true projection in such cases consists of intentionally showing such features swung out of position in one view so as to present the idea of symmetry and show the true relationship of the features at the same time. For example, while the radially arranged holes in a flange (Fig. 6.42) should always be shown in their true position in the circular view, they should be shown in a revolved position in the other view in order to show their true relationship with the rim.

Radial ribs and radial spokes are similarly treated. The true projection of such features may create representations that are unsymmetrical and misleading. The preferred conventional method of treatment, by preserving symmetry, produces representations that are more easily understood and that at the same time are much simpler to draw. Figure 6.43 illustrates the preferred treatment for radial ribs.

6.34. Representation of fillets and rounds.

Interior corners, which are formed on a casting by unfinished surfaces, always are filled in (filleted) at the intersection in order to avoid possible fracture at that point. Sharp corners are also difficult to obtain and are avoided for this reason as well (Fig. 6.44). Exterior corners are rounded for appearance and for the comfort of persons who must handle the part when assembling or repairing the machine on which the part is used. A rounded internal corner is known as a *fillet;* a rounded external corner is known as a *round.*

When two intersecting surfaces are machined, however, their intersection will become a sharp corner. For this reason, all corners formed by unfinished surfaces should be shown "broken" by small rounds, and all corners formed by two finished surfaces or one finished surface and one unfinished surface should be shown "sharp." Although in the past it has been the practice to allow pattern makers to use their judgment about the size of fillets and rounds, many present-day companies require their designers and draftsmen to specify their size even though their exact size may not be important.

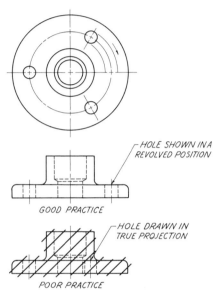

HOLE SHOWN IN A
REVOLVED POSITION

GOOD PRACTICE

HOLE DRAWN IN
TRUE PROJECTION

POOR PRACTICE

Fig. 6.42. Radially arranged holes.

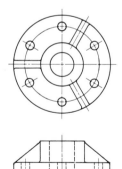

Fig. 6.43. Conventional treatment of radially arranged ribs.

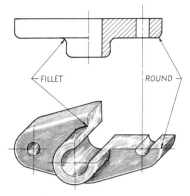

Fig. 6.44. Fillets and rounds.

Since fillets and rounds eliminate the intersection lines of intersecting surfaces, they create a special problem in orthographic representation. To treat them in the same manner as they would be treated if they had large radii results in views that are misleading. For example, the true projection view in Fig. 6.45(c) confuses the reader, because at first glance it does not convey the idea that there are abrupt changes in direction. To prevent such a probable first impression and to improve the descriptive value of the view, it is necessary to represent these theoretically nonexisting lines. These characteristic lines are projected from the approximate intersections of the surfaces, with the fillets disregarded.

Figure 6.46 illustrates the accepted conventional method of representing the "run-out" intersection of a fillet in cases where a plane surface is tangent to a cylindrical surface. Although run-out arcs such as these are usually drawn freehand, a French curve or a bow instrument may be used. If they are drawn with the bow instrument, a radius should be used that is equal to the radius of the fillet,

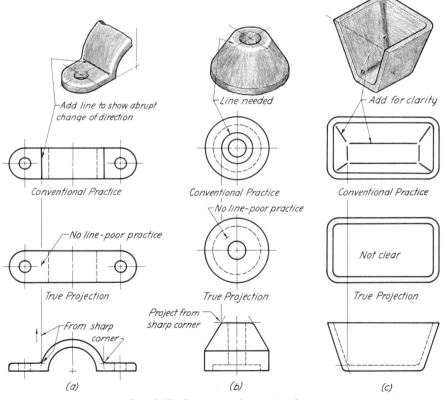

Fig. 6.45. Conventional practice of representing nonexisting lines of intersection.

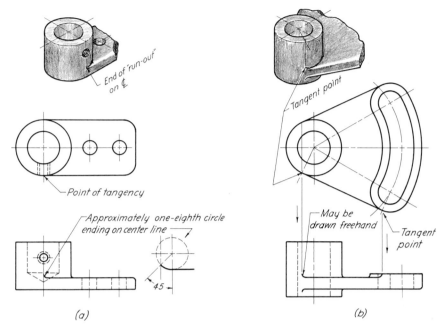

Fig. 6.46. The conventional treatment for fillets.

and the completed arc should form approximately one-eighth of a circle.

The generally accepted methods of representing intersecting fillets and rounds are illustrated in Fig. 6.47. The treatment, in each of the cases shown, is determined by the relationship existing between the sizes of the intersecting fillets and rounds. Figure 6.47 shows several illustrations of accepted conventional methods used to represent run-outs.

6.35. Conventional breaks.

A relatively long piece of uniform section may be shown to a larger scale, if a portion is broken out so that the ends can be drawn closer together (Fig. 6.48). When such a scheme is employed, a conventional break is used to indicate that the length of the representation is not to scale. The American Standard conventional breaks, shown in Fig. 6.49, are used on either detail or assembly drawings. The break representations for indicating the broken ends of rods, shafts, tubes, and so forth, are designed to reveal the characteristic shape of the cross section in each case. Although break lines for round sections may be drawn freehand, particularly on small views, it is better to draw them with either an irregular curve or a bow instrument. The breaks for wood sections, however, always should be drawn freehand.

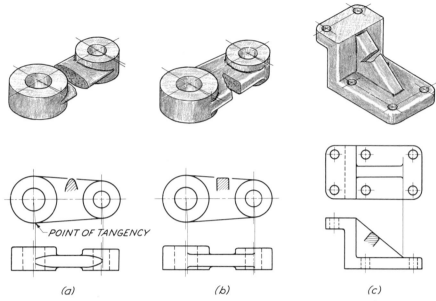

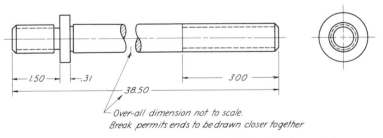

POINT OF TANGENCY

(a)   (b)   (c)

Fig. 6.47. The approximate methods of representing intersecting fillets, rounds.

6.36. Ditto lines. When it is desirable to minimize labor in order to save time, ditto lines may be used to indicate a series of identical features. For example, the threads on the shaft shown in Fig. 6.50 are just as effectively indicated by ditto lines as by a completed profile representation. When ditto lines are used, a long shaft of this type may be shortened without actually showing a conventional break.

6.37. A conventional method for showing a part in alternate positions. A method frequently used for indicating an alternate position of a part or a limiting position of a moving part is shown in Fig. 6.51. The dashes forming the object lines of the view showing the alternate position should be of medium weight. The phantom

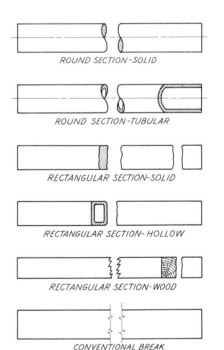

ROUND SECTION-SOLID

ROUND SECTION-TUBULAR

RECTANGULAR SECTION-SOLID

RECTANGULAR SECTION- HOLLOW

RECTANGULAR SECTION-WOOD

CONVENTIONAL BREAK

Fig. 6.49. Conventional breaks.

1.50   .31

38.50

300

Over-all dimension not to scale.
Break permits ends to be drawn closer together

Fig. 6.48. A broken-out view.

Fig. 6.50. Ditto lines.

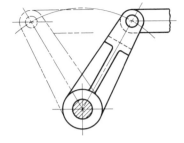

Fig. 6.51. Alternate positions.

line shown in Fig. 3.46 is recommended for representing an alternate position.

6.38. Conventional representation. Conventional representations are used by engineers of all fields to represent many of the details that occur repeatedly on their drawings. Symbols are used on topographic drawings, architectural drawings, electrical drawings, and machine drawings. No engineer serving in a professional capacity can very well escape their use.

Most of the illustrations that are shown in Fig. 6.52 should be easily understood. However, the crossed-lines (diagonals) symbol has two distinct and different meanings. First, this symbol may be used on a drawing of a shaft to indicate the position of a surface for a bearing or, second, it may indicate that a surface perpendicular to the line of sight is flat. These usages are illustrated with separate examples.

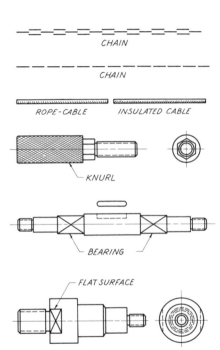

Fig. 6.52. Conventional symbols.

PROBLEMS

The problems that follow are intended primarily to furnish study in multiview projection through the preparation of either sketches or instrumental drawings. Many of the problems in this chapter, however, may be prepared in more complete form. Their views may be dimensioned as are the views of working drawings, if the student will study carefully the beginning of the chapter covering dimensioning before attempting to record size description (Chap. 17). All dimensions should be placed in accordance with the general rules of dimensioning.

The views shown in a sketch or drawing should be spaced on the paper with aim for balance within the border lines. Ample room should be allowed between the views for the necessary dimensions. If the views are not to be dimensioned, the distance between them may be made somewhat less than would be necessary otherwise.

Before starting to draw, the student should reread Sec. 6.24 and study Fig. 6.30, which shows the steps in making a multiview drawing. The preparation of a preliminary sketch always proves helpful to the beginner.

All construction work should be done in light lines with a sharp hard pencil. A drawing should be checked by an instructor before the lines are "heavied in," unless the preliminary sketch was checked beforehand.

SURFACE NUMBER ON PICTORIAL	PROJECTS AS LINE OR SURFACE		
	NUMBER ON TOP VIEW	NUMBER ON FRONT VIEW	NUMBER ON END VIEW
I			
II			

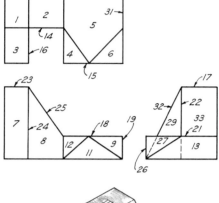

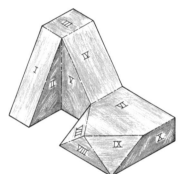

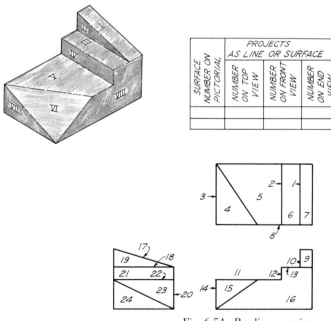

Fig. 6.53. Reading exercise.

1-2. (Figs. 6.53–6.54.) Draw a table similar to that shown in Fig. 6.36 and fill in the required information for each of the surfaces designated on the pictorial drawing by a Roman numeral. Draw the necessary guide lines and letter the column headings and information in ⅛ in. capitals.

3. (Fig. 6.55.) A line is missing from each of the three-view drawings. When the correct missing line is found, the three views of each object will be consistent with one another. *Suggestion:* A good method of visualizing these objects is to sketch them pictorially or to cut a model from a piece of modeling clay, a cake of soap, or an ordinary potato.

4. (Fig. 6.56.) Add the missing line or lines in one view of each of the three-view drawings. When the missing line or lines have been determined, the three views of each object will be consistent with one another.

5-6. (Figs. 6.57–6.58.) Draw or sketch the third view for each of the given objects.

7-12. (Figs. 6.59–6.64.) Reproduce the given views and draw the required view. Show all hidden lines.

13-24. (Figs. 6.65–6.76.) Sketch, freehand, the necessary views of the given objects as assigned. The selected length for the unit will determine the size of the views. Assume any needed dimensions that are not given in units.

SURFACE NUMBER ON PICTORIAL	PROJECTS AS LINE OR SURFACE		
	NUMBER ON TOP VIEW	NUMBER ON FRONT VIEW	NUMBER ON END VIEW

Fig. 6.54. Reading exercise.

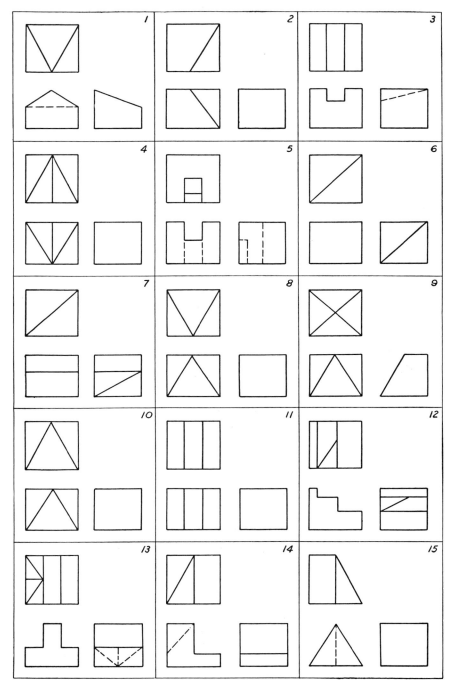

Fig. 6.55. Missing-line exercises.

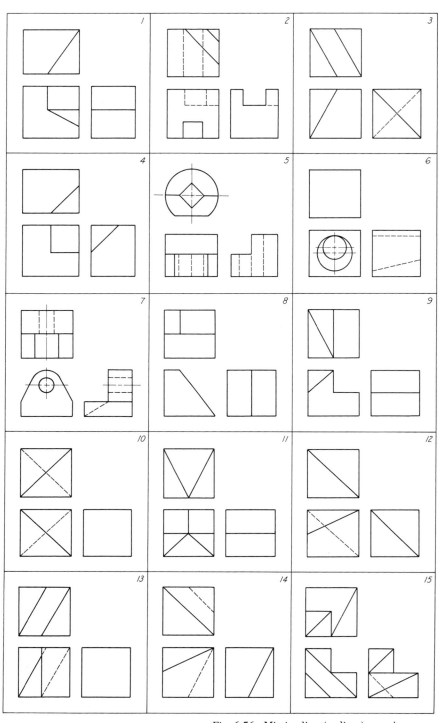

Fig. 6.56. Missing-line (or lines) exercises.

Fig. 6.57. Third-view problems.

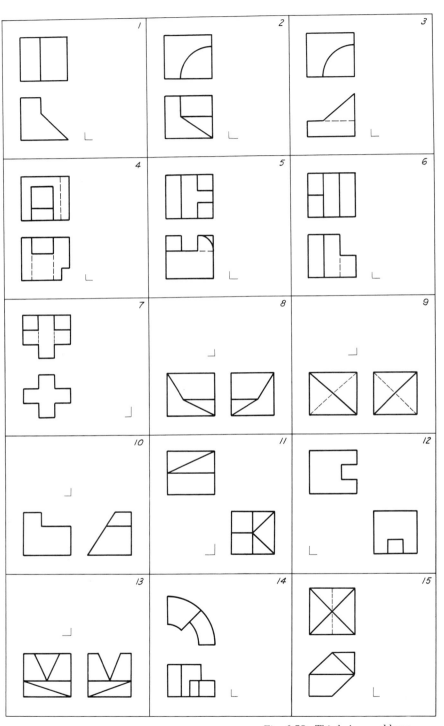

Fig. 6.58. Third-view problems.

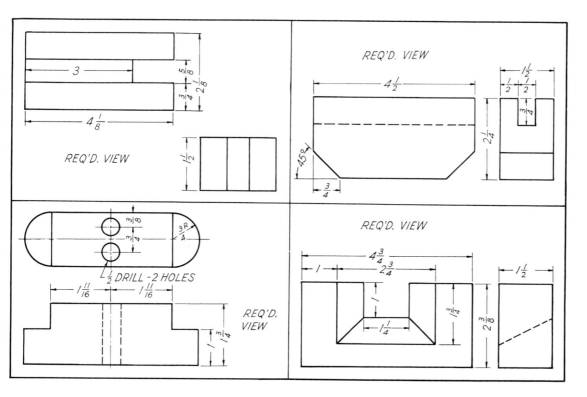

Fig. 6.59

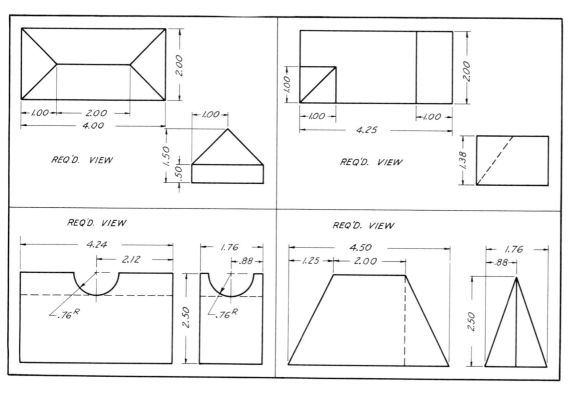

Fig. 6.60

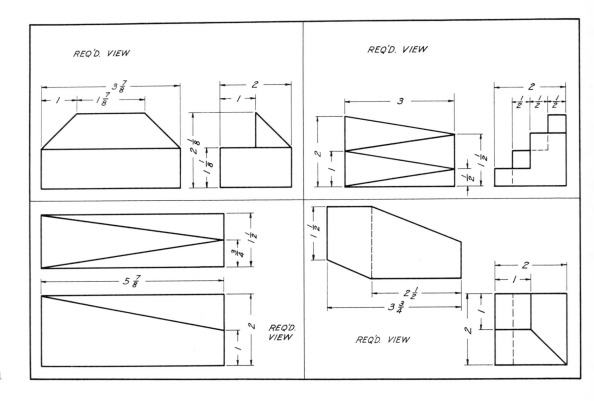

Fig. 6.61

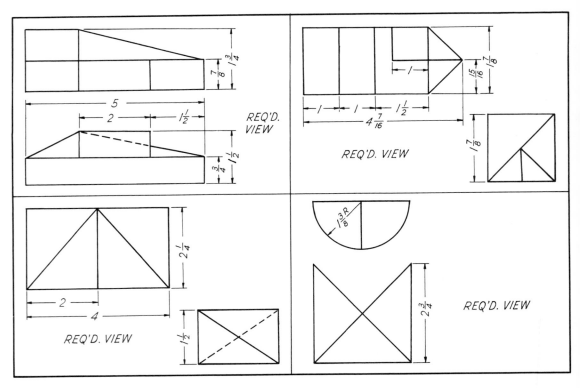

Fig. 6.62

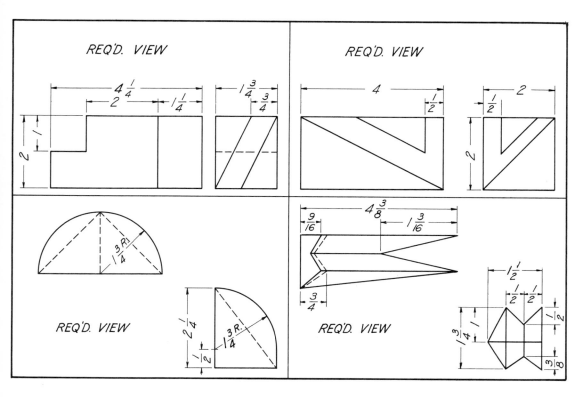

Fig. 6.63

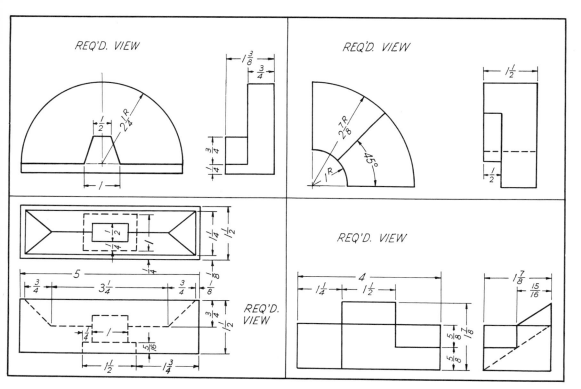

Fig. 6.64

Fig. 6.65. Stop block.

Fig. 6.66. Angle block.

Fig. 6.67. Adjustment block.

Fig. 6.68. Slip block.

Fig. 6.69. Alignment block.

Fig. 6.70. Control bracket.

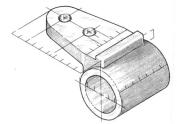

Fig. 6.71. Shaft bracket.

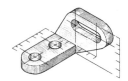

Fig. 6.72. Automatic feed bracket.

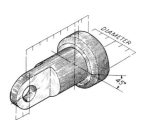

Fig. 6.73. Guide.

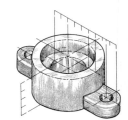

Fig. 6.74. Collar bracket.

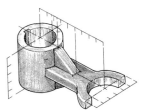

Fig. 6.75. Shifter.

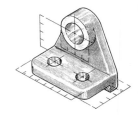

Fig. 6.76. Support bracket.

25-70. (Figs. 6.77–6.122.) These problems are designed to give the student further study in multiview drawing. The views of the drawings of the given objects may or may not be dimensioned.

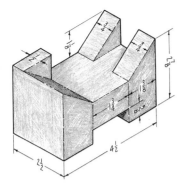

Fig. 6.77. Rest block.

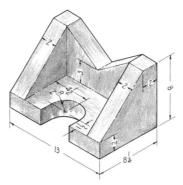

Fig. 6.78. V-rest.

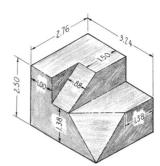

Fig. 6.79. Corner block.

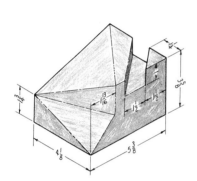

Fig. 6.80. Adjustment block.

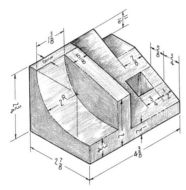

Fig. 6.81. Stop block.

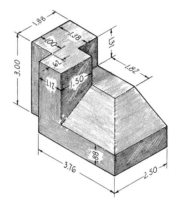

Fig. 6.82. Angle block.

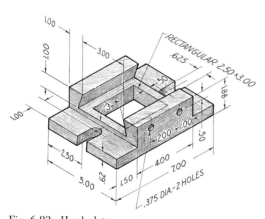

Fig. 6.83. Head plate.

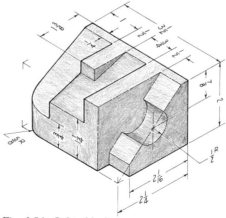

Fig. 6.84. Safety block.

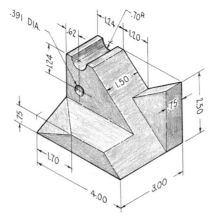

Fig. 6.85. Terminal block.

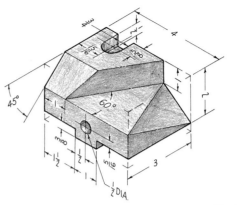

Fig. 6.86. Locating block.

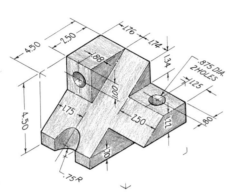

Fig. 6.87. Cross stop.

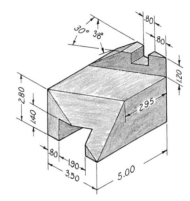

Fig. 6.88. End block.

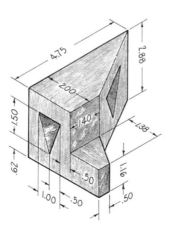

Fig. 6.89. Bevel block.

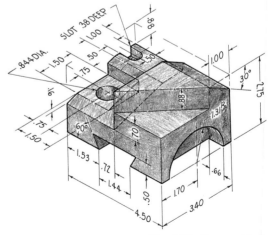

Fig. 6.90. Bumper block.

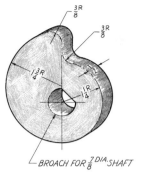

Fig. 6.91. Cam.

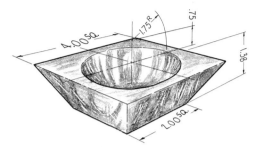

Fig. 6.92. Ash tray.

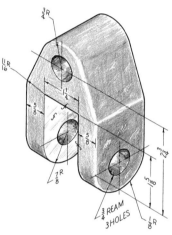

Fig. 6.93. Hinge link.

Fig. 6.94. Bearing block.

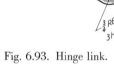

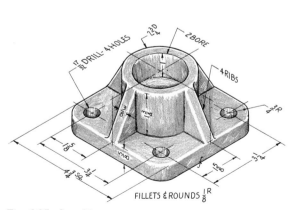

Fig. 6.95. Stanchion support.

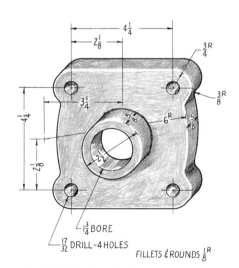

Fig. 6.96. Regulator body cover.

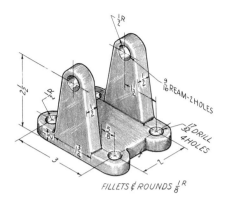

FILLETS & ROUNDS $\frac{1}{8}$ R

Fig. 6.97. Support bracket.

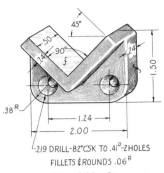

.219 DRILL-82°CSK TO .41^D-2HOLES
FILLETS & ROUNDS .06^R

Fig. 6.98. Corner stop.

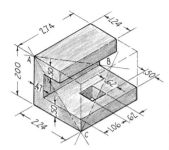

Fig. 6.99. Stabilizer block.

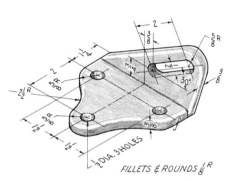

FILLETS & ROUNDS $\frac{1}{8}$ R

Fig. 6.100. Mounting bracket.

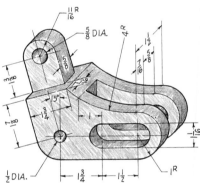

Fig. 6.101. Pivot guide.

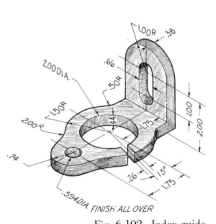

.594 DIA. FINISH ALL OVER

Fig. 6.102. Index guide.

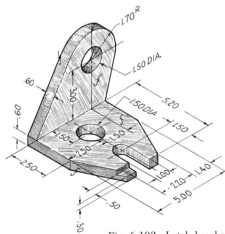

Fig. 6.103. Latch bracket.

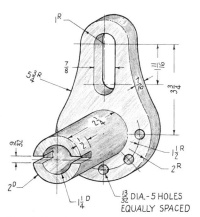

Fig. 6.104. Slotted guide.

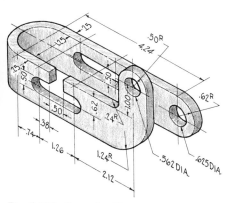

Fig. 6.106. Control guide.

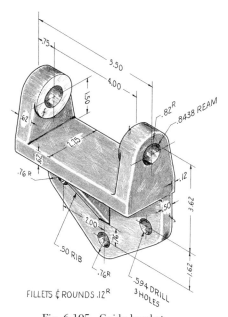

FILLETS & ROUNDS .12R

Fig. 6.105. Guide bracket.

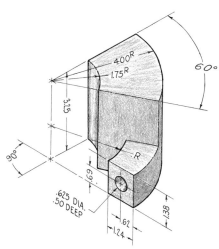

Fig. 6.107. Jaw block.

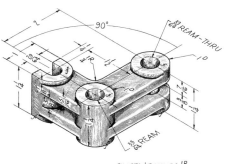

FILLETS & ROUNDS $\frac{1}{8}$R

Fig. 6.108. Shifter link.

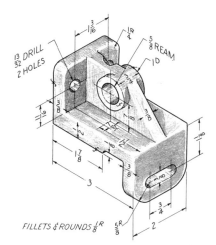

Fig. 6.109. Support bracket.

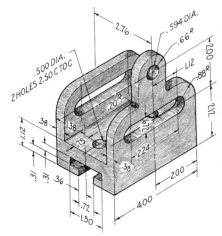

Fig. 6.110. Control guide.

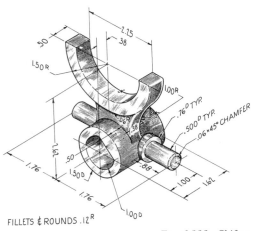

Fig. 6.111. Shifter.

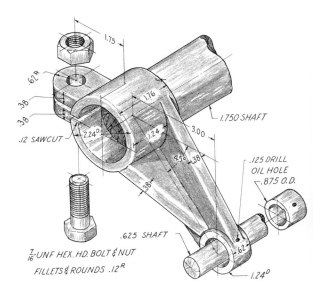

Fig. 6.112. Shaft bracket.

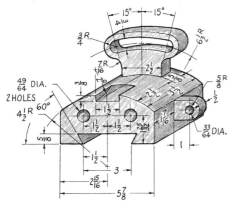

Fig. 6.113. Sliding guide.

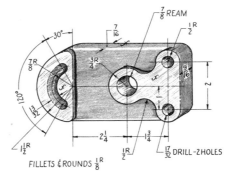

Fig. 6.114. Control plate.

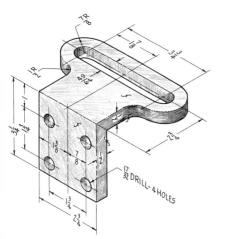

Fig. 6.115. Guide bracket.

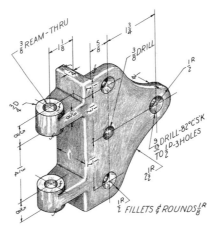

Fig. 6.116. Corner bracket.

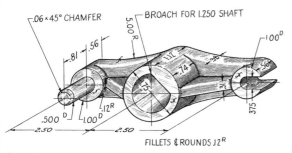

Fig. 6.117. Stud guide.

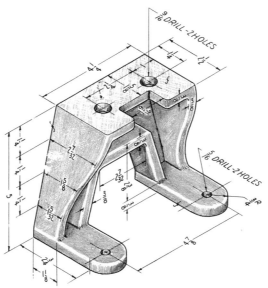

Fig. 6.118. Lathe leg.

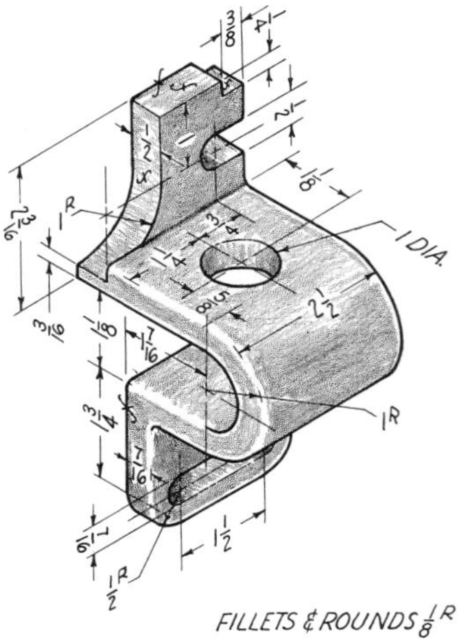

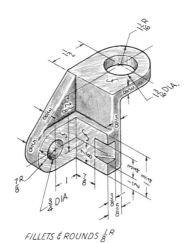

FILLETS & ROUNDS $\frac{1}{8}$R

Fig. 6.120. Ejector bracket.

71. (Fig. 6.123.) Make a complete orthographic drawing of the tube holder.

72. (Fig. 6.124.) Make a drawing of the bell crank. The bell crank is a part of the control mechanism of a vertical single-spindle boring machine. The rod which extends downward connects with a foot-operated control. The link carries the movement to the drive unit. *Supplementary design data:* (1) The distance from the pivot center of the crank to the center of the connecting pin for the rod is 3½ in., and the distance from the center of the crank to the pin con-

FILLETS & ROUNDS $\frac{1}{8}$R

Fig. 6.119. Guide clip.

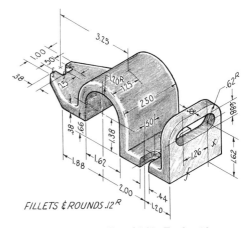

FILLETS & ROUNDS .12^R

Fig. 6.121. Feed guide.

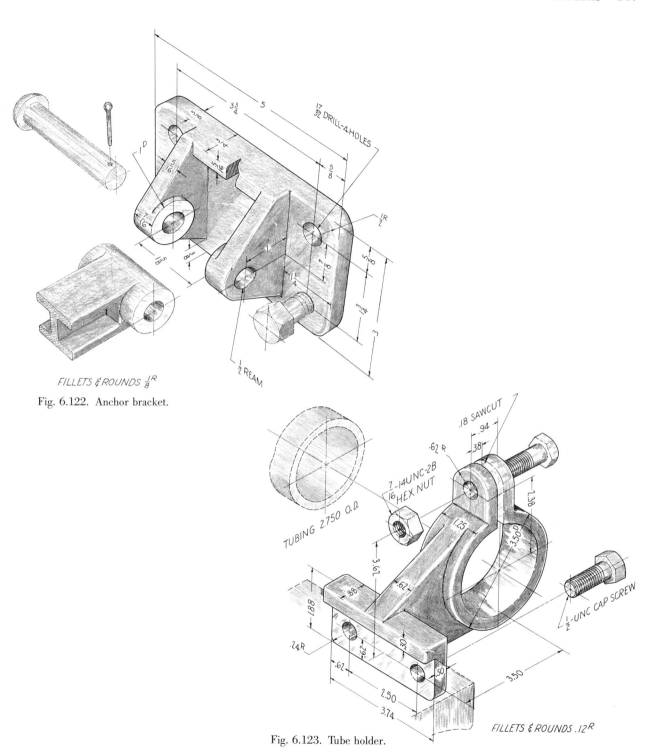

FILLETS & ROUNDS $\frac{1}{8}R$

Fig. 6.122. Anchor bracket.

Fig. 6.123. Tube holder.

necting the link is 2½ in. (2) The limiting position for any counterclockwise movement of the bell crank is as shown; namely, that the line connecting the centers of the pivot and the rod-pin is horizontal. The crank is to be drawn to allow the rod a 1½ in. downward movement. The upper arm of the crank is to be located so that there will be exactly ⅛ in. clearance between the arm and the housing when the crank is in the extreme clockwise position. The horizontal distance from the pivot center to the left face of the housing is 1⅝ in. (3) The end of the rod through which the pin passes is 1½ in. in diameter, and ⅜ in. thick. Allow adequate clearance. (4) The crank pivots about a 1 in.-diameter shoulder screw which is screwed into the bracket. (5) The crank is of cast iron. Fillets and rounds ⅛ in. R except as noted.

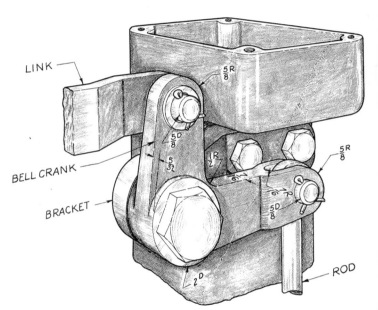

Fig. 6.124. Bell crank.

FREEHAND DRAFTING

7.1. Value of freehand drafting. Free-hand technical drafting is primarily the language of those in responsible charge of the development of technical designs and plans. Chief engineers, chief drafts-men, designers, and squad bosses have found that the best way to present their

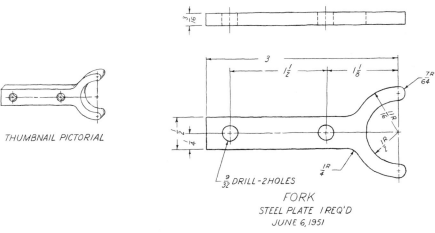

THUMBNAIL PICTORIAL

$\frac{9}{32}$ DRILL - 2 HOLES

FORK
STEEL PLATE 1 REQ'D
JUNE 6, 1951

Fig. 7.1. Working sketch.

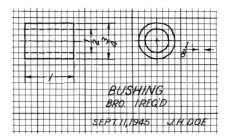

BUSHING
BRO. 1 REQ'D
SEPT. 11, 1945   J.H. DOE

Fig. 7.2. Sketches on cross-section paper.

ideas for either a simple or complex design is through the medium of sketches. Sketches may be schematic, as are those that are original expressions of new ideas, or they may be instructional, their purpose being to convey ideas to draftsmen or shopmen. Some sketches, especially those prepared for the manufacture of parts that are to replace worn or broken parts on existing machines, may resemble complete working drawings.

Since the importance of freehand drafting very often is underestimated, the purpose of this discussion is to amplify training in this phase. The young prospective engineer should understand, when beginning his studies, that sketching, and not mechanical drafting, will be his ultimate form of expression and that he must be able to prepare complete sketches that will present his ideas and decisions to subordinates in an understandable manner. Figure 7.1 is an example of a working sketch.

7.2. Sketching materials. For the type of sketching discussed here, the required materials are an F pencil, a soft eraser, and some paper. In the industrial field, men who have been improperly trained in sketching often use straightedges and cheap pocket compasses that they could well dispense with if they would adopt the correct technique. Preparing sketches with instruments consumes much unnecessary time.

For the person who cannot produce a satisfactory sketch without guide lines, cross-section paper is helpful. Ordinarily, the ruling on this paper forms one-inch squares which are subdivided into one-eighth or one-tenth inch squares. Such paper is especially useful when sketching to scale is desirable (Fig. 7.2).

7.3. Projections. Although freehand drafting lacks the refinement given by mechanical instruments, it is based upon the same principles of projection and conventional practices that apply to multiview, pictorial, and the other divisions of mechanical drawing. For this reason, one must be thoroughly familiar with projection, in all of its many forms, before he is adequately trained to prepare sketches.

7.4. Technique of lines. Freehand lines quite naturally will differ in their appearance from mechanical ones. A well-executed freehand line will never be perfectly straight and absolutely uniform in weight, but an effort should be made to approach *exacting uniformity*. As in the case of mechanical lines, they should be black and clear and not broad and fuzzy (see Fig. 7.3).

7.5. Sharpening the sketching pencil. A sketching pencil should be sharpened, on a file or piece of sandpaper, to a conical point. The point then should be rounded slightly, on the back of the sketch pad or on another sheet of paper, to the correct degree of dullness. When rounding the point, the pencil should be rotated to prevent the formation of sharp edges.

7.6. Straight lines. The pencil should rest on the second finger and be held loosely by the thumb and index finger about 1 to 1½ in. above the point.

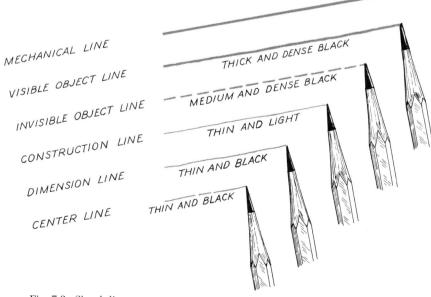

Fig. 7.3. Sketch lines.

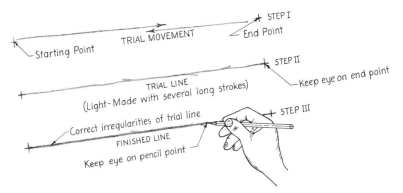

Fig. 7.4. Steps in sketching a straight line.

Horizontal lines are sketched from left to right with an easy arm motion that is pivoted about the muscle of the forearm. The straight line thus becomes an arc of infinite radius.

When sketching a straight line, it is advisable to first mark the end points with light dots or small crosses (Fig. 7.4). The complete procedure for sketching a straight line is as follows:

1. Mark the end-points.
2. Make a few trial motions between the marked points to adjust the eye and hand to the contemplated line.
3. Sketch a *very* light line between the points by moving the pencil in two or three sweeps. When sketching the trial line, the eye should be on the point toward which the movement is directed. With each stroke, an attempt should be made to correct the most obvious defects of the stroke preceding, so that the finished trial line will be relatively straight.
4. Darken the finished line, keeping the eye on the pencil point on the trial line. The final line, replacing the trial line, should be distinct, black, uniform, and straight.

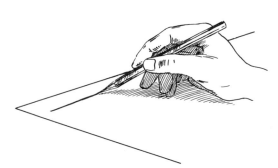

Fig. 7.5. Sketching horizontal lines.

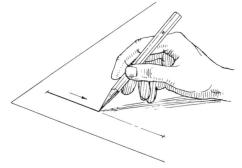

Fig. 7.6. Sketching vertical lines.

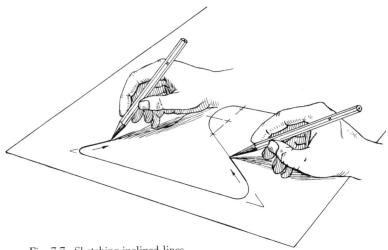

Fig. 7.7. Sketching inclined lines.

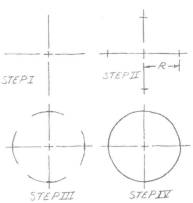

Fig. 7.8. Sketching small circles.

It is helpful to turn the paper through a *convenient angle* so that the horizontal and vertical lines assume a slight inclination (Fig. 7.5). A horizontal line, when the paper is in this position, is sketched to the right and upward, thus allowing the arm to be held slightly away from the body and making possible a free arm motion.

Short vertical lines may be sketched either downward or upward, without changing the position of the paper. When sketching downward, the arm is held slightly away from the body and the movement is toward the sketcher (see Fig. 7.6). To sketch vertical lines upward, the arm is held well away from the body.

By turning the paper, a long vertical line may be made to assume the position of a horizontal line and can be sketched with the same general movements used for the latter.

Inclined lines running upward from lower left to upper right may be sketched upward with the same movements used for horizontal lines, but those running downward from upper left to lower right are sketched with the general movements used for either horizontal or vertical ones, depending upon their inclination (Fig. 7.7). Inclined lines may be more easily sketched by turning the paper to make them conform to the direction of horizontal lines.

7.7. Circles. Small circles may be sketched by marking radial distances on perpendicular center lines (Fig. 7.8). These distances can be marked off either by eye or by measuring with a marked strip of paper (Fig. 7.9). Larger circles may be constructed more accurately by sketching two or more diagonals, in addition to the center lines, and by sketching short construction lines perpendicular to each, equidistant from the center. Tangent to these lines, short arcs are drawn perpendicular to the radii. The circle is completed with

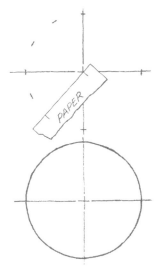

Fig. 7.9. Marking off radial distances.

a light construction line, and all defects are corrected before darkening (Fig. 7.10).

7.8. Ellipses. An ellipse of good proportion may be sketched within an enclosing rectangle. The rectangle, since it is used merely as an aid in forming the ellipse, should be drawn with very light lines, and the required ellipse should be sketched tangent to the sides.

7.9. Making a sketch. When making orthographic working sketches, a systematic order should be followed and all the rules and conventional practices used in making working drawings should be applied. The following procedure is recommended:

1. Examine the object, giving particular attention to detail.
2. Determine which views are necessary.
3. "Block in" the views, using light construction lines.
4. Complete the detail and darken the object lines.

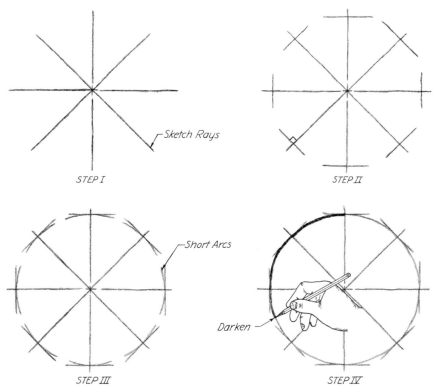

Fig. 7.10. Sketching large circles.

5. Sketch extension lines and dimension lines, including arrowheads.

6. Complete the sketch by adding dimensions, notes, title, date, sketcher's name or initials, and so on.

7. Check the entire sketch carefully to see that no dimensions have been omitted.

The progressive steps in making a working sketch of an object are shown in Fig. 7.11.

7.10. Making sketches of parts for the purpose of replacement and repair. It quite frequently is necessary to make working sketches of broken or worn parts. Such sketches are used instead of mechanical drawings because they can be made and sent to the shop in a much shorter time. The procedure given in Sec. 7.9 should be followed carefully when making sketches to be used by workmen in the shops.

7.11. Measurements and measuring instruments. If a sketch is to serve as a working drawing, it must contain all the necessary dimen-

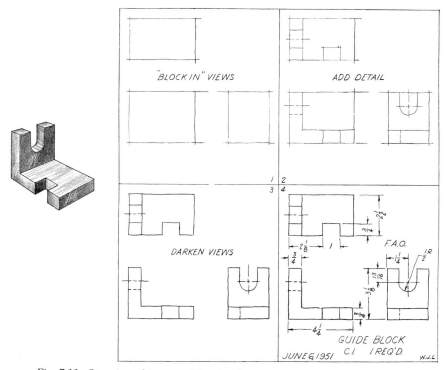

Fig. 7.11. Steps in making a working sketch.

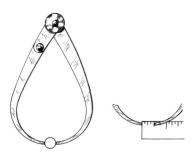

Fig. 7.12. Outside calipers.

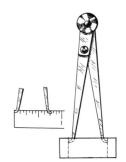

Fig. 7.13. Inside calipers.

sions and instructional notes needed by the workmen. If a sketch is for the manufacture of a part that is to replace a worn or broken part in an existing machine, measurements must be taken from the original part with the same general types of measuring devices to be used in manufacturing the new part. The instrument selected for each particular detail should be of a type that will allow measurements to be made with the correct degree of accuracy. For most machine parts, a steel scale and a set of inside and outside calipers will prove sufficient. When more accurate measurements are necessary, a micrometer must be used. In any case, the selection of the instrument for a measurement should be determined by exercising good judgment. Figure 7.12 shows how the outside calipers are used to take measurements from an object. Figure 7.13 shows the use of the inside calipers for measuring the diameter of a hole.

When taking measurements, certain practices are recommended. For example, to obtain the distance between holes (shown on the sketch as between centers), measure the distance between corresponding edges. To locate other features and to take off size dimensions, measure from a finished surface whenever possible, for a finished surface is usually a mating surface. The man in the shop must work from such a surface if he is to produce a part accurate enough to function in the existing machine.

7.12. The title. A title is far more important on a working sketch than many persons realize. It serves to identify the sketch and usually contains additional valuable information such as (1) the type of material, (2) the number required, (3) the name or initials of the sketcher, and (4) the date.

7.13. Proportions. The beginner must recognize the importance of being able to estimate comparative relationship between the width, height, and depth of an object being sketched. The complete problem of proportioning a sketch also involves relating the estimated dimensions for any component parts such as slots, holes, and projections to the over-all dimensions of the object. It is not the practice to attempt to estimate actual dimensions, for sketches are not usually made to scale. Rather one must decide, for example, that the width of the object is twice its height, that the width of a given slot is equal to one-half the width of the object, and that its depth is approximately one-fourth of the over-all height.

To become proficient at sketching one must learn to recognize proportions and be able to compare dimensions "by eye." Until he is able to do so, he can not really "think with his pencil." Some can develop a keen eye for proportion with only a limited amount of practice and can maintain these estimated proportions when

making the views of the sketch. Others have alternatingly discour-
aging and encouraging experiences. Discouragement comes when
one's knowledge of sketching is ahead of his ability and he has not
had as much practice as he needs. The many who find it difficult
to make the completed views of a sketch agree with the estimated
proportions of the object may at the start use the graphical method
shown in Fig. 7.14(a), (b), and (c). This method is based on the
fact that a rectangle (enclosing a view) may be divided to obtain
intermediate distances along any side that are in such proportion
of the total length as one-half, one-fourth, one-third and so forth.
Those who start with this rectangle method as an aid in proportioning must realize that they should abandon its use when they have
developed their eye and sketching skill so that it is no longer needed.

Sketching must be done rapidly and the addition of unnecessary
lines consumes much valuable time. Furthermore, the addition of
construction lines distract the reader, and it is certain that they do
not contribute to the neatness of the sketch.

The mid-point of a rectangle is the point of intersection of the
diagonals, as shown in Fig. 7.14(a). A line sketched through this
point that is perpendicular to any side will establish the mid-point
of that side. Should it be necessary to determine a distance that is
equal to one-fourth the length of a side, say AC, the quarter-point
may be located by repeating this procedure for the small rectangle
representing the upper left-hand quarter of $ABCD$.

With the mid-point J located by the intersecting diagonals of
the small rectangle representing one-fourth of the larger rectangle
$EFGH$ as in (b), the one-third point along FH may be located by
sketching a line from point G through J and extending it to line
FH. The point K at the intersection of these lines establishes the
needed one-third distance.

To determine one-sixth of the length of a side of a rectangle as
in (c), sketch a line from N through point P as was done in (b) to
determine a one-third distance. Point Q at which the line NP crosses

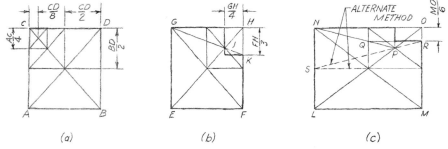

Fig. 7.14. Methods of proportioning a rectangle representing
the outline of a view.

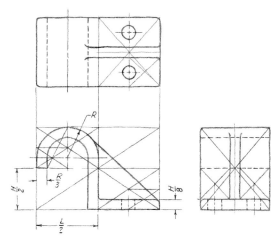

Fig. 7.15. The rectangle method applied in making an orthographic sketch.

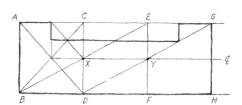

Fig. 7.16. The build-up method.

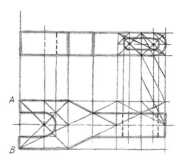

Fig. 7.17. An orthographic sketch —build-up method.

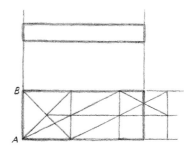

Fig. 7.18. Using combined methods.

the centerline of the rectangle establishes the one-sixth distance along the centerline.

Figure 7.15 shows how this method for dividing the sides of a rectangle might be used to proportion an orthographic sketch.

The square may be used to proportion a view after one dimension for the view has been assumed. In using this method, additional squares are added to the initial one having the assumed length as one side (Fig. 7.16). As an example, suppose that it has been estimated that the front view of an object should be three times as long as it is high. In Fig. 7.16 the height of the view has been represented by the line *AB* sketched to an assumed length. The first step in making the construction is to sketch the initial square *ABCD* and extend *AC* and *BD* to indefinite length, being certain that the overall length from *A* and *D* will be slightly greater than three times the length of *AB*. Then the center line must be sketched through the intersection of *AD* and *BC*. Now *BX* extended to *E* locates *EF* to form the second square, and *DY* extended to point *G* locates the line *GH*. Line *AG* will be three times the length of *AB*.

Figure 7.17 shows how the build-up method might be used to make an orthographic sketch. The starting line is *AB*. The three principal squares were divided as needed using the method for proportioning a rectangle.

The method for determining a length that is equal to some full number and fractional number of times a given height is shown in Fig. 7.18. In this case the length of the block is two and one-half times the height *AB*.

7.14. Use of an overlay sheet. An overlay sheet may be used to an advantage in making any sketch that is complicated with details (Fig. 7.19). In this case, a quick sketch showing the general outline of the principal parts is made first in a rather rough form. Then an overlay sheet is placed over this outline sketch and the lines are

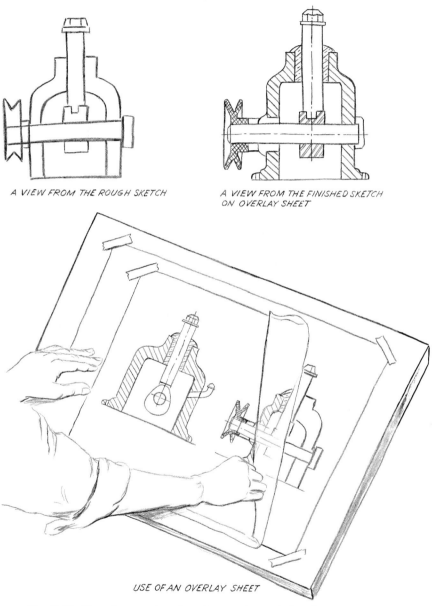

A VIEW FROM THE ROUGH SKETCH

A VIEW FROM THE FINISHED SKETCH
ON OVERLAY SHEET

USE OF AN OVERLAY SHEET

Fig. 7.19. Use of an overlay sheet for creating a final and complete sketch of a mechanism.

retraced. In doing so, slight corrections can be made for any known errors existing in the proportions of the parts or in the position of any of the lines of the original rough sketch. When this has been done, the representations of the related minor parts are added. If at any time one becomes discouraged with a sketch that he is making and feels that a new start is needed, an overlay sheet should be used, for there are usually many features on his existing sketch that may be retraced with a great saving of time.

7.15. Use of technical sketching-design by an engineer. When an engineer is involved in the planning and direction of a project, he finds it necessary to prepare numerous sketches—entirely freehand. Without the ability to prepare quick and accurate sketches as they are needed for both exploratory and explanatory purposes, he would find himself immeasurably handicapped. In fact, the lack of this ability would reduce his professional efficiency as much as if he were actually tongue-tied or illiterate. Use of the freehand drafting technique enables one to make frequent changes very rapidly when developing an original idea for a design or when modifying a design that has already won partial acceptance.

By making numerous idea sketches an engineer finally is able to crystallize his thoughts and settle some of the perplexing problems that usually arise to plague him. If he employed instruments to prepare these drawings that are a necessary aid to his thinking, he would find that he was wasting much of his valuable time, for numerous drawings would be required and quite a few might finally be discarded after varied ideas had been explored and found to be unsatisfactory.

In "thinking with a pencil" an engineer's very environment makes the use of instruments undesirable, for much of his work may be done at his office desk, at the conference table, or in the laboratory where instruments are not readily at hand. It is because of the conditions under which he works that he must learn to sketch rapidly and well and to resist the temptation to use a straightedge and compass. To use any aids whatsoever takes away much of the practical advantage to be gained from sketching.

Figure 7.20 shows an idea sketch that was prepared to satisfy the need for a connector for a mechanical control unit. Sketches of this type may be turned over to a draftsman for complete development.

In studying the techniques of sketching, it is advisable to read this chapter and Chapter 11 at the same time, for multiview and pictorial sketches may be used together when "thinking with the pencil."

An engineer's sketches may show either an idea for a complete unit, or a small subassembly of the unit. Some may be made to show only a few related parts around which a problem exists.

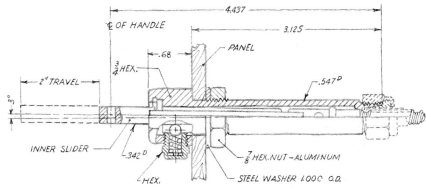

Fig. 7.20. A sketch for a connector of a remote control unit (*Courtesy Teleflex, Inc.*).

An engineer must usually supply explanatory sketches to the draftsmen who are assisting him in developing a project, for the draftsmen quite frequently come face-to-face with minor problems as the drawings are being prepared.

A wiring diagram in sketch form is shown in Fig. 7.21. This diagram appeared on the original idea sketch shown in Fig. 11.4 in the chapter on pictorial sketching.

PROBLEMS

The problems presented with this chapter have been selected to furnish practice in freehand drafting. The individual pieces that appear in pictorial form have been taken from a wide variety of mechanisms used in different fields of engineering. The student may be required to prepare complete working sketches of these parts if his instructor desires. Such an assignment, however, would presuppose an understanding of the fundamentals of dimensioning as they are presented in the beginning sections of Chapter 17.

A complete set of working sketches may be prepared for a unit mechanism where all of the related parts are shown in pictorial. As part of the assignment an instructor may require a student to prepare a sketch showing all of the parts assembled.

The problems given as assembly drawings provide practice in making sketches of individual parts as they are assigned. In sketching a part given on an assembly drawing, the student gains experience in reading drawings and in understanding the functions of different parts. Problems of this type develop the student's power to visualize, for he is forced to form a mental picture of the complete shape of the piece as well as to see the shape of its component forms.

Screw threads may be shown by using either the schematic or simplified form of representation as shown in Figs. 16.12 and 16.13. The

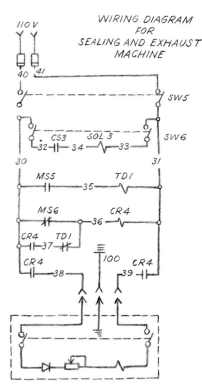

Fig. 7.21. A wiring diagram (*Courtesy General Electric Company*).

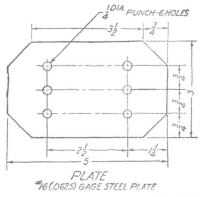

PLATE
#16 (0625) GAGE STEEL PLATE

Fig. 7.22

student should read Sec. 16.9. If a specification is to be given for the thread, it will be necessary to read the appropriate sections in Chapter 16 that cover the specification of screw threads.

The following practical one-view working sketches were selected to provide practice in lettering and sketching. The pictorial representations of practical machine parts offer the opportunity for practice in sketching and further study of multiview projection.

1-6. (Figs. 7.22–7.27.) Reproduce an assigned one-view sketch on a sheet of sketching paper.

7-27. (Figs. 7.28–7.48.) Sketch, freehand, the necessary views of the given objects as assigned. The selected length for the unit will determine the size of the views. Assume any needed dimensions that are not given in units.

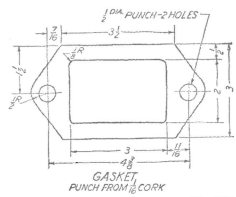

GASKET,
PUNCH FROM 1/16 CORK

Fig. 7.23

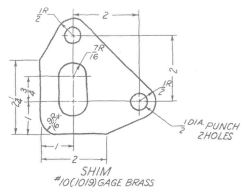

SHIM
#10 (1019) GAGE BRASS

Fig. 7.24

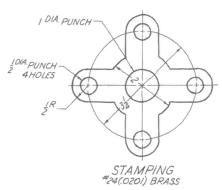

STAMPING
#24 (0201) BRASS

Fig. 7.25

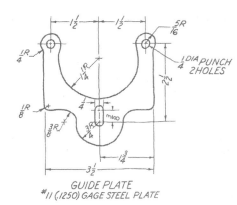

GUIDE PLATE
#11 (1250) GAGE STEEL PLATE

Fig. 7.26

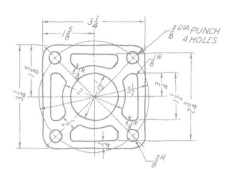

GASKET,
PUNCH FROM $\frac{1}{16}$ CORK

Fig. 7.27

Fig. 7.28. V-rest.

Fig. 7.29. Support block.

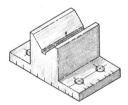

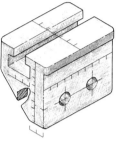

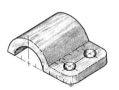

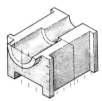

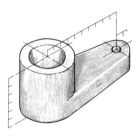

Fig. 7.30. Wedge block.

Fig. 7.31. End block.

Fig. 7.32. Offset guide.

Fig. 7.33. Bearing block.

Fig. 7.34. Corner block.

Fig. 7.35. V-block.

Fig. 7.36. Control rod bracket.

Fig. 7.37. Link.

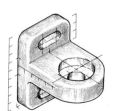

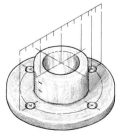

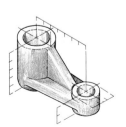

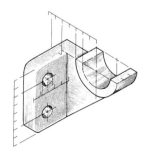

Fig. 7.38. Bearing bracket.

Fig. 7.39. End plate.

Fig. 7.40. Trip bracket.

Fig. 7.41. Offset bracket.

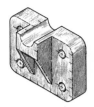

Fig. 7.42. Support bracket.

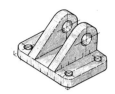

Fig. 7.43. Strut bracket.

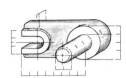

Fig. 7.44. Stud guide.

Fig. 7.45. Feed rod bracket.

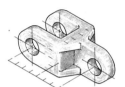

Fig. 7.46. Link.

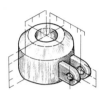

Fig. 7.47. Feeder cone.

Fig. 7.48. Bracket.

28-44. (Figs. 7.49–7.65.) These problems are designed to give the student further study in multiview representation and, at the same time, offer him the opportunity to apply good line technique to the preparation of sketches.

Only the necessary views on which all of the hidden lines are to be shown should be drawn.

If dimensions are to be given, ample space must be allowed between the views for their placement. The beginning sections of Chapter 17 present the basic principles of size description.

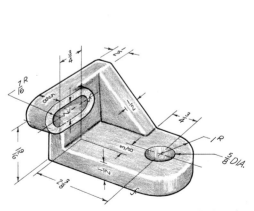

Fig. 7.49. Rod guide.

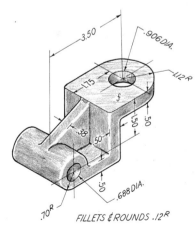

Fig. 7.50. Control rod bracket.

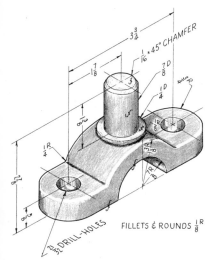

Fig. 7.51. Stud bracket.

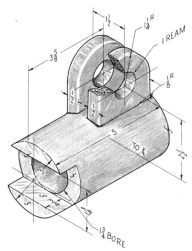

Fig. 7.52. Control guide.

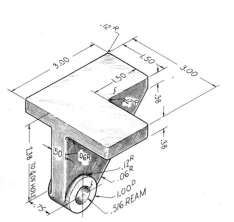

Fig. 7.53. Tool rest.

Fig. 7.54. Shifter bracket.

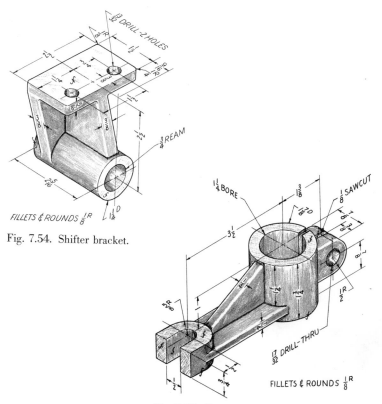

Fig. 7.55. Shifter.

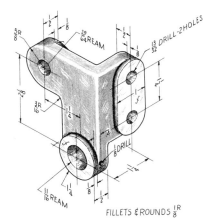

FILLETS & ROUNDS $\frac{1}{8}$R

Fig. 7.56. Link.

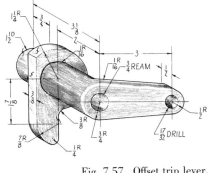

Fig. 7.57. Offset trip lever.

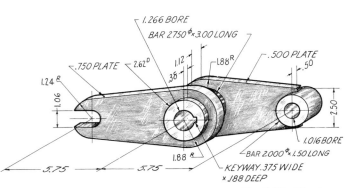

1.266 BORE

BAR 2.750 Φ × 3.00 LONG

.750 PLATE

.500 PLATE

1.24 R

1.016 BORE

BAR 2.000 Φ × 1.50 LONG

KEYWAY .375 WIDE × .188 DEEP

Fig. 7.58. Idler lever.

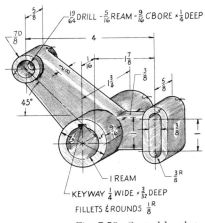

$\frac{19}{64}$ DRILL - $\frac{5}{16}$ REAM - $\frac{9}{16}$ C'BORE × $\frac{1}{4}$ DEEP

1 REAM

KEYWAY $\frac{1}{4}$ WIDE × $\frac{3}{32}$ DEEP

FILLETS & ROUNDS $\frac{1}{8}$R

Fig. 7.59. Control bracket.

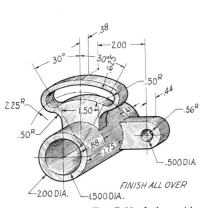

.500 DIA.

FINISH ALL OVER

2.00 DIA.

1.500 DIA.

Fig. 7.60. Index guide.

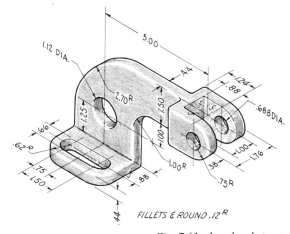

1.12 DIA.

.688 DIA.

FILLETS & ROUND .12 R

Fig. 7.61. Arm bracket.

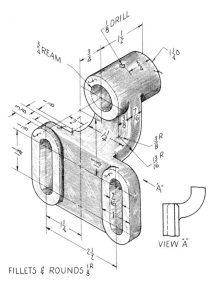

Fig. 7.62. Bearing bracket.

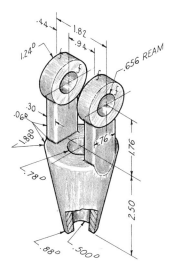

Fig. 7.63. Socket.

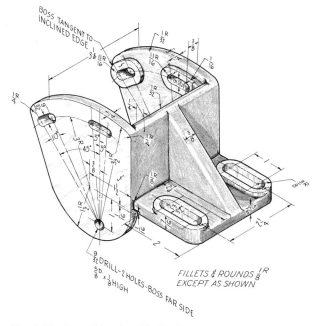

Fig. 7.64. Control bracket (airplane).

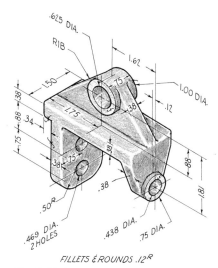

Fig. 7.65. Rear support bracket.

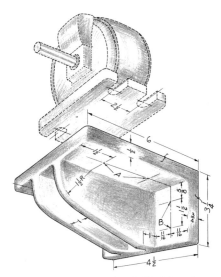

Fig. 7.66. Motor base.

45. (Fig. 7.66.) Make a complete three-view sketch of the motor base. The ribs are ⅜ in. thick. At points *A*, four holes are to be drilled for ½ in. bolts that are to be 2½ in. center to center in one direction and 3⅛ in. in the other. At points *B*, four holes are to be drilled for ½ in. bolts that fasten the motor base to a steel column. Fillets and rounds are ⅛ R.

46. (Fig. 7.67.) Make a three-view orthographic sketch of the motor bracket.

47-48. (Fig. 7.68.) Make a complete three-view sketch of the tool rest and/or the tool rest bracket. The rectangular top surface of the tool rest is to be 1⅛ in. above the center line of the hole for the ⁷⁄₁₆ in. bolt. The over-all dimensions of the top are 1¼ in. × 2½ in. It is to be ¼ in. thick. The over-all dimensions of the rectangular pad of the bracket are 1¼ in. × 1⅞ in. The center line of the adjustment slot is ⁹⁄₁₆ in. above the center line of the top holes in the rectangular pad and the distance from center line to center line of the slot is 1⅜ in. The bracket is to be fastened to a housing with ¼ in. round head machine screws.

49-50. (Fig. 7.69.) Make an orthographic sketch of the stud arm and/or the clamp arm (read Sec. 16.9).

51. (Fig. 7.70.) Make an orthographic sketch of the base of the milling jack (read Sec. 16.9).

52-53. (Fig. 7.71.) Make a multiview sketch of the base and/or the pipe roll.

54. (Fig. 7.71.) Make an orthographic sketch of the pipe stand (read Sec. 16.9).

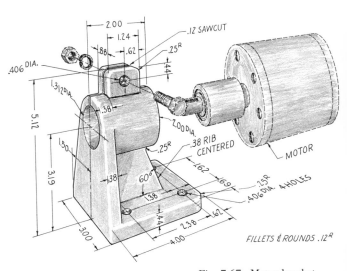

Fig. 7.67. Motor bracket.

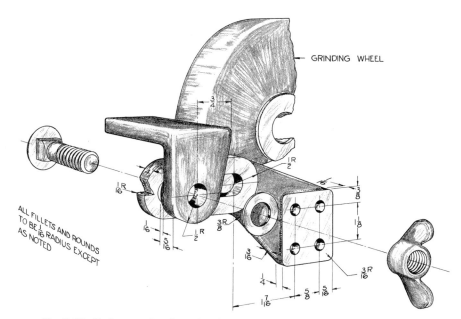

Fig. 7.68. Tool rest and tool rest bracket.

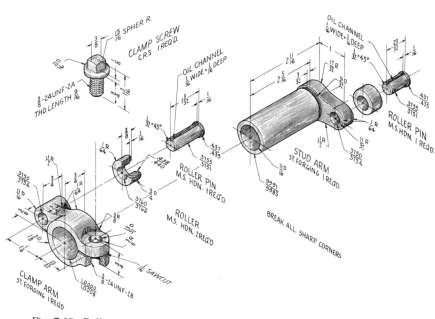

Fig. 7.69. Roller rest.

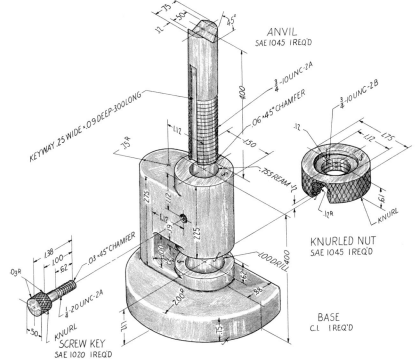

Fig. 7.70. Milling jack.

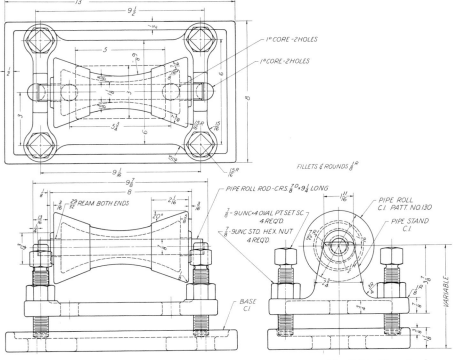

Fig. 7.71. Pipe stand.

55-56. (Fig. 7.72.) Make a multiview sketch of the base and/or the swivel fitting.

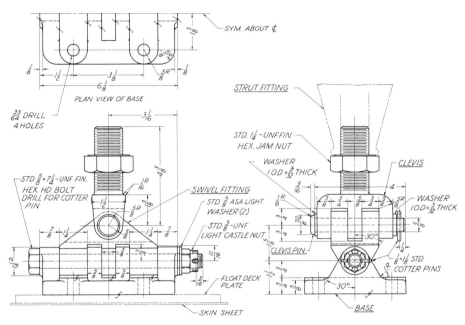

Fig. 7.72. Flexible joint.

AUXILIARY VIEWS: PRIMARY AND SECONDARY

8.1. Introduction. When it is desirable to show the true size and shape of an irregular surface, which is inclined to two or more of the coordinate planes of projection, a view of the surface must be projected on a plane parallel to it. This imaginary projection plane

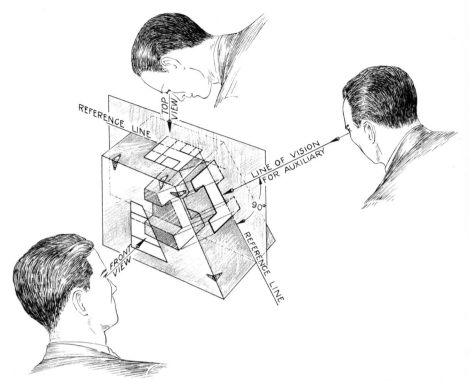

Fig. 8.1. Theory of projecting an auxiliary view.

is called an *auxiliary plane*, and the view obtained is called an *auxiliary view* (Fig. 8.1).

The theory underlying the method of projecting principal views applies also to auxiliary views. In other words, an auxiliary view shows an inclined surface of an object as it would appear to an observer stationed an infinite distance away (Fig. 8.2).

8.2. The use of auxiliary views. In commercial drafting, an auxiliary view ordinarily is a partial view showing only an inclined surface. The reason for this is that a projection showing the entire object adds very little to the shape description. The added lines are likely to defeat the intended purpose of an auxiliary view. For example, a complete drawing of the casting in Fig. 8.3 must include an auxiliary view of the inclined surface in order to show the true shape of the surface and the location of the holes. Compare the views in (*a*) and (*b*) and note the confused appearance of the view in (*b*). In technical schools, some instructors require that an auxiliary view show the entire object, including all invisible lines. Such a requirement, though impractical commercially, is justified in the

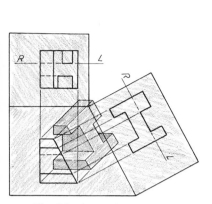

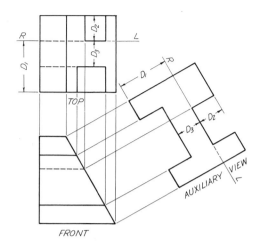

Fig. 8.2. An auxiliary view.

classroom, for the construction of a complete auxiliary view furnishes excellent practice in projection.

A partial auxiliary view often is needed to complete the projection of a foreshortened feature in a principal view. This second
important function of auxiliary views is illustrated in Fig. 8.16 and
explained in Sec. 8.13.

8.3. Types of auxiliary views.   Although auxiliary views may have
an infinite number of positions in relation to the three principal
planes of projection, primary auxiliary views may be classified into

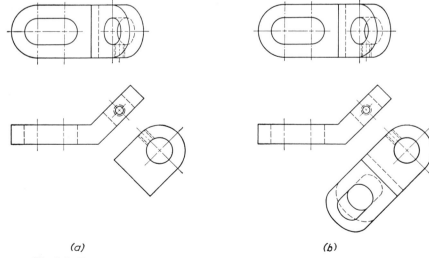

(a)   (b)

Fig. 8.3. Partial and complete auxiliary views.

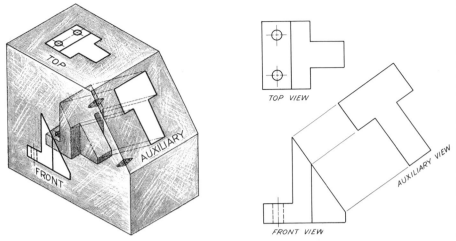

Fig. 8.4. Auxiliary view projected from front view.

three general types in accordance with position relative to the principal planes. Figure 8.4 shows the first type where the auxiliary plane is perpendicular to the frontal plane and inclined to the horizontal plane of projection. Here the auxiliary view and top view have one dimension that is common to both, the depth. Note that the auxiliary plane is hinged to the frontal plane, and that the auxiliary view is projected from the front view.

In Fig. 8.5 the auxiliary plane is perpendicular to the horizontal plane and inclined to the frontal and profile planes of projection. The auxiliary view is projected from the top view, and its height is the same as the height of the front view.

The third type of auxiliary view, as shown in Fig. 8.6, is projected from the side view and has a common dimension with both

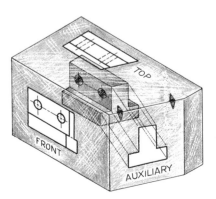

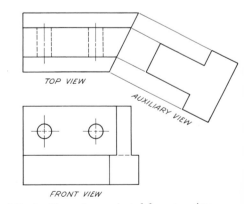

Fig. 8.5. Auxiliary view projected from top view.

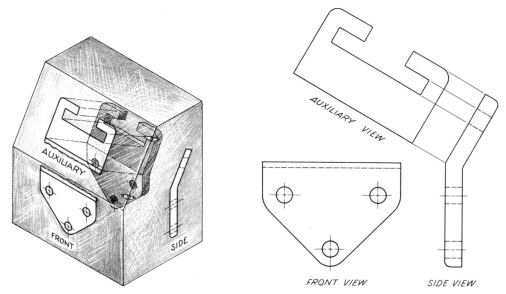

Fig. 8.6. Auxiliary view projected from side view.

the front and top views. To construct it, distances may be taken from either the front or top view.

All three types of auxiliary views are constructed similarly. Each is projected from the view that shows the slanting surface as a line, and the distances for the view are taken from the other principal view that has a common dimension with the auxiliary. A careful study of the three illustrations will reveal the fact that the inclined auxiliary plane is always hinged to the principal plane to which it is perpendicular.

8.4. Symmetrical and unsymmetrical auxiliary views. Since auxiliary views are either symmetrical or unsymmetrical about a center line or reference line, they may be termed (1) symmetrical, (2) unilateral, or (3) bilateral, according to the degree of symmetry. A symmetrical view is drawn symmetrically about a center line, the unilateral view entirely on one side of a reference line, and the bilateral view on both sides of a reference line.

8.5. To draw a symmetrical auxiliary view. When an inclined surface is symmetrical, the auxiliary view is "worked" from a center line (Fig. 8.7). The first step in drawing such a view is to draw a center line parallel to the inclined line that represents an edge view of the surface. If the object is assumed to be enclosed in a glass box, this center line may be considered the line of intersection of the auxiliary plane and an imaginary vertical center plane. There

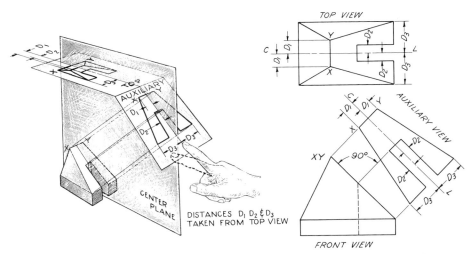

Fig. 8.7. A symmetrical auxiliary view of an inclined surface.

are professional draftsmen who, not acquainted with the "glass" box, proceed without theoretical explanation. Their method is simply to draw a working center line for the auxiliary view and a corresponding line in one of the principal views.

Although, theoretically, this working center line may be drawn at any distance from the principal view, actually it should be so located to give the whole drawing a balanced appearance. If not already shown, it also must be drawn in the principal view showing the true width of the inclined surface.

The next step is to draw projection lines from each point of the sloping face, remembering that the projectors make an angle of 90° with the inclined line representing the surface. With the projectors drawn, the location of each point in the auxiliary can be established by setting the dividers to each point's distance from the center line in the principal view and transferring the distance to the auxiliary view. For example, point X is projected to the auxiliary by drawing a projector from point X in the front view perpendicular to the center line. Since its distance from the center line in the top view is the same as it is from the center line in the auxiliary view, the point's location along the projector may be established by using the distance taken from the top view. In the case of point X, the distance is set off from the center line toward the front view. Point Y is set off from the center line away from the front view. A careful study of Fig. 8.7 reveals the fact that if a point lies between the front view and the center line of the top view, it will lie between the front view and the center line of the auxiliary view, and, conversely, if it lies away from the front view with reference to the center line of the top view, it will lie away from the front view with reference to the center line of the auxiliary view.

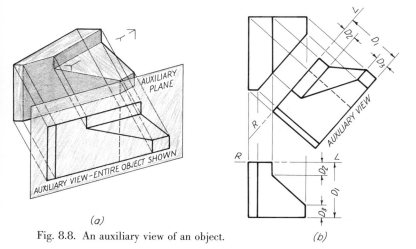

(a)

Fig. 8.8. An auxiliary view of an object.   *(b)*

Figure 8.8 shows an auxiliary view of an entire object. In constructing such a view, it should be remembered that the projectors from all points of the object are perpendicular to the auxiliary plane, since the observer views the entire figure by looking directly at the inclined surface. The distances perpendicular to the auxiliary reference line were taken from the front view.

8.6. Unilateral auxiliary views. When constructing a unilateral auxiliary view, it is necessary to work from a reference line that is drawn in a manner similar to the working center line of a symmetrical view. The reference line for the auxiliary view may be considered to represent the line of intersection of a reference plane coinciding with an outer face and the auxiliary plane (Fig. 8.9).

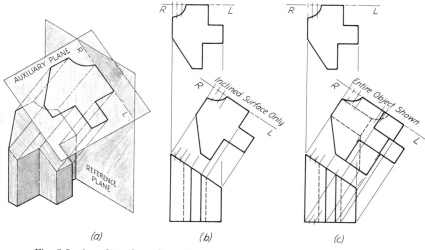

(a)   *(b)*   *(c)*

Fig. 8.9. A unilateral auxiliary view.

The intersection of this plane with the top plane establishes the reference line in the top view. All the points are projected from the edge view of the surface, as in a symmetrical view, and it should be noted in setting them off that they all fall on the same side of the reference line.

8.7. Bilateral auxiliary views. The method of drawing a bilateral view is similar to that of drawing a unilateral view, the only difference being that in a bilateral view the inclined face lies partly on both sides of the reference plane, as shown in Fig. 8.10.

8.8. Curved lines in auxiliary views. To draw a curve in an auxiliary view, the draftsman must plot a sufficient number of points to insure a smooth curve (see Fig. 8.11). The points are projected first to the inclined line representing the surface in the front view and then to the auxiliary view. The distance of any point from the center line in the auxiliary view is the same as its distance from the center line in the end view.

8.9. Projection of a curved boundary. In Fig. 8.11, the procedure is illustrated for plotting the true size and shape of an inclined surface, bounded by a curved outline. A similar procedure can be followed to plot a curve, such as the one on the left end of the object shown in Fig. 8.12, in an auxiliary view. Since the points on the curved outline of the vertical surface are being viewed from the same direction as those on the curved boundary of the inclined surface, the projectors from points on both surfaces will be parallel. From the pictorial drawing, it can be observed that points A and A^1 and B and B^1 lie on elements of the cylindrical surface. Also it should

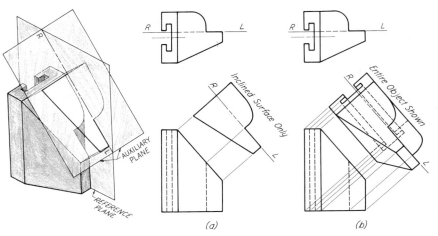

Fig. 8.10. A bilateral auxiliary view.

be noted that A and A' are the same distance from the reference plane as are B and B'. It is for this reason that point A' in the auxiliary view is at the intersection of the projector from A' in the front view and a line through A in the auxiliary view, drawn parallel to the reference line RL.

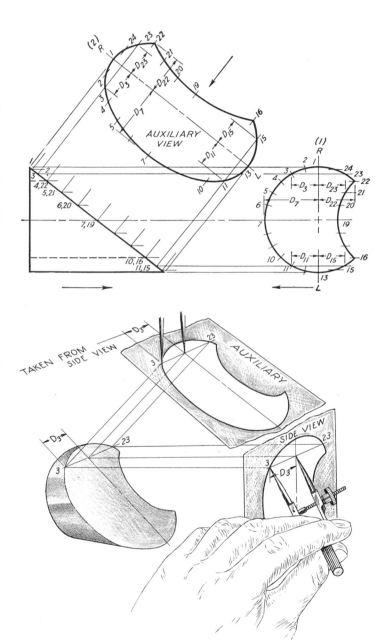

Fig. 8.11. Curved line auxiliary view.

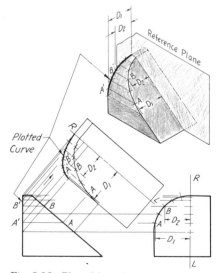

Fig. 8.12. Plotted boundary curves.

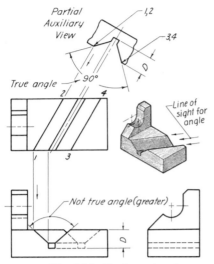

Fig. 8.13. To determine the true dihedral angle between inclined surfaces.

8.10. Dihedral angles. Frequently, an auxiliary view may be needed to show the true size of a dihedral angle, that is, the true size of the angle between two planes. In Fig. 8.13, it is desirable to show the true size of the angle between the planes forming the V-slot by means of a partial auxiliary view as shown. The direction of sight (see pictorial) must be taken parallel to the edge lines 1–2 and 3–4 so that these lines will appear as points and the surfaces forming the dihedral angle will project as line views in the auxiliary view. The reference line for the partial auxiliary view would necessarily be drawn perpendicular to the lines 1–2 and 3–4 in the top view. Since the plane upon which the auxiliary view is projected is a vertical one, height dimensions were used, that is, distances in the direction of the dimension D in the auxiliary view, were taken from the front view.

8.11. To construct an auxiliary view, practical method. The usual steps in constructing an auxiliary view are shown in Fig. 8.14. The illustration should be studied carefully, as each step is explained on the drawing.

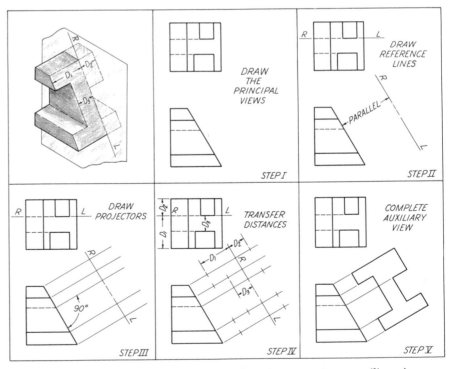

Fig. 8.14. Steps in constructing an auxiliary view.

8.12. Auxiliary and partial views. Often the use of an auxiliary view allows the elimination of one of the principal views (top or side) or makes possible the use of a partial principal view. The shape description furnished by the partial views shown in Fig. 8.15 is sufficient for a complete understanding of the shape of the part. The use of partial views simplifies the drawing, saves valuable drafting time, and tends to make the drawing easier to read.

A break line is used at a convenient location to indicate an imaginary break for a partial view.

8.13. The use of an auxiliary view to complete a principal view. As previously stated, it is frequently necessary to project a foreshortened feature in one of the principal views from an auxiliary view. In the case of the object shown in Fig. 8.16, the foreshortened projection of the inclined face in the top view can be projected from the auxiliary view. The elliptical curves are plotted by projecting points from the auxiliary view to the front view and from there to the top view. The location of these points in the top view with respect to the center line is the same as their location in the auxiliary view with respect to the auxiliary center line. For example, the distance D_1 from the center line in the top view is the same as the distance D_1 from the auxiliary center line in the auxiliary view.

The steps in preparing an auxiliary view and using it to complete a principal view are shown in Fig. 8.17.

8.14. Secondary (oblique) auxiliary views. Frequently an object will have an inclined face that is not perpendicular to any one of

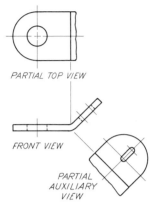

Fig. 8.15. Partial views.

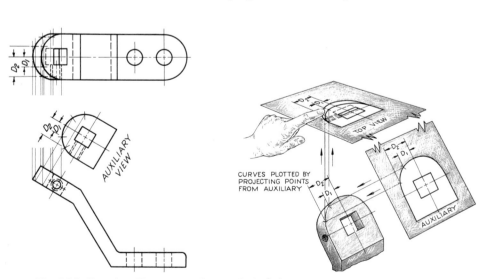

Fig. 8.16. Use of auxiliary to complete a principal view.

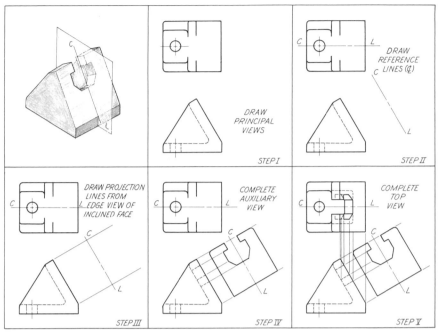

Fig. 8.17. Steps in preparing an auxiliary view and completing a principal view.

the principal planes of projection. In such cases it is necessary to draw two auxiliary views (Fig. 8.18). The primary auxiliary view is constructed by projecting the figure upon a primary auxiliary plane that is perpendicular to the inclined surface and one of the principal planes. This plane may be at any convenient location. In the illustration, the primary auxiliary plane is perpendicular to the frontal plane. Note that the inclined face appears as a straight line in the primary auxiliary view. Using this view as a regular view, the secondary auxiliary view may be projected upon a plane parallel to the inclined face. Figure 8.18(b) shows a practical application of the theoretical principles shown pictorially in (a).

It is suggested that the student turn to Chapter 12 and read Sec. 12.25 in which the procedure for drawing the normal (true shape) view of an oblique surface is presented step by step.

Figure 8.19 shows the progressive steps in preparing and using a secondary auxiliary view of an oblique face to complete a principal view. Reference planes have been used as datum planes from which to take the necessary measurements. Step II shows the partial construction of the primary auxiliary view in which the inclined surface appears as a line. Step III shows the secondary auxiliary view projected from the primary view and completed, using the

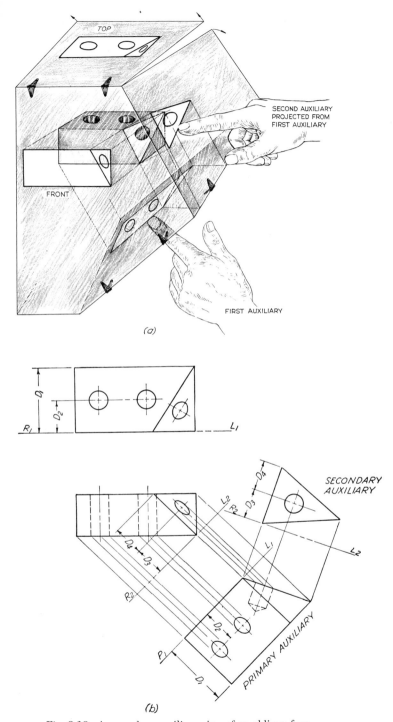

Fig. 8.18. A secondary auxiliary view of an oblique face.

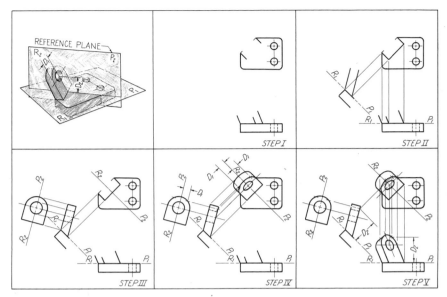

Fig. 8.19. Steps in drawing a secondary auxiliary view and using it to complete a principal view.

known measurements of the lug. The primary auxiliary view is finished by projecting from the secondary auxiliary view. Step IV illustrates the procedure for projecting from the secondary auxiliary view to the top view through the primary auxiliary in order to complete the foreshortened view of the lug. It should be noted that distance D_1 taken from reference plane R_2P_2 in the secondary auxiliary is transferred to the top view because both views show the same width distances in true length. A sufficient number of points should be obtained to allow the use of an irregular curve. Step V shows the projection of these points on the curve to the front view. In this case the measurements are taken from the primary auxiliary view because the height distances from reference plane R_1P_1 are the same in both views.

8.15. True length of a line. The true length of an oblique line may be determined either by means of an auxiliary view or by revolution of the line: Separate discussions of the procedure to be followed in the application of these methods are given in Chapters 12 and 13. To determine the true length of a line by revolution, see Sec. 12.43. To find the true length through the use of an auxiliary view, read Sec. 12.11.

8.16. Line of intersection. It is frequently necessary to represent a line of intersection between two surfaces when making a multi-

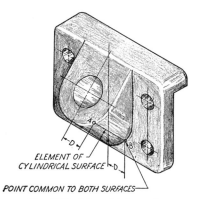

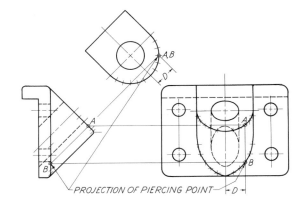

ELEMENT OF
CYLINDRICAL SURFACE ⌐D⌐

POINT COMMON TO BOTH SURFACES

Fig. 8.20. Line of intersection.

PROJECTION OF PIERCING POINT ⌐ D ⌐

view drawing involving an auxiliary view. Figure 8.20 shows a method for drawing the line of intersection on a principal view. In this case the scheme commonly used for determining the intersection involves the use of elements drawn on the surface of the cylindrical portion of the part as shown on the pictorial drawing. These elements such as *AB*, are common to the cylindrical surface. Point *B* where the element pierces the flat surface, is a point that is common to both surfaces and, therefore, lies on the line of intersection.

On the orthographic views, element *AB* appears as a point on the auxiliary view and as a line on the front view. The location of the projection of the piercing point on the front view is visible upon inspection. Point *B* is found in the other principal view by projecting from the front view and setting off the distance *D* taken from the auxiliary view. The distance *D* of point *B* from the center line is a true distance for both views. The center line in the auxiliary view and side view can be considered as the edge view of a reference plane or datum plane from which measurements can be made.

PROBLEMS

The problems shown in Fig. 8.21 are designed to give the student practice in constructing auxiliary views of the inclined surfaces of simple objects formed mainly by straight lines. They will provide needed drill in projection if, for each of the objects, an auxiliary is drawn showing the entire object. Complete drawings may be made of the objects shown in Figs. 8.22–8.32. If the views are to be dimensioned, the student should adhere to the rules of dimensioning given in Chapter 17 and should not take too seriously the locations for the dimensions on the pictorial representations.

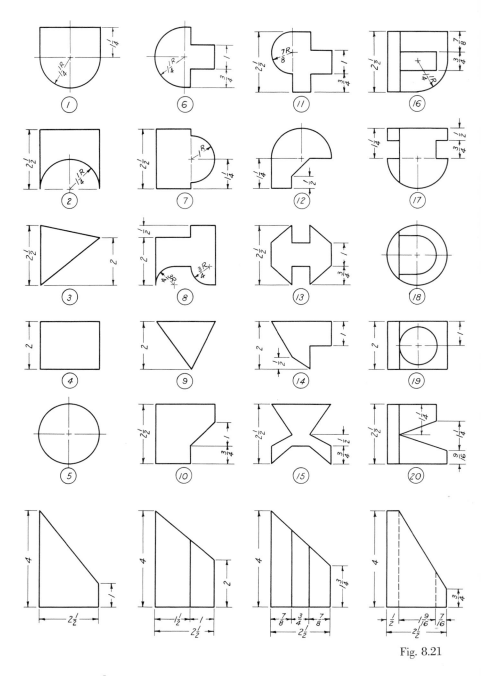

Fig. 8.21

1. (Fig. 8.21.) Using instruments, reproduce the given views of an assigned object and draw an auxiliary view of its inclined surface.

2. (Fig. 8.22.) Draw the views that would be necessary on a working drawing of the *vibrator cap*.

3. (Fig. 8.23.) Draw the views that would be necessary on a working drawing of the *boiler bracket*.

4. (Fig. 8.24.) Draw the views that would be necessary on a working drawing of the *feeder bracket*.

5. (Fig. 8.25.) Draw the necessary views of the anchor clip. It is suggested that the top view be a partial one and that the auxiliary view show only the inclined surface.

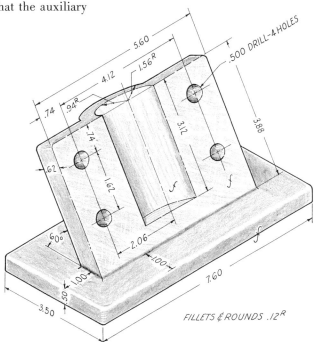

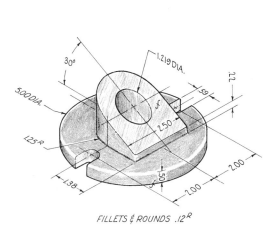

Fig. 8.22. Vibrator cap.

Fig. 8.23. Boiler bracket.

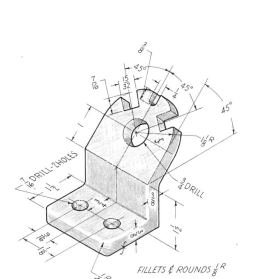

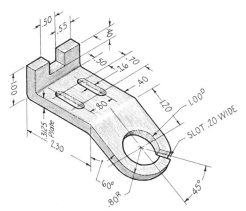

Fig. 8.24. Feeder bracket.

Fig. 8.25. Anchor clip.

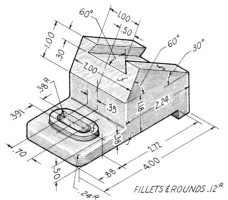

FILLETS & ROUNDS .12^R

Fig. 8.26. Dovetail bracket.

6. (Fig. 8.26.) Draw the views that would be necessary on a working drawing of the dovetail bracket.

7. (Fig. 8.27.) Draw the necessary views of the offset guide. It is suggested that partial views be used, except in the view where the inclined surface appears as a line.

8. (Fig. 8.28.) Draw the necessary views of the hinge bracket.

9. (Fig. 8.29.) Draw the necessary views of the anchor bracket. Make partial views for the top and end views.

10. (Fig. 8.30.) Draw the necessary views of the clutch stop.

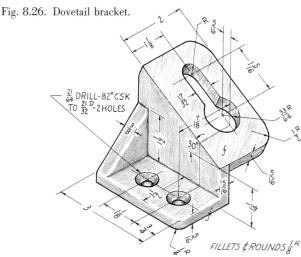

$\frac{21}{64}$ DRILL-82° C'S'K
TO $\frac{21}{32}$ D - 2 HOLES

FILLETS & ROUNDS $\frac{1}{8}$^{R}

Fig. 8.27. Offset guide.

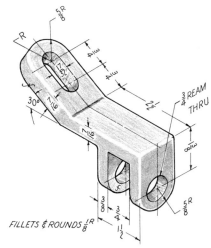

FILLETS & ROUNDS $\frac{1}{8}$^{R}

Fig. 8.28. Hinge bracket.

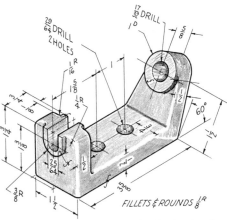

$\frac{29}{64}$ DRILL
2 HOLES

$\frac{17}{32}$ DRILL

FILLETS & ROUNDS $\frac{1}{8}$^{R}

Fig. 8.29. Anchor bracket.

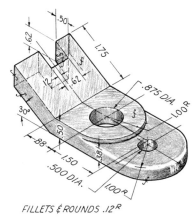

.875 DIA.

.500 DIA.

FILLETS & ROUNDS .12^R

Fig. 8.30. Clutch stop.

11. (Fig. 8.31.) Draw the necessary views of the cut-off clip.

12. (Fig. 8.32.) Draw the necessary views of the ejector clip.

13. (Fig. 8.33.) Draw the views as given. Complete the top view.

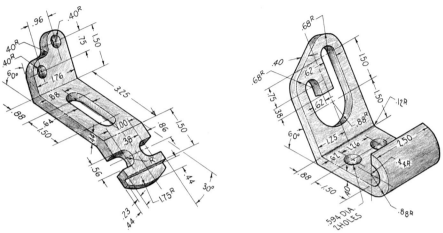

Fig. 8.31. Cut-off clip.

Fig. 8.32. Ejector clip.

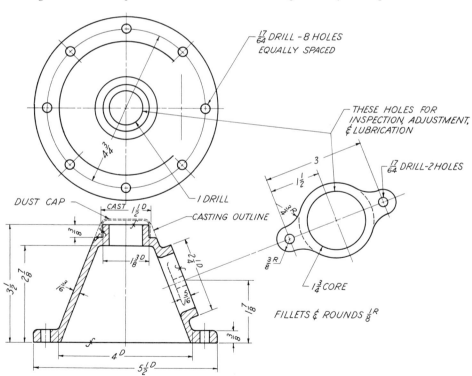

Fig. 8.33. Housing cover.

14. (Fig. 8.34.) Draw the views as given. Complete the auxiliary view and the front view.

15. Make a multiview drawing of the airplane engine mount shown in Fig. 8.35. The engine mount is formed of three pieces of steel plate welded to a piece of steel tubing. The completed drawing is to consist of four views. It is suggested that the front view be the view obtained by looking along and parallel to the axis of the tube.

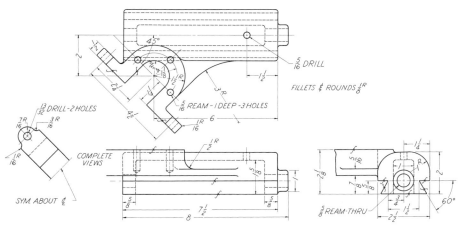

Fig. 8.34. Sliding tool base.

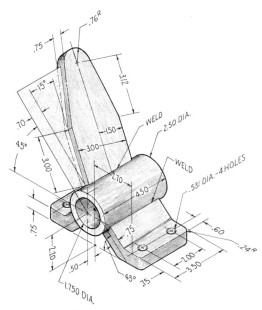

Fig. 8.35. Airplane engine mount.

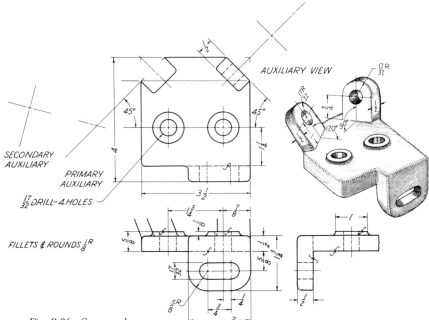

Fig. 8.36. Cross anchor.

The remaining views that are needed are an auxiliary view showing only the inclined lug, a side view that should be complete with all hidden lines shown, and a partial top view with the inclined lug omitted.

16. (Fig. 8.36.) Draw the views as given and add the required primary and secondary auxiliary views.

17. (Fig. 8.37.) Draw the necessary views of the tool holder.

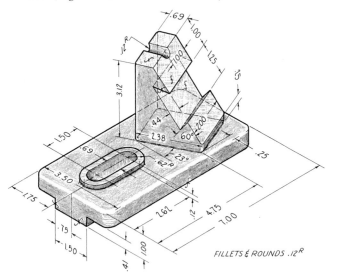

Fig. 8.37. Tool holder.

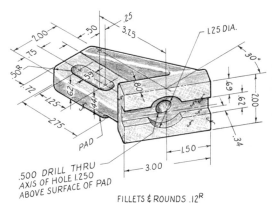

Fig. 8.38. Locating slide.

18. (Fig. 8.38.) Draw the necessary views of the locating slide.

19. (Fig. 8.39.) Using instruments, reproduce the given views of an assigned object and draw a secondary auxiliary view that will show the true size and shape of the inclined surface.

20. (Fig. 8.40.) Draw the layout for the support anchor as given and then, using the double auxiliary view method, complete the views as required.

The plate and cylinder are to be welded. Since the faces of the plate show as oblique surfaces in the front and top views, double auxiliary views are necessary to show the thickness and the true shape.

Start the drawing with the auxiliary views that are arranged horizontally on the paper, then complete the principal views. The inclined face of the cylinder will show as an ellipse in top and front views; but do not show this in the auxiliary view that shows the true shape (4.00 in. square) of the plate.

How would you find the view that shows the true angle between the inclined face and the axis of the cylinder?

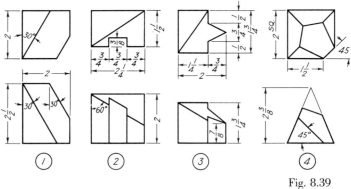

Fig. 8.39

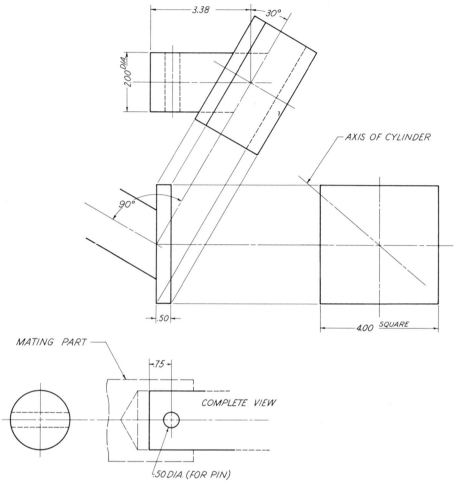

Fig. 8.40. Support anchor.

SECTIONAL VIEWS

9.1. Sectional views (Fig. 9.1). Although the invisible features of a simple object usually may be described on an exterior view by the use of hidden lines, it is unwise to depend upon a perplexing mass of such lines to describe adequately the interior of a complicated

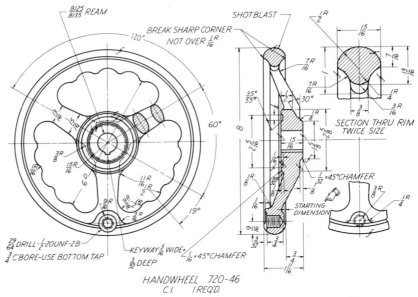

Fig. 9.1. A working drawing with sectional views (*Courtesy Warner and Swasey Co.*).

object or an assembled mechanism. Whenever a representation becomes so confused that it is difficult to read, it is customary to make one or more of the views "in section" (Fig. 9.2). A view "in section" is one obtained by imagining the object to have been cut by a cutting plane, the front portion being removed so as to reveal clearly the interior features. Figure 9.3(*a*) illustrates the use of an imaginary cutting plane. The resulting section (front) view, accom-

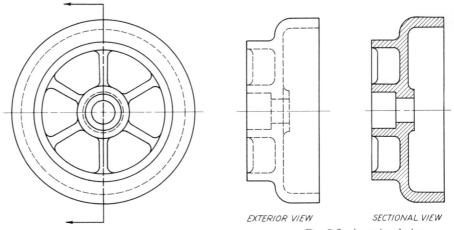

EXTERIOR VIEW   SECTIONAL VIEW

Fig. 9.2. A sectional view.

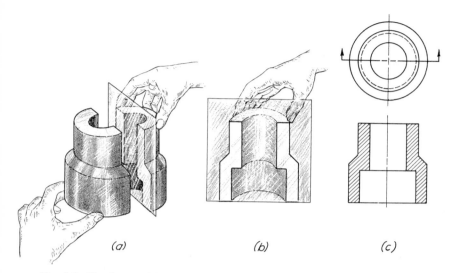

(a)   (b)   (c)

Fig. 9.3. The theory of the construction of a sectional view.

panied by a top view, is shown in Fig. 9.3(c). At this point it should be understood that a portion is shown removed only in a sectional view, not in any of the other views [see Fig. 9.3(c)].

When the cutting plane cuts an object lengthwise, the section obtained is commonly called a longitudinal section; when crosswise, it is called a cross section. It is designated as being either a full section, a half section, or a broken section. If the plane cuts entirely across the object, the section represented is known as a *full section*. If it cuts only halfway across a symmetrical object, the section is a *half section*. A *broken section* is a partial one which is used when less than a half section is needed.

On a completed sectional view, fine section lines are drawn across the surface cut by the imaginary plane, to emphasize the contour of the interior (see Sec. 9.8).

9.2. A full section. Since a cutting plane that cuts a full section passes entirely through an object, the resulting view will appear as illustrated in Fig. 9.3(c). Although the plane usually passes along the main axis, it may be offset (see Fig. 9.4) to reveal important features.

A full sectional view, showing an object's characteristic shape, usually replaces an exterior front view; however, one of the other principal views, side or top, may be converted into a sectional view if some interior feature thus can be shown to better advantage or if such a view is needed in addition to a sectioned front view.

The procedure in making a full sectional view is simple, in that

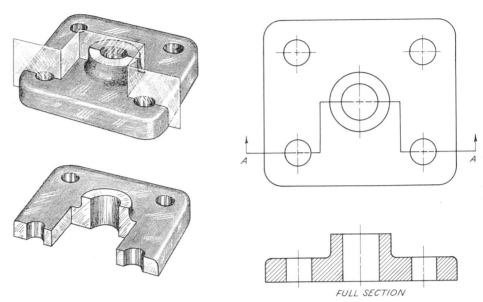

Fig. 9.4. An offset cutting plane.

FULL SECTION

the sectional view is an orthographic one. The imaginary cut face of the object simply is shown as it would appear to an observer looking directly at it from a point an infinite distance away. In any sectional view, it is considered good practice to omit all invisible lines unless such lines are necessary to clarify the representation. Even then they should be used sparingly.

9.3. A half section. The cutting plane for a half section removes one quarter of an object. The plane cuts halfway through to the axis or center line so that half the finished sectional view appears in section and half appears as an external view (see Fig. 9.5). This type of sectional view is used when a view is needed showing both the exterior and interior construction of a symmetrical object. Good practice dictates that hidden lines be omitted from both halves of the view unless they are absolutely necessary for dimensioning purposes or for explaining the construction. Although the use of a solid object line to separate the two halves of a half section has been approved by the Society of Automotive Engineers and has recently been accepted by the American Standards Association [Fig. 9.6(a)], many draftsmen prefer to use a center line as shown in Fig. 9.6(b). They reason that the removal of a quarter of the object is theoretical and imaginary and that an actual edge, which would be implied by a solid line, does not exist. The center line is taken as denoting a theoretical edge.

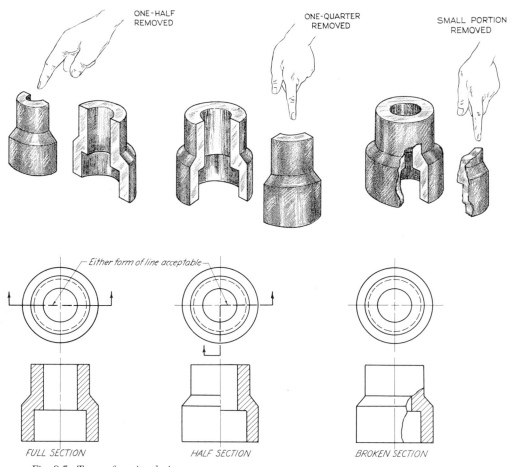

ONE-HALF REMOVED

ONE-QUARTER REMOVED

SMALL PORTION REMOVED

Either form of line acceptable

FULL SECTION

HALF SECTION

BROKEN SECTION

Fig. 9.5. Types of sectional views.

9.4. A broken section. A broken or partial section is used mainly to expose the interior of objects so constructed that less than a half section is required for a satisfactory description (Fig. 9.7). The object theoretically is cut by a cutting plane and the front portion is removed by breaking it away. The "breaking away" gives an irregular boundary line to the section.

9.5. A revolved section. A revolved section is useful for showing the true shape of the cross section of some elongated object, such as a bar, or some feature of an object, such as an arm, spoke, or rib (Figs. 9.1 and 9.8).

To obtain such a cross section, an imaginary cutting plane is passed through the member perpendicular to the longitudinal axis, and then is revolved through 90° to bring the resulting view into

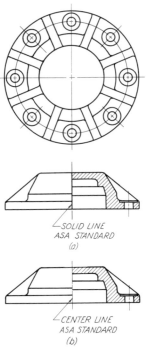

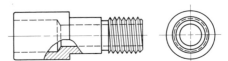

SOLID LINE
ASA STANDARD
(a)

CENTER LINE
ASA STANDARD
(b)

Fig. 9.6. A half section.

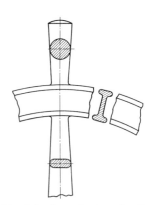

Fig. 9.7. A broken section.

Fig. 9.8. A revolved section.*

the plane of the paper (Fig. 9.9). When revolved, the section should show in its true shape and in its true revolved position, regardless of the location of the lines of the exterior view. If any lines of the view interfere with the revolved section, they should be omitted (Fig. 9.10). It sometimes is advisable to provide an open space for the section by making a break in the object (see Fig. 9.8).

9.6. Detail or removed sections. A detail section is similar to a revolved section, except that it does not appear on an external view but, instead, is drawn "out of place," and appears adjacent to it (Fig. 9.11). There are two good reasons why detail sections frequently are desirable. First, their use may prevent a principal view of an object, the cross section of which is not uniform, from being cluttered with numerous revolved sections (Fig. 9.11). Second, they may be drawn to an enlarged scale in order to emphasize detail and allow for adequate dimensioning (Fig. 9.12).

Whenever a detail section is used, there must be some means of identifying it. Usually this is accomplished by showing the cutting plane on the principal view and then labeling both the plane and the resulting view, as shown in Fig. 9.12.

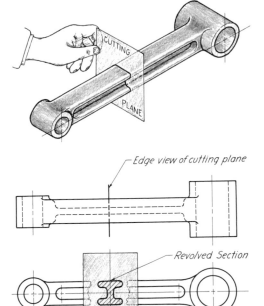

Edge view of cutting plane

Revolved Section

Cutting plane revolved

Fig. 9.9. A revolved section and cutting plane.

* ASA Y14.2–1957.

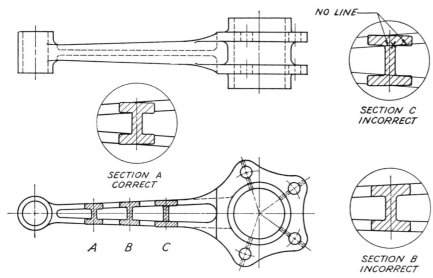

Fig. 9.10. Revolved sections.

9.7. Phantom sections. A phantom or hidden section is a regular exterior view upon which the interior construction is emphasized by crosshatching an imaginary cut surface with dotted section lines (see Fig. 9.13). This type of section is used only when a regular section or a broken section would remove some important exterior

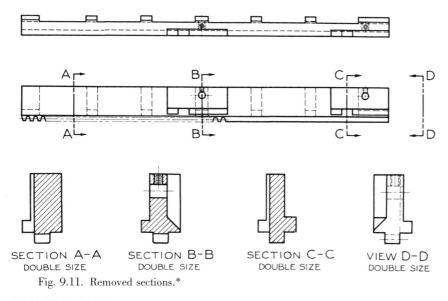

SECTION A-A
DOUBLE SIZE

SECTION B-B
DOUBLE SIZE

SECTION C-C
DOUBLE SIZE

VIEW D-D
DOUBLE SIZE

Fig. 9.11. Removed sections.*

* ASA Y14.2–1957.

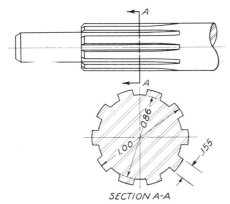

SECTION A-A

Fig. 9.12. A detail section.

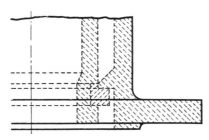

Fig. 9.13. A phantom section.

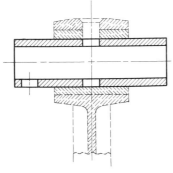

Fig. 9.14. Phantom sectioning—adjacent parts.

detail, or, in some instances, to show an accompanying part in its relative position with regard to a particular part (Fig. 9.14). Instead of using a broken line with dashes of equal length, the phantom line shown in Fig. 3.46 could have been used to represent the outline of the adjacent parts shown in Fig. 9.14.

9.8. Section lining. Section lines are light continuous lines drawn across the imaginary cut surface of an object for the purpose of emphasizing the contour of its interior. Usually they are drawn at an angle of 45° except in cases where a number of adjacent parts are shown assembled (see Fig. 9.18).

To be pleasing in appearance, these lines must be correctly executed. While on ordinary work they are spaced about $\frac{3}{32}$ in. apart, there is no set rule governing their spacing. They simply should be spaced to suit the drawing and the size of the areas to be crosshatched. For example, on small views having small areas, the section lines may be as close as $\frac{1}{32}$ in., while on large views having large areas they may be as far apart as $\frac{1}{8}$ in. In the case of very thin plates, the cross section is shown "solid black" (Fig. 9.15).

The usual mistake of the beginning student is to draw the lines too close together. This, plus the unavoidable slight variations, causes the section lining to appear streaked. Although several forms of mechanical section liners are available, most draftsmen do their spacing by eye. The student is advised to do likewise, being careful to see that the initial pitch, as set by the first few lines, is maintained across the area. To accomplish this, he should check back from time to time to make sure there has been no slight general increase or decrease in the spacing. An example of correct section lining is shown in Fig. 9.16(a), and, for comparison, examples of faulty practice may be seen in Fig. 9.16(b), (c), and (d). Experienced draftsmen realize that nothing will do more to ruin the appearance of a drawing than carelessly executed section lines.

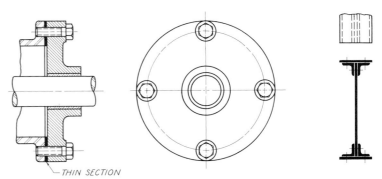

THIN SECTION

Fig. 9.15. Thin sections.

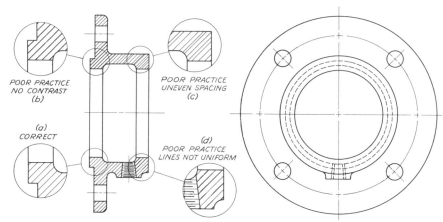

Fig. 9.16. Faults in section lining.

As shown in Fig. 9.17, the section lines on two adjacent pieces should slope at 45° in opposite directions. If a third piece adjoins the two other pieces, as in Fig. 9.18(*a*), it ordinarily is section-lined at 30°. An alternate treatment, which might be used, would be to vary the spacing without changing the angle. On a sectional view showing an assembly of related parts, *all portions of the cut surface of any part must be section-lined in the same direction, for a change would lead the reader to consider the portions as belonging to different parts. Furthermore, to allow quick identification, each piece (and all identical pieces) in every view of the assembly drawing should be section-lined in the same direction.*

Shafts, bolts, pins, rivets, balls, and so on, whose axes lie in the plane of section are not treated the same as ordinary parts. Having no interior construction to be shown, they are drawn in full and thus tend to make the adjacent sectioned parts stand out to better advantage (Fig. 9.19).

Whenever section lines drawn at 45° with the horizontal are parallel to part of the outline of the section (see Fig. 9.20), it is advisable to draw them at some other angle (say 30° or 60°). Those drawn as in (*a*) and (*c*) produce an unusual appearance that

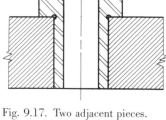

Fig. 9.17. Two adjacent pieces.

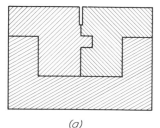

(*a*)   (*b*)

Fig. 9.18. Three adjacent pieces.

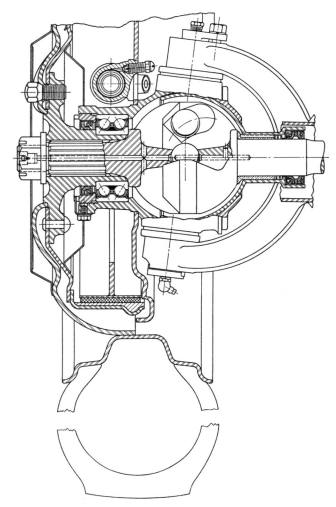

Fig. 9.19. Treatment of shafts, fasteners, ball bearings, and other parts (*Courtesy New Departure, Division General Motor Sales Corp.*).

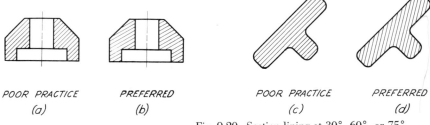

POOR PRACTICE
(a)

PREFERRED
(b)

POOR PRACTICE
(c)

PREFERRED
(d)

Fig. 9.20. Section lining at 30°, 60°, or 75°.

is contrary to what is expected. Note the more natural effect obtained in (*b*) and (*d*) by sloping the lines at 30° and 75°.

9.9. Outline sectioning. Very large surfaces may be section-lined around the bounding outline only, as illustrated in Fig. 9.21.

9.10. The symbolic representation for a cutting plane. The symbolic lines that are used to represent the edge view of a cutting plane are shown in Fig. 9.22. The line is as heavy as an object line and is composed of either alternate long and short dashes or a series of dashes of equal length. The latter form is used in the automobile industry and has been approved by the SAE (Society of Automotive Engineers) and the American Standards Association. On drawings of ordinary size, when alternate long and short dashes are used for the cutting plane line, the long dashes are ¾ in. long, the short dashes ⅛ in. long, and the spaces ⅟₃₂ in. wide. When drawn in ink, the dashes are ⅟₄₀ in. to ⅟₃₂ in. wide, depending on the size of the drawing. When drawn in pencil on manila paper, they are made with a medium pencil.

Arrowheads are used to show the direction in which the imaginary cut surface is viewed, and reference letters are added to identify it (Fig. 9.23).

Whenever the location of the cutting plane is obvious, it is common practice to omit the edge-view representation, particularly in the case of symmetrical objects. If it is shown, however, and coincides with a center line, it takes precedence over the center line.

9.11. Summary of the practices of sectioning.

1. A cutting plane may be offset in order to cut the object in such a manner as to reveal an important detail that would not be shown if the cutting plane were continuous (Fig. 9.4).

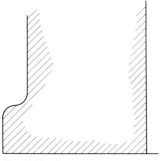

Fig. 9.21. Outline sectioning.

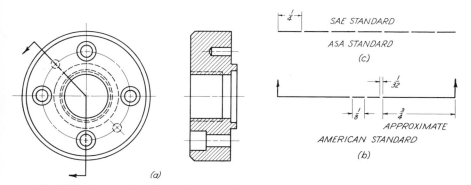

Fig. 9.22. Cutting plane lines (American Standard).

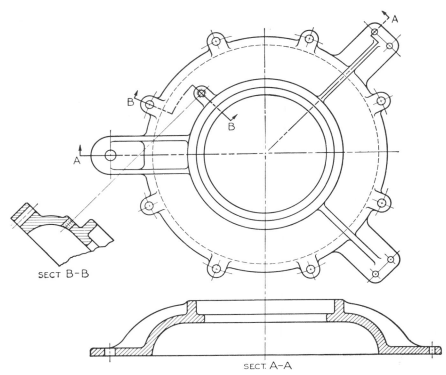

SECT B-B

SECT. A-A

Fig. 9.23. A sectional view.*

2. All visible lines beyond the cutting plane for the section are usually shown.

3. Invisible lines beyond the cutitng plane for the section are usually not shown, unless they are absolutely necessary to clarify the construction of the piece. In a half section, they are omitted in the unsectioned half, and either a center line or a solid line is used to separate the two halves of the view (Figs. 9.5 and 9.6).

4. On a view showing assembled parts, the section lines on adjacent pieces are drawn in opposite directions at an angle of 45° (Fig. 9.17).

5. On an assembly drawing, the portions of the cut surface of a single piece in the same view or different views always should be section-lined in the same direction, with the same spacing (Fig. 9.19).

6. The symbolic line indicating the location of the cutting plane may be omitted if the location of the plane is obvious (Fig. 9.1).

* ASA Y14.2–1957.

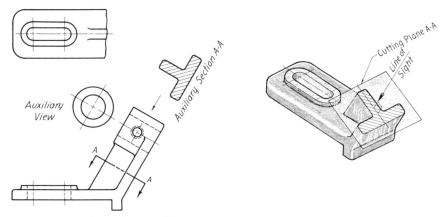

Fig. 9.24. An auxiliary section.

7. On a sectioned view showing assembled pieces, an exterior view is preferred for shafts, rods, bolts, nuts, rivets, and so forth, whose axes are in the plane of section (Fig. 9.19).

9.12. Auxiliary sections. A sectional view, projected upon an auxiliary plane, is sometimes necessary to show the shape of a surface cut by a plane, or to show the cross-sectional shape of an arm, rib, and so forth, inclined to any two or all three of the principal planes of projection (Fig. 9.24). When a cutting plane cuts an object, as in Fig. 9.24, arrows should show the direction in which the cut surface is viewed. Auxiliary sections are drawn by the usual method for drawing auxiliary views. When the bounding edge of the section is a curve, it is necessary to plot enough points to obtain a smooth one. Section 8.11 explains in detail the method for constructing the required view. A section view of this type usually shows only the inclined cut surface.

9.13. Conventional sections. Sometimes a less confusing sectioned representation is obtained if certain of the strict rules of projection are violated as explained in Chapter 6. For example, an unbalanced and confused view results when the sectioned view of the pulley shown in Fig. 9.25 is drawn in true projection, as in (a). It is better practice to preserve symmetry by showing the spokes as if they were aligned into one plane, as in (c). Such treatment of unsymmetrical features is not misleading, since their actual arrangement is revealed in the circular view. The spokes are not sectioned in the preferred view. If they were, the first impression would be that the wheel had a solid web (b) (see Fig. 9.26).

When there are an odd number of holes in a flange, as is the case with the part in Fig. 9.27, they should be shown aligned in

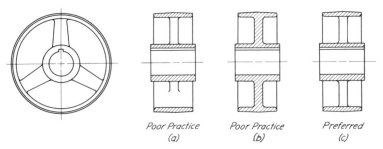

Fig. 9.25. Conventional treatment of spokes in section.

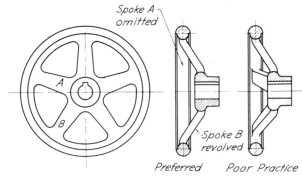

Fig. 9.26. Spokes in section.*

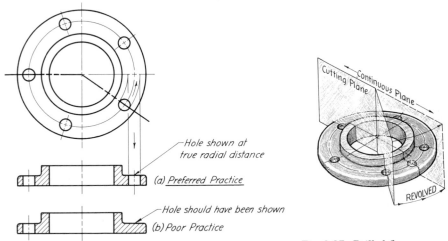

Fig. 9.27. Drilled flanges.

* ASA Y14.2–1957.

the sectioned view so as to reveal their true location with reference to the rim and the axis of the piece. To secure the so-called aligned section, one usually considers the cutting plane to be bent to pass through the angled hole as shown in the pictorial drawing. Then, the bent portion of the plane (with the hole) is imagined to be revolved until it is aligned with the other portion of the cutting plane. As straightened-out the imaginary continuous plane produces the preferred section view shown in (*a*).

Figure 9.28 shows another example of conventional representation. The sectional view is drawn as if the upper projecting lug had been swung until the portion of the cutting plane through it formed a continuous plane with the other portion (see Sec. 6.31). It should be noted that the hidden lines in the sectioned view are necessary for a complete description of the construction of the lugs.

9.14. Ribs in section. When a machine part has a rib cut by a plane of section (Fig. 9.29), a "true" sectional view taken through the rib would prove to be false and misleading, because the cross-hatching on the rib would cause the object to appear "solid." The preferred treatment is to omit arbitrarily the section lines from the rib, as illustrated by Fig. 9.29(*a*). The resulting sectional view may be considered the view that would be obtained if the plane were offset to pass just in front of the rib (*b*).

An alternate conventional method, approved but not used as frequently, is illustrated in Fig. 9.30. This practice of omitting alternate section lines sometimes is adopted when it is necessary to emphasize a rib that might otherwise be overlooked.

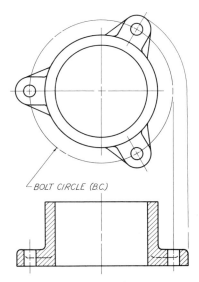

Fig. 9.28. Revolution of a portion of an object.

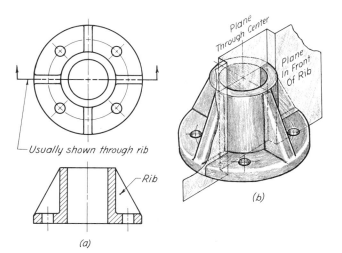

Fig. 9.29. Conventional treatment of ribs in section.

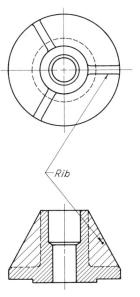

Fig. 9.30. Alternate treatment of ribs in section.

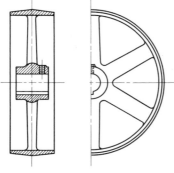

Fig. 9.31. A half view.

9.15. Half views. When the space available is insufficient to allow a satisfactory scale to be used for the representation of a symmetrical piece, it is considered good practice to make one view a half view, as shown in Fig. 9.31. The half view, however, must be the top or side view and not the front view, which shows the characteristic contour. The half view should be the rear half.

9.16. Material symbols. The section-line symbols recommended by the American Standards Association for indicating various materials are shown in Fig. 9.32. Code section lining ordinarily is not used on a working (detail) drawing of a separate part. It is considered unnecessary to indicate a material symbolically when its exact specification must also be given as a note. For this reason, and in order to save time as well, the easily drawn symbol for cast iron is commonly used on detail drawings for all materials. Contrary to this general practice, however, some few chief draftsmen insist that symbolic section lining be used on all detail drawings prepared under their supervision.

Code section lining usually is employed on an assembly section showing the various parts of a unit in position, because a distinction between the materials causes the parts to "stand out" to better advantage. Furthermore, a knowledge of the type of material of

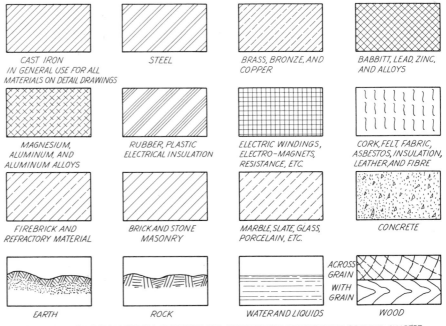

FOR OTHER SYMBOLS FOR MATERIALS IN SECTION AND ELEVATION SEE ARCHITECTURAL DRAWING CHAPTER

Fig. 9.32. Material symbols.

which an individual part is composed often helps the reader to identify it more quickly and understand its function.

PROBLEMS

The following problems were designed to emphasize the principles of sectioning. It is not recommended that a great amount of time be spent on them, as more practice in applying the fundamentals of sectioning is offered the student by problems at the end of the chapter on working drawings. Those orthographic drawings that are prepared from the pictorials of objects may be dimensioned if the elementary principles of dimensioning (Chapter 17) are carefully studied.

1. (Fig. 9.33.) Reproduce the top view and change the front view into a full section view in accordance with the indicated cutting plane.

2. (Fig. 9.34.) Reproduce the top view and change the front and side views into sectional views that will be in accordance with the indicated cutting planes.

3. (Fig. 9.35.) Draw a front view of the pulley (circular view) and a side view in full section.

4. (Fig. 9.36.) Reproduce the top view of the rod support and draw the front view in full section. Read Sec. 6.33 before starting to draw.

5. (Fig. 9.37.) Draw a front view of the "V" pulley (circular view) and a side view in full section.

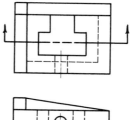
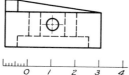

Fig. 9.33. Mutilated block.

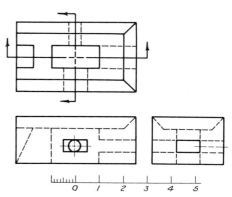

Fig. 9.34. Mutilated block.

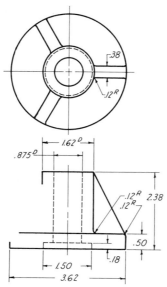

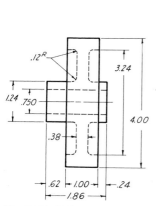

Fig. 9.35. Pulley.

Fig. 9.36. Rod support.

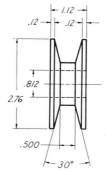

Fig. 9.37. "V" pulley.

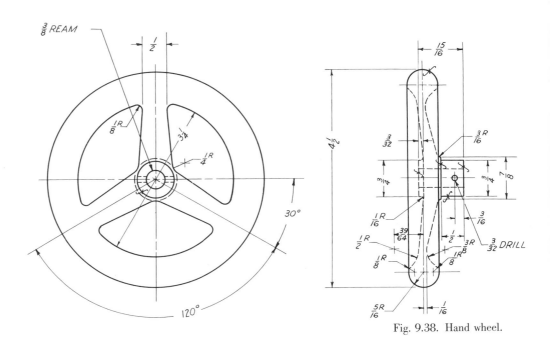

Fig. 9.38. Hand wheel.

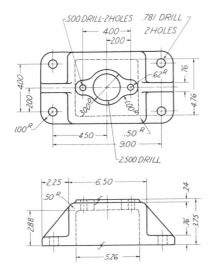

Fig. 9.39. Control housing cover.

6. (Fig. 9.38.) Reproduce the two views of the hand wheel and change the right-side view into a full section.

7. (Fig. 9.39.) Reproduce the top view of the control housing cover and convert the front view to a full section.

8. (Fig. 9.40.) Reproduce the circular front view of the pump cover and convert the right-side view to a full section.

9. (Fig. 9.41.) Make a full sectional view of the "rectangular view" of the piston head. Reproduce the circular view.

10. (Fig. 9.42.) Reproduce the front and top views of the steady brace. Complete the top view and draw the required side view and auxiliary section. Since this is a structural drawing, the figure giving the value of a distance appears above on unbroken dimension line in accordance with the custom in this field of engineering. The slope (45°) of the inclined member to which the plates are welded is indicated by a slope triangle with 12 in. legs.

This problem has been designed to make it necessary for the student to test his power of visualization if he is to determine the shape of the inclined structural member. Good judgment must be exercised in determining the location of the third hole in each plate. All hidden object lines should be shown.

11-24. (Figs. 9.43–9.56.) These problems may be dimensioned, as are working drawings. For each object, the student should draw all

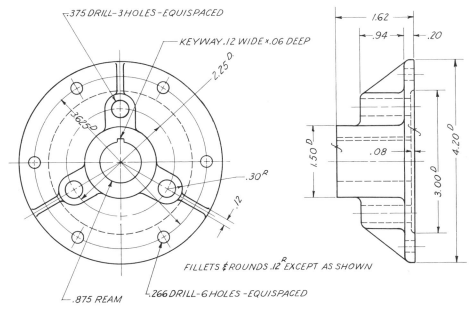

.375 DRILL-3 HOLES-EQUISPACED

KEYWAY .12 WIDE × .06 DEEP

2.25 D.

3.625 D.

.30 R

.12

.875 REAM

.266 DRILL-6 HOLES-EQUISPACED

FILLETS & ROUNDS .12 R EXCEPT AS SHOWN

1.62

.94

.20

1.50 D

.08

3.00 D

4.20 D

Fig. 9.40. Pump cover.

the views necessary for a working drawing of the part. Good judgment should be exercised in deciding whether the sectional view should be a full section or a half section. After the student has made his decision, he should consult his class instructor.

The end guide has five ribs (Fig. 9.56).

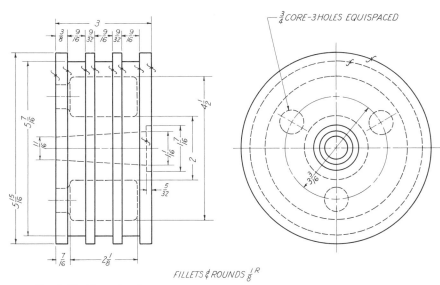

$\frac{3}{4}$ CORE-3 HOLES EQUISPACED

3

$\frac{3}{8}$ $\frac{9}{16}$ $\frac{9}{32}$ $\frac{9}{16}$ $\frac{9}{32}$ $\frac{9}{16}$

$4\frac{1}{2}$

$5\frac{7}{16}$

$\frac{11}{16}$

$\frac{7}{16}$

$\frac{1}{16}$

2

$\frac{5}{32}$

$5\frac{15}{16}$

$\frac{3}{16}$

$\frac{7}{16}$

$2\frac{1}{8}$

FILLETS & ROUNDS $\frac{1}{8}$ R

Fig. 9.41. Piston head.

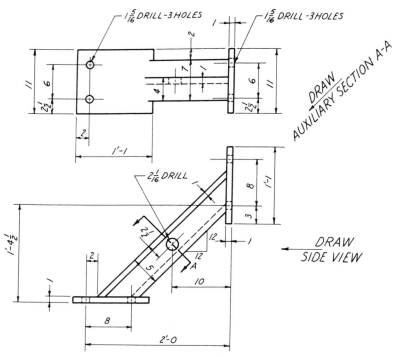

Fig. 9.42. Steady brace.

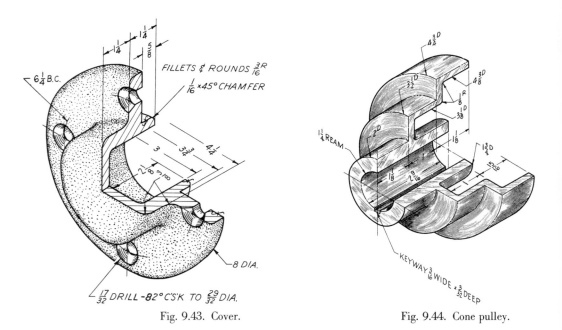

Fig. 9.43. Cover.

Fig. 9.44. Cone pulley.

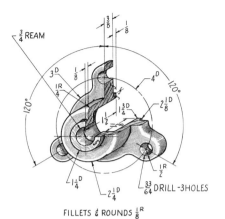

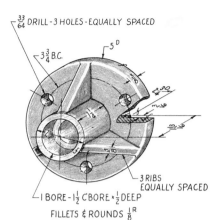

Fig. 9.45. End cap.

FILLETS & ROUNDS $\frac{1}{8}$R

Fig. 9.46. Rod yoke.

I BORE - $1\frac{1}{2}$ CBORE × $\frac{1}{2}$ DEEP

FILLETS & ROUNDS $\frac{1}{8}$R

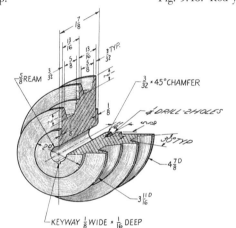

Fig. 9.47. "V" motor pulley.

KEYWAY $\frac{1}{8}$ WIDE × $\frac{1}{16}$ DEEP

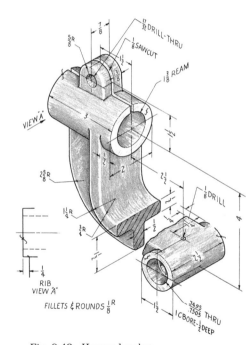

Fig. 9.48. Hanger bracket.

RIB VIEW "A"

FILLETS & ROUNDS $\frac{1}{8}$R

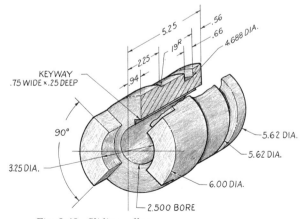

Fig. 9.49. Sliding collar.

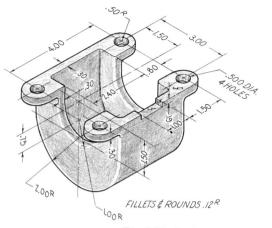

Fig. 9.50. Strainer pan.

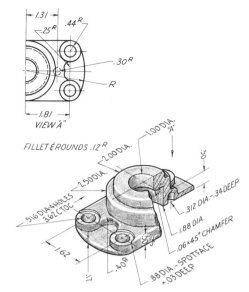

Fig. 9.51. Control housing cover.

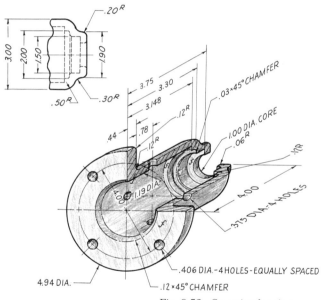

Fig. 9.52. Centering bearing.

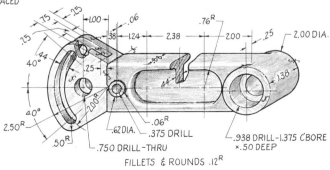

Fig. 9.53. Slotted guide link.

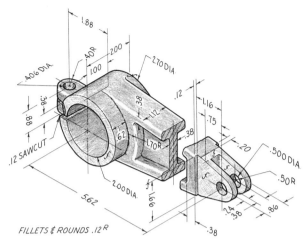

Fig. 9.54. Shifter link.

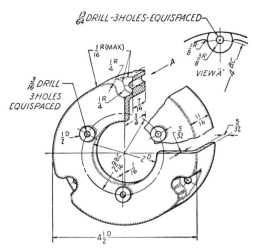

Fig. 9.55. Cover.

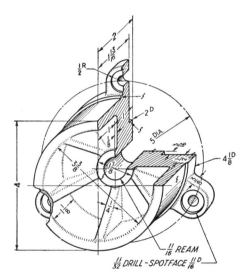

Fig. 9.56. End guide.

25. (Fig. 9.57.) Make a multiview drawing of the drum. The drum rotates when it is forced along the shaft into contact with the constantly rotating driving cone. The driving cone is fixed to the rotating shaft by a Pratt and Whitney key to insure rotary motion with the shaft, and by a taper pin to prevent longitudinal axial movement. As the drum rotates it winds or unwinds a cable. The shaft is driven by a system of gears that is not shown. The partial orthographic views show the operating mechanism for sliding the drum along the shaft into contact with the driving cone. If after studying the drawings carefully you have further questions, please consult your instructor. *Supplementary information:* (1) The outside diameter of the drum is 30 in. The diameter of the opening in the drum for the backing drum cone is 29¼ in. and the taper is 2½ in. per ft. (2) The diameter of the cable section is 18 in., and the width of opening for the cable is 10 in. (3) The dimensions of the hub are: 8 in. outside diameter (O.D.) and 12⅜ in. over-all length. (4) The O.D. of the bushing is 4¼ in. (5) There are six ⅝ in.-thick ribs which are equally spaced. (6) The hole in the hub for an oil fitting is tapped for a ¼ in. pipe thread. The hole which is to provide access to the threaded hole is drilled ¾ in. in diameter. The tapped hole is 6³⁄₁₆ in. from the face of the hub. (7) The small hole for attaching the cable is ¹³⁄₁₆ in. It is located ¾ in. from the face of the flange. (8) The thickness of all sections except for the ribs is ¾ in. (9) There are 124 copper rivets required to fasten the brake lining to the drum. The holes in the drum are to be drilled ¼ in. in diameter and are countersunk at 90°. (10) All small radii are ¾ in. R.

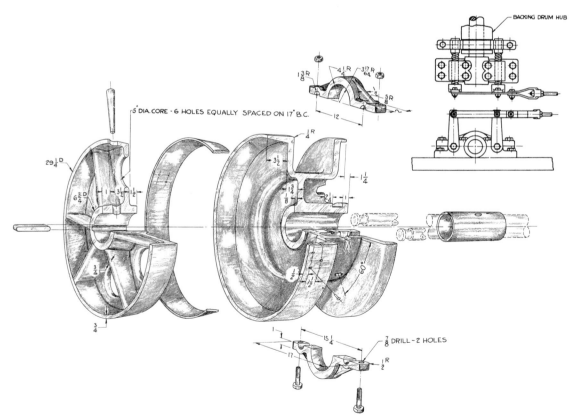

Fig. 9.57. Hoisting machine—drum, cone, and collar.

26. (Fig. 9.57.) Make a multiview drawing of the driving cone. *Supplementary information:* (1) The surface of the driving cone which contacts the lining in the drum is tapered. The taper is 2½ in. per ft. (2) The diameter of the shaft on which the driving cone is fixed is 3¾ in. (3) It is suggested that a No. 34 Pratt and Whitney and No. 12 Std. taper be used for the driving cone. Taper pins have a taper of ¼ in. per ft. (4) The 5-in. diam. holes are to be cored in the casting.

10

PICTORIAL DRAWING

10.1. Introduction. An orthographic drawing of two or more views describes an object accurately in form and size but, since each of the views shows only two dimensions without any suggestion of depth, such a drawing can convey information only to those who are familiar with graphic representation. For this reason, multiview drawings are used mainly by engineers, draftsmen, contractors, and shopmen.

Frequently, however, engineers and draftsmen find they must use conventional picture drawings to convey specific information to persons who do not possess the trained imagination necessary to construct mentally an object from views. To make such drawings, several special schemes of one-plane pictorial drawing have been devised that combine the pictorial effect of perspective with the advantage of having the principal dimensions to scale. But pictorial drawings, in spite of certain advantages, have disadvantages that limit their use. A few of these are as follows:

1. Some drawings frequently have a distorted, unreal appearance that is disagreeable.
2. The time required for execution is, in many cases, greater than for an orthographic drawing.
3. They are difficult to dimension.
4. Some of the lines cannot be measured.

Even with these limitations, pictorial drawings are used extensively for catalogs, Patent Office records, piping diagrams, and furniture designs (Fig. 10.1). Occasionally they are used, in one form or another, to supplement and clarify machine and structural details which would be difficult to visualize (Fig. 10.2).

10.2. Divisions of pictorial drawing. Single-plane pictorial drawings are classified in three general divisions: (1) axonometric pro-

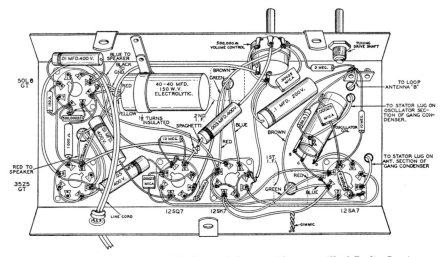

Fig. 10.1. Pictorial diagram (*Courtesy Allied Radio Corp.*).

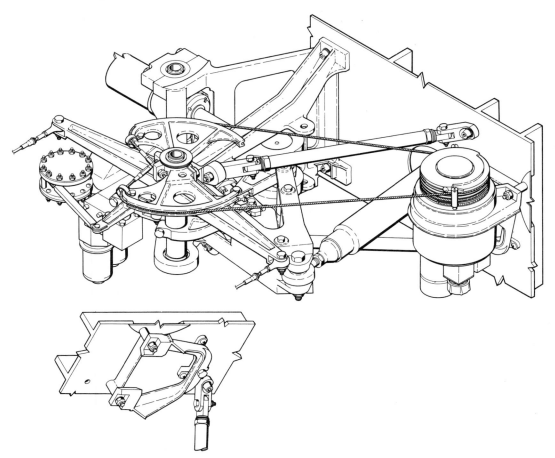

Fig. 10.2. A pictorial illustration (*Courtesy Lockheed Aircraft Corp.*).

jection, (2) oblique projection, and (3) perspective projection (Fig. 10.3).

Perspective methods produce the most realistic drawings, but the necessary construction is more difficult and tedious than the construction required for the conventional methods classified under

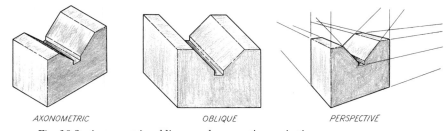

AXONOMETRIC   OBLIQUE   PERSPECTIVE

Fig. 10.3. Axonometric, oblique, and perspective projection.

the other two divisions. For this reason, engineers customarily use some form of either axonometric or oblique projection. Modified methods, which are not theoretically correct, are often used to produce desired effects.

10.3. Divisions of axonometric projection. Theoretically, axonometric projection is a form of orthographic projection. The distinguishing difference is that only one plane is used instead of two or more, and the object is turned from its customary position so that three faces are displayed (Fig. 10.4). Since an object may be placed in a countless number of positions relative to the picture plane, an infinite number of views may be drawn which will vary in general proportions, lengths of edges, and sizes of angles. For practical reasons, a few of these possible positions have been classified in such a manner as to give the recognized divisions of axonometric projection: (1) isometric, (2) dimetric, and (3) trimetric.

Isometric projection is the simplest of these, because the principal axes make equal angles with the plane of projection and the edges are therefore foreshortened equally.

10.4. Isometric projection. If the cube in Fig. 10.4 were revolved through an angle of 45° about an imaginary vertical axis, as shown in II, and is then tilted forward until its body diagonal is perpendicular to the vertical plane, the edges would be foreshortened equally and the cube would be in the correct position to produce an isometric projection.

The three front edges, called isometric axes, make angles of approximately 35° 16′ with the vertical plane of projection or pic-

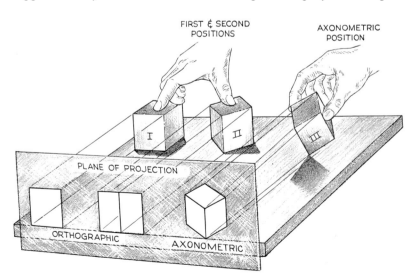

Fig. 10.4. Theory of axonometric projection.

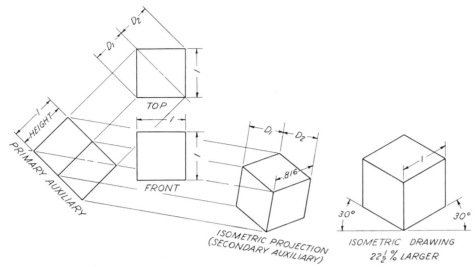

Fig. 10.5. Comparison of isometric projection and isometric drawing.

ture plane. In this form of pictorial, the angles between the projections of these axes are 120°, and the projected lengths of the edges of an object, along and parallel to these axes, are approximately 81 per cent of their true lengths. It should be observed that the 90° angles of the cube appear in the isometric projection as either 120° or 60°.

Now, if instead of turning and tilting the object in relation to a principal plane of projection, an auxiliary plane is used that will be perpendicular to the body diagonal, the view projected on the plane will be an axonometric projection. Since the auxiliary plane will be inclined to the principal planes upon which the front, top, and side views would be projected, the auxiliary view, taken in a position perpendicular to the body diagonal, will be a secondary auxiliary view, as shown in Fig. 10.5.

10.5. Isometric scale. An isometric scale (proportional scale) for laying off distances parallel to isometric axes may be made by the simple graphical method shown in Fig. 10.6. Usually, the scale is drawn along the edge of a strip of paper or cardboard. Its use is illustrated in Fig. 10.7.

10.6. Isometric drawing. Objects seldom are drawn in true isometric projection, the use of an isometric scale being inconvenient and impractical. Instead, a conventional method is used in which all foreshortening is ignored, and actual true lengths are laid off along isometric axes and isometric lines. To avoid confusion and

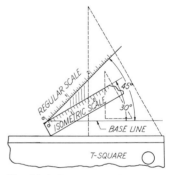

Fig. 10.6. Isometric scale.

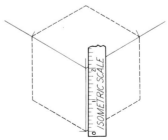

Fig. 10.7. Use of an isometric scale.

to set this method apart from true isometric projection, it is called isometric drawing.

The isometric drawing of a figure is slightly larger (approximately 22½%) than the isometric projection, but, since the proportions are the same, the increased size does not affect the pictorial value of the representation (see Fig. 10.5). The use of a regular scale makes it possible for a draftsman to produce a satisfactory drawing with a minimum expenditure of time and effort.

In isometric drawing, lines that are parallel to the isometric axes are called *isometric lines*.

10.7. To make an isometric drawing of a rectangular object. The procedure followed in making an isometric drawing of a rectangular block is illustrated in Fig. 10.8. The three axes that establish the front edges, as shown in (*b*), should be drawn through point *A* so that one extends vertically downward and the other two upward to the right and left at an angle of 30° from the horizontal. Then the actual lengths of the edges may be set off, as shown in (*c*) and (*d*), and the remainder of the view completed by drawing lines parallel to the axes through the corners thus located, as in (*e*) and (*f*).

Hidden lines, unless absolutely necessary for clearness, always should be omitted on a pictorial representation.

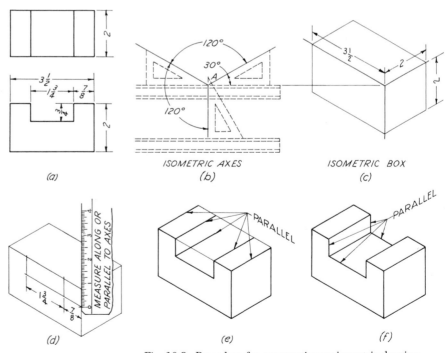

Fig. 10.8. Procedure for constructing an isometric drawing.

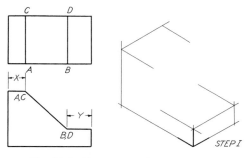
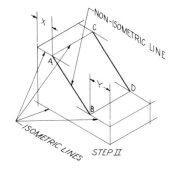

Fig. 10.9. Nonisometric lines.

10.8. Nonisometric lines. In a pictorial view, the lines that are oblique to the isometric axes are called *nonisometric lines*. Since a line of this type does not appear in its true length and cannot be measured directly, its position and projected length must be established by locating its extremities. In Fig. 10.9, *AB* and *CD*, which represent the edges of the block, are nonisometric lines. The location of *AB* is established in the pictorial view by locating points *A* and *B*. Point *A* is on the top edge, *X* distance from the left side surface. Point *B* is on the upper edge of the base, *Y* distance from the right side surface. All other lines coincide with or are parallel to the axes and, therefore, may be measured off with the scale.

The pictorial representation of an irregular solid containing a number of nonisometric lines may be conveniently constructed by the box method; that is, the object may be enclosed in a rectangular box so that both isometric and nonisometric lines may be located by points of contact with its surfaces and edges (see Fig. 10.10).

A study of Figs. 10.9 and 10.10 reveals the important fact that lines that are parallel on an object are parallel in the pictorial view, and, conversely, lines that are not parallel on the object are not parallel on the view. It is often possible to eliminate much tedious

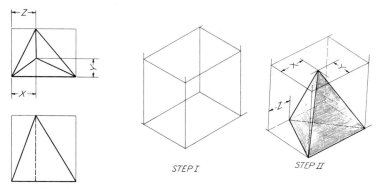

Fig. 10.10. Box construction.

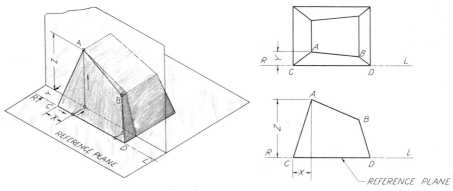

Fig. 10.11. Co-ordinate construction.

construction work by the practical application of the principle of parallel lines.

10.9. Coordinate construction method. When an object contains a number of inclined surfaces, such as the one shown in Fig. 10.11, the use of the coordinate construction method is desirable. In this method, the end-points of the edges are located in relation to an assumed isometric base line located upon an isometric reference plane. For example, the line *RL* is used as a base line from which measurements are made along isometric lines, as shown. The distances required to locate point *A* are taken directly from the orthographic views.

Irregular curved edges are most easily drawn in isometric by the offset method, which is a modification of the coordinate construction method (Fig. 10.12). The position of the curve readily can be established by plotted points that may be located by measuring along isometric lines.

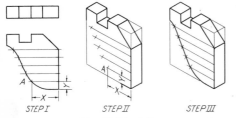

STEP I   *STEP II*   *STEP III*

Fig. 10.12. Offset construction.

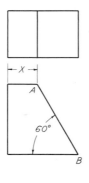
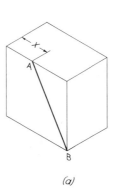
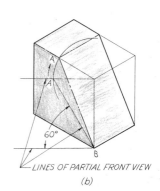

(a)   *(b)*

Fig. 10.13. Angles in isometric.

10.10. Angles in isometric drawing. When nonisometric lines are located by angular measurements (Fig. 10.13), it is necessary to draw at least a partial orthographic view of the object and take off the dimensions. The scale should be the same as that of the pictorial view (*a*). A practical application of this principle, to the construction of an isometric drawing of a 60° angle, is shown in (*b*). By making this construction at the place where the angle is to appear on the isometric drawing, the position of the required line is obtained graphically.

10.11. Circle and circle arcs in isometric drawing. In isometric drawing, a circle appears as an ellipse. The tedious construction required for plotting an ellipse accurately (Figs. 10.14 and 10.15) often is avoided by using some approximate method of drawing. The representation thus obtained is accurate enough for most work, although the true ellipse, which is slightly narrower and longer, is more pleasing in shape (Fig. 10.14). For an approximate construction, a four-center method is generally used.

To draw an ellipse representing a pictorial circle, a square is conceived to be circumscribed about the circle in the orthographic projection. When transferred to the isometric plane in the pictorial view, the square becomes a rhombus (isometric square) and the circle an ellipse tangent to the rhombus at the mid-points of its sides. If the ellipse is to be drawn by the four-center method (Fig. 10.16), the points of intersection of the perpendicular bisectors of the sides of the rhombus will be centers for the four arcs forming the approximate ellipse. The two intersections that lie on the corners of the rhombus are centers for the two large arcs, while the remaining intersections are centers for the two small arcs. Furthermore, the length along the perpendicular from the center of each arc to the point at which the arc is tangent to the rhombus (mid-point) will

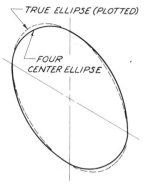

Fig. 10.14. Pictorial ellipses.

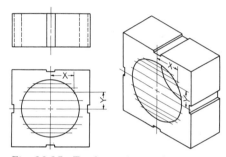

Fig. 10.15. To plot an isometric circle.

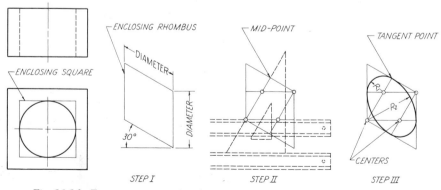

Fig. 10.16. Four-center approximation.

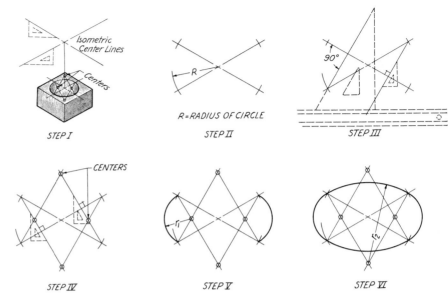

Fig. 10.17. Steps in drawing a four-center isometric circle (ellipse).

be the radius. All construction lines required by this method may be made with a T-square and a 30° ×60° triangle.

The amount of work may be still further shortened, and the accuracy of the construction improved, by following the procedure shown in Fig. 10.17. The steps in this method are:

Step I. Draw the isometric center lines of the required circle.

Step II. Using a radius equal to the radius of the circle, strike arcs across the isometric center lines.

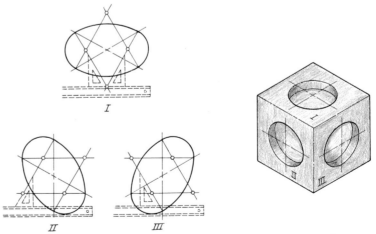

Fig. 10.18. Isometric circles.

Steps III–IV. Through each of these points of intersection erect a perpendicular to the other isometric center line.

Steps V–VI. Using the intersection points of the perpendiculars as centers and lengths along the perpendiculars as radii, draw the four arcs that form the ellipse (see Fig. 10.18).

A circle arc will appear in pictorial representation as a segment of an ellipse. Therefore, it may be drawn by using as much of the four-center method as is required to locate the needed centers (see Fig. 10.19). For example, to draw a quarter circle, it is only necessary to lay off the true radius of the arc along isometric lines drawn through the center and to draw intersecting perpendiculars through these points.

To draw isometric concentric circles by the four-center method, a set of centers must be located for each circle (Fig. 10.20).

When several circles of the same diameter occur in parallel planes, the construction may be simplified. Figure 10.21 shows two views of a cylinder and its corresponding isometric drawing. The centers for the ellipse representing the upper base are found in the usual way, while the four centers for the lower base are located by moving the centers for the upper base downward a distance equal to the height of the cylinder. It should be noted that corresponding centers lie along an isometric line parallel to the axis of the cylinder.

Circles and circle arcs in nonisometric planes are plotted by using the offset or coordinate method (Fig. 10.22). Sufficient points for establishing a curve are located by transferring measurements from the orthographic views to isometric lines in the pictorial view, as illustrated for point A.

The pictorial representation of a sphere is the envelope of all of the great circles which could be drawn on the surface. In isometric drawing, the great circles appear as ellipses and a circle is their envelope. In practice it is necessary to draw only one ellipse,

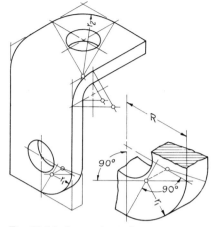

Fig. 10.19. Isometric circle arcs.

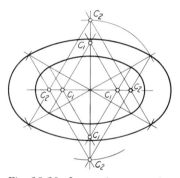

Fig. 10.20. Isometric concentric circles.

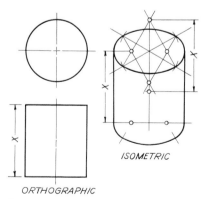

Fig. 10.21. Isometric parallel circles.

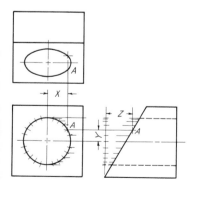

Fig. 10.22. Circles in nonisometric planes.

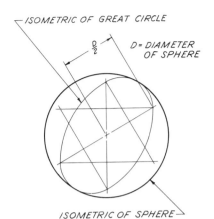

Fig. 10.23. Isometric drawing of a sphere.

(a)   (b)   (c)   (d)

Fig. 10.24. Convenient positions of axes.

using the true radius of the sphere and the four-center method of construction. The diameter of the circle is the long diameter of the ellipse (Fig. 10.23).

10.12. Positions of isometric axes. It sometimes is desirable to place the principal isometric axes so that an object will be in position to reveal certain faces to a better advantage (Fig. 10.24).

The difference in direction should cause no confusion, since the angle between the axes and the procedure followed in constructing the view are the same for any position. The choice of the direction may depend upon the construction of the object, but usually this is determined by the position from which the object ordinarily is viewed.

Reversed axes are used in architectural work to show a feature as it would be seen from a natural position below (*b*).

Sometimes long objects are drawn with the long axis horizontal, as shown in Fig. 10.25.

10.13. Isometric sectional views (Fig. 10.26). Generally, an isometric sectional view is used for showing the inner construction of an object, when there is a complicated interior to be explained or when it is desirable to emphasize features that would not appear in a usual outside view. Sectioning in isometric drawing is based upon the same principles as sectioning in orthographic drawing. Isometric planes are used for cutting an object, and the general procedure followed in constructing the representation is the same as for an exterior view.

Figure 10.26 shows an isometric half section. It is easier, in

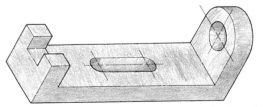

Fig. 10.25. Main axis horizontal—long objects.

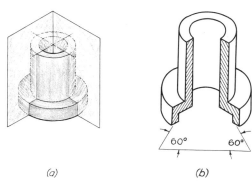

(a)   (b)

Fig. 10.26. Isometric half section.

this case, to outline the outside view of the object in full and then remove a front quarter with isometric planes.

Figure 10.27 illustrates a full section in isometric. The accepted procedure for constructing this form of sectional view is to draw the cut face and then add the portion that lies behind.

Section lines should be sloped at an angle that produces the best effect, but they should never be drawn parallel to object lines. In Fig. 10.28, (a) illustrates the slope that is correct for most drawings, while (b), (c), and (d) show the poor effect produced when this phase of section lining is ignored. Ordinarily, isometric section lines are drawn at 60°.

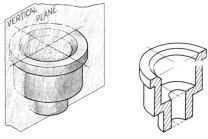

Fig. 10.27. Isometric full section.

10.14. Dimetric projection. The view of an object that has been so placed that two of its axes make equal angles with the plane of projection is called a *dimetric projection*. The third axis may make either a smaller or larger angle. All of the edges along or parallel to the first two axes are foreshortened equally, while those parallel to the third axis are foreshortened a different amount. It might be said that dimetric projection, a division of axonometric projection, is like isometric projection in that the object must be placed to satisfy specific conditions. Similarly, a dimetric projection may be

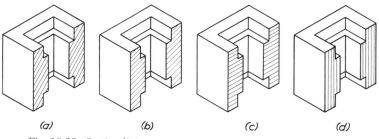

(a)   (b)   (c)   (d)

Fig. 10.28. Section lining.

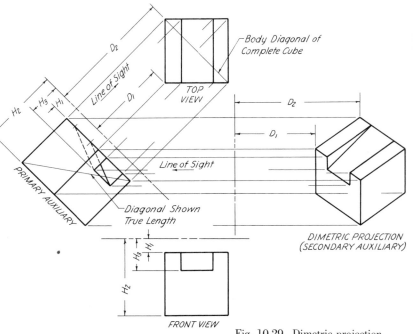

Fig. 10.29. Dimetric projection.

DIMETRIC DRAWING (APPROX.)
(a)

DIMETRIC AXES
(b)

Fig. 10.30. Approximate dimetric drawing.

drawn by using the auxiliary view method. Figure 10.29 shows the front, top, primary auxiliary, and secondary auxiliary view of a part. The secondary auxiliary view is the dimetric projection. The procedure is the same as for an isometric projection (see Fig. 10.5), except that the line of sight is taken in the direction necessary to obtain the desired dimetric projection. Obviously, an infinite number of dimetric projections is possible.

In practical application, dimetric projection is sometimes modified so that regular scales can be used to lay off measurements to assumed ratios. This is called *dimetric drawing* [Fig. 10.30(a)].

The angles and scales may be worked out* for any ratios such as 1:1:½ (full size:full size:half size); 1:1:¾ (full size:full size: three-fourths size). For example, the angles for the ratios 1:1:½ are 7° 11′ and 41° 25′. After the scales have been assumed and the angles computed, an enclosing box may be drawn in conformity to the angles and the view completed by following the general procedure used in isometric drawing, except that two scales must be used. The positions commonly used, along with the scale ratios and corresponding angles, are shown in Fig. 10.30(b). The first scale given in each ratio is for the vertical axis. Since obviously two of

---

* Formula: $\cos \alpha = -\sqrt{2s_1{}^2s_2{}^2 - s_2{}^4}/2s_1s_2$. In this formula, α is one of the equal angles; s_1 is one of the equal scales; s_2 is the third scale.

the axes are foreshortened equally, while the third is foreshortened in different ratio, two scales must be used. This is an effective method of representation.

10.15. Trimetric projection. A trimetric projection of an object is the view obtained when each of the three axes makes a different angle with the plane of projection. Figure 10.31 illustrates the application of the auxiliary view method to the construction of a trimetric projection. It must be noted that the object shown in Fig. 10.31 is rectangular and that the line of sight for the primary auxiliary view was not taken perpendicular to the body diagonal of a cube as in the case of the dimetric projection illustrated in Fig. 10.29. This form of pictorial representation has been used to some extent by certain aircraft companies for the preparation of production illustrations.

10.16. Oblique projection. In oblique projection, the view is produced by using parallel projectors that make some angle other than 90° with the plane of projection. Generally, one face is placed parallel to the picture plane and the projection lines are taken at

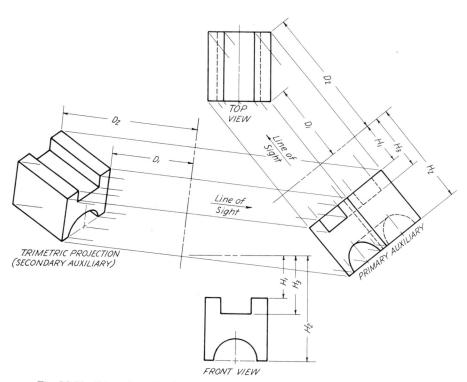

Fig. 10.31. Trimetric projection.

45°. This gives a view that is pictorial in appearance, as it shows the front and one or more additional faces of an object. In Fig. 10.32, the orthographic and oblique projections of a cube are shown. When the angle is 45°, as in this illustration, the representation is sometimes called cavalier projection. It is generally known, however, as an oblique projection or an oblique drawing.

10.17. Principle of oblique projection. The theory of oblique projection can be explained by imagining a vertical plane of projection in front of a cube parallel to one of its faces (Fig. 10.32). When the projectors make an angle of 45° in any direction with the picture plane, the length of any oblique projection $A'B'$ of the edge AB is equal to the true length of AB. Note that the projectors could be parallel to any element of a 45° cone having its base in the plane of projection. With projectors at this particular angle (45°), the face parallel to the plane is projected in its true size and shape and the edges perpendicular to the picture plane are projected in their true length. If the projectors make a greater angle, the oblique projection will be shorter, while if the angle is less, the projection will be longer.

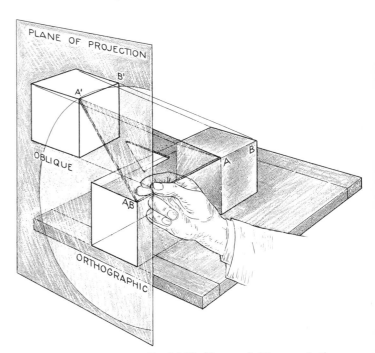

Fig. 10.32. Theory of oblique projection.

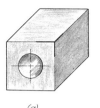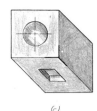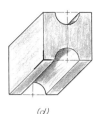

(a)   *(b)*   *(c)*   *(d)*

Fig. 10.33. Various positions of the receding axis.

10.18. Oblique drawing. This form of drawing is based upon three mutually perpendicular axes along which, or parallel to which, the necessary measurements are made for constructing the representation. Oblique drawing differs from isometric drawing principally in that two axes are always perpendicular to each other while the third (receding axis) is at some convenient angle, such as 30°, 45°, or 60° with the horizontal (see Fig. 10.34). It is somewhat more flexible and has the following advantages over isometric drawing: (1) circular or irregular outlines on the front face show in their true shape; (2) distortion can be reduced by foreshortening along the receding axis; and (3) a greater choice is permitted in the selection of the positions of the axes. A few of the various views that can be obtained by varying the inclination of the receding axis are illustrated in Fig. 10.33. Usually, the selection of the position is governed by the character of the object.

10.19. To make an oblique drawing. The procedure followed in constructing an oblique drawing of an adjustable guide is illustrated in Fig. 10.34. The three axes that establish the perpendicular edges in (*b*) are drawn through point *O* representing the front corner. *OA* and *OB* are perpendicular to each other and *OC* is at any desired angle (say 30°) with the horizontal. After the width, height, and depth have been set off, the front face may be laid out in its true size and shape, as in (*c*), and the view can be completed by drawing lines parallel to the receding axes through the established corners. The circle and semicircle are shown parallel to the picture plane in order to avoid distortion and because, from the draftsman's standpoint, it is easier to draw a circle than to construct an ellipse.

In general, the procedure for constructing an oblique drawing is the same as for an isometric drawing.

10.20. Rules for placing an object. Generally, the most irregular face, or the one containing the most circular outlines, should be placed parallel to the picture plane, in order to minimize distortion and simplify construction. By following this practice, all or most

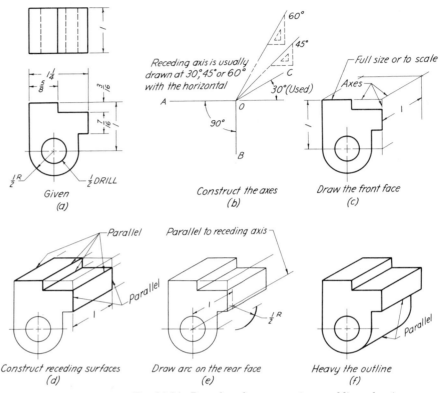

Fig. 10.34. Procedure for constructing an oblique drawing.

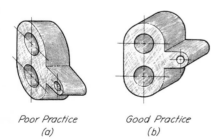

Poor Practice
(a)

Good Practice
(b)

Fig. 10.35. Irregular contour parallel to picture plane.

of the circles and circle arcs can be drawn with a compass, and the tedious construction that would be required to draw their elliptical representations in a receding plane is eliminated. In selecting the position of an object, two rules should be followed. The first is to place the face having the most irregular contour, or the most circular outlines, parallel to the picture plane. Note in Fig. 10.35 the advantage of following this rule.

When the longest face of an object is used as the front face, the pictorial view will be distorted to a lesser degree and, therefore, will have a more realistic and pleasing appearance. Hence, the second rule is to place the longest face parallel to the picture plane. Compare the views shown in Fig. 10.36 and note the greater distortion in (*a*) over (*b*).

If these two rules clash, the first should govern. It is more desirable to have the irregular face show its true shape than it is to lessen the distortion in the direction of the receding axis.

10.21. Angles, circles, and circle arcs in oblique. As previously stated, angles, circles, and irregular outlines on surfaces parallel to

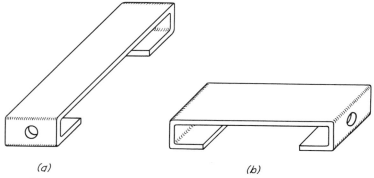

Fig. 10.36. Long axis parallel to picture plane.

the plane of projection show in true size and shape. When located on receding faces, the construction methods used in isometric drawing usually may be applied. Figure 10.37 shows the method of drawing the elliptical representation of a circle on an oblique face. Note that the method is identical with that used for constructing isometric circles, except for the slight change in the position of the axes.

Circle arcs and circles on inclined planes must be plotted by using the offset or coordinate method (Fig. 10.38).

10.22. Reduction of measurements in the direction of the receding axis.
An oblique drawing often presents a distorted appearance that is unnatural and disagreeable to the eye. In some cases the view constructed by this scheme is so misleading in appearance that it is unsatisfactory for any practical purpose. As a matter of interest, the effect of distortion is due to the fact that the receding lines are parallel and do not appear to converge as the eye is accustomed to anticipating (Fig. 10.39).

The appearance of excessive thickness can be overcome somewhat by reducing the length of the receding lines. For practical purposes, measurements usually are reduced one-half, but any scale

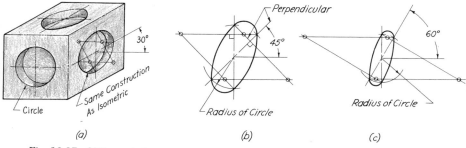

Fig. 10.37. Oblique circles.

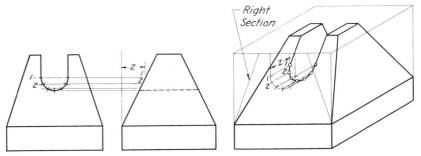

Fig. 10.38. Curved outlines on an inclined plane.

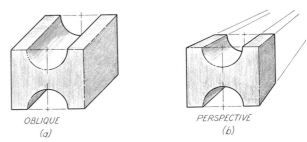

OBLIQUE
(a)

PERSPECTIVE
(b)

Fig. 10.39. Comparison of oblique and perspective.

of reduction may be arbitrarily adopted if the view obtained will be more realistic in appearance. When the receding lines are drawn one-half their actual length, the resulting pictorial view is called a cabinet drawing. Figure 10.40 shows an oblique drawing (a) and a cabinet drawing (c) of the same object, for the purpose of comparison.

10.23. Oblique sectional views. Oblique sectional views are drawn to show the interior construction of objects. The construction pro-

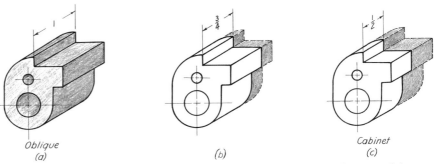

Oblique
(a)

(b)

Cabinet
(c)

Fig. 10.40. Foreshortening in the direction of the receding axis.

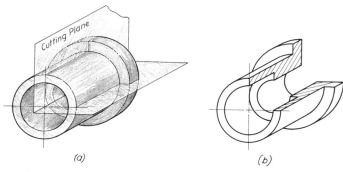

Fig. 10.41. Oblique half section.

cedure is the same as for an isometric sectional view, except that oblique planes are used for cutting the object. An oblique half section is illustrated in Fig. 10.41.

10.24. Pictorial dimensioning. The dimensioning of isometric and other forms of pictorial working drawings is done in accordance with the following rules:

1. Draw extension and dimension lines (except those dimension lines applying to cylindrical features) parallel to the pictorial axes in the plane of the surface to which they apply (Fig. 10.42).
2. If possible, apply dimensions to visible surfaces.
3. Place dimensions on the object, if, by so doing, better appearance, added clearness, and easy readings result.

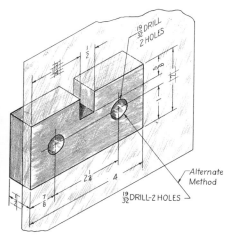
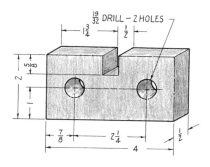

Fig. 10.42. Extension and dimension lines in isometric (left); numerals, fractions, and notes in oblique (right).

4. Notes may be lettered either in pictorial or as on ordinary drawings. When lettered as on ordinary drawings the difficulties encountered in forming pictorial letters are avoided (Fig. 10.42).

5. Make the figures of a dimension appear to be lying in the plane of the surface whose dimension it indicates, by using vertical figures drawn in pictorial (Fig. 10.42). (Note: Guide lines and slope lines are drawn parallel to the pictorial axes.)

10.25. Conventional treatment of pictorial drawings. When it is desirable for an isometric or an oblique drawing of a casting to present a somewhat more or less realistic appearance, it becomes necessary to represent the fillets and rounds on the unfinished surfaces. One method, commonly used by draftsmen, is shown in Fig. 10.43(*b*). On the drawing in (*a*), all of the edges have been treated as if they were sharp. The conventional treatment for threads in pictorial is illustrated in (*b*).

10.26. Perspective. In perspective projection, an object is shown much as the human eye or camera would see it at a particular point. Actually, it is a geometric method by which a picture can be projected upon a picture plane in much the same way as in photography. Perspective drawing differs from the methods previously discussed in that the projectors or visual rays intersect at a common point known as the *station point* (see Fig. 10.47).

Since perspective shows an object as it appears instead of showing its true shape and size, it is rarely used by engineers. It is more extensively employed by architects to show the appearance

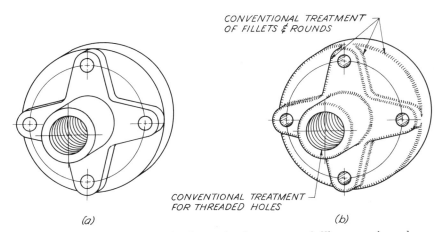

Fig. 10.43. Conventional treatment of fillets, rounds, and threads in pictorial.

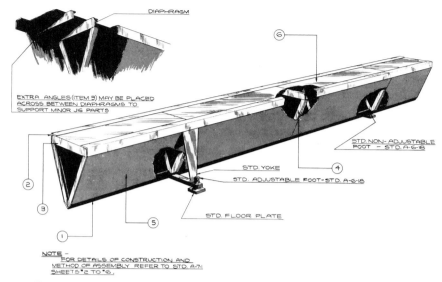

DIAPHRAGM

EXTRA ANGLES (ITEM 3) MAY BE PLACED
ACROSS BETWEEN DIAPHRAGMS TO
SUPPORT MINOR JIG PARTS

STD. NON-ADJUSTABLE
FOOT - STD. A-6-18

STD. YOKE

STD. ADJUSTABLE FOOT-STD. A-6-18

STD. FLOOR PLATE

NOTE –
FOR DETAILS OF CONSTRUCTION AND
METHOD OF ASSEMBLY REFER TO STD. A-7-1
SHEETS *2 TO *6.

Fig. 10.44. A production illustration. Prepared by Victory
Aircraft Limited (*Courtesy Crafting Mfg. Co.*).

of proposed buildings, by artist-draftsmen for production illustrations, and by illustrators in preparing advertising drawings.

Figure 10.2 shows a type of production illustration that has been
widely used in assembly departments as an aid to those persons who
find it difficult to read an orthographic assembly. This form of presentation, which may show a mechanism both exploded and assembled,
has made it possible for industrial concerns to employ semitrained
personnel. Figure 10.44 shows a type of industrial drawing made
in perspective that has proved useful in aircraft plants. Because of
the growing importance of this type of drawing, and also because
engineers frequently will find perspective desirable for other purposes, its elementary principles should be discussed logically in this
text. Other books on the subject, some of which are listed in the
bibliography, should be studied by architectural students and those
interested in a more thorough discussion of the various methods.

The fundamental concepts of perspective can be explained best
if the reader will imagine himself looking through a picture plane
at a formal garden with a small pool flanked by lamp posts, as
shown in Fig. 10.45. The point of observation, at which the rays
from the eye to the objects in the scene meet, is called the *station
point,* and the plane upon which the view is formed by the piercing
points of the visual rays is known as the *picture plane* (*PP*). The
piercing points reproduce the scene, the size of which depends upon
the location of the picture plane.

It should be noted that objects of the same height intercept a

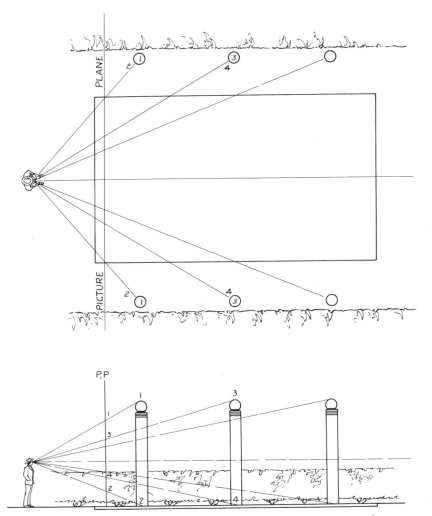

Fig. 10.45. The picture plane.

greater distance on the picture plane when close to it than when farther away. For example, rays from the lamp post at 2 intercept a distance 1–2 on the picture plane, while the rays from the pole at 4, which actually is the same height, intercept the lesser distance 3–4. From this fact it should be observed that the farther away an object is, the smaller it will appear, until a point is reached at which there will be no distance intercepted at all. This happens at the horizon.

Figure 10.46 shows the scene observed by the man in Fig. 10.45 as it would be formed on the picture plane. The posts farther from the picture plane diminish in height, as each one has a height on

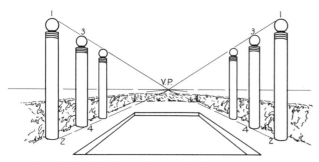

Fig. 10.46. The picture (perspective).

the picture plane equal to the distance it intercepts, as shown in Fig. 10.45. The lines of the pool and hedge converge to the center of vision or vanishing point, which is located directly in front of the observer, on the horizon.

10.27. Perspective nomenclature. Figure 10.47 illustrates pictorially the accepted nomenclature of perspective drawing. The *horizon line* is the line of intersection of the horizontal plane through the observation point (eye of the observer) and the picture plane. The horizontal plane is known as the *plane of the horizon*. The *ground line* is the line of intersection of the ground plane and the picture plane. The *CV point* is the center of vision of the observer. It is located directly in front of the eye in the plane of the horizon on the horizon line.

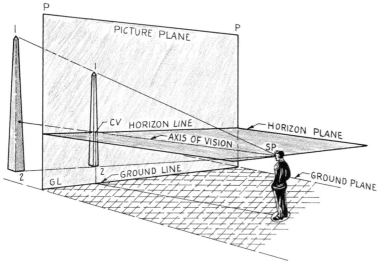

Fig. 10.47. Nomenclature.

10.28. Location of picture plane. The picture plane is usually placed between the object and the *SP* (station point). In parallel perspective (Sec. 10.34) it may be passed through a face of the object in order to show the true size and shape of the face.

10.29. Location of the station point. Care must be exercised in selecting the location for the station point, for its position has much to do with the appearance of the finished perspective drawing. A poor choice of position may result in a distorted perspective that will be decidedly displeasing to the eye.

In general, the station point should be offset slightly to one side and should be located above or below the exact center of the object. However, it must be remembered that the center of vision must be near the center of interest for the viewer.

One should always think of the station point as the viewing point, and its location should be where the object can be viewed to the best advantage. It is desirable that it be at a distance from the picture plane equal to at least twice the maximum dimension (width, height, or depth) of the object, for at such a distance, or greater, the entire object can be viewed naturally, as a whole, without turning the head.

A wide angle of view is to be avoided in the interest of good picturization. It has been determined that best results are obtained when the visual rays from the station point (*SP*) to the object are kept within a cone having an angle of not more than 30° between diametrically opposing elements (see Fig. 10.48).

In locating an object in relation to the picture plane, it is advisable to place it so that both of the side faces do not make the same angle with the picture plane and thus will not be equally visible. It is common practice to choose angles of 30° and 60° for rectangular objects.

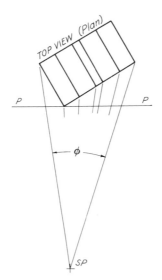

Fig. 10.48. Angle of vision.

10.30. Position of the object in relation to the horizon. When making a perspective of a tall object, such as a building, the horizon usually is assumed to be at a height above the ground plane equal to the standing height of a man's eye, normally about 5 ft 6 in.

A small object may be placed either above or below the horizon (eye level), depending upon the view desired. If an object is above the horizon, it will be seen looking up from below as shown in Fig. 10.49. Should the object be below the horizon line, it will be seen from above.

10.31. Lines. The following facts should be recognized concerning the perspective of lines:

1. Parallel horizontal lines vanish at a single *VP* (vanishing point). Usually the *VP* is at the point where a line parallel to the system through the *SP* pierces the *PP* (picture plane).

2. A system of horizontal lines has its *VP* on the horizon.

3. Vertical lines, since they pierce the picture plane at infinity, will appear vertical in perspective.

4. When a line lies in the picture plane, it will show its true length because it will be its own perspective.

5. When a line lies behind the picture plane, its perspective will be shorter than the line.

10.32. Perspective by multiview projection. Adhering to theory that a perspective drawing is formed upon a picture plane by visual rays from the eye to the object, as illustrated in Fig. 10.45, a perspective can be drawn by using multiview projection (see Fig. 10.50). The multiview method may be the easiest for a student to understand but it is not often used by an experienced person because considerable more line work is required if the scene or object to be represented is at all complicated. The top and side views are drawn in multiview projection and the picture plane (as an edge view) and the station point are shown in each case. SP^H and its related views of the rays are in the top view while SP^P and its projections of the rays belong to the side view. The front view of the picture plane is in the plane of the paper.

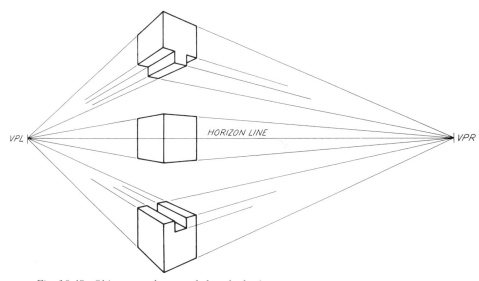

Fig. 10.49. Objects on, above, or below the horizon.

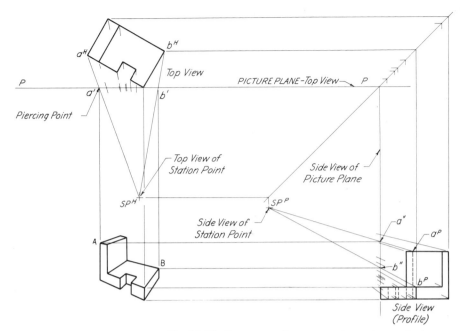

Fig. 10.50. Perspective drawing—orthographic method.

After the preliminary layout has been completed point A may be located in the perspective by the following procedure:

Step I. Draw the top view ($SP^H a^H$) and the side view ($SP^P a^P$) of the visual ray from the eye to point A.

Step II. From a' (the top view of the piercing point of the ray) draw a projection line downward.

Step III. From a'' (the side view of the piercing point) draw a horizontal projection line to intersect the one drawn from a'. Point A of the perspective is at this intersection.

Point B and the other points that are needed for the perspective representation are found in the same manner as point A.

10.33. Types of perspective. In general, there are two types of perspective: *parallel perspective* and *angular perspective*. In parallel perspective, one of the principal faces is parallel to the picture plane and is its own perspective. All vertical lines are vertical, and the receding horizontal lines converge to a single vanishing point. In angular perspective, the object is placed so that the principal faces are at an angle with the picture plane. The horizontal lines converge at two vanishing points.

10.34. Parallel perspective. Figure 10.51 shows the parallel perspective of a rectangular block. The *PP* line is the top view of the picture plane, SP_H is the top view of the station point, and *CV* is the center of vision. The receding horizontal lines vanish at *CV*. The front face, since it lies in the picture plane, is its own perspective and shows in its true size. The lines representing the edges back of the picture plane are found by projecting downward from the points at which the visual rays pierce the picture plane, as shown by the top views of the rays. Figure 10.52 shows a parallel perspective of a cylindrical machine part.

10.35. Angular perspective. Figure 10.53 shows pictorially the graphical method for the preparation of a two-point perspective drawing of a cube. To visualize the true layout on the surface of a sheet of drawing paper, it is necessary to revolve mentally the horizontal plane downward into the vertical or picture plane. Upon completion of Sec. 10.35, it is suggested that the reader turn back and endeavor to associate the development of the perspective in Fig. 10.54 with the pictorial presentation in Fig. 10.53. For a full understanding of the construction in Fig. 10.54, it is necessary to differentiate between the lines that belong to the horizontal plane and those that are on the vertical or picture plane. In addition, it must be fully realized that there is a top view for the perspective

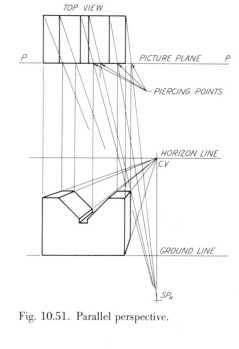

Fig. 10.51. Parallel perspective.

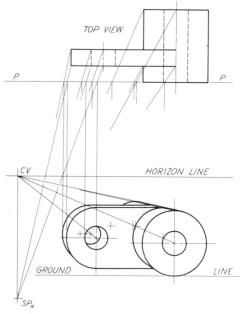

Fig. 10.52. Circles in parallel perspective.

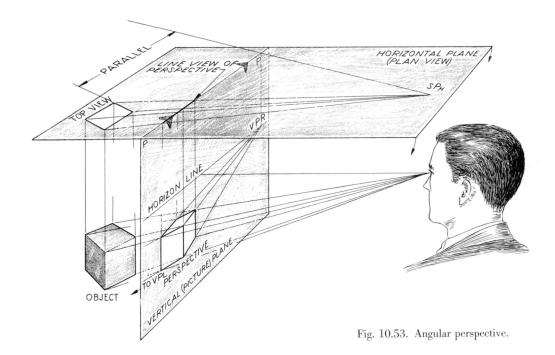

Fig. 10.53. Angular perspective.

that is a line, and that in this line view lie the points that must be projected downward to the perspective representation (front view).

Figure 10.54 shows an angular perspective of a block. The block has been placed so that one vertical edge lies in the picture plane. The other vertical edges are parallel to the plane, while all of the horizontal lines are inclined to it so that they vanish at the two vanishing points, *VPL* and *VPR*, respectively.

In constructing the perspective shown in this illustration, an orthographic top view was drawn in such a position that the visible vertical faces made angles of 30° and 60° with the picture plane. Next, the location of the observer was assumed and the horizon line was established. The vanishing points *VPL* and *VPR* were found by drawing a 30° line and a 60° line through the *SP*. Since these lines are parallel to the two systems of receding horizontal lines, each will establish a required vanishing point at its intersection with the picture plane. The vertical line located in the picture plane, which is its own perspective, was selected as a measuring line on which to project vertical measurements from the orthographic front view. The lines shown from these division points along this line to the vanishing points (*VPL–VPR*) established the direction of the receding horizontal edge lines in the perspective. The position of the back edges was determined by projecting downward from the points at which the projectors from the station point (*SP*) to the corners of the object pierced the picture plane, as shown by the top view of the object and projectors.

10.36. Use of measuring lines. Whenever the vertical front edge of an object lies in the picture plane, it can be laid off full length in the perspective, because, theoretically, it will be in true length in the picture formed on the plane by the visual rays (see Fig. 10.54). Should the near vertical edge lie behind the picture plane, as is the case with the edge line *AB* in Fig. 10.55, the use of a measuring line becomes desirable. The measuring line *a'b'* is the vertical edge *AB* moved forward to the picture plane where it will appear in its true height. Some prefer to think of the vertical side as being extended to the picture plane so that the true height of the side is revealed. The length and position of *AB* is established in the perspective picture by first drawing vanishing lines from *a'* and *b'* to *VPR*; then, the top view of the edge in the picture plane (point *X*) is projected downward to the front view picturization. Points *A* and *B* must fall on the vanishing lines from *a'* and *b'* to *VPR* respectively.

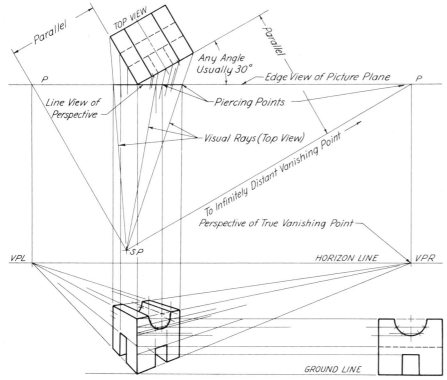

Fig. 10.54. Angular perspective.

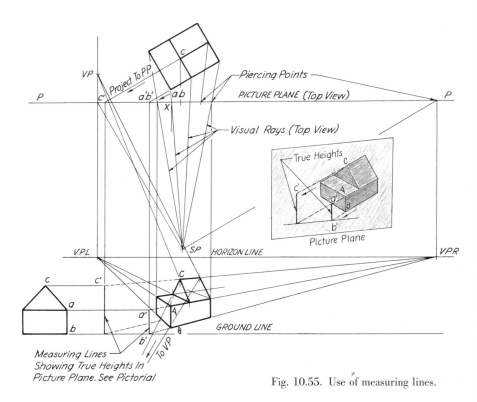

Fig. 10.55. Use of measuring lines.

A measuring line may be used to establish the "picture height" of any feature of an object. For example, in Fig. 10.55 the vertical measuring line through c' was used as needed to locate point C and the top line of the object in the perspective.

10.37. Vanishing points for inclined lines. In general, the perspective of any inclined straight line can be found by locating the end-points of the line perspectively. By this method, an end-point may be located by drawing the perspective representations of any two horizontal lines intersecting at the end-point. Where several parallel inclined lines vanish to the same vanishing point, it may prove to be worth while to locate the *VP* for the system in order to conserve time and achieve a higher degree of accuracy.

Just as in the case of other lines, the vanishing point for any inclined line may be established by finding the piercing point in the picture plane (*PP*) of a line through *SP* parallel to the given inclined line.

In Fig. 10.56 the inclined lines are *AB* and *CD*. If one is to understand the construction shown for locating vanishing point *VPI*, he must recognize that vertical planes vanish in vertical lines and that a line in a vertical plane will vanish at a point on the vanishing line of the plane. The preceding statements being true, the vanishing point *VPI* for line *CD* must lie at some point on a vertical line through *VPR*, since *CD* and *CE* lie in the same vertical plane. *VPI* is the point at which a line drawn parallel (in space) to *CD* through *SP* pierces the picture plane.

On the drawing, the distance *D* that *VPI* is above *VPR* may be found easily through the construction of a right triangle with *SPQ* as a base. Angle β is the slope angle for line *CD* (see side view). The needed distance *D* is the line *QR* or the short leg of the triangle.

10.38. Use of measuring points. Frequently, it is desirable to use measuring points in preparing a perspective drawing, because their use permits the laying off of a series of direct measurements that can be transferred quickly and accurately to the perspective. Measuring points are, in reality, special vanishing points that are used to establish distances in perspective along perspective lines.

To understand the measuring point method, one must realize that, in theory, a vertical face is rotated into the picture plane so that direct measurements may be made along the horizontal ground line to the same scale as the top view. In Fig. 10.57 the vertical

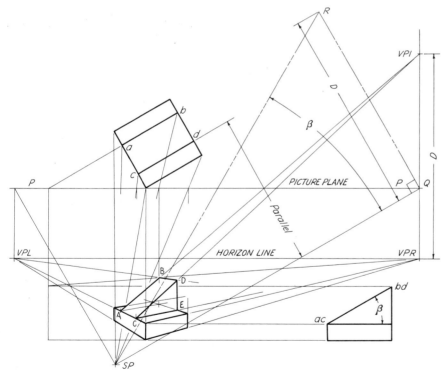

Fig. 10.56. Vanishing point for inclined lines.

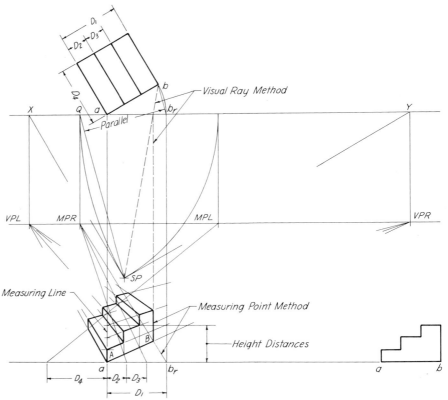

Fig. 10.57. Use of measuring points.

face containing line *AB* was revolved into the picture plane to position ab_r. The vanishing point of the line bb_r is *MPR*. The position of *MPR* was established by first drawing a line from *SP* parallel to bb_r to a piercing point in the picture plane and, then, projecting to the horizon line.

Another method for determining the location of measuring points is included in this same illustration. By this second method, the location of a measuring point can be readily found by swinging an arc with the plan view of the vanishing point as a center and using a radius equal to the distance from this center to the *SP*. For example, the location of *MPR* on the horizon was determined by swinging an arc from *Y* using the distance from *Y* to *SP* as a radius. The point of intersection of this arc and picture plane (in plan) projected to the horizon established the position of *MPR* for use in preparing the perspective drawing shown. *MPL* was similarly located.

The scaled lengths (D_1, D_2 and D_3) laid off along ab_r, when vanished to *MPR*, established the desired lengths along the line *AB*, which represents the perspective of the lower edge of the object.

Height distances were laid off along the measuring line through the vertical edge lying in the picture plane at *a*. With width, height, and depth distances established, the perspective drawing was completed by following the procedure given in Sec. 10.35.

10.39. Circles in perspective. If a circle is on a surface that is inclined to the picture plane (*PP*), its perspective will be an ellipse. It is the usual practice to construct the representation within an enclosing square by finding selected points along the curve in the perspective as shown in Fig. 10.58(*a*). Any points might be used, but it is recommended that points be located on 30° and 60° lines.

In (*a*), the perspective representation of the circle was found by using visual rays and parallel horizontal lines in combination. In starting the construction, the positions of several selected points, located on the circumference and lying on horizontal lines in the plane of the circle, were established in both views. After these lines had been drawn in the perspective in the usual manner, the location of the points along them were determined through the use of visual rays as shown. Specifically, the position of a point in the perspective was found by projecting downward from the piercing point of the ray from the point and the picture plane (see line view) to the perspective view of the line on which the point must lie. In (*b*), the same method was applied to construct the perspective view of a circle in a horizontal plane. It should be noted in this case that the horizontal lines, as established in the top view, were extended to

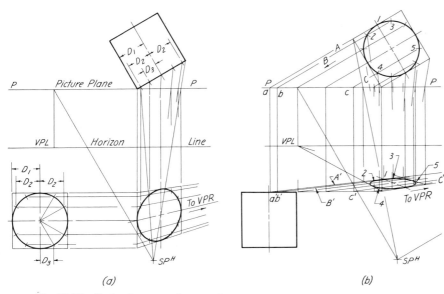

(a)   (b)

Fig. 10.58. Circles in perspective.

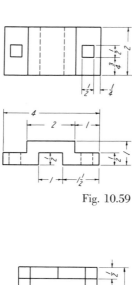

cut the picture plane so that the true height of these lines at the plane could be used in the perspective view for locating the endpoints of the perspective representations (at the left).

Fig. 10.59

PROBLEMS

The student will find that a preliminary sketch will facilitate the preparation of isometric and oblique drawings of the problems of this chapter. On such a sketch he may plan the procedure of construction. Since many engineers frequently find it necessary to prepare pictorial sketches during discussions with untrained persons who cannot read orthographic views, it is recommended that some problems be sketched freehand on either plain or pictorial grid paper (see Fig. 11.38). Additional problems may be found at the end of Chapter 11.

1-13. (Figs. 10.59–10.71.) Prepare instrumental isometric drawings or freehand sketches of the objects as assigned.

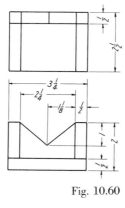

Fig. 10.60

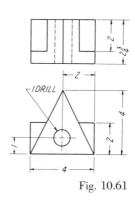

Fig. 10.61

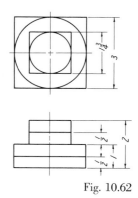

Fig. 10.62

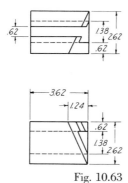

Fig. 10.63

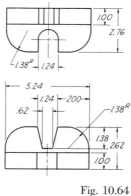

Fig. 10.64

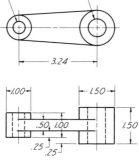

Fig. 10.65

14-20. (Figs. 10.65–10.71.) Prepare instrumental oblique drawings or freehand sketches of the objects as assigned.

21. (Fig. 10.72). Make an isometric drawing of the differential spider.

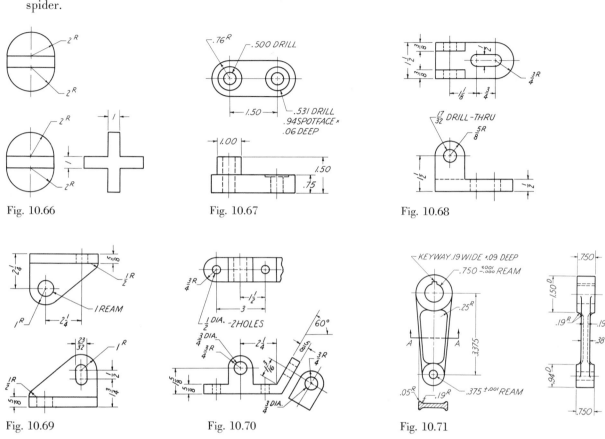

Fig. 10.66   Fig. 10.67   Fig. 10.68

Fig. 10.69   Fig. 10.70   Fig. 10.71

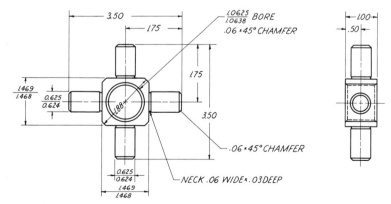

Fig. 10.72. Differential spider.

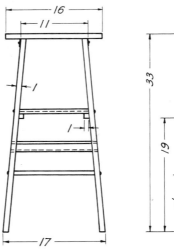

Fig. 10.73. Stepladder.

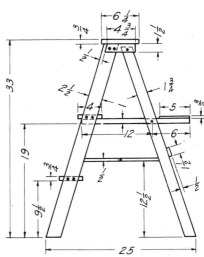

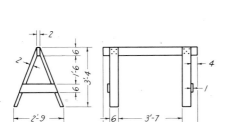

Fig. 10.74. Sawhorse.

22. (Fig. 10.73.) Make an isometric drawing of the stepladder. Select a suitable scale.

23. (Fig. 10.74.) Make an isometric drawing of the sawhorse. Select a suitable scale.

24. (Fig. 10.75.) Make an oblique drawing of the locomotive driver nut.

25. (Fig. 10.76.) Make an oblique drawing of the adjustment cone.

26. (Fig. 10.77.) Make an oblique drawing of the fork.

27. (Fig. 10.78.) Make an oblique drawing of the feeder guide.

28. (Fig. 10.79.) Make an isometric drawing of the hinge bracket.

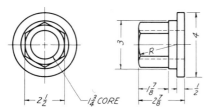

Fig. 10.75. Locomotive driver nut.

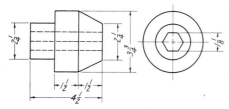

Fig. 10.76. Adjustment cone.

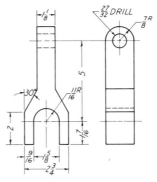

Fig. 10.77. Fork.

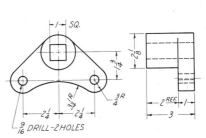

Fig. 10.78. Feeder guide.

29. (Fig. 10.80.) Make an isometric drawing of the alignment bracket.

30. (Fig. 10.81.) Make an isometric drawing of the stop block.

31. (Figs. 10.76–10.78.) Make a parallel perspective drawing as assigned.

32. (Figs. 10.79–10.81.) Make an angular perspective drawing as assigned.

33. (Fig. 10.82.) Make a pictorial drawing (oblique, isometric, or perspective) of the slotted bell crank.

34. (Fig. 10.83.) Make a pictorial drawing (oblique, isometric, or perspective) of the control guide.

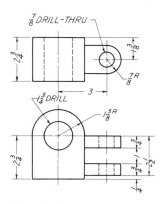

Fig. 10.79. Hinge bracket.

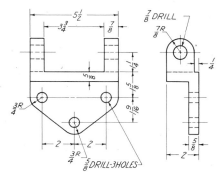

Fig. 10.80. Alignment bracket.

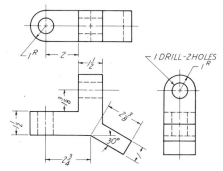

Fig. 10.81. Stop block.

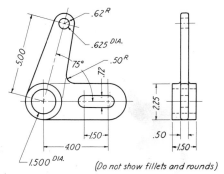

(Do not show fillets and rounds)

Fig. 10.82. Slotted bell crank.

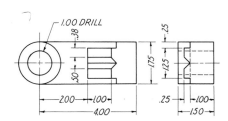

Fig. 10.83. Control guide.

PICTORIAL SKETCHING

11.1. Introduction. From the earliest times pictorial representations have been the means of conveying the ideas of one person to another person and of one group to another group (Fig. 11.1). There is little doubt that our ancestors traced out in the dust on the cave floor

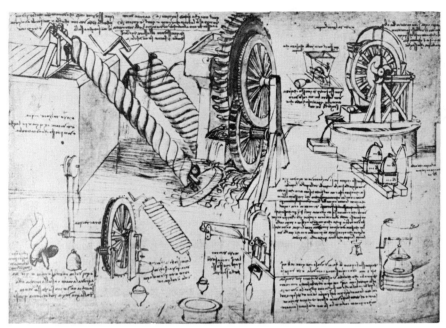

Fig. 11.1. Sketch showing Archimedean screw and wheel by Leonardo da Vinci (1452–1519), engineer, scientist, and painter (*From Collections of Fine Arts Department, International Business Machines Corporation*).

many crude pictures to supplement their gutteral utterances. On their cave walls these same primitive men and women drew pictures which today convey to others the stories of their lives. They used the only permanent means they were aware of at that time.

At present, we have at our command the spoken languages, which no doubt developed from limited semi-intelligent throat sounds, and the written languages, graphical and symbolic in form. The descriptive powers of the various forms of presentation may be compared in Fig. 11.2. The use of sign language representation, (*a*) is rather easy to learn and may be quickly executed but interpretation is restricted to persons who understand the particular language in which it is presented. The multiview representation, shown in (*b*), may be understood universally by persons who have been trained in its use. However, the given views will prove to be almost meaningless to the many who have not had the advantage of needed training. What then is the one form of representation that can be understood and may be used by all? It is the pictorial form shown in (*c*).

It is necessary that an engineer be capable of executing well-proportioned and understandable freehand pictorial sketches, for it is one of the most important modes of expression that he has available for use. Like other means for conveying ideas, when depended upon alone it will usually prove to be inadequate. However, when used in combination with the written or spoken language and related graphical representations, it makes a full understanding by others become sure and not just possible. Each method of expression is at hand to supplement another to convey the intended idea.

The engineer should be capable of speaking his own language and possibly one foreign language fluently; he should be able to write so as to present his ideas clearly and accurately; he should be familiar with the graphical method of presenting shape through the use of multiviews; and finally, he should be competent to execute well-proportioned and understandable pictorial sketches, which are needed to clarify and insure complete transfer of his ideas to others.

The engineer is a creative person living in a world where all that he creates must exist in space. He must visualize space conditions, space distances, and movement in space. In addition he must be able to retain as well as alter the image of his idea, which will at the very start exist only in his mind.

As his idea forms the engineer nearly always resorts to sketching to organize his thoughts quickly and more clearly visualize the problems that appear. The first ideas may be sketched in pictorial form as they are visualized. Later, in making a preliminary study, a combination of orthographic design sketches and pictorial sketches may quickly pile upon his desk as problems are recognized and pos-

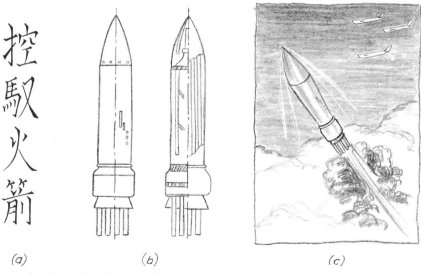

(a)   (b)   (c)

Fig. 11.2. Graphic methods for presenting ideas (symbolic, multiview, and pictorial).

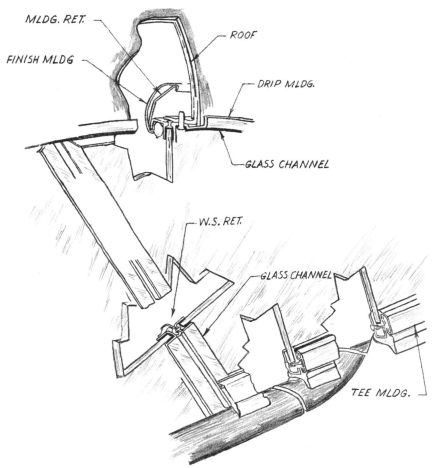

Fig. 11.3. A sketch showing a detail of construction (*Courtesy General Motors Corp.*).

sible solutions are recorded for reference and for conferences with others.

The engineer's use of sketches, both pictorial and orthographic, continues throughout the preliminary design stages and into the development and detailing stages (Fig. 11.3). This comes about because he is usually called upon to serve as both planner and director. Throughout all stages in the development of a structure, he must solve problems and clarify instructions. Very often a pictorial sketch of some detail of construction will prove to be more intelligible and will convey the idea much better than an orthographic sketch, even when dealing with an experienced draftsman or detailer.

Design sketches may be done in the quiet of the engineer's office or amid the confusion of the conference table. To meet the requirement of speed of preparation, one must resist all temptation to use instruments of any type and rely on the pencil alone, for the true measure of the quality of a finished sketch is neatness and good proportion rather than the straightness of the lines. A pictorial sketch need not be an artistic masterpiece to be useful.

Students may employ pictorial sketches to advantage as an aid in visualizing and organizing problems. Sales engineers may frequently include pictorial sketches with orthographic sketches when preparing field reports on the needs and suggestions of the firm's customers.

With some training anyone can prepare pictorial sketches that will be satisfactory for all practical purposes. Artistic ability is not needed. This fact is important, for many persons lack only the necessary confidence to start making pictorial sketches.

Training for making pictorial sketches must include the presentation of basic fundamentals, as is done with other how-to-do-it subjects. As learning the mechanics of English does not make one a creative writer, so training in sketching will not make one a creative engineer. However, sketching is the means of recording creative thoughts.

Some design sketches, drawn by an electrical engineer, are shown in Fig. 11.4. These sketches were prepared in making a study of the wiring to the electronic control panel for an automatic machine.

11.2. Thinking with a pencil. As an attempt is made to bring actuality to a plan, sketches undergo constant change as different ideas develop. An eraser may be in constant use or new starts may be made repeatedly, even though one should think much and sketch only when it would appear to be worthwhile. Sketching should be done as easily and freely as writing, so that the mind is always centered on the idea and not on the technique of sketching. To reach the point where one can "think with the pencil" is not easy. Continued practice is necessary until one can sketch with as little thought as to how it is done as he gives to how he uses a knife and fork at the dinner table.

Two idea sketches for the dashboard panel of an automobile are shown in Fig. 11.5. Persons who prepare sketches for the styling division of a company must have a feeling for beauty as well as an understanding of engineering design. The engineer of the future must be style conscious if his product is to enjoy a sales advantage over that of a competitor.

Figure 11.6 shows a form of sketch that might be made by an industrial engineer interested in improving assembly methods. A set of sketches of this type might be prepared to compare the present table arrangement with the planned arrangement, or for present-

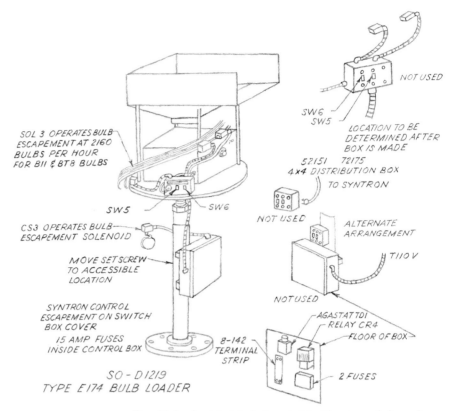

SOL 3 OPERATES BULB
ESCAPEMENT AT 2160
BULBS PER HOUR
FOR B11 & BT8 BULBS

NOT USED

SW6
SW5

LOCATION TO BE
DETERMINED AFTER
BOX IS MADE

52151 72175
4×4 DISTRIBUTION BOX

TO SYNTRON

NOT USED

ALTERNATE
ARRANGEMENT

T110V

SW5   SW6

CS3 OPERATES BULB
ESCAPEMENT SOLENOID

MOVE SET SCREW
TO ACCESSIBLE
LOCATION

SYNTRON CONTROL
ESCAPEMENT ON SWITCH
BOX COVER
15 AMP FUSES
INSIDE CONTROL BOX

NOT USED

AGASTAT TD1
RELAY CR4
FLOOR OF BOX

8-142
TERMINAL
STRIP

2 FUSES

SO - D1219
TYPE E174 BULB LOADER

Fig. 11.4. A pictorial design sketch (*Courtesy of General Electric Company*).

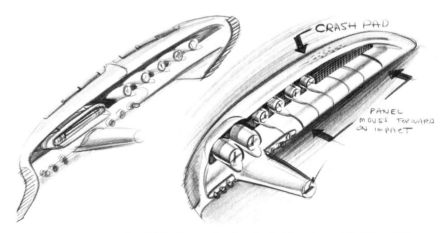

CRASH PAD

PANEL
MOVES FORWARD
ON IMPACT

Fig. 11.5. Design sketches for dashboard panel "Wildcat III" (*Courtesy General Motors Corp.*).

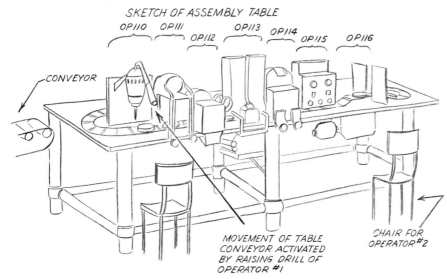

SKETCH OF ASSEMBLY TABLE

OP110 OP111 OP112 OP113 OP114 OP115 OP116

CONVEYOR

MOVEMENT OF TABLE
CONVEYOR ACTIVATED
BY RAISING DRILL OF
OPERATOR #1

CHAIR FOR
OPERATOR #2

Fig. 11.6. A planning sketch as made by an industrial engineer.

ing a new and well thought out plan to experienced employees and interested persons at the management level for their comments.

11.3. Mechanical methods of sketching. Many engineers have found that they can produce satisfactory pictorial sketches by using one of the so-called mechanical methods. They rely on these methods because of their familiarity with the procedures used in making pictorial drawings with instruments.

It has been assumed that the student has read Chapter 7 covering "Freehand Drafting," for the techniques discussed there apply to pictorial sketching.

The practices presented in Chapter 10 for the mechanical methods, axonometric, oblique, and perspective, are followed generally in pictorial sketching, except that angles are assumed and lengths are estimated. For this reason, one must develop an eye for good proportion before he will be able to create a satisfactory pictorial sketch that will be in no way misleading.

11.4. Isometric sketching. Isometric sketching starts with three isometric lines, called axes, which represent three mutually perpendicular lines. One of these axes is sketched vertically, the other two at 30° with the horizontal. In Fig. 11.7 (step I), the near front corner of the enclosing box lies along the vertical axis, while the two visible receding edges of the base lie along the axes receding to the left and to the right.

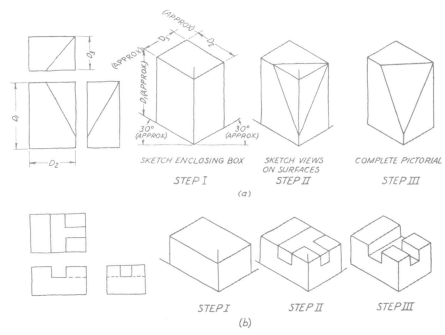

Fig. 11.7. Steps in isometric sketching.

If the object is of simple rectangular form as in Fig. 11.7, it may be sketched by drawing an enclosing isometric box (step I) upon the surfaces of which the orthographic views may be sketched (step II). Care must be taken in assuming lengths and distances so that the finished view (step III) will have relatively correct proportions. In constructing the enclosing box (step I), the vertical edges are parallel to the vertical axis, and edges receding to the right and to the left are parallel to the right and left axes, respectively.

Objects of more complicated construction may be "blocked in" as shown in Fig. 11.8. Note that the projecting cylindrical features are enclosed in "isometric" prisms, and that the circles are sketched within isometric squares. The procedure in Fig. 11.8 is the same as in Fig. 11.7, except that three enclosing isometric boxes are needed in the formation of the final representation instead of one.

In sketching an ellipse to represent a circle pictorially, an enclosing "isometric square" (rhombus) is drawn having sides equal approximately to the diameter of the true circle (step I, Fig. 11.9). The ellipse is formed by first drawing arcs tangent to the mid-points of the sides of the isometric square in light, sketchy pencil lines (step II). In finishing the ellipse (step III) with a dark, heavy line, care must be taken to obtain a nearly elliptical shape.

Figure 11.10 shows the three positions for an isometric circle.

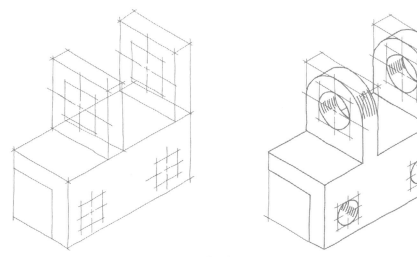

Fig. 11.8. Blocking in an isometric sketch.

Note that the major axis is horizontal for an ellipse on a horizontal plane (I).

11.5. Proportioning. As stated in Chapter 7, one should eventually be able to judge lengths and recognize proportions. Until this ultimate goal has been reached, the graphical method presented in Fig. 7.14 may be used with pictorial sketching (Fig. 11.11). The procedures as used are identical, the only recognizable difference being that the rectangle in the first case now becomes a rhomboid. Figure 11.12 illustrates how the method might be applied in making a sketch of a simple object. The enclosing box was sketched first with light lines, and then the graphical method was applied as shown to locate the points at one-quarter and one-half of the height. To establish the line of the top surface that is at a distance equal to one-third of the length from the end, a construction line was sketched from A to the mid-point B to locate C at the point of intersection of AB with the diagonal. Point C will fall on the required line.

SKETCH "ISOMETRIC SQUARE"
STEP I

SKETCH SHORT ARCS
STEP II

COMPLETE ELLIPSE
STEP III

Fig. 11.9. Isometric circles.

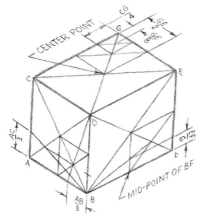

Fig. 11.11. Method for proportioning a rhomboid.

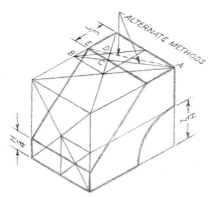

Fig. 11.12. Proportioning method applied.

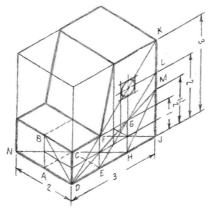

Fig. 11.13. The build-up method.

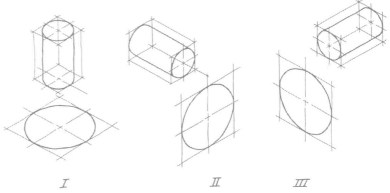

Fig. 11.10. Isometric circles.

One might also use the build-up method (Fig. 7.16) to lay off the estimated proportions of an object. This method is particularly easy to apply when using an approximation of isometric. Suppose that the proportions are to be as shown in Fig. 11.13, and that the axes have been sketched through point D, one being vertical while the other two are at 30° upward to the right and to the left.

A start is made by drawing the two rhombuses $ABCD$ and $CDEF$. The interesting facts that can be observed are:

1. A horizontal line through point C intersects the inclined axes at points H and N, the lower corner points of adjacent rhombuses.
2. A horizontal line through point F intersects the right-hand axis at point J, the far corner of the third rhombus.
3. Line DF extended locates point K. Line KJ is equal in length to the sum of the lengths of the sides of three of the isometric squares (rhombuses).
4. Line EG extended locates point L at two units above DJ.
5. Line DG extended locates the mid-point M of line KJ.

After this means of proportioning has been used a few times, a student will discover the possibilities that are offered by this method of building up an object, and he will become aware that there are varied ways of locating the needed points.

The object shown in Fig. 11.13 can also be thought of as being built-up of cubes. The hidden lines at the lower corner complete the outline of the initial cube. More will be written about the use of cubes when sketching in perspective is presented in the latter portion of this chapter.

11.6. Dimetric sketching. A sketch may be made on dimetric axes to lessen distortion and obtain a more effective representation. In preparing dimetric sketches, one of the axes is usually made vertical and the other two in a choice of several possible arrangements. The two most widely used arrangements of positions are those shown in Figs. 11.14 and 11.15. Either of these arrangements will give a well-proportioned view. When the two receding axes are sketched so that they are at approximately 15° with the horizontal, all dimensions taken in the direction of either receding axis are assumed to be approximately three-fourths those in the direction of the vertical axis. In other words, in dimetric sketching an attempt is made to approximate a similar dimetric drawing made with instruments, where a full scale would be used for all dimensions parallel to the vertical axis and a three-fourths size scale for dimensions in the direction of either of the receding axes. If the angles for the receding axes are approximately 7° and 45°, the dimensions along the vertical axis and the 7° axis are considered to be at full size, and those dimensions that are parallel to the axis at 45° are made to appear to be one-half of their assumed lengths.

11.7. Sketches in isometric. In making a sketch in isometric, an experienced person frequently foreshortens the distances in the direction of either of the receding axes until the proportions satisfy the eye. In addition, some who are a little more confident will make the receding lines converge slightly. A pictorial sketch treated in this manner is said to be in pseudoperspective.

A sketch giving the parts of a simple mechanism arranged for assembly is shown in Fig. 11.17.

11.8. Sketches in oblique. A sketch in oblique shows the front face without distortion, in its true shape. It has this one advantage over axonometric projection, even though the final result usually will not present so pleasing an appearance. It is not recommended for objects having circular or irregularly curved features on any but the front plane or in a plane parallel to it.

The beginner who is familiar with axonometric sketching will have very little difficulty in preparing a sketch in oblique, for in general the methods of preparation presented in the previous sections apply to both. The principal difference between these two forms of sketching is in the position of the axes, oblique sketching being unlike the axonometric in that two of the axes are at right angles to each other. The third axis may be at any convenient angle as indicated in Fig. 11.19.

Figure 11.18 shows the steps in making an oblique sketch using the proportioning methods previously explained for dividing a rec-

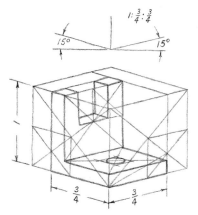

Fig. 11.14. Pictorial sketch (dimetric)—receding axes at approximately 15°.

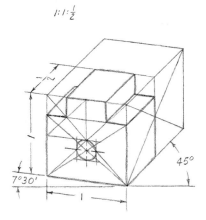

Fig. 11.15. Pictorial sketch (dimetric)—receding axes at approximately 7° and 45°.

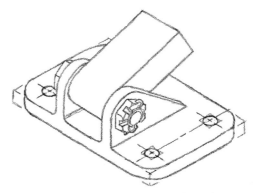

Fig. 11.16. An idea sketch in isometric.

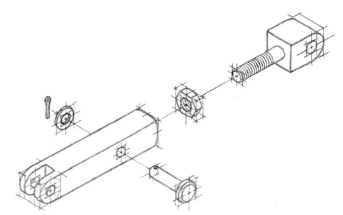

Fig. 11.17. A sketch of a simple mechanism.

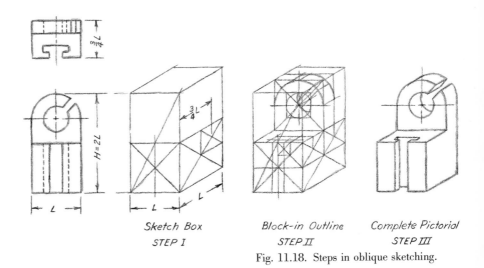

Sketch Box
STEP I

Block-in Outline
STEP II

Complete Pictorial
STEP III

Fig. 11.18. Steps in oblique sketching.

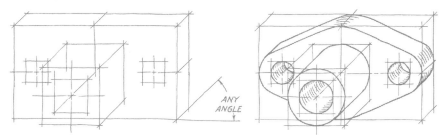

Fig. 11.19. Blocking in an oblique sketch.

tangle and a rhomboid. The receding lines are made parallel when a sketch is made in oblique projection.

The distortion and illusion of extreme elongation in the direction of the receding axis may be minimized by foreshortening to obtain proportions that are more realistic to the eye and by making the receding lines converge slightly. The resulting sketch will then be in a form of pseudoperspective, which resembles parallel perspective to some extent.

11.9. Perspective sketching. A sketch that has been prepared in accordance with the concepts of perspective will present a somewhat more pleasing and realistic effect than one in oblique or axonometric projection. A perspective sketch actually presents an object as it would appear when observed from a particular point. The recognition of this fact, along with an understanding of the concepts that an object will appear smaller at a distance than when it is close, and that horizontal lines converge as they recede until they meet at a vanishing point, should enable one to produce sketches having a perspective appearance.

Figure 11.20 shows a parallel or one-point perspective which bears some resemblance to an oblique sketch. All faces in planes parallel to the front show their true shape. Figure 11.21 is an angular perspective.

11.10. Principles of perspective sketching. Many engineers hesitate to make perspective sketches, thinking that either too much construction will be needed or that they must have some artistic ability. Both of these ideas are false, for almost anyone who can understand the theory of perspective and can abide by a few simple rules can make a satisfactory representation in perspective. Since sketches that are prepared in perspective surpass those made by any of the other methods, the time consumed in learning to use perspective is well spent.

A two-point perspective sketch shows an object as it would appear to the human eye at a fixed point in space and not as it actu-

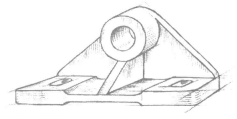

Fig. 11.20. A sketch in parallel perspective.

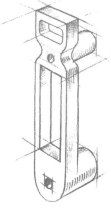

Fig. 11.21. A sketch in angular perspective.

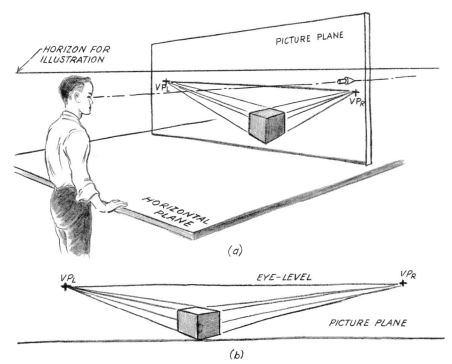

Fig. 11.22. Theory of angular perspective.

ally exists. In perspective, all parallel receding lines converge. Should these receding lines be horizontal, they will converge at a vanishing point on the eye-line. Those lines extending towards the right converge to a vanishing point to the right (VP_R); and those to the left converge to the left (VP_L). These vanishing points are at

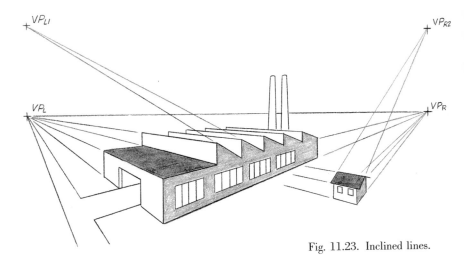

Fig. 11.23. Inclined lines.

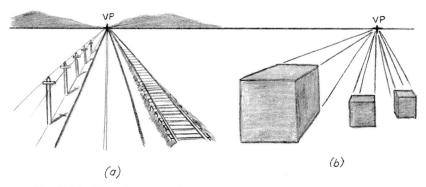

Fig. 11.24. One point perspective.

the level of the observer's eye (Fig. 11.22). A system of lines that is neither perpendicular nor horizontal will converge to a *VP* for inclined lines (Fig. 11.23).

In one-point perspective one of the principal faces is parallel to the picture plane. All of the vertical lines will appear as vertical, and the receding horizontal lines converge to a single vanishing point (Fig. 11.24).

Those interested in a complete discussion of the geometry of perspective drawing should read Secs. 10.26 through 10.39. The beginner should make two or three mechanically drawn perspectives at the start to fix the fundamentals of the methods of perspective projection in his mind, even though there is some difference between sketching what one sees or imagines and true geometrical perspective.

In making a sketch in artist's perspective, several fundamental concepts must be recognized.

First, a circle sketched in perspective will appear as an ellipse (Fig. 11.25). The long diameter of an ellipse representing a circle on a horizontal plane is always in a horizontal direction.

Second, if an object or a component part of an object is above the eye-line, it will be seen from below. Should the object be below the eye-line, it will be seen from above (Fig. 11.25). The farther the object is removed above or below the eye-line, the more one can see of the top or the bottom surface. In particular, it can be noted in Fig. 11.25(b) that an ellipse broadens as it is moved away from the eye-line.

Third, the nearest vertical edge of an object will be the longest vertical line of the view as shown in Fig. 11.25(a). When two or more objects of the same actual height appear in a perspective sketch, their represented heights will decrease in the view as they near the vanishing point (Fig. 11.26).

Finally, the station point *SP* should be considered as being far enough away from the object so that the vanishing points will not

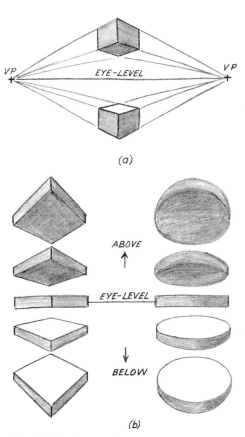

Fig. 11.25. Objects above and below the eye-line.

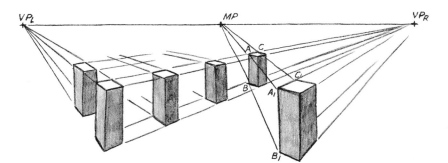

Fig. 11.26. Objects near and far.

be too close together. Should they be too close, the picture will be distorted (Fig. 11.27).

It is interesting to note that an object may be moved forward in the perspective picture by using the method shown in Fig. 11.26. Lines drawn from a point MP on the horizon line through the corner-points A and B of the block to the rear establish the height of corner-points A_1 and B_1 of the object in its forward position. Edge-line A_1B_1 will be in correct length for the perspective.

11.11. Determining proportions. When an object exists only as an image in one's mind, all proportions can be assumed. However, when sketching by eye an object that already exists, it becomes necessary to be able to compare the relationship between the depth, width and height dimensions as they are seen. That is, some sort of a measuring stick is needed to compare these lengths in the proportions that they are being seen at the fixed position of the observer, who is at some distance from the object itself. To satisfy this need most sketchers use the most convenient thing that is available— their sketching pencil. Apparent lengths can be determined along the body of the pencil held at arm's length in a plane perpendicular to the line of sight, as shown in Fig. 11.28. One marks with the

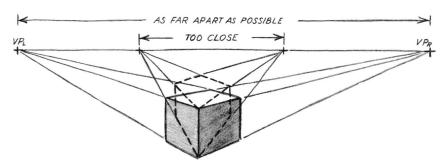

Fig. 11.27. Location of the vanishing points.

Fig. 11.28. Obtaining proportions by means of the pencil.

tip of the thumbnail the length on the object that is covered from the top of the pencil downward. With this basic distance established, the arm is rotated until the pencil coincides with another edge of the object and then an estimate is made as to whether the second line is to be made one-fifth, one-fourth, one-half, or three-fourths as long as the first. To make an estimate of a proportion in terms closer than in fifths is impractical and unnecessary.

The pencil may also be used to determine the direction of a line that will be inclined on a sketch. To do this the sketch board should be held in a position directly in front of the observer and perpendicular to the line of sight. Then the pencil is rotated at arm's length until it coincides with the line of the object. This apparent direction is brought in from space to the paper by moving the pencil parallel to its original position back to the sketch board.

Frequently, it will be possible to transfer an observed length for a starting-line directly from the pencil to the sketch. However, since it is usually undesirable to do this because the resulting sketch will be too large for the paper, the length of one line to start the sketch must be assumed. This first line determines the size of the sketch and all of the other lines must be proportionally related to it.

This method of using the pencil as a measuring stick for determining relative proportions can be used when making sketches that are either in orthographic projection or in some form of pictorial.

Objects that are of the same height and equally spaced may be located in perspective by using the method illustrated in Fig. 11.29. To apply this method, three lines must first be drawn to the vanishing point (*VP*). These lines, sketched from the first and near pole,

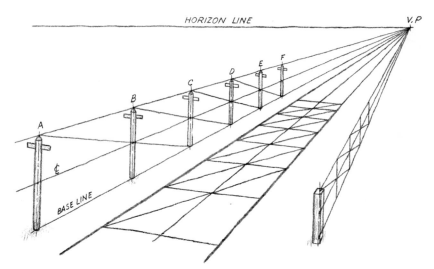

Fig. 11.29. Spacing by the diagonal line method.

should finally join the top-points, the base-points, and the mid-points of all poles. If a line should be sketched from the top of pole *A* straight through the mid-point of pole *B*, the intersection of this line with the base line will locate pole *C*. Likewise, a line sketched from the top of *B* through the mid-point of *C* will locate the base-point for pole *D*. Pole *E* and other additional poles may be located similarly.

The method just presented, known as the diagonal line method, is an adaptation of the rectangle method discussed in Sec. 7.13. For those who need some graphical assistance in determining receding distances, at least until they develop an artistic sense for relating proportions in perspective, the method illustrated in Fig. 7.14 may

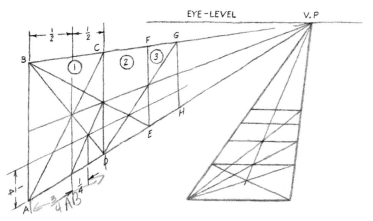

Fig. 11.30. Proportioning the perspective square.

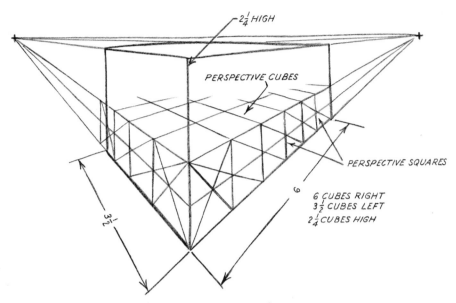

Fig. 11.31. Proportioning with the perspective cube.

be extended and modified for use as shown in Figs. 11.30 and 11.31. The method illustrated in Fig. 11.31, which is known as the "perspective cube" method, combines the use of perspective cubes and the division of their faces as perspective squares.

11.12. To make a perspective sketch. The application of the perspective cube to the construction and division of an enclosing box is shown in Fig. 11.32. The construction of a required perspective by steps is as follows:

Step I. Sketch the eye-line. This line should be well towards the top of the sheet of sketch paper.

Step II. Locate VP_L and VP_R on the eye-line. These vanishing points should be placed as far apart as possible (see Fig. 11.27).

Step III. Assume the position and length for the near front edge AB. The length of this line, along with the spacing of the vanishing points, establishes the size of the finished sketch. The position of AB determines how the visible surfaces are to appear. For instance, if the line AB had been moved downward from the position shown in (*a*), much more of the top surface would be seen in (*b*) and (*c*). Should AB have been moved to the right from its position shown in (*a*), the left side would have become more prominent. If AB were placed midway between the two vanishing points, then both the front and left side surfaces would be at 45° with the picture plane for the perspective. As

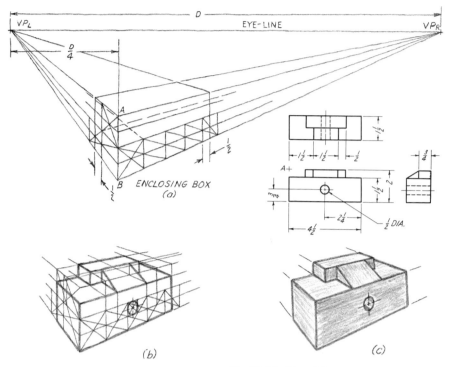

Fig. 11.32. Use of the perspective cube.

it has been placed in (a), the side face is at 60° to the picture plane while the front face is at 30°. Before establishing the position for the near front edge, one must decide which surfaces are the most important surfaces and how they may best be displayed in the sketch.

Step IV. Sketch light construction lines from points A and B to each vanishing point.

Step V. Determine the proportions for the enclosing box, in this case 4½, 2, and 1½, and mark off one inch units along AB.

Step VI. Sketch perspective squares, representing the faces of one inch cubes, starting at AB and working toward each vanishing point. In cases where an over-all length must be completed with a partial unit, a full perspective square must be sketched at the end.

Step VII. Subdivide any of the end squares if necessary and sketch-in the enclosing box (a).

Step VIII. Locate and block-in the details, subdividing the perspective squares as is required to establish the location of any detail. When circles are to be sketched in perspective by a beginner, it is advisable to sketch the enclosing box first using light lines (*b*).

Step IX. Darken the object lines of the sketch. Construction lines may be removed and some shading added to the surfaces as shown in (*c*), if desired (read Sec. 11.13).

A sketch in one-point perspective might be made as shown in Fig. 11.33. For this particular sketch the enclosing box was made to the assumed over-all proportions for the part. Then the location of the details was established by subdividing the regular rectangle of the front face of the enclosing box and the perspective rectangle of the right side.

11.13. Pencil shading. The addition of some shading to the surfaces of a part will force its form to stand out against the white surface of the sketching paper and will increase the effect of depth in a view that might otherwise appear to be somewhat flat.

Seldom are engineers able to do creditable work in artistic shading with cast shadows included as they could many years ago when training in art was part of an engineer's education. It is unfortunate that they lack this training at the present time, for art and design go hand in hand. This is especially true today, for a pleasing and appealing styling sells more products than good mechanical design (Fig. 11.5).

Within the scope of this chapter, written for beginning students, it will only be possible to present a few simple rules as a guide for those making a first attempt at surface shading. However, continued

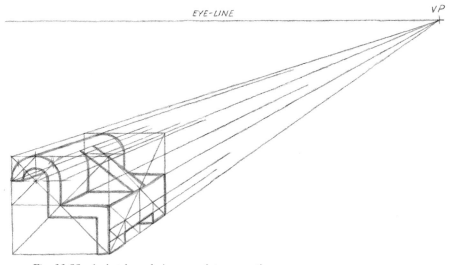

Fig. 11.33. A sketch made in one-point perspective.

practice and some thought should lead one to the point where he can do a creditable job of shading and definitely improve a pictorial sketch.

When shading an imaginary part, an engineer may consider the source of the light to be located in a position to the left, above, and in front of the object. Of course, if the part actually exists and is being sketched by viewing it, then the sketcher should attempt to duplicate the degrees of shade and shadows as they are observed.

With the light source considered to be to the left, above, and in front of the object, a square part would be shaded as shown in Fig. 11.34(a). The use of gradation of tone on the surfaces gives additional emphasis to the depth. To secure this added effect by shading, the darkest tone on the surface that is away from the light must be closest to the eye. As the surface recedes the tone must be made lighter in value with a faint trace of reflected light showing along the entire length of the back edge. On the lighted side, the lightest area must be closest to the eye as indicated by the letter L_1 in (a). To make this lighted face appear to go into the distance, it is made darker as it recedes, but it should never be made as dark as the lightest of the dark tones on the dark surface.

Shading a cylindrical part is not as easy to do as shading a rectangular part but, if it is realized that practically half of the cylinder is in the light and half in the dark and that the lightest light and the darkest dark fall along the elements at the quarter points of each half, then one should not find the task too difficult (b). The two extremes are separated by lighter values of shade. The first quarter on the lighted side must be made lighter than the last quarter on the dark side. In starting at the left and going counterclockwise there is a dark shade of light blending into the full light at the first quarter point. From this point and passing the center to the dark line, the tone should become gradually darker. If vertical lines are used for shading, they should be spaced closer and closer together

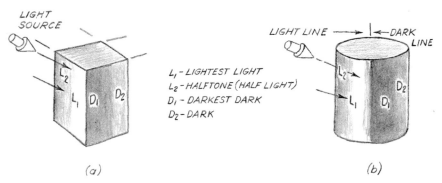

L₁ - LIGHTEST LIGHT
L₂ - HALFTONE (HALF LIGHT)
D₁ - DARKEST DARK
D₂ - DARK

(a)   (b)

Fig. 11.34. Shading rectangular and cylindrical parts.

as they approach the dark line. The extreme right-hand quarter should show the tones of reflected light.

There are two ways that pencil shading may be applied. If the paper has a medium rough surface, solid tone shading may be used with one shade blending into the other. For the best results, the light tones are put on first over all areas to be shaded. The darker tones are then added by building up lighter tones to the desired intensity for a particular area. For this form of shading, a pencil with flattened point is used.

The other form of shading, and the one that is best suited for quick sketches, is produced with lines of varied spacing and weight. Light lines with wide spacing are used on the light areas and heavy lines that are closely spaced give the tone for the darkest areas. No lines are needed for the lightest of the light areas.

11.14. Conventional treatment of fillets, rounds, and screw threads. Sketches that are not given full pencil shading may be given a more or less realistic appearance by representing the fillets and rounds of the unfinished surfaces as shown in Fig. 10.43 in the preceding chapter. The conventional treatment for screw threads is shown in (b) of the same illustration.

11.15. Idea sketches. A pictorial sketch may be used to advantage in studying an idea for a complete unit, as was done for the quick-acting clamp shown in Fig. 11.35. Another example is given in Fig. 11.36, where a suggested arrangement for a remote control system is shown. Only a minimum number of lines were used to suggest the outline of the boat, for using unnecessary lines on a sketch is undesirable since they make the sketch more difficult to understand.

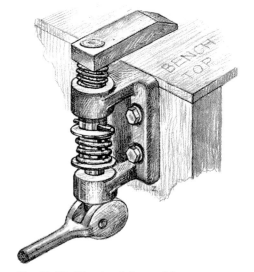

Fig. 11.35. Idea sketch for a quick acting machine clamp.

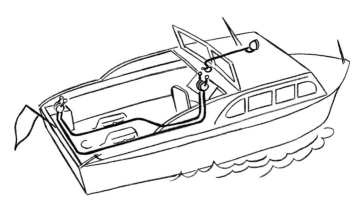

Fig. 11.36. Idea sketch showing remote control system for a motor boat (*Courtesy Teleflex, Inc.*).

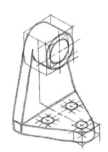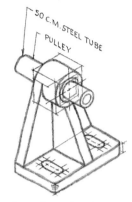

Fig. 11.37. Successive idea sketches made to determine the form for a control rod bracket.

In Fig. 11.37 the results of some progressive thinking on a particular problem are shown. The changes that an original design may undergo result from the minor problems that usually develop and from new ideas which seem to improve it. Frequently these new ideas come as casual thoughts of one's colleagues, or they may arise in a formal way around a conference table when those who represent the design and production departments of a firm meet with the representatives of management and prospective customers. Each new idea that is presented must be thoroughly explored before being discarded as unnecessary or undesirable.

At such conferences, the representation of an idea in some pictorial form assures one that there will be a complete understanding of an idea by all of those who are present, be they engineers or business men.

After a rather complete pictorial representation has once been prepared to show a suggested change for an existing mechanism or for showing an entirely new idea for a nonexistent structure, subsequent alterations may be represented on transparent overlay sheets (see Sec. 7.14). The sketch on the overlay is made by tracing as much of the original sketch as is needed. Sometimes it will be desirable to make the sketch on the overlay nearly complete; while at other times all that will be needed is a complete sketch of a particular detail along with a few additional lines that will suggest the outline of the main structure or mechanism.

Idea sketches of single parts are made frequently when deciding upon the form that the part must take if it is to fulfill its function. In making such sketches, it is a rare occasion when the first sketch made by the engineer or draftsman proves to be satisfactory (Fig. 11.37). Usually several ideas must be considered and discarded before one is found that will satisfy all concerned with the design or alteration that is being developed.

11.16. Creative sketching—beginning student. The spark that sets one off on an engineering project is not the touch of genius, but rather an open-minded recognition of the urgent need and the economic possibilities afforded. Very little is known as to why some possess the inherent drive that is behind all forms of creativity while others do not, but the opportunity to exercise some creativeness and thoughtful judgment will aid one and strengthen one's confidence. For this reason a few of the problems offered are presented so as to require the beginning student to create single parts that will satisfy some particular requirements. In preparing the sketches for these problems, emphasis must necessarily be placed on the form of the part and on the technique of sketching. Finished sketches can be evaluated only on quality, originality, and how well the part as represented will fulfill the need. Structural strength and correctness of design, although important, must be overlooked.

One often becomes discouraged with his efforts towards creating even simple parts, when he becomes aware of the amount of time that he is taking in making repeated attempts to satisfy conditions and requirements. The student, however, should remember that creative work must necessarily be time consuming, for step by step guidance is not at hand. Furthermore, the value of creative work can never be measured in terms of time or money. For instance, would it be reasonable to evaluate a creation of our great Thomas A. Edison in terms of the number of hours that he worked on that particular project?

When the mind seems to be stalled on dead-center, it will often be helpful to start a sketch of just anything that might meet the requirements, for as one's mind and pencil work together, new ideas may make an appearance.

11.17. Materials—technique. For pictorial sketching, the materials needed are an HB or F pencil, a soft eraser, and some paper. Although one should become proficient in sketching on plain white bond paper, a specially ruled paper, shown in Fig. 11.38, can be used by those who need the help of guide lines.

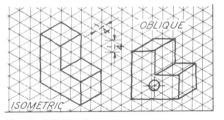

Fig. 11.38. Sketches on isometric paper.

11.18. Illustration sketches showing mechanisms exploded. A sketch of a mechanism showing the parts in exploded positions along the principal axes is shown in Fig. 11.39. Through the use of such sketches those who have not been trained to read multiview drawings may readily understand how a mechanism should be assembled, for both the shapes of the parts and their order of assembly, as denoted by their space relationship, is shown in pictorial form.

Illustration sketches may be made for discussions dealing with ideas for a design, but more frequently they are prepared for explanatory purposes to clarify instructions for preparing illustration draw-

Horizon Line

TO VP_L ←

TO VP_R →

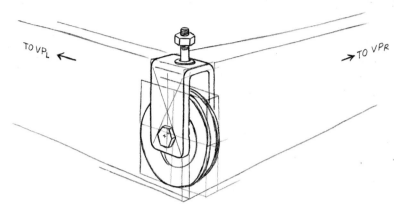

TO VP_L ←

→ TO VP_R

Block-in assembly in outline

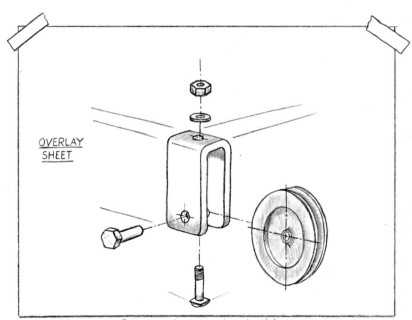

OVERLAY
SHEET

Retrace parts on overlay sheet in
exploded positions from assembly sketch

Fig. 11.39. A sketch showing the parts of a mechanism in
exploded positions.

ings in a more finished form as assembly illustrations, advertising illustrations, catalogue illustrations, and illustrations for service and repair charts.

Many persons find that it is desirable, when preparing sketches of exploded mechanisms, to first block in the complete mechanism with all of the parts in position. At this initial stage of construction, the parts are sketched in perspective in rough outline and the principal axes and object lines are extended part way towards their vanishing points.

When the rough layout has been completed to the satisfaction of the person preparing the sketch, an overlay sheet is placed over the original sketch and the parts are traced directly from the sketch beneath in exploded positions along the principal axes and along the axes of holes. Frequently some beginners make a traced sketch of each individual part and place the sketches in exploded positions before preparing the finished sketch. Others with more experience accomplish the same results by first tracing the major part along with the principal axes and then moving the overlay sheet as required to trace off the remaining parts in their correct positions along the axes.

It should be recognized that in preparing sketches of exploded mechanisms in this manner the parts are not shown perspectively reduced although they are removed from their original place in the pictorial assembly outward and towards the vanishing points. To prepare a sketch of this type with all of the parts shown in true geometrical perspective would result in a general picture which would be misleading and one that would be apt to confuse the nontechnical person because some parts would appear much too large or too small to be mating parts.

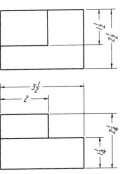

Fig. 11.40

PROBLEMS

The problems presented in this chapter were selected to give practice in preparing pictorial sketches—axonometric, oblique, or perspective. In addition to developing proficiency in sketching, these problems offer the student further opportunity to gain experience in reading drawings. Additional problems that are suitable for pictorial sketching may be found in Chapter 10.

1-6. (Figs. 11.40–11.45.) Make freehand isometric sketches of the objects as assigned.

7-12. (Figs. 11.40–11.45.) Make freehand dimetric sketches of the objects as assigned.

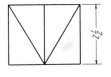

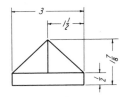

Fig. 11.41

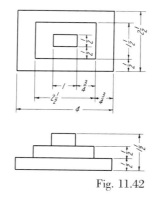

Fig. 11.42

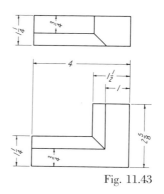

Fig. 11.43

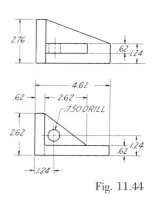

Fig. 11.44

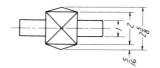

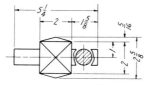

Fig. 11.45

13-18. (Figs. 11.40–11.45.) Make freehand perspective sketches of the objects as assigned.

19-21. (Figs. 11.46–11.48.) Make freehand oblique sketches of the objects as assigned.

22-26. (Figs. 11.49–11.53.) Make freehand isometric sketches of the objects as assigned.

27. (Fig. 7.71.) Make a pictorial sketch of a part from the pipe stand as assigned.

28. (Fig. 18.36.) Make a pictorial sketch of the base of the tool holder.

29. (Fig. 7.72.) Make a pictorial sketch of a part from the flexible joint as assigned.

30. (Fig. 11.54.) Make a pictorial sketch of the base of the self-aligning shaft support.

31. (Fig. 11.54.) Make a pictorial sketch of the yoke of the self-aligning shaft support.

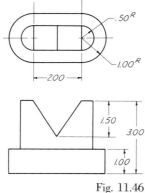

Fig. 11.46

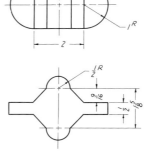

Fig. 11.47

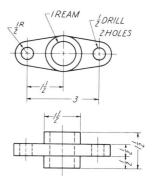

Fig. 11.48

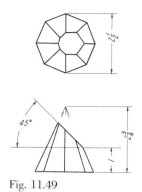

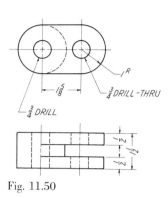

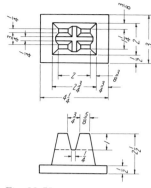

Fig. 11.49

Fig. 11.50

Fig. 11.51

The following problems are offered as suggestions to stimulate creativity and give some additional experience in both pictorial and multiview sketching. Students who have an inclination to design useful mechanisms should be encouraged to select a problem for themselves, for the creative mind works best when directed to a task in which it already has some interest. However, the young beginner should confine his activities to ideas for simple mechanisms that do not require extensive training in machine design and the engineering sciences.

32. Prepare design sketches (both pictorial and multiview) for an open-end wrench to fit the head of a bolt (regular series) having a body diameter of 1 in. Give dimensions on the multiview sketch and specify the material.

33. Prepare design sketches (both pictorial and multiview) for a wrench having a head with four or more fixed openings to fit the heads of bolts having nominal diameters of ⅝ in., ¾ in., ⅞ in., and 1 in. Dimension the multiview sketch and specify the material.

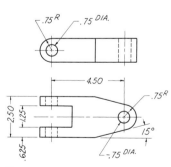

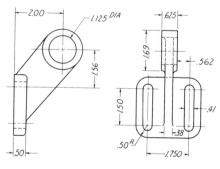

(Do not show fillets and rounds)

Fig. 11.52

Fig. 11.53

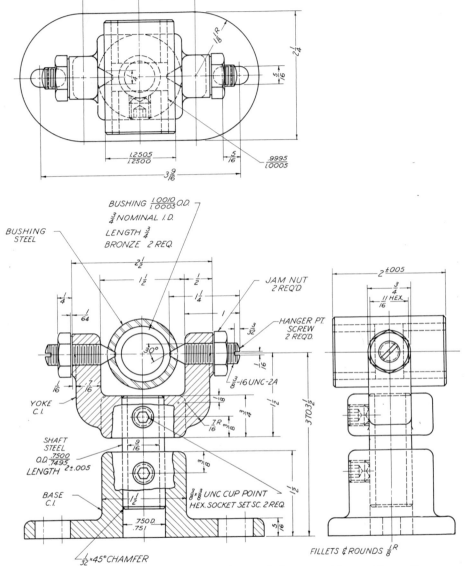

Fig. 11.54. Self-aligning shaft support (*Courtesy Boston Gear Works, Inc.*).

34. Prepare a series of design sketches for a bumper hitch (curved bumper) for attaching a light two-wheel trailer to a passenger automobile. Weight of trailer is 295 lb.

35. Prepare sketches for a hitch for a glider. The design should allow for release of the cable at the glider after the glider has become air-borne by being pulled by a jeep on the ground.

36. Prepare sketches for a hangar bracket to support a ½ in. control rod. The bracket must be attached to a vertical surface to which the control rod is parallel. The distance between the vertical surface and the center line of the control rod is 4 in.

37. Prepare sketches for a mechanism to be attached to a two-wheel hand truck to make it easy to move the truck up and down stairs with a heavy load.

38. Prepare sketches for a quick-acting clamp that can be used to hold steel plates in position for making a lap weld.

39. Prepare a pictorial sketch of a bracket that will support an instrument panel at an angle of 45° with a vertical bulkhead to which the bracket will be attached. The bracket should be designed to permit the panel to be raised or lowered a height distance of 4 in. as desired.

40. Prepare sketches for an adjustable pipe support for a 1½ in. pipe that is to carry a chemical mixture in a factory manufacturing paint. The pipe is overhead and is to be supported at 10 ft intervals where the adjustable supports can be attached to the lower chords of the roof trusses. The lower chord of a roof truss is formed by two angles 2½ × 2½ × 5⁄16 that are separated by 3⁄8 in.-thick washers.

12

BASIC DESCRIPTIVE GEOMETRY: POINTS, LINES, PLANES, CURVED AND WARPED SURFACES

12.1. Introduction. On many occasions, problems arise in engineering design which may be solved quickly by applying the basic principles of orthographic projection.

If one thoroughly understands the solution for each of the problems presented, he should find it easy, at a later time, to analyze and solve almost any of the practical problems he may encounter. In this chapter only one method of solution for each type of problem will be shown. In some cases, there are several alternative methods which can be found in any standard text on Descriptive Geometry.

It should be pointed out at the very beginning, that to solve most types of problems one must apply the principles and methods used to solve a few basic problems such as: (1) to find the true length of a line, (2) to find the point projection of a line, and (3) to find the true size and shape of a surface. To find information such as the angle between surfaces, the angle between lines, or the clearance between members of a structure, one must use, in proper combination, the methods of solving these basic problems. Success in solving problems by projection depends largely upon the complete understanding of the principles of projection, the ability to visualize space conditions, and the ability to analyze a given situation. Since the ability to analyze and to visualize are of utmost importance in engineering design, the student is urged to develop these abilities by resisting the temptation to memorize step procedures.

12.2. The projection of a point. Figure 12.1(*a*) shows the projection of point S upon the three principle planes of projection and a supplementary plane A. The notation used is as explained in Sec. 6.8. Point s^F is the view of point S on the frontal plane; s^H is the view of S on the horizontal plane; and s^P is its view on the profile plane. For convenience and ease in recognizing the projected view

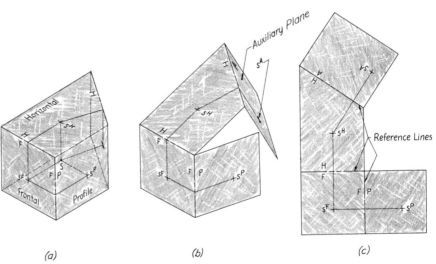

(a)   (b)   (c)

Fig. 12.1. Frontal, horizontal, profile, and auxiliary views of a point S.

of a point on a supplementary plane, the supplementary planes are designated as A-planes and O-planes. A (auxiliary) planes are always perpendicular to one of the principal planes. Point s^A is the view of S on the A-plane. The view of S on an O (oblique) plane would be designated s^O. Additional O-planes are identified as O_1, O_2, O_3, etc. in the order that they follow the first O-plane.

Since it is necessary to represent on one plane (the working surface of our drawing paper) the views of point S which lie on mutually perpendicular planes of projection, the planes are assumed to be hinged so that they can be revolved as shown in Fig. 12.1(b) until they are in a single plane as in (c). The lines about which the planes of projection are hinged are called reference lines. A reference line is identified by the use of capital letters representing the adjacent planes as FH, FP, FA, HA, AO, and so forth (see Fig. 12.1).

It is important to note in (c) that the projections s^F and s^H fall on a vertical line; s^F and s^P lie on a horizontal line, and s^H and s^A lie on a line perpendicular to the reference line HA. In each case this results from the fact that point S and its projections on adjacent planes lie in a plane perpendicular to the reference line for those planes [see Fig. 12.1(a)]. This important principal of projection determines the location of views when the relationship of lines and planes form the problem.

12.3. The projection of a straight line. Capital letters are used for designating the end-points of the actual line in space. In the projected views, these points are identified as shown in Fig. 12.2. The student should read Sec. 6.8, which presents the principles of mul-

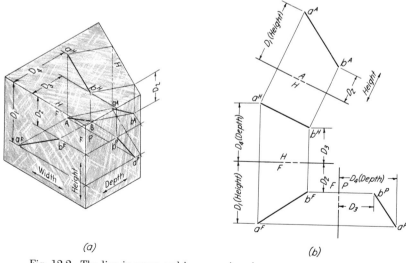

(a)   (b)

Fig. 12.2. The line in space and in successive views.

tiview drawing. In particular, he should study the related illustration which shows some typical line positions.

12.4. Projection of a plane in space. Theoretically, a plane is considered to be flat and unlimited in extent. A plane can be delineated graphically by: (1) two intersecting lines, (2) a line and a point not on the line, (3) two parallel lines, and lastly, (4) three points, not on a straight line. For graphical purposes and to facilitate the solution of space problems as presented in this chapter, planes will be bounded and usually triangular. The space picture and multiview representation of a plane *ABC* are given in Fig. 12.3. The pictorial at the left in (*a*) shows the projected views on the principal planes of projection. In (*b*) the planes are shown being opened outward so as to be in the plane of the paper as in (*c*). It should be noted that plane *ABC* projects as a line (edge view) on the auxiliary plane. The three points *A*, *B*, and *C* of the plane are projected in the same manner as the single point *S* in Fig. 12.1 and are identified similarly (a^F, a^H, a^P, a^A, etc.).

12.5. Analysis of views. It may be desirable at this point to review and restate some of the principles of projection which must be thoroughly understood.

First, each of the principal views of a drawing shows two dimensions. The *F* (frontal) view gives height and width; the *H* (horizontal) view reveals width and depth; and, the *P* (profile) view, height and depth. Each principal view has a dimension common with each of the other views.

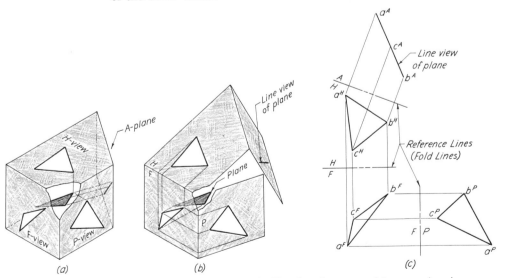

Fig. 12.3. The plane in space and in successive views.

What then are the basic relationships of projection that can be observed from a study of the four views in Fig. 12.2? They might be stated as follows:

1. Since the two views of a point, projected on adjacent planes, will be on a straight line that is perpendicular to the reference line for the planes, a point in one view may be projected to an adjacent view (*b*).

2. Since the *F*-, *P*-, and *A*-planes shown are all perpendicular to the *H*-plane, the distance D_1 that *A* is below the *H*-plane is the same in all three views. The height distance D_2 for point *B* locates point b^A in the *A*-view and could be transferred from the *F*-view when constructing a required *A*-view.

3. Since both the *H*- and *P*-planes are perpendicular to the *F*-plane, the depth distances D_3 and D_4 are the same in both the *H*- and *P*-views.

4. Since the two outside planes of three successive planes of projection are perpendicular to the central plane, the distance of the projected views of a point from the respective reference lines will be equal. Figure 12.4 shows a series of views and the related dimensions.

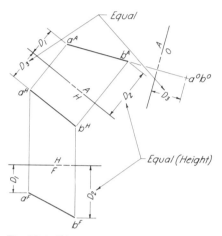

Fig. 12.4. Dimensions on consecutive planes.

From these observations it should be evident that a needed view may be obtained by first drawing projectors from a view that will become a central view, and then laying off along these projection lines (from the reference line) the corresponding distances measured from the reference line of the central plane to the projections of the points on the adjacent view, *i.e.*, to locate b^A construct a projector perpendicular to *HA* and lay off the distance D_2.

12.6. Classification of lines. As has been indicated, a straight line in space can be described graphically on the surface of a sheet of drawing paper by showing the necessary principal and supplementary views and by labeling its extremities. In the written discussion in this chapter a particular line may be identified as being either; (1) vertical, (2) horizontal, (3) inclined, or (4) oblique (Fig. 12.5).

A vertical line has only one direction, perpendicular to the "earth's surface." It can be a frontal-line and a profile-line in that it will be parallel to both of these principal planes of projection. Since a vertical line will be perpendicular to the horizontal plane of projection it will appear on that plane as a point.

A horizontal line may have an infinite number of positions but it must have all points of equal elevation. It may also be an inclined line when its position is related to the frontal and profile planes of projection.

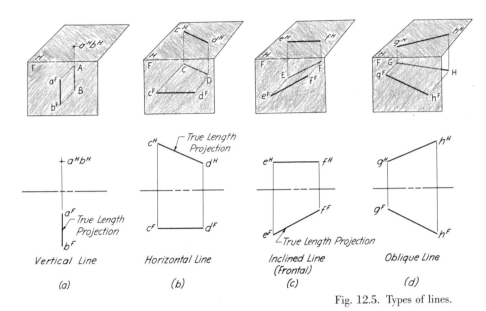

Fig. 12.5. Types of lines.

An inclined line is one that is parallel to the frontal or profile planes of projection. It is always parallel to one of the principal planes of projection and is inclined to the others.

An oblique line is inclined to all of the principal planes of projection. It can be neither vertical or horizontal, nor can it ever be a frontal, horizontal, or profile line.

12.7. A point on a line. When a point is on a line, the projected views of that point must appear on all of the respective views of the line. Thus, in Fig. 12.6(a) point X is on line AB because x^H lies on $a^H b^H$ while x^F is on $a^F b^F$.

In Fig. 12.6(b), the point Y does not lie on line CD because y^F, the frontal view of point Y, does not lie on the frontal view $c^F d^F$.

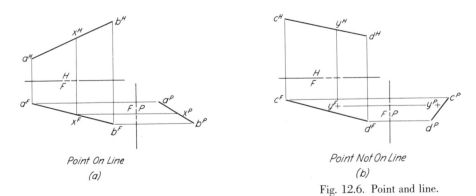

Fig. 12.6. Point and line.

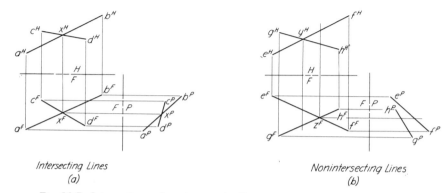

Intersecting Lines
(a)

Nonintersecting Lines
(b)

Fig. 12.7. Intersecting and nonintersecting lines.

12.8. Intersecting and nonintersecting lines. When two lines intersect they meet or cut each other at a common point [Fig. 12.7(a)]. The projections of this point must lie on the same projector. In Fig. 12.7(a), the lines AB and CD meet at point X and the projection of this point of intersection x^H must lie directly above x^F. Likewise, the projected point x^P must lie on a horizontal projector from x^F.

In Fig. 12.7(b) it can be discovered after careful inspection of all views that the lines EF and GH do not intersect. At a first glance at the top (horizontal) view it would appear that they do intersect at point Y but the projection line extended downward from y^H reveals the fact that this is not true because y^F cannot lie on both lines [except at a common point of crossing, as in (a)].

12.9. Parallel lines. Any two lines in space must be either: (1) parallel, (2) intersecting, or (3) nonintersecting and nonparallel (called *skew lines*). Figure 12.7(a) shows intersecting lines while Fig. 12.7(b) shows skew lines. Parallel lines are shown in Fig. 12.8.

It might be stated as a rule of projection, with one exception, that when two lines are parallel their projections will be parallel in every view (Fig. 12.8). In other words the lines will appear to be parallel in every view in which both appear. This is true even though in specific views they may appear as points or their projections may coincide. In either case they are still parallel because both conditions indicate that the lines have the same direction. The exception that has been mentioned occurs when the F- and H-projections of two inclined profile lines are shown. For proof of parallelism a supplementary view should be drawn which may or may not be the profile view.

The true or shortest distance between two parallel lines can be determined on the view which will show these lines as points. The true distance can be measured between the points (Fig. 12.8).

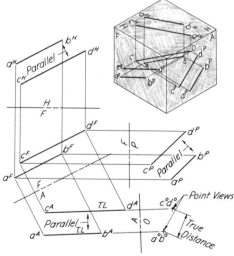

Fig. 12.8. Parallel lines.

12.10. To determine the true length of a line. An observer can see the true length of a line when he looks in a direction perpendicular to it. It is suggested that the student hold a pencil before him and move it into the following typical line positions to observe the conditions under which the pencil, representing a line, appears in true length.

1. *Vertical line.* The vertical line is perpendicular to the horizontal and will therefore appear as a point in the H (top) view. It will appear in true length in the F (frontal) view, in true length in the P (profile) view, and in true length in any auxiliary view that is projected upon an auxiliary plane that is perpendicular to the horizontal plane of projection.

2. *Horizontal line.* The horizontal line will appear in true length when viewed from above because it is parallel to the H-plane of projection and its end-points are theoretically equidistant from an observer looking downward.

3. *Inclined line.* The inclined line will show true length in the F-view or P-view, for by definition (Sec. 12.6) an inclined line is one that is parallel to either the F-plane or the P-plane of projection. However, it can not be parallel to both planes of projection at the same time.

4. *Oblique line.* The oblique line will not appear in true length in any of the principal views because it is inclined to all of the principal planes of projection. It should be apparent that in viewing the pencil alternately from the directions used to obtain the principal views, namely from the front, above, and side, that one end of the pencil is always farther away from the observer than the other. Only when looking directly at the pencil from such a position that the end-points are equidistant from the observer can the true length be seen. On a drawing, the true length projection of an oblique line will appear in a supplementary A (auxiliary) view that is parallel to the line.

12.11. To determine the true length of an oblique line. In order to find the true length of an oblique line, it is necessary to select an auxiliary plane of projection which will be parallel to the line (Figs. 12.9 and 12.10).

Given: The F (frontal) view $a^F b^F$ and the H (top) view $a^H b^H$ of the oblique line AB (Fig. 12.9).

Solution: (1) Draw the reference line HA parallel to the projection $a^H b^H$. The A-plane for this reference line will be parallel to AB and perpendicular to the H-plane (see pictorial drawing). (2) Draw lines of projection from points a^H and b^H perpendicular to the reference line. (3) Transfer height measurements from the

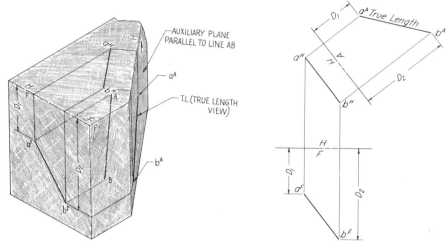

Fig. 12.9. To find the true length of an oblique line.

F-view to the A-view to locate a^A and b^A. In making this transfer
of measurements, the student should attempt to visualize the space
condition for the line and understand that, since the F-view and
A-view both show height and because the planes of projection for
these views are perpendicular to the H-plane, the perpendicular
distance D_1 from the reference line HF to point a^F must be the same
as the distance D_1 from reference line HA to point a^A.

The projection $a^A b^A$ shows the true length of the line AB.

It was not necessary to use an auxiliary plane perpendicular to
the H-plane to find the true length of line AB in Fig. 12.9. The

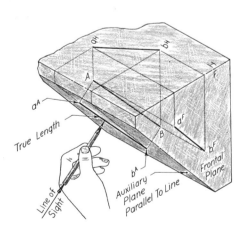

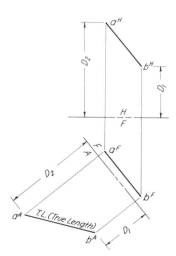

Fig. 12.10. To find the true length of a line.

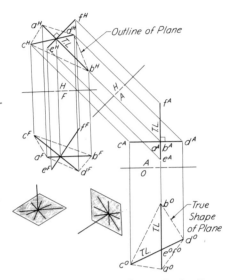

Fig. 12.11. Perpendicular lines.

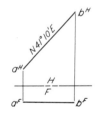

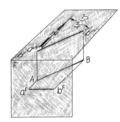

Fig. 12.12. The bearing of a line.

auxiliary plane could just as well have been perpendicular to either the F- or P-planes. Figure 12.10 shows the use of an auxiliary plane perpendicular to the frontal plane to find the true length of the line. In this case the auxiliary view has depth distances in common with the top view as indicated.

12.12. Perpendicular lines. Lines that are perpendicular in space will have their projections perpendicular in any view which shows either or both of the lines in true length. A second rule of perpendicularity might be that, when a line is perpendicular to a plane, it will be perpendicular to every line in that plane. A careful study of Fig. 12.11 will verify these rules. For instance, it should be noted that the lines AB and CD lie in a plane which is outlined with broken lines and that $e^H f^H$ is perpendicular to $a^H b^H$ because $a^H b^H$ shows the true length of the line AB. In the A-view, we see that $e^A f^A$ is perpendicular to the line view of the plane and is therefore perpendicular to both AB and CD. The O-view shows the true shape (TSP) of the plane and the line EF as a point. This again verifies the fact that EF is perpendicular to the plane and to lines AB and CD. Otherwise line EF would not appear as a point. Note also, that the O-view shows the true length (TL) of AB and CD.

12.13. Bearing of a line. The bearing of a line is the horizontal angle between the line and a north-south line. A bearing is given in degrees with respect to the meridian and is measured from 0° to 90° from either north (N) or south (S). The bearing reading indicates the quadrant in which the line is located by use of the letters N and E, S and E, S and W, or N and W, as N 31° E or S 42° 10′ W. The bearing of a line is measured in the H-view (Fig. 12.12).

12.14. The azimuth of a line. The azimuth of a line may be given in degrees from either the north or south. In the past, it has been customary to reckon azimuth in degrees from the south in clockwise direction from 0° to 360° (Fig. 12.13). Thus a line 10° east of north would have an azimuth of 190°. Recently, our armed services decided that the measurement of azimuth angles from the north in a clockwise direction best suited their needs. Although the U.S. Coast and Geodetic Survey defines azimuth as the clockwise angle from either the north or south, tables show that this organization continues to reckon azimuth from the south.

12.15. The slope of a line. In engineering practice the position of a line is given frequently by specifying both the bearing and slope. The slope or grade of a line is the inclination of the line with the horizontal. Slope may be expressed either in percentage, in which case it is the rise in elevation in feet per one-hundred feet of horizontal length, or as an angle in degrees and minutes. The slope of a line can be seen and measured only in a view which shows vertical height and the line in true length (Fig. 12.14).

12.16. Point view of a line. It was pointed out in the first section of this chapter that the solutions of many types of problems depended upon an understanding of a few basic constructions. One of these basic constructions involves the finding of the view showing the point view or point projection of a line. For instance, this construction is followed when it is necessary to determine the dihedral angle between two planes, for the true size of the angle will appear in the view which shows the line common to the two planes as a point.

A line will show as a point on a projection plane that is perpendicular to the line. The observer's direction of sight must be along and parallel to the line. When a line appears in true length on one of the principal planes of projection, only an auxiliary view is needed to show the line as a point. However, in the case of an oblique line both an auxiliary and an oblique view are required, for a point view must always follow a true length view. In other words, the plane of projection for the view showing the line as a point must be adjacent to the plane for the true view and be perpendicular to it.

Given: The *F*-view $a^F b^F$ and the *H*-view $a^H b^H$ of the oblique line *AB* (Fig. 12.15).

Solution: (1) Draw the view showing the *TL* (true length) of *AB*. This is an auxiliary view drawn as explained in Sec. 12.11.

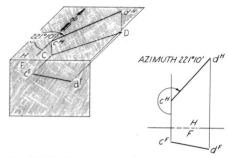

Fig. 12.13. The azimuth of a line.

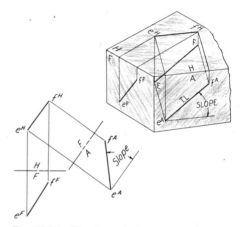

Fig. 12.14. The slope of a line.

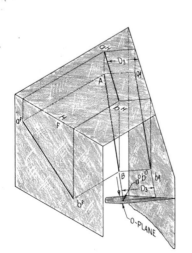

Fig. 12.15. The point view of a line.

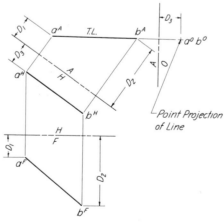

Auxiliary Plane Perpendicular
to Horizontal Plane

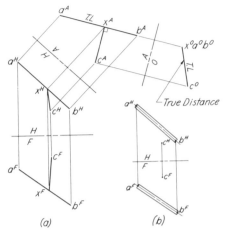

(a)   (b)

Fig. 12.16. To find the shortest distance from a point to a line.

(2) Draw reference line AO perpendicular to the true length projection $a^A b^A$. This reference line is for an O-plane that is perpendicular to the A-plane. (3) Draw a projection line from $a^A b^A$ and transfer the distance D_3 from the H-view to the O-view. It should be noted from the pictorial drawing that the distance D_3 is common to both of these views, and that points a^O and b^O coincide to give a point or end view of line AB.

12.17. To find the shortest distance from a point to a line. The shortest distance between a given point and a given straight line must be measured along a perpendicular drawn from the point to the line. Since lines that are perpendicular will have their projections show perpendicular in any view showing either or both lines in true length (Sec. 12.12), the perpendicular must be drawn in the view showing the given line in true length.

Given: The F- and H-views of the line AB and point C (Fig. 12.16).

Solution: (1) Draw the A (auxiliary) view showing the true length view $a^A b^A$ of line AB and view c^A of point C. (2) Draw $c^A x^A$ perpendicular to $a^A b^A$. Line $c^A x^A$ is a view of the required perpendicular from point C to its juncture with line AB at point X. (3) Draw reference line AO parallel to $c^A x^A$. This reference line locates an O-plane which will be parallel to the perpendicular CX and perpendicular to the A-plane. The O-view will show the true length of CX. Line CX does not show true length in any of the other views.

12.18. To find the shortest distance between two skew lines. As was stated in Sec. 12.9, any two lines that are not parallel and do not intersect are called *skew lines.* The shortest distance between any such lines must be measured along one line and only one line that can be drawn perpendicular to both. This common perpendicular can be drawn in a view which is taken to show one line as a point. Its projection will be perpendicular to the view of the other line and will show in true length (Fig. 12.17).

Given: The F- and H-views of two skew lines AB and CD.

Solution: (1) Draw an A-view adjacent to the H-view so as to show line AB in true length ($a^A b^A$). Line CD should also be shown in this same view ($c^A d^A$). (2) Draw reference line AO perpendicular to $a^A b^A$ and draw the O-view in which line AB will appear as a point ($a^O b^O$). It is in this view that the exact location of the required perpendicular can be established. (3) Draw the line $e^O f^O$ through point $a^O b^O$ perpendicular to $c^O d^O$. The shortest distance between the skew lines now appears in true distance as the length of $e^O f^O$.

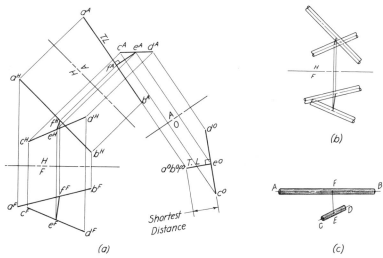

Fig. 12.17. To find the shortest distance between two skew lines.

Although line CD does not appear in true length in the O-view, $e^O f^O$ does, and hence $c^O d^O$ and $e^O f^O$ will appear perpendicular. (4) Complete the A-view by first locating point e^A on $c^A d^A$ and then draw $e^A f^A$ parallel to reference line AO. (5) Locate points E and F in the H- and F-views remembering that point E is located on line CD and point F on line AB.

In engineering design an engineer frequently has to locate and find the length of the shortest line between two skewed members in order to determine clearance or the length of a connecting member. In underground construction work one might use this method to locate a connecting tunnel. For another method see Sec. 12.37.

In Fig. 12.17(b) and (c) we see the two rods for which the clearance distance was determined in (a). Lines AB and CD represent the center lines of the rods.

12.19. The direct or natural method. In the solution of space problems, many persons prefer to think of the object or the parts as being definitely fixed in position with no change taking place. The engineer or draftsman then simply imagines that he changes his position to look at the object or structural members, as he should to determine the information needed. This method is sometimes called the direct method and is identical with the so-called natural method discussed in Sec. 6.4 when the object is considered as being fixed in position.

Up to this point the "glass-box" and supplementary planes of projection have been used freely to present the solution of problems dealing with points and lines because the "glass-box" is useful in explaining the theory of projection and in understanding the position of the views on the surface of a sheet of drawing paper. However, since both the "glass-box" method with planes of projection and the direct method produce the same results, the student should use the method which seems to be best suited to his thinking. In either case, the same notations for the identification of points, lines, and reference lines must be used.

12.20. A plane. As stated previously, a plane may be defined and located by: (1) three points, (2) a straight line and a point, (3) two intersecting straight lines, or (4) two parallel straight lines. Although usually a plane is limited in extent and is bounded by straight or curved lines, it is frequently necessary to consider a plane to extend

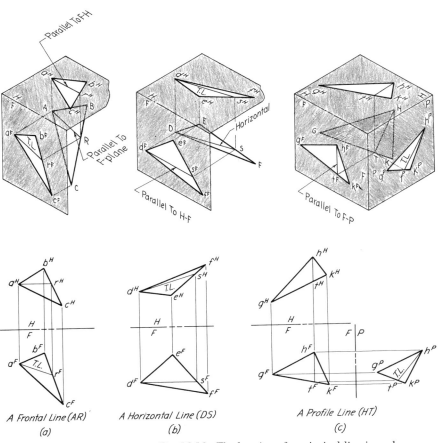

Fig. 12.18. The location of a principal line in a plane.

indefinitely in order to solve some of the problems that are encountered.

12.21. The principal lines of a plane (Fig. 12.18). Those lines which are parallel to the principal planes of projection are the *principal lines of a plane.* A principal line may be either a horizontal line, a frontal line, or a profile line. Principal lines are true length lines and one such line may be drawn in any plane so as to appear true length in any one of the principal views as desired. This is an important principle that is the basis for the solution of many problems involving lines and planes.

12.22. A point in a plane. It is necessary at times to determine whether or not a given point lies in a given plane. A check can be made easily, since any point in a plane must be on a line in the plane. Furthermore, since any two nonparallel lines in the given plane must intersect, the point lies in the plane if a line drawn through it intersects other lines in the plane. In Fig. 12.19, the point M lies in the plane ABC since a line CX, drawn through M, intersects the line AB at point X. Point N does not lie in the plane because a line drawn through the point from C does not intersect line AB.

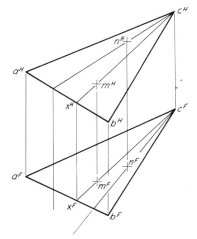

Fig. 12.19. Point in a plane.

12.23. The strike and dip of a plane. Mining engineers and geologists employ the terms strike and dip to describe the direction and inclination of strata of the earth's formations. The *strike* of a plane is the direction of a horizontal line in the plane. Strike is specified by the bearing of the line. The *dip* of a plane is the slope angle of the plane (angle the plane makes with the horizontal).

12.24. To obtain the edge view of a plane. When a plane is vertical, an edge view of it will be seen from above and it will be represented by a line in the top view. Should a plane be horizontal, it will appear as an edge in the frontal view. However, planes are not always vertical or horizontal; frequently they are inclined or oblique to the principal planes of projection.

Finding the edge view of a plane is a basic construction that is used to determine the slope of a plane (dip), to determine clearance, and to establish perpendicularity. The method presented here is part of the construction used to obtain the true size and shape of a plane, to determine the angle between a line and plane, and to establish the location at which a line pierces a plane.

The edge view of an oblique plane can be obtained by viewing the plane with direction of sight parallel to it. The edge view will then appear in an auxiliary view. When the auxiliary view shows height, the slope of the plane is shown (Fig. 12.20).

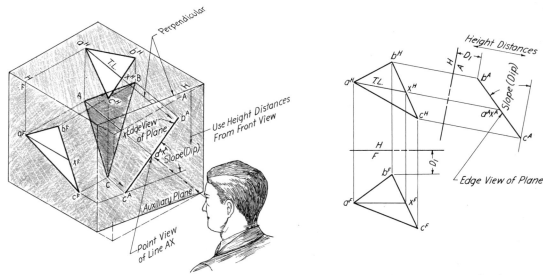

Fig. 12.20. To find the edge view of a plane.

Given: The *F*- and *H*-views of plane *ABC*.

Solution: (1) Draw the horizontal line *AX* in the plane. Because *AX* is parallel to the horizontal, $a^F x^F$ will be horizontal and must be drawn before the position of $a^H x^H$ can be established. (2) Draw reference line *HA* perpendicular to $a^H x^H$. (3) Construct the *A*-view which will show the plane *ABC* as a straight line. Since the *F*-view and *A*-view have height as a common dimension, the distances used in constructing the *A*-view were taken from the *F*-view. It should be noted by the reader that an edge view found by projecting from the front view will show the angle that the plane makes with the *F*-plane. Similarly, the edge view found by projecting from the side view will show the angle with the *P*-plane.

12.25. To find the true shape (*TSP*) of an oblique plane.

Finding the true shape of a plane by projection is another of the basic constructions that the student must understand, for it is used to determine the solution of two of the problems which are to follow. In a way, the construction shown in Fig. 12.21 is a repetition of that shown in Fig. 8.18. However, repetition in the form of another presentation should help even those students who feel they understand the method for finding the true shape of an oblique surface of an object.

To see the true size and shape of an oblique plane an observer must view it with a line of sight perpendicular to it. To do this he must, as the first step in the construction, obtain an edge view of the plane. An *O*-view taken from the *A*-view will then show the true shape of the plane.

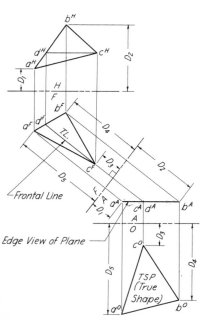

Fig. 12.21. To find the true shape (*TSP*) of an oblique plane.

Given: The *F*- and *H*-views of plane *ABC*.

Solution: (1) Draw a frontal line *CD* in plane *ABC*. (2) Draw reference line *FA* perpendicular to $c^F d^F$ and construct the *A*-view showing the edge view of the plane. The auxiliary view has depth in common with the *H*-view. (3) Draw reference line *AO* parallel to the edge view in the *A*-view and construct the *O*-view which will show the true size and shape of plane *ABC*. The needed distances from the reference line to points in the *O*-view are found in the *F*-view.

12.26. To determine the angle between a line and a given plane. The true angle between a given line and a given plane will be seen in the view which shows the plane as an edge (a line) and the line in true length. The solution shown in Fig. 12.22 is based on this premise. The solution as presented might be called the *edge view method.*

Given: The *F*- and *H*-views of plane *ABC* and line *ST*.

Solution: (1) Draw the frontal line *BX* in the plane *ABC*. (2) Draw reference line *FA* perpendicular to $x^F b^F$ and construct the *A*-view. This view will show plane *ABC* as line ($a^A b^A c^A$); however, since this view does not show *ST* in true length, the true angle is not shown. (3) Draw reference line *AO* parallel to the edge view of the plane and construct the *O*-view that will show line *ST* viewed obliquely and plane *ABC* in its true size and shape. (4) Draw reference line OO_1 parallel to $s^O t^O$.

Line $s^{O_1} t^{O_1}$ will show the true length of *ST* in this second oblique view. Plane *ABC* will be seen again as an edge (line) for

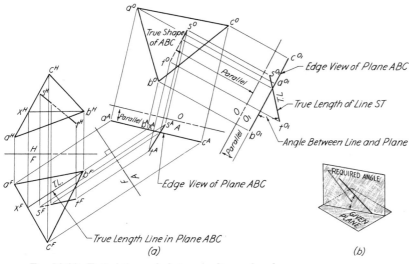

Fig. 12.22. To find the angle between a line and a plane.

it now appears on an adjacent view taken perpendicular to the view showing true shape (*TSP*). The required angle can now be measured between the true length view of line *ST* and the edge view of plane *ABC*.

In the illustration in Fig. 12.22 three supplementary views were required to obtain the true angle. If the plane had appeared as an edge in one of the given views, only two supplementary views would have been needed; if it had appeared in true shape in a given view only one additional view, properly selected to show the plane as an edge and the line in true length, would be needed.

12.27. To determine the true angle between two intersecting oblique lines. Since, as previously stated, two intersecting lines establish a plane, the true angle between the intersecting lines may be seen in a true shape view of a plane containing the lines (Fig. 12.21). In Fig. 12.23 line *AC* completes plane *ABC* containing the given lines *AB* and *BC*. It is necessary to find the true angle between *AB* and *BC*.

Solution: (1) Draw the frontal line *XC*. (2) Draw reference line *FA* perpendicular to $c^F x^F$ and construct the *A*-view showing an edge view of plane *ABC*. (3) Draw reference line *AO* parallel to the edge view $a^A c^A b^A$ and construct the *O*-view which will show the *TSP* of plane *ABC*. In this view it is desirable to show only the given lines. The true angle between *AB* and *BC* is shown by $a^O b^O c^O$. As a

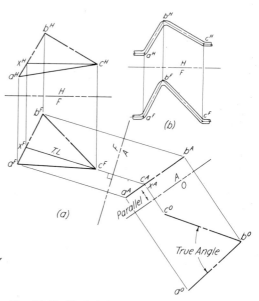

Fig. 12.23. To find the true angle between two intersecting lines.

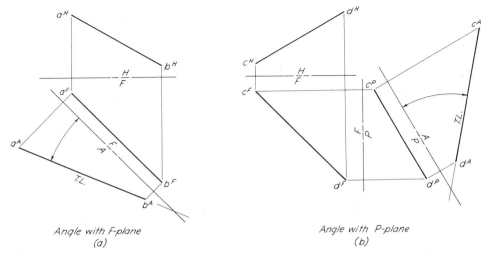

Fig. 12.24. Angle between a line and a principal plane.

Angle with F-plane
(a)

Angle with P-plane
(b)

practical application this method might be used to determine the angle between two adjacent sections of bent rod as shown in (*b*).

12.28. To determine the angle between a line and a principal plane. As stated in Sec. 12.26, the angle between a given line and a given plane will be seen in the view which shows the plane as an edge (a line) and the line in true length. Since the method for finding the slope of a line, which is also the angle between the line and *H*-plane has been discussed previously in Sec. 12.15 and illustrated in Fig. 12.14, the two illustrations in Fig. 12.24 show only the method for the determination of the angle between a line and the *F*-plane and a line and the *P*-plane. The same analysis is used as for finding the slope of a line. In (*a*) the angle between the given line and the *F*-plane is shown between the true length projection of the line and the reference line for an auxiliary plane perpendicular to the *F*-plane. For finding the angle that a line makes with the *P*-plane, the auxiliary plane is taken perpendicular to the *P*-plane.

12.29. To find the piercing point of a line and a plane. Determining the location of the point where a line pierces a plane is another fundamental operation with which one must be familiar. A line, if it is not parallel to a plane, will intersect the plane at a point that is common to both. In a view showing the plane as an edge, the piercing point appears where the line intersects (cuts) the edge view. This method is known as the edge view method to distinguish it from the cutting plane method which may be found in Chapter 13.

The simple cases occur when the plane appears as an edge in one of the principal views. The general case, for which we use an oblique plane, is given in Fig. 12.25.

Given: Plane *ABCD* and line *ST*.

Solution: (1) Draw the frontal line *AX* in *ABCD*. (2) Draw reference line *FA* perpendicular to $a^F x^F$ and construct the *A*-view showing an edge view of the plane as line $a^A b^A c^A d^A$ and the view of the line $s^A t^A$. Point p^A where the line cuts the edge view of the plane is the *A*-view of the piercing point. (3) Project point *P* back from the *A*-view first to the *F*-view and then to the *H*-view.

12.30. Visibility. Most often visibility can be determined by inspection of the given views and by remembering: (1) that the extreme outline (outside lines) is always visible, (2) that an edge or corner closest to the viewer is visible, and (3) that an edge or corner falling within the outline and away from the viewer will generally be invisible. A study of the two views of Fig. 12.26(*a*) reveals that in the frontal view, part of the outline of the block must be invisible because the horizontal (top) view shows clearly that the rod is in front of the block, so as to hide a portion of it when viewed from the front. Part of the outline of the block in the horizontal view must be shown as being invisible as well, for the front view shows that the rod is between the observer and the block when looking downward from above.

To assist one in determining visibility in cases where this is difficult to do without resorting to an extra view, a general method has been devised. This method, as it applies to the views of a solid, is illustrated in Fig. 12.26(*b*) (see pictorial). In the horizontal (top) view lines $a^H b^H$, $b^H c^H$, $c^H o^H$, and $o^H a^H$ must all be visible because

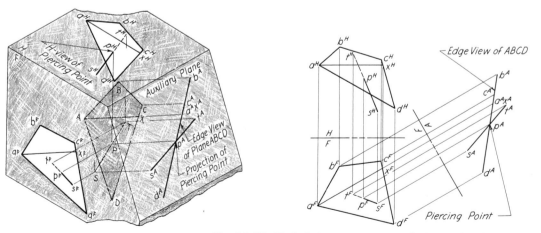

Fig. 12.25. To find the piercing point of a line and a plane.

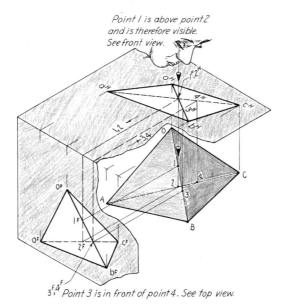

Point 1 is above point 2
and is therefore visible.
See front view.

Point 3 is in front of point 4. See top view.

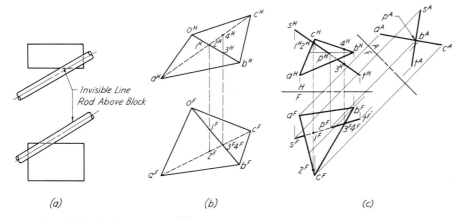

Invisible Line
Rod Above Block

(a)   (b)   (c)

Fig. 12.26. To determine visibility.

they form the outline of the view. However, since a^Hc^H and o^Hb^H fall inside the view, their visibility must be determined. Although in this particular case this question could be answered by inspection of the given views, the general method will be applied. In considering o^Hb^H and a^Hc^H the apparent intersection is in reality two points, one above the other. One point is on OB and the other on AC. To apply our general method, suppose that these points on the edges of the solid be assigned the numbers 1 and 2, which will be seen in the H-view as 1^H and 2^H. Although in the H-view these points are coincident, the frontal view shows that 1^F is on o^Fb^F and is well above 2^F, which lies on $a^F c^F$. Since point 1 on OB is above point 2 on AC, edge OB is visible when the solid is viewed from above.

In the frontal view $o^F b^F$ and $a^F c^F$ must be considered for visibility. Numbers 3 and 4 will be assigned to the points on these edges. This time 3^F and 4^F are coincident in the frontal view. When 3^H and 4^H are located in the horizontal view, it becomes evident that point 4 is in back of point 3 and lies on the edge of AC. Therefore, since point 4 is farther from the observer than point 3, edge AC must be invisible.

In Fig. 12.26(c) this method for determining visibility is shown applied to an oblique plane and a line which pierces it. The student is urged to analyze the solution carefully.

12.31. To find the shortest distance from a point to a plane.
Frequently it is desirable to determine the shortest distance from a point to a plane in order to check clearance and for other reasons.

The edge view method shown in Fig. 12.27 may be used when it becomes necessary to draw a perpendicular to a plane through a given point, for the problems solutions are related. The student should recognize this fact as he studies this section.

The shortest distance from a point to a plane must be measured along a perpendicular from the point to the plane. This perpendicular can be seen in true length in any view that shows an edge view of the plane.

Given: Plane ABC and point D.

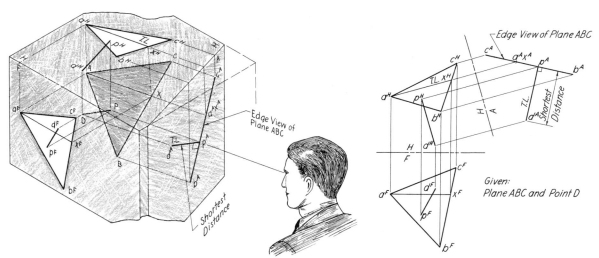

Fig. 12.27. To find the shortest distance from a point to a plane.

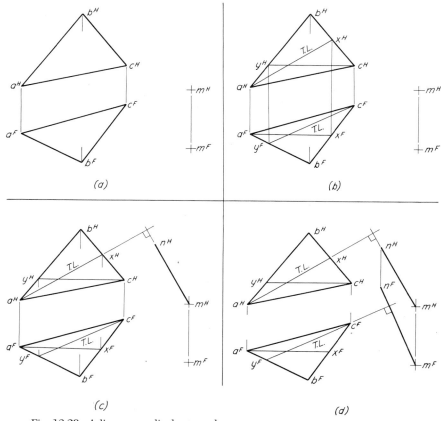

Fig. 12.28. A line perpendicular to a plane.

Solution: (1) Draw the horizontal line *AX* in plane *ABC*. (2) Draw reference line *HA* perpendicular to $a^H x^H$ and construct the *A*-view showing an edge view of the plane and point *D*. (3) Draw a perpendicular to the edge view of the plane through d^A. This establishes the location of p^A, the *A*-view of the point where the perpendicular pierces the plane. (4) Measure $d^A p^A$ to obtain the shortest distance. (5) Draw a line through d^H parallel to reference line *HA* and project p^A to the *H*-view to establish the location of p^H. Line $d^H p^H$ must be parallel to *HA* because the adjacent *A*-view shows the true length of the perpendicular. (6) Locate p^F in the *F*-view. Point p^F is the same distance from reference line *HF* as p^A is from reference line *HA*.

12.32. To construct a line perpendicular to a plane (Fig. 12.28).
The procedure presented in Sec. 12.31 for finding the shortest distance from a point to a plane is a method of drawing a line perpendicular to a plane. However, when establishing the direction of

the perpendicular is the only requirement and its length is unimportant, the relationship that applies is: if a line is perpendicular to a plane, it is perpendicular to every line in that plane. Furthermore, since a plane can be defined by two intersecting lines, it follows that if a line is perpendicular to a plane, the line must be perpendicular to two intersecting lines in the plane. In reality, the discussion and presentation given here is a further development of the discussion given in Sec. 12.12.

Given: The plane ABC and a point M through which a line is to be constructed perpendicular to the plane [see (*a*)].

Solution: Draw the principal lines AX and CY as illustrated in (*b*). Then, as shown in (*c*), draw the H-view of a line MN perpendicular to the true length view of the line AX. Point N is located at an arbitrary distance along line MN. From observing the H-view only, it should be noted that the view proves that, no matter how the F-view of MN will appear finally when drawn, the line MN is perpendicular to line AX (read Sec. 12.12). For the last step [see (*d*)], draw the F-view of the line MN perpendicular to the true length view of line CY. As before, this view alone proves that line MN is perpendicular to line CY. Considering both views (H-view and F-view), line MN is perpendicular to both AX and CY that are intersecting lines in plane MNO. Thus, line MN is perpendicular to the given plane ABC.

12.33. To construct a plane perpendicular to a given line.

The procedure illustrated in Fig. 12.29, for constructing a plane perpendicular to a line should be recognized as being a reverse appli-

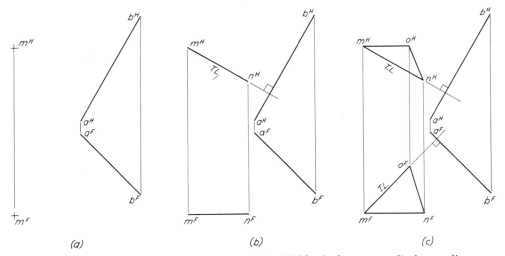

| (a) | (b) | (c) |

Fig. 12.29. A plane perpendicular to a line.

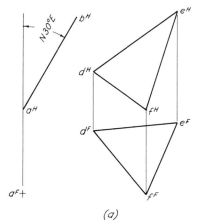 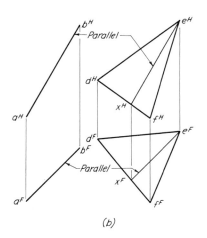

Fig. 12.30. A line parallel to a plane.

cation of the method given in Sec. 12.32 for constructing a line perpendicular to a plane.

Given: The line *AB* and a point *M* through which a plane is to be passed perpendicular to *AB* [see (*a*)].

Solution: Draw a horizontal line *MN* with the true length view perpendicular to line *AB* as shown in (*b*). Then, draw a frontal line *MO* with the true length view perpendicular to line *AB* as in the case of line *MN.* Since the line *AB* is perpendicular to both lines *MN* and *MO,* it is perpendicular to the plane *MNO* [see (*c*)].

12.34. To construct a line parallel to a plane (Fig. 12.30). If a line is parallel to a plane, the line must be parallel to some line in that plane.

Given: The plane *DEF* and the point *A.* A line *AB* having a bearing of N30°E is to be drawn parallel to the plane *DEF* [see (*a*)].

Solution: Draw a line in the plane *DEF* having the same bearing as the required line. (In this case, draw $e^H x^H$ parallel to $a^H b^H$.) Then, draw the *F*-view of the line *AB* ($a^F b^F$) parallel to the *F*-view of the line *EX* as shown in (*b*).

12.35. To construct a plane parallel to a line (Fig. 12.31). In some situations that arise, it becomes necessary to pass a plane through a line in such a manner that the plane will be parallel to another line.

Given: The two skew lines *AB* and *EF* [see (*a*)]. It is required that a plane *ABC* be constructed parallel to the line *EF.*

Solution: Construct line *BC* parallel to the line *EF* as shown in (*b*). The lines *AB* and *BC* define a plane parallel to the line *EF.*

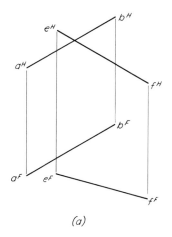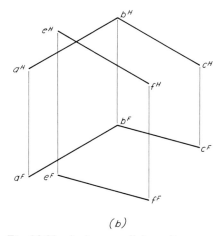

Fig. 12.31. A plane parallel to a line.

12.36. To determine the angle between two skew lines (Fig. 12.32). Sometimes it is necessary to measure the angle between two skew lines. To determine this angle, construct a plane through one of the lines such that the plane is parallel to the other line as explained in Sec. 12.35. Then, draw the view that will reveal the true shape of the plane. Since this projected view will show both of the given lines in their true length, the angle between them can be measured. Read Sec. 12.37 and study Fig. 12.32(b).

12.37. Shortest distance of specified slope between two skew lines (Fig. 12.32). In Sec. 12.18 a method for determining the shortest distance between two skew lines was discussed. By means of the particular method presented it was shown that the shortest distance could be found in the view showing one of the skew lines as a point. This problem could have been solved as well by a different construction, as given here, which leads to results that are often useful.

Given: The lines *AB* and *CD*.

Solution: Construct the plane *ABX* parallel to the line *CD* and draw the *A*-view showing an edge view of the plane as line $b^A x^A y^A a^A$ and the view of the line *CD* as $c^A d^A$ [see (*a*)]. At this point, several possibilities for construction are offered that provide different results, depending upon the position selected for the *O*-plane upon which the second auxiliary (*O*-view) is projected.

In (*b*), when the *O*-plane is parallel to the lines, the true length of both lines is shown and the angle between them can be measured. This is as explained in Sec. 12.36. Now, since both lines show in true length projection in this *O*-view, a line perpendicular to both (the shortest distance between two skew lines) will appear in end view at the point where the projected views of these lines cross. The true length of the perpendicular MN is revealed in the A-view when the point projection m^0n^0 is projected back. Locating the F-view and H-view of MN completes the drawing.

When the O-plane is placed as shown in (c), perpendicular to the AH reference line, the point s^0r^0, where the projected views of the lines cross, is the end view of the line RS, the shortest horizontal line between the given two skew lines. The true length of RS can be found in the H-view.

If the shortest line of a specified slope (other than $0°$) is desired, a "slope directrix" must first be drawn in the A-view at the specified slope with the HA reference line as shown in (d). In the O-view (second auxiliary) set up perpendicular to this slope directrix, the required line is located as before at the point (t^0v^0) where the projected views of AB and CD cross. The true length of TV can be measured in the A-view.

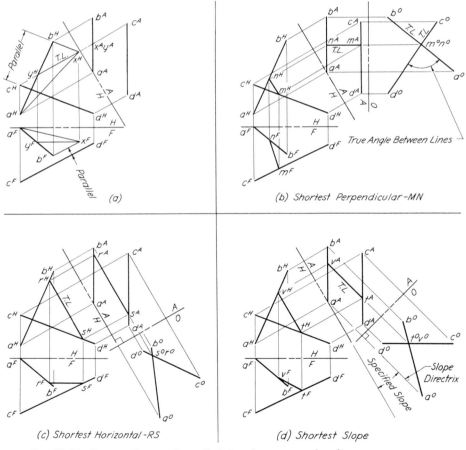

Fig. 12.32. Shortest distance of specified slope between two skew lines.

12.38. To find the line of intersection of two planes. The intersection of two planes can be found by using an edge view method. That is, a view of the line of intersection can be seen in an auxiliary view which shows one plane as an edge. However, the required line of intersection can be found quickly and without resorting to an extra view if the cutting plane method shown in Fig. 12.33 is used. Those who are interested can find the edge view method in almost any good descriptive geometry text. In the limited coverage of this book it is impossible to present all of the alternate methods that one might find advantageous. However, the simple basic constructions that have been given will serve most of the needs of the professional man.

Since any two planes that are not parallel will intersect in a straight line it is necessary to find only two points that lie in both planes to fix the line in position and direction. To find these required two points, one could select any two lines in one plane and find the piercing points of these lines. This would be more work than is necessary. The cutting plane method is much easier.

The cutting plane method requires the use of only two cutting planes. Although these planes may be taken at random, as far as position is concerned, each must show as an edge view in one of the given views. In order to clarify the theory underlying this method, a pictorial view has been added to Fig. 12.33. It should be noted that when a third plane cuts two given planes the intersection lines for all three planes meet at a point P_1. This point P_1 is one of two points along the line of intersection that must be found.

Given: The planes *ABCD* and *EFG*.

Solution: (1) Draw the edge view of cutting plane CP_1 in the

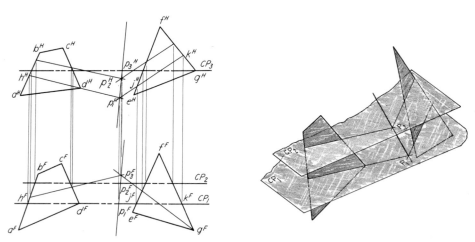

Fig. 12.33. To find the line of intersection of two planes.

F-view. Although drawn through point *D* it could have been taken elsewhere. The intersection of CP_1 and plane *ADCD* is line *DH*. CP_1 also intersects plane *EFG* along the line *JK*. The *F*-views of these lines appear in the cutting plane line CP_1. (2) Find the *H*-views of *DH* and *JK* and extend them to establish the location of $p_1{}^H$, the *H*-view of point P_1 on the line of intersection. (3) Project $p_1{}^H$ downward to locate point $p_1{}^F$, the *F*-view of point P_1. (4) Draw the edge view of CP_2 in the *F*-view. (5) Locate point $p_2{}^H$ and $p_2{}^F$ by following the general procedure set forth for locating the *H*- and *F*-views of point P_1. (6) Locate the *H*-view of the line of intersection by drawing a line through $p_1{}^H$ and $p_2{}^H$. (7) Locate the *F*-view of the line of intersection.

Although point P_1 and P_2 definitely establish the line of intersection, it is well to take a third plane (CP_3) as a check.

12.39. To find the dihedral angle between two planes.
The angle between two planes is known as a *dihedral angle*. The true size of this angle between intersecting planes may be seen in a plane that is perpendicular to both. For this condition as set forth, the intersecting planes will appear as edges and the line of intersection of the two planes as a point. The true angle may be measured between the edge views of the planes (Fig. 12.34).

Given: The intersecting planes *ABCD* and *CDEF*. The line of intersection is line *CD* as shown in the pictorial drawing.

Solution: (1) Draw reference line *FA* parallel to $c^F d^F$ and construct the *A*-view. This view will show *CD* in true length ($c^A d^A$). (2) Draw reference line *AO* perpendicular to $c^A d^A$ and construct the adjacent *O*-view. Since this view was taken looking along line *CD*, points *C* and *D* are coincident and appear as a single point identified as $c^O d^O$. The intersecting planes show as edge views and the true angle between the given planes may be measured between these edge view lines. When two planes are given that do not intersect, the dihedral angle may be found after the line of intersection has been determined.

12.40. Perpendicular planes (Fig. 12.35).
If two planes are perpendicular, some line in one plane must be perpendicular to the other plane. Hence, the proof of perpendicular planes as well as the construction of perpendicular planes is based on the discussion in Sec. 12.32.

Given: The plane *MNO* and the line *AB*. A plane *ABC* is to be constructed perpendicular to the plane *MNO*.

Solution: Draw the two principal lines *MX* and *OY* in plane *MNO*. Then, construct the line *AC* so that it is perpendicular to plane *MNO* (read Sec. 12.32). The plane *ABC* is then, by defini-

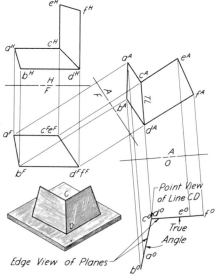

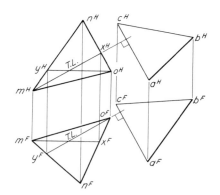

Fig. 12.34. To find the dihedral angle between two planes.

Fig. 12.35. Perpendicular planes.

tion, perpendicular to the plane *MNO*. Point *C* is arbitrarily located along the line *AC* and line *AC* could have been drawn from any point along *AB*.

When it is necessary to prove whether or not two planes are perpendicular, the construction is started by drawing two principal lines in one plane as in Fig. 12.35. Then, through some point in the other plane a line must be constructed that is perpendicular to the first plane. If it is determined that this line lies in the second plane, the planes are perpendicular. If it does not lie in the plane, the planes are not perpendicular.

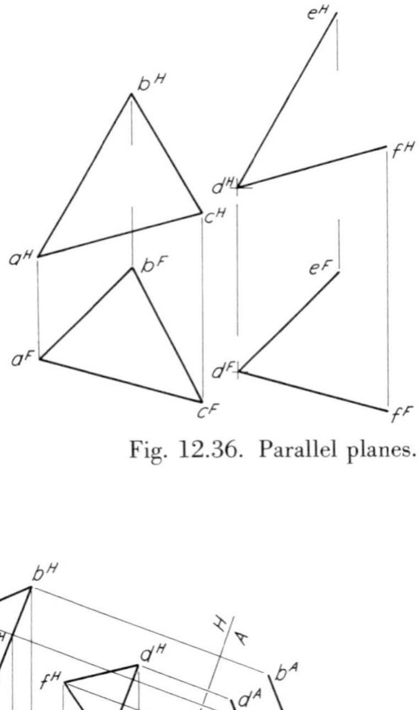

12.41. Parallel planes (Fig. 12.36). If two planes are parallel, then for every line in one plane there must be a parallel line in the second plane. However, since two intersecting lines define a plane, it is sufficient to say that there must be two intersecting lines in one plane parallel to two intersecting lines in the second plane.

Given: The plane *ABC* and point *D*. A plane *DEF* is to be constructed through point *D* parallel to the given plane *ABC*.

Solution: Construct: (1) line *DE* parallel to line *AB*, and (2) line *DF* parallel to the line *AC*. Plane *DEF* is parallel to the plane *ABC*. Points *E* and *F* were arbitrarily chosen along their respective lines.

When it is necessary to determine whether or not two given planes are parallel, a line is selected in one plane and a check is made to determine if there is a parallel line in the other plane. However, even if there is a line parallel to the one first selected this alone is not sufficient proof of parallel planes as the lines in question might be parallel to the line of intersection of the two planes. Therefore, for a complete and certain proof, the procedure must be repeated for a second set of lines which intersect the first set. Read Sec. 12.42 that follows.

12.42. The distance between two parallel planes. When two planes are parallel their edge views will appear as parallel lines in the same view. The clearance or perpendicular distance between them can be measured in this view (Fig. 12.37). The existence of planes as parallel lines in a view is another proof that they are parallel.

12.43. To find the true length of a line by revolution. In engineering layout work, it frequently is necessary to determine the true length of a line when constructing the development of a surface. The true lengths must be found of those lines that are not parallel to any coordinate plane and, therefore, appear foreshortened in all the principal views. A practical, as well as the theoretical procedure, is to revolve any such oblique line into a position parallel to a co-

Fig. 12.36. Parallel planes.

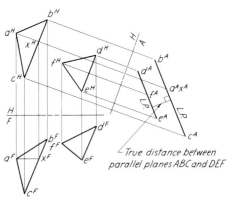

Fig. 12.37. Distance between parallel planes.

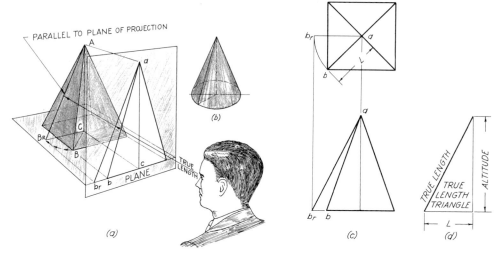

Fig. 12.38. True length of a line, revolution method.

ordinate plane so that its projection on that particular plane will be the same length as the line. In Fig. 12.38(a), this is illustrated by the edge AB on the pyramid. AB is oblique to the coordinate planes and its projections are foreshortened. If this edge line is imagined to be revolved until it becomes parallel to the frontal plane, then the projection ab_r in the front view will be the same length as the true length of AB.

A practical application of this method is shown in Fig. 12.38(c). The true length of the edge AB, in Fig. 12.38(a), would be found by revolving its top projection into the position ab_r representing AB revolved parallel to the frontal plane, and then projecting the end-point b_r down into its new position along a horizontal line through b. The horizontal line represents the horizontal plane of the base in which the point B travels as the line AB is revolved.

Note in Fig. 12.38(a) and (b) that the true length of a line is equal to the hypotenuse of a right triangle whose altitude is equal to the difference in the elevation of the end-points and whose base is equal to the top projection of the line. With this fact in mind, many persons determine the true length of a line by constructing a true-length triangle similar to the one illustrated in Fig. 12.38(d).

Students who lack a thorough understanding of the principles of projection, and find it difficult to determine whether or not a projection of a line in one of the principal views shows the true length of the line, should study carefully the following facts:

1. If the projection of a line shows the true length of a line, one of the other projections must appear as a horizontal line, a

vertical line, or a point on one of the other views of the drawing.

2. If the top and front views of a line are horizontal, then both views show the true length.

3. If the top view of a line is a point, the front and side views show the true length.

4. If the front view of a line is a point, the top and side views show the true length.

5. If the top and front views of a line are vertical, the side view shows the true length.

6. If the side projection of a line is a point, the top and front views show the true length.

7. If the front view of a line is horizontal and the top view is inclined, the top inclined view shows the true length.

8. If the top view of a line is horizontal and the front view is inclined, the front inclined view shows the true length.

12.44. Edge view of a plane by revolution. For some problems, it may be desirable to determine the edge view of a plane by revolution. This is accomplished by revolving the plane about an axis in a manner such that each of the lines will have the same angular displacement as shown in Fig. 12.39. The method, as applied, consists of selecting a principal line in the plane and revolving this line, along with the other lines of the plane, until the principal line appears as a point, for, as has been proven elsewhere, when any line in a plane projects as a point in one view, the plane will appear as an edge (line) in that view.

Given: The plane ABC.

Solution: Select a principal line in the plane, in this case the line AX. Revolve the line AX about a vertical axis through point A until the line appears as a point in the F-view. Revolve points B and C about the same axis and through the same angle. This is done by first revolving b^H and c^H along circular paths to the new positions b^H_r and c^H_r in the H-view. The revolved F-view, projected from the H-view revolved, then shows the edge view of the given plane.

In studying the illustration, it should be noted that in the front view, where the axis would be seen in true length, that the points move in a direction perpendicular to the axis.

When the revolution of a plane has been a step in the solution of a problem, the student should keep in mind the fact that revolving the plane has changed its spatial relationship with other points and/or lines in the problem unless they too have been revolved as were points B and C.

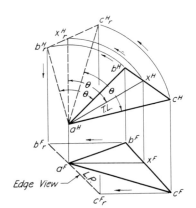

Fig. 12.39. Edge view of a plane by revolution.

12.45. True shape of a plane by revolution. The true shape of a plane may be easily found by first revolving to find the edge view of the plane as explained in Sec. 12.44. Then a second revolution of the plane must be made, about an axis that appears as a point along the edge view, until the plane is parallel to a principal plane of projection as shown in Fig. 12.40. The true shape view of the plane will then appear on the principal plane to which the given plane is now parallel. In the illustration, the plane was first revolved about an imaginary vertical axis having an implied point projection at a^H and then about an axis appearing as a point at $c^F_{r_1}$, on the edge view until the plane was parallel to the H-plane of projection. In the true shape view $(a^H_{r_2} b^H_{r_2} c^H_{r_1})$ the principal line AX again shows true length.

12.46. To draw the views of a line that makes specified angles with two of the principal planes of projection. In Fig. 12.41, the solution shown is for a line 1¾ in. long through A, making an angle of 45° with the H-plane and 30° with the F-plane. As illustrated by the pictorial representation, this line is an element that is common to two right cones whose slant heights are equal. The apex of both cones is at A and the required line is the common element AB.

Solution: (1) Starting with the F-view, draw the triangular representation of a right cone, all of whose elements make 45° with

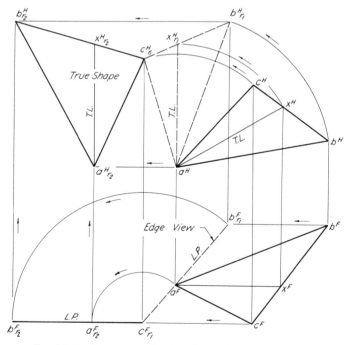

Fig. 12.40. True shape of a plane by revolution.

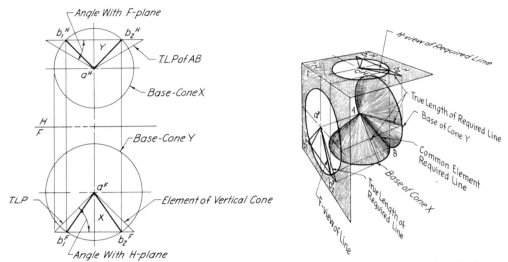

Fig. 12.41. Line that makes specified angles with the principal planes of projection.

the horizontal and are 1¾ in. long. Draw the circular view of the base of this cone in the *H*-view. (2) In the *H*-view, draw the triangular representation of a right cone having all elements at 30° with the *F*-plane and 1¾ in. long. Draw the circular view of this cone in the *F*-view. Point *B*, the other end of the required line, is at the intersection of the bases of these cones (see pictorial). When only the angles are specified, there are eight possible positions for a line through point *A*. Two of these positions are shown in the illustration.

SURFACES: SINGLE-CURVED AND WARPED

12.47. Curved surfaces. There are situations encountered in engineering practice where both the engineer and engineering draftsman must be familiar with single-curved and warped surfaces. The draftsman in particular must be capable of preparing correct representations of these surfaces since a wide variety of mechanical parts, such as gears, cams, and screw conveyors, depend upon curved and warped surfaces for proper performance of their function. Elsewhere, contoured surfaces are encountered on chutes, dams, ship hulls, automobile bodies, aircraft fuselages, and building roofs. The engineer on his part must have at least a basic knowledge of the solution of problems relating to curved and warped surfaces for the success of a design, requiring such surfaces, is his responsibility alone. Sufficient information is given in this chapter to solve ordinary problems. More complete coverage may be found in the textbooks listed in the Bibliography under Descriptive Geometry.

12.48. Classification of surfaces. As stated in Sec. 13.2, those surfaces that are generated by a moving straight line, called a genera-trix, are known as *ruled surfaces*, while those generated by a curved line are known as *double-curved surfaces*. Only ruled surfaces (single-curved and warped) will be treated in the discussions that follow. Read Secs. 13.2 and 13.3.

12.49. Terms relating to the generation of surfaces. The follow-ing terms will be used in discussions covering the generation and delineation of surfaces:

Surface–the area generated by a moving line (see Fig. 12.42).

Generatrix–a straight or curved line, the movement of which generates a surface (see Fig. 12.42). Any specific position of the generatrix is an element of the surface.

Directrix–a line (straight or curved) which guides the movement of the generatrix. A surface may have one or more directrices (Fig. 12.42).

Director–a plane to which a generatrix, as it moves, remains parallel (Fig. 12.42).

Plane surface–a surface generated by a straight-line generatrix, guided by parallel straight-line directrices (Fig. 12.42).

Ruled surface–a surface generated by a straight line (cylinder, cone, and convolute). A ruled surface is developable (see Figs. 12.42 and 12.45).

Single-curved surface–a ruled surface (developable) having either parallel or intersecting elements.

Double-ruled surface–a surface that can be ruled by two differ-ent straight line generatrices. It is a surface on which two intersecting lines may be drawn through any point (Fig. 12.42–hyperbolic paraboloid).

Warped surface–a ruled surface (nondevelopable) in which con-secutive straight line elements are nonparallel and do not inter-sect (Fig. 12.42–hyperboloid of revolution and cylindroid).

Double-curved surface–a surface generated by a moving curved line (sphere, ellipsoid, torus, paraboloid of revolution, hyper-boloid of revolution, etc.) (see Figs. 4.63 and 12.47).

Surface of revolution–a surface generated by either a straight- or curved-line generatrix rotating about an axis. When a straight-line generatrix is either parallel to or intersects the axis, a single-curved surface is generated. When the straight-line generatrix is not parallel to the axis and does not intersect it, a warped surface, known as a hyperboloid of revolution of one nappe (one sheet), is generated (see Fig. 12.47).

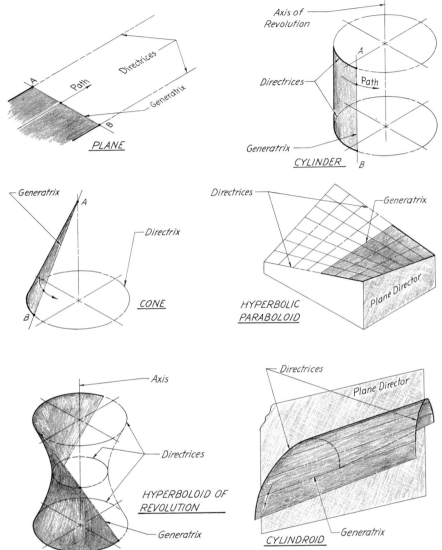

Fig. 12.42. Generated surfaces-plane, single-curved and warped.

12.50. Single-curved surfaces. The three types of single-curved surfaces are cylinders, cones, and convolutes.

As shown in Fig. 12.42 a cylinder is generated by a straight-line generatrix moving parallel to another straight line serving as an axis of revolution. The directrix may be any curved line but usually it will be either circular or elliptical.

A cone is generated by the motion of a straight-line generatrix having one end at a fixed point and the other end on a curved line directrix as shown in Fig. 12.42.

A convolute surface is generated by the motion of a straight line that constantly remains tangent to a space curve. As shown in Fig. 12.45 a helical convolute is generated when the space curve is a helix. In practice, the surface is usually limited by a horizontal base plane where the intersection is the involute of the base circle of the cylindrical helix.

12.51. Warped surfaces. A warped surface is generated by a straight-line generatrix that is constantly changing in direction and it may be said that for each type of warped surface the generatrix moves in accordance with a law associated with that particular type of surface. In general the common warped surfaces are generated by using either: (1) two linear directrices and a generatrix always at a constant angle with one directrix, (2) three linear directrices, or (3) two linear directrices along with a plane director. The various types of helicoids are generated through the use of the two directrices and a generatrix in motion at a constant angle with one directrix as mentioned in (1). For hyperboloids of revolution three directrices may be used [item (2)]. The hyperbolic paraboloids, the conoids, and the cylindroids are all generated by a straight-line generatrix moving parallel to a plane director while touching two linear directrices.

12.52. Tangents to curves. Theoretically, a straight line is tangent to a curved line when both coincide for an infinitesimal distance at the tangent point, the point of contact. To satisfy this definition of tangency, the straight-line tangent must lie in the same plane as the curve at the point of tangency. In testing for the tangency on an orthographic drawing, it is necessary to know that when a line is tangent to a curve this tangent relationship will appear in all views. This being true one should not assume that a line is tangent to a curve merely because there is an appearance of tangency in one of the orthographic views.

In Fig. 12.43(a), (b), (c), and (d) the geometrical methods are shown that are commonly used for constructing straight-line tangents to the conic curves. Since the construction in each case has already been explained in Chapter 4, all discussion has been purposely omitted here.

Since the generatrix for a helical convolute is a straight line moving always tangent to a helix, it is necessary that one be able to draw a tangent to a helix before he attempts to construct the representation of a helical convolute (read Sec. 4.64). To allow a choice of procedures, alternate methods for constructing a tangent to a helix have been shown in Fig. 12.43(e). Both are closely based on the same principle. In the H-view, the projection of the tangent XY will be tangent to the circular right section of the cylinder at point 5. Then, knowing that the slope of the tangent at point 5 will be equal to the helix angle (see development) an auxiliary view showing the true slope may be constructed that will give the height distance D of x^F in the frontal view. In applying the second method, the length 5 to y^H is made equal to the arc length 5–3 so that the height of Y in the frontal view will be the same as the height of point 3 and y^F will be on the line through 3.

12.53. To draw a line or plane tangent to a curved surface. A line is tangent to a surface when it is tangent to a line on the surface. In Fig. 12.44(a) the line AB is tangent to the cylindrical surface at point T because it is tangent to the circular right section at that point. For the same reason the line CD is tangent to the cone in (b). A line will also be tangent to the surface of a cylinder or cone

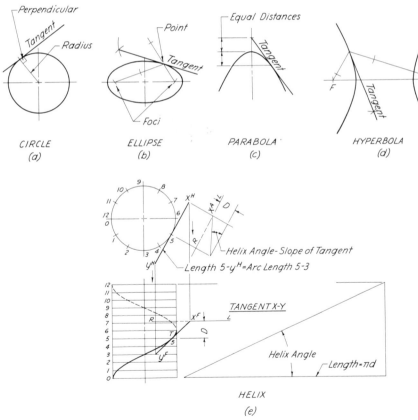

Fig. 12.43. Tangents to curves—conic curves and helix.

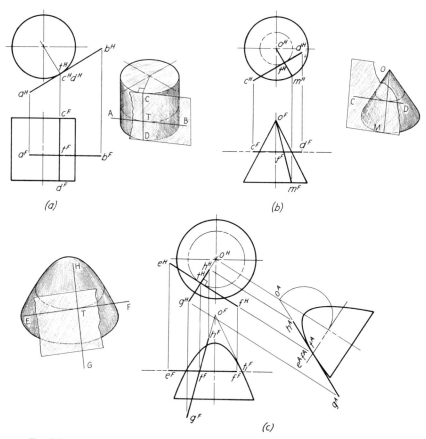

Fig. 12.44. To draw a line or plane tangent to
a curved surface.

when it is drawn tangent to any of the possible sections or base
curves. In the case of cylinders, the needed line might be drawn
tangent to an ellipse representing an elliptical section, while for
cones the curve for the section might be either an ellipse, a parabola, or a hyperbola.

Since any pair of intersecting straight lines determines a plane,
a plane tangent to a single-curved surface at a given point can be
defined by an element of the surface and a line tangent to the surface through the point, as illustrated in Fig. 12.44(a) and (b). In
(a) the tangent plane touches the cylinder all along the element CD
through the point T, and, similarly in (b) the plane is tangent to
the conical surface along OM through T.

In (c) a plane is to be drawn tangent to a paraboloid (surface
of revolution) and point T is the designated point of tangency. The
first of the two lines needed to define the plane can be drawn tan-

gent to the circle which represents the right section that would be cut by a horizontal plane through T (see pictorial). On the multiview representation this is accomplished by drawing $e^H f^H$ tangent to the circle through t^H. Then the F-view of EF ($e^F f^F$) can be easily established by projecting the end-points of the line downward from the H-view to the edge view of the cutting plane. At this point, there are two possible approaches to the same end which is to draw the second line GH tangent to the surface through T. As shown, an A-view can be constructed that will make it possible to draw a view of GH ($g^A h^A$) tangent to the contour curve through a point view of EF ($e^A f^A$). With this done, the H- and F-views of GH can be found by projection. A more practical approach, however, is to assume that point T can be revolved in the horizontal cutting plane until it lies on the contour curve in the F-view at $t_1{}^F$. The line drawn tangent to the curve at $t_1{}^F$ locates o^F on the axis. Then, since point O will not change position when point T is counterrevolved back to its original position, $o^F t^F$ will establish the position of the F-view of GH ($g^F h^F$). The required tangent plane has now been defined by the intersecting lines EF and GH.

Some knowledge of planes that are tangent to surfaces of revolution is essential for under certain conditions a tangent line can best be established by first locating a tangent plane.

12.54. To draw the representation of a helical convolute. As stated in Sec. 12.50, a helical convolute is generated by the motion of a straight line that constantly remains tangent to a helix. Such a surface is theoretically unlimited in extent; however, in practice it is usually limited in some manner as shown in Fig. 12.45 where the surface was purposely extended to the horizontal plane of the base. The intersection of the convolute and the horizontal plane in this case is the involute of the circular base of the helix cylinder (read Sec. 4.57). The first step in preparing a multiview representation of a helical convolute, similar to the one illustrated is to construct, say a three-quarter turn helix, using the given diameter and lead. Then, the elements shown in the H-view are drawn tangent to the circle view of the helix at the division points. With this accomplished the involute to the base circle, that will establish the base points of the elements, must be drawn in the H-view, beginning with point A which is the starting point of the helix in the base plane. The F-views of the elements are drawn from their respective points of tangency on the helix to their base points as located in the F-view. The procedure to be followed in constructing a helix is explained in Sec. 4.64.

A helical convolute of this general form might be the surface of a conveyor screw. Convolute surfaces often form transition pieces.

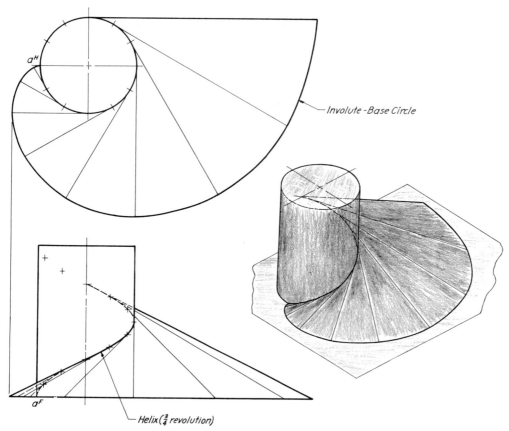

Fig. 12.45. Right-hand helical convolute—extended to the base plane of the cylinder.

12.55. To draw the representation of a right helicoid.

The right helicoid can be thought of as being generated by a straight-line generatrix moving perpendicular to the axis and always in contact with an inner helix and an outer helix that are coaxial. A helicoid is represented by its constructed helices and elements as illustrated in Fig. 12.46 where one full turn of the helices is shown. In the top view the elements appear as radial lines, while in the front view they are horizontal. Equal divisions of the lead and equally spaced division points on the circumference of each of the helix circles establish the positions of the end-points on equally spaced elements. It may be said then, that the drawing of the representation of a right helicoid in its simplest form involves the construction of two cylindrical helices having the same lead and starting with the same element. It should be noted from Fig. 12.46 that visibility is treated as if the inner cylinder were opaque.

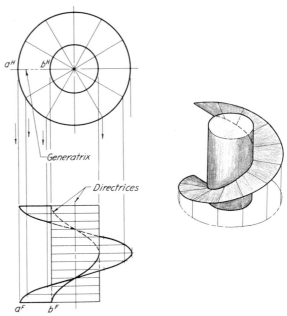

Fig. 12.46. A right helicoid.

The procedure to be followed in constructing a helix is explained in Sec. 4.64. The construction of an oblique helicoid, having a generatrix that intersects the axis at a constant angle other than 90°, is similar to the construction already described for the right helicoid.

12.56. To draw a hyperboloid of revolution. A hyperboloid of revolution of one nappe is usually generated by a straight-line generatrix in contact with three circular directrices centered on the same axis as shown by the pictorial drawing in Fig. 12.42. In Fig. 12.47, the generatrix is the line AB intersecting the directrices at points 1 and 1' and the gorge circle at a point where the line will be closest to the axis about which it revolves. A hyperboloid of revolution is delineated by drawing a series of elements representing successive positions of the generating line (see Sec. 12.51). The H- and F-views of an element of the surface, as for example 1–1' in Fig. 12.47, are determined by: (1) drawing $a^H b^H$ tangent to the gorge circle in the H-view, (2) finding the intersection points 1 and 1' of the line AB and the two circular directrices in the H-view, and (3) projecting points 1 and 1' to the F-view. Since two positions of the element are possible from this H-view projection of the generatrix two elements 1–1' could be drawn in the front view, each sloping in an opposite direction with the one shown by a broken line being an element of the second generation. After additional

elements, such as 2–2′ and 3–3′, representing successive positions
of the generatrix AB have been drawn, the representation may be
completed by drawing the hyperbolic outline using the elements as
an envelope. Should additional points be needed on the hyperbolic
outline of the F-view, such as x_R and y_R, any point on any element
may be revolved along a circular path until it is in a position to be
on the contour outline. For example, either point x^1, x^2, or x^3 can
be selected and moved along its circular path into position by first
revolving the H-view of the selected point to the horizontal center
line and then projecting downward to a horizontal line drawn
through the original position of x^1 in the F-view. This is equivalent
to revolving a point on the surface along a path around a circular
right section. Points on the lower portion of the outline, such as
y_R, would be found in a similar manner.

The hyperboloid, being a double-ruled surface, may be fabricated
using steel rods welded into a lattice work with the rods having the
positions of elements of two generations. Some cooling towers have
been constructed in this manner. A more important application,
however, arises in the design of skew gearing, that is, the design of
hypoid gears.

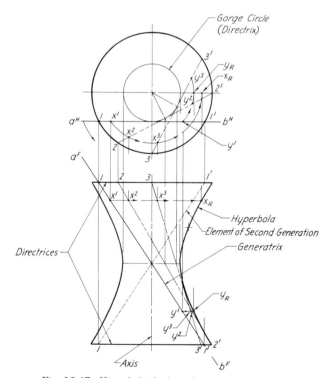

Fig. 12.47. Hyperboloid of revolution.

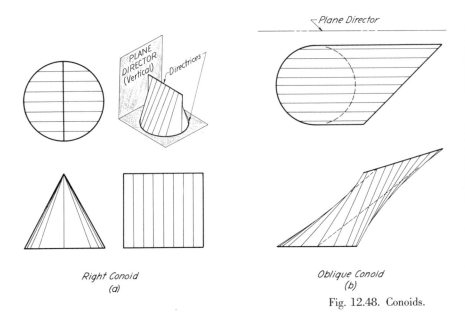

Right Conoid
(a)

Oblique Conoid
(b)

Fig. 12.48. Conoids.

12.57. To draw the representation of a conoid. The conoid is a warped surface that is generated by a straight-line generatrix moving in contact with a curved-line directrix and a straight-line directrix while remaining parallel to a plane director (see Sec. 12.51). Conoids are represented as shown in Fig. 12.48 by drawing the two directrices and a series of elements. In both (a) and (b) the directrices are the circle and straight line, as is indicated on the pictorial drawing in (a). It should be noted that the elements of the oblique conoid meet the straight-line directrix at an angle other than 90° and that the straight-line directrix is not perpendicular to the plane director as in the case of the right conoid. However, in both (a) and (b) the plane director is a frontal plane that has an edge view representation in the H-view.

12.58. To draw the representation of a cylindroid. A cylindroid is generated by a straight-line generatrix moving parallel to a plane director and in contact with two linear curved-line directrices. This warped surface is represented orthographically by showing the directrices in both views and by drawing a selected series of elements. It should be noted in Fig. 12.49 that a vertical plane director was used, and that the H-view of the elements were drawn parallel to the line view of this plane to which they must be parallel by definition. In making this drawing, the points of intersection of the elements and the line views of the directrices in the H-view were projected to the F-view to establish the F-views of the elements.

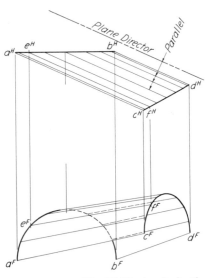

Fig. 12.49. A cylindroid.

Ordinarily this surface is used to connect curves at different levels that lie in nonparallel planes, as in the case of the example shown.

12.59. To draw the representation of a hyperbolic paraboloid. This warped surface is generated by a straight-line generatrix moving in contact with two skew lines while always remaining parallel to a plane director. In Fig. 12.50, *AB* and *CD* are the given directrices. With the views of these linear directrices drawn and the position of the vertical plane director established (see *H*-view) each directrix was divided into the same number of equal parts, in this illustration, eight. Then, since the plane director is vertical, the *H*-views of the elements had to be drawn first before they could be located in the *F*-view. Practically, it is customary to number the division points consecutively along each directrix in both views and then draw each straight-line element through points having corresponding numbers as shown. The fact that this surface may be doubly ruled by taking the first and last elements of the first generation as directrices of the second generation (see Fig. 12.42) makes it possible to construct the strongly braced curved surfaces of roofs using straight members. In addition, this warped surface is quite commonly used for bridge abutments, for wing walls, and for the bows of ships.

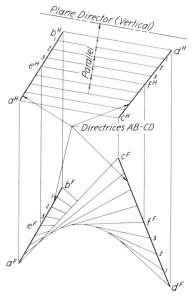

Fig. 12.50. A hyperbolic paraboloid.

PROBLEMS

The problems of this chapter have been selected and arranged to offer the student an opportunity to apply the basic principles of descriptive geometry.

The problems in Groups I to V and VIII can be reproduced to a suitable size by transferring the needed distances from the drawing to the scale that has been provided for each group of problems. The distances, as they are determined, should be laid off on the drawing paper using a full-size scale. The spacing between views may be increased, if necessary, to prevent the possible overlapping of the views of the finished drawing.

All of the drawings of a group in the groups mentioned above may be reproduced on a $11'' \times 17''$ sheet of drawing paper, or one or more problems, as selected and assigned, may be drawn on an $8\frac{1}{2}'' \times 11''$ sheet.

1. (Fig. 12.51.) Group I. This group of problems offers a student the opportunity to visualize space situations and to determine the position of lines by applying the principles of projection.

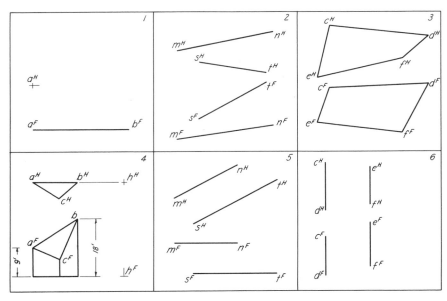

Fig. 12.51. Problems, Group I.

1. Draw the *H*-view of the 3.4 in. line *AB*.

2. Show proof that the lines *ST* and *MN* are or are not in a plane.

3. Show proof that *ECDF* is or is not a plane.

4. *By observation only*, estimate the height of the post *H* shown in the *H*-view and partially drawn in the *F*-view. The top of the post is in the plane of *ABC*.

5. Without using additional views show proof that lines *MN* and *ST* are or are not in a plane.

6. Show proof that the lines *CD* and *EF* are not parallel.

2. (Fig. 12.52.) Group II. These problems are intended to give some needed practice in manipulating views to obtain certain relationships of points and lines.

1. Determine the distance between points *A* and *B*.

2. Draw the *H*- and *F*-views of a ½-in. perpendicular erected from point *N* of the line *MN*.

3. Draw the *H*-view of the 3¾ in. line *ST*.

4. Draw the *H*- and *F*-views of a plane represented by an equilateral triangle and containing line *AB* as one of the edges. The added plane *ABC* is to be at an angle of 30° with plane *ABDE*.

5. If the figure *MNOP* is a plane surface, an edge view of the surface would appear as a line. Draw such a view to determine whether or not *MNOP* is a plane.

6. A vertical pole with top O is held in place by three guy wires. Determine the slope in tangent value of the angle for the guy wire which has a bearing of N23°W.

3. (Fig. 12.53.) Group III. This group of problems offers the opportunity to determine the piercing point of a line and plane. Included also is the requirement to determine the visibility of lines in views.

1. Complete the H- and F-views of the tetrahedron $ABCD$. Show proof for the visibility of the lines.

2. The arrow S will pierce the plane $ABCD$ at point P. Draw the F (frontal) view of the arrow.

3. Two views of a sphere and two views of an arrow are shown. The arrow moves in the direction shown at S^H. Locate the F- and H-views of the piercing point where the arrow enters the sphere.

4. Two views of a sphere and two views of an arrow are shown. Without using an ellipse in your construction, locate the F- and H-views of the piercing point where the arrow enters the sphere.

5. F (frontal) and A (auxiliary) views of a square base pyramid with vertex at O are shown incomplete. Complete the two views and show proof of the visibility of the lines.

6. H- and F-views of a cone and an arrow are shown. Show the H- and F-views of the piercing points of the arrow as it enters and passes out of the cone.

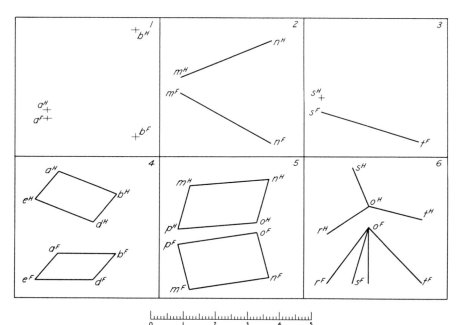

Fig. 12.52. Problems, Group II.

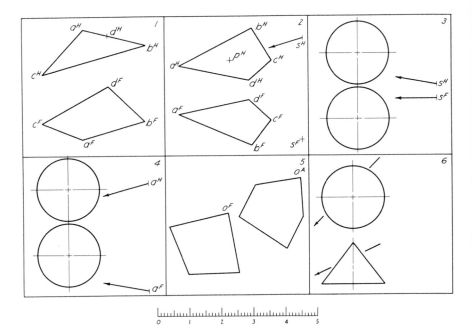

Fig. 12.53. Problems, Group III.

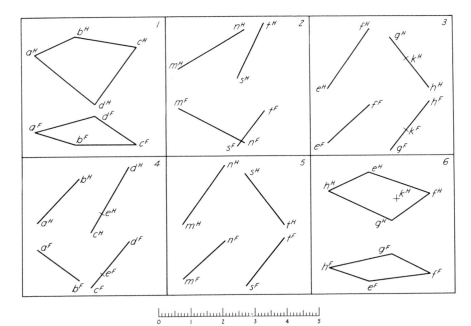

Fig. 12.54. Problems, Group IV.

4. (Fig. 12.54.) Group IV. In this group of problems it is required to determine the shortest distance between skew lines and the angle formed by intersecting lines.

1. Show proof that the plane *ABCD* is an oblique plane.

2. Determine the shortest distance between the lines *MN* and *ST*.

3. Through point *K* on line *GH* draw the *F*- and *H*-views of a line that will be perpendicular to line *EF*.

4. Determine the angle between line *AB* and a line intersecting *AB* and *CD* at the level of point *E*.

5. Through a point on line *MN* that is 1¼ in. from point *N*, draw the *F*- and *H*-views of a line that will be perpendicular to line *ST*.

6. Erect a 1 in. perpendicular at point *K* in the plane *EFGH*. Connect the outer end-point *L* of the perpendicular with *F*. Determine the angle between *LF* and *KF*.

5. (Fig. 12.55.) Group V. These problems require that the student determine the angle between a line and a plane and the angle between two given planes.

1. Determine the angle between the planes *MNQP* and *RST*.

2. Determine the angle between the line *ST* and:
    (a) The *H*-plane.
    (b) The *F*-plane.

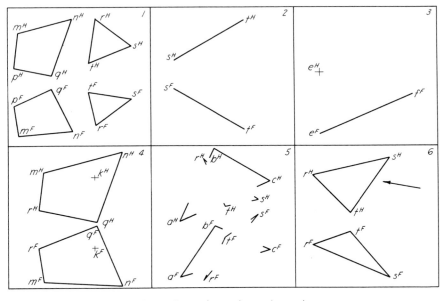

Fig. 12.55. Problems, Group V.

3. The line *EF* has a bearing of N53°E. What angle does this line make with the *P*-plane?

4. Draw the *F*- and *H*-views of a line through point *K* that forms an angle of 35° with plane *MNQR*.

5. The top and front views of planes *ABC* and *RST* are partially drawn.
    (a) Complete the views including the line of intersection.
    (b) Determine the angle between the line of intersection and the *H* plane of projection.

6. Two views of a plane *RST* and the top view of an arrow are shown. The arrow, pointing downward and toward the left, is in a plane that forms an angle of 68° with plane *RST*. The arrow point is ¼ in. from the plane *RST*.
    (a) Draw the front view of the arrow.
    (b) Draw the top and front views of the line of intersection of the 68° plane and plane *RST*.

The following two groups of problems have been designed for a single problem on an 8½″ × 11″ sheet of drawing paper, using the following coordinate system:

A point is designated as: *A*(2½, 1, 3). This is interpreted as follows:

1st number	the distance, in inches, of the front and top views of point *A* to the right of the left edge of the sheet.
2nd number	the distance, in inches, of the front view above the lower edge of the sheet.
3rd number	the distance, in inches, of the top view above the lower edge of the sheet.

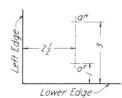

The illustration shows the plotting of point *A*(2½, 1, 3). A point given as *B*(3, 2, *z*) would mean that the exact position of the top view is unknown.

6. Group VI. This group offers practice in the manipulation of lines and planes.

1. Given plane *A*(3, 3, 5) *B*(4, 4, 7½) *C*(5½, 1½, 6) and points *R*(3½, 3, *z*), *S*(6½, *y*, 7), and *T*(1½, 2½, 6½).
    (a) Determine whether or not point *T* is coplanar with plane *ABC*.
    (b) Determine the missing views of points *R* and *S* so that the points lie in the plane *ABC*.

2. Given point *D*(3, 3, 4½). Construct a line *DE* which has a bearing of N60°E, slopes downward at 30°, and is 4 in. long.

3. Given lines *A*(1, 3, 5) *B*(3, 2, 6) and *C*(2½, 2, 4) *D*(3½, 4, 6). Determine the angle between these skew lines.

4. Given the lines *AB* and *CD* as designated in Problem 3. Determine the shortest horizontal line between the skew lines.

5. Given the lines *AB* and *CD* as designated in Problem 3. Determine the shortest line that slopes downward from *CD* to *AB* at 30°.

6. Given plane *R*(4½, 2, 4½) *S*(6½, 1½, 6½) *T*(7½, 3½, 5½). Determine the true shape of the plane using the methods of revolution.

7. Group VII. These problems offer practice in the perpendicular and parallel relations of lines and planes.

1. Given plane *A*(3, 2½, 6½) *B*(4½, 4½, 5½) *C*(5½, 3½, 7½) and point *M*(3½, 4, 8).
    (a) Construct a line *MN* perpendicular to plane *ABC*. Point *N* is 2 in. to the right of point *M*.
    (b) Find the point where line *MN* intersects plane *ABC* and show proper visibility with respect to the plane.

2. Given line *C*(1½, 5, 6½) *D*(3½, 3, 5½) and point *K*(7, 4, 7). Construct a plane *KLM* which is perpendicular to line *CD*. The lines *KL* and *KM* can be of any length.

3. Given planes *M*(1, 3½, 5½) *N*(2½, 2½, 8) *O*(3½, 4½, 7) and *R*(4½, 3, 6) *S*(5, 5, 8) *T*(7, y, 7½). Complete the front view of plane *RST* so that plane *RST* is perpendicular to plane *MNO*.

4. Given plane *A*(2, 6½, 8) *B*(3, 6, 8½) *C*(4, 7, 7½) and line *D*(5, 6, z) *E*(6½, 7, 8). Construct line *DE* parallel to plane *ABC*. This problem fits the upper half of an 8½″ × 11″ sheet.

5. Given lines *R*(1½, 1½, 4½) *T*(3½, 2½, 3) and *M*(5, 2½, 3) *N*(7, 2, 4). Construct a plane *MNO* that is parallel to line *RT*. This problem fits the lower half of an 8½″ × 11″ sheet.

6. Given planes *A*(2, 6½, 8) *B*(3, 6, 7½) *C*(4, 7, 8½) and *M*(5, 6, 7½) *N*(6, 7, 8½) *O*(7½, 6½, 8). Determine whether or not plane *ABC* is parallel to plane *MNO*. Show proof.
This problem fits the upper half of an 8½″ × 11″ sheet.

7. Given planes *D*(1½, 2, 4) *E*(3, 1, 4½) *F*(4, 2½, 3) and *R*(4½, y, 3½) *S*(6, 1½, 4½) *T*(7, 2, z). Complete the views of plane *RST* so that it is parallel to plane *DEF*.
This problem fits the lower half of an 8½″ × 11″ sheet.

8. (Fig. 12.56.) Group VIII. These problems are intended to offer a general review of the fundamental methods as presented in this chapter.

1. Determine the angle between the two center lines at each of the bends in the rod.

2. The *F*- and *H*-views of two rods are shown. Determine the shortest distance between the centerlines.

3. The walls of a cooling room are shown in plan and elevation (*F*- and *H*-views). Determine the length of the pipe in the given position.

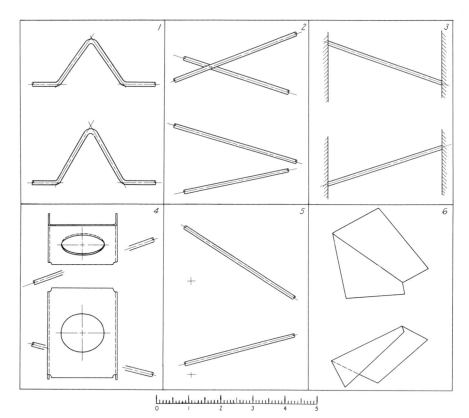

Fig. 12.56. Problems, Group VIII.

4. Determine the location of the point where the centerline of the rod would pierce the plane of the bulkhead shown.

5. The cross lines indicate the position of a point P from which it is desired to know the shortest distance to the centerline of the rod. Determine this distance.

6. The F- and H-views of intersecting planes are shown. Determine the true angle between these planes.

9. (Fig. 12.57.) A trough for the passage of cans of 4 in. diam. was made of hard wood ¾ in. thick. The V shape of the trough was such that the centerlines of the cans and the top edge of the trough were in the same plane. The inside surfaces of the trough measured 5 in. along a side. Show the H- and F-views of an 18 in. section of the trough using the F- and H-views of the centerline AB as the centerline of the cans.

10. (Fig. 12.58.) The F- and H-views of a certain control system involving pipe lines and cables operating over pulleys are shown. Find the shortest distance between the cable and the outside of the

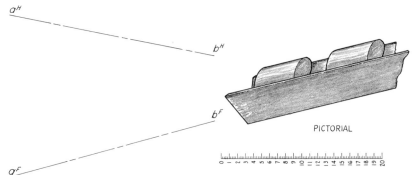

Fig. 12.57. Trough.

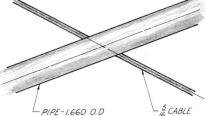

pipe (O.D. 1.660 in.) at a position where the cable runs under the pipe.

11. (Fig. 12.59.) An airplane takes off from a carrier at point *C* and flies in a direction of N68°W while gaining altitude at an angle of 15°. At what horizontal distance from the take-off point will the plane be at the nearest vertical height from the ground? Use the tangent method for laying out the direction of flight.

12. (Fig. 12.60.) A vein of ore, the top layer of which proved to be a plane surface, was located by the following borings: Hole A, at a depth of 15.0 ft; B, at a depth of 26.0 ft; C, at a depth of 68.0 ft; and D, at a depth of 80.0 ft.

Because an old riverbed provided a roadbed for transportation to a highway near by, it was decided to tunnel directly west and downward at an angle of 15° with the horizontal from point *M* to gain access to the ore vein.

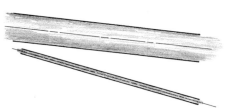

Fig. 12.58. Clearance for control cable.

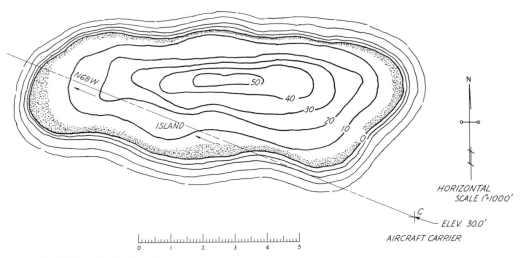

Fig. 12.59. Flight of airplane.

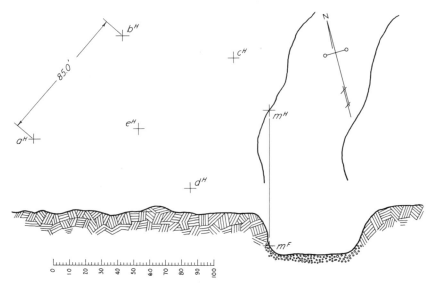

Fig. 12.60. Tunnel problem.

(a) What was the length of the tunnel needed to reach the ore vein?

(b) How deep would a check hole need to be drilled at position *E* to strike the ore?

13. (Fig. 12.61.) A plot of ground is shown with contours and sections. Along cutting plane *AB* the positions for a number of drilled holes are shown. Each of the drilled holes struck a vein of ore at depths as follows:

    Hole 1 on contour 40′ at 15 ft.

    Hole 2 on contour 50′ at 34 ft.

    Hole 3 on contour 30′ at 20 ft.

Another hole on contour 40′ (4) struck the ore vein at 10 ft. Determine the "strike" and the "dip" of the ore vein.

14. (Fig. 12.62.) Group IX. These problems are intended to offer the opportunity to apply some of the methods that are commonly used in preparing multiview drawings of curved and warped surfaces.

1. Assuming the helix cylinder to be opaque, draw the front and top views of the helical convolute that would be generated by a line moving tangent to the given left-hand helix. Show the intersection of the convolute and the indicated horizontal plane.

2. Construct the two views of one turn of a right helicoid with the generating line being perpendicular to and intersecting the axis.

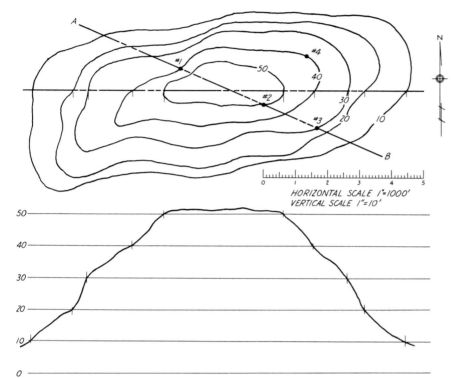

Fig. 12.61. Strike and dip problem.

The helicoidal surface is to be considered to extend only between the cylinders.

3. Draw the two views of a forming roller that is a circular hyperboloid of revolution.

4. Draw the top and side views of the conoid that serves as a transition between a semicircular form and the upper edge *AB* of a vertical rectangular plane.

5. Draw the *H*- and *F*-views of the cylindroid.

6. Draw the *H*- and *F*-views of a hyperbolic paraboloid using the two skew lines *AB* and *CD* as directrices.

15. A chute for carrying packages from the second floor to the mail room 12 ft below is to be in the form of a right-hand helicoid of three complete turns. The center core (cylinder) is to be 2 ft in diameter. The package track (helicoidal surface) is to have a width of 3 ft and is to have a 6 in. high guard plate along the outer edge. Draw the top and front views for one turn of the chute.

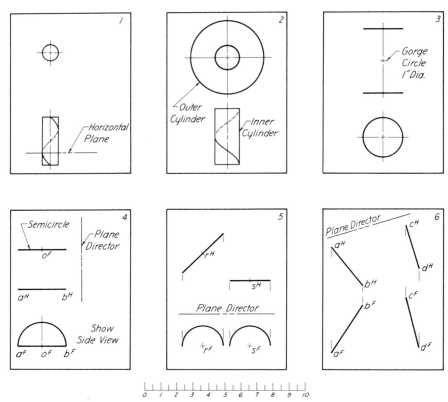

Fig. 12.62. Problems, Group IX.

13

DEVELOPMENTS AND INTERSECTIONS

13.1. Introduction. A comprehensive study of intersections and developments is logically a part of the subject of descriptive geometry. A few of the many practical applications that can be handled without advanced study in projection, however, are presented in this chapter. Desired lines of intersection between geometric surfaces may be obtained by applying the principles of orthographic projection with which the student is already familiar. Although developments are laid out and are not drawn by actual projection in the manner of exterior views, their construction nevertheless requires the application of orthographic projection in finding the true lengths of elements and edges.

13.2. Geometric surfaces. A geometric surface is generated by the motion of a geometric line, either straight or curved. Surfaces that are generated by a moving straight line are known as *ruled surfaces*, and those generated by a curved line are known as *double-curved surfaces*. Any position of the generating line, known as a *generatrix*, is called an *element of the surface*.

Ruled surfaces include planes, single-curved surfaces, and warped surfaces.

A *plane* is generated by a straight line moving in such a manner that one point touches another straight line as it moves parallel to its original position.

A *single-curved surface* is generated by a straight line moving so that in any two of its near positions it is in the same plane.

A *warped surface* is generated by a straight line moving so that it does not lie in the same plane in any two near positions.

Double-curved surfaces include surfaces that are generated by a curved line moving in accordance with some mathematical law.

13.3. Geometric objects. Geometric solids are bounded by geometric surfaces. They may be classified as follows:

1. Solids bounded by plane surfaces:
   Tetrahedron, cube, prism, pyramid, and others.
2. Solids bounded by single-curved surfaces:
   Cone and cylinder (generated by a moving straight line).
3. Solids bounded by warped surfaces:
   Conoid, cylindroid, hyperboloid of one nappe, and warped cone.
4. Solids bounded by double-curved surfaces:
   Sphere, spheroid, torus, paraboloid, hyperboloid, and so on (surfaces of revolution generated by curved lines).

A: DEVELOPMENTS

13.4. Introduction. A layout of the complete surface of an object is called a *development* or *pattern*. The development of an object bounded by plane surfaces may be thought of as being obtained by turning the object, as illustrated in Figs. 13.1 and 13.2, so as to unroll the imaginary enclosing surface upon a plane. Practically, the drawing operation consists of drawing the successive surfaces in their true size with their common edges joined.

The surfaces of cones and cylinders also may be unrolled upon a plane. The development of a right cylinder (Fig. 13.3) is a rectangle having a width equal to the altitude of the cylinder and a length equal to the cylinder's computed circumference (πd). The development of a right circular cone (Fig. 13.4) is a sector of a circle having a radius equal to the slant height of the cone and an arc length equal to the circumference of its base.

Warped and double-curved surfaces cannot be developed accurately, but they may be developed by some approximate method. Ordinarily, an approximate pattern will prove to be sufficiently accurate for practical purposes if the material of which the piece is to be made is somewhat flexible.

Plane and single-curved surfaces (prisms, pyramids, cylinders, and cones), which can be accurately developed, are said to be developable. Warped and double-curved surfaces, which can be only approximately developed, are said to be nondevelopable.

13.5. Practical developments. On many industrial drawings, a development must be shown to furnish the necessary information for making a pattern to facilitate the cutting of a desired shape from sheet metal. Because of the rapid advance of the art of manufacturing an ever-increasing number of pieces by folding, rolling, or pressing cut sheet-metal shapes, one must have a broad knowledge of the methods of constructing varied types of developments. Patterns also are used in stone cutting as guides for shaping irregular faces.

A development of a surface should be drawn with the inside face up, as it theoretically would be if the surface were unrolled or unfolded as illustrated in Figs. 13.1–13.4. This practice is further justified because sheet-metal workers must make the necessary punch marks for folding on the inside surface.

Although in actual sheet-metal work extra metal must be allowed for lap at seams, no allowance will be shown on the developments in this chapter. Many other practical considerations have been purposely ignored, as well, in order to avoid confusing the beginner.

13.6. To develop a right truncated prism. Before the development of the lateral surface of a prism can be drawn, the true lengths of the edges and the true size of a right section must be determined. In the right truncated prism, shown in Fig. 13.5, the true lengths

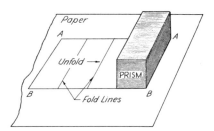

Fig. 13.1. The development of a prism.

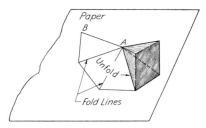

Fig. 13.2. The development of a pyramid.

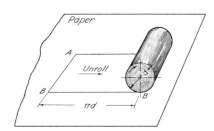

Fig. 13.3. The development of a cylinder.

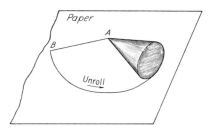

Fig. 13.4. The development of a cone.

of the prism edges are shown in the front view and the true size of the right section is shown in the top view.

The lateral surface is "unfolded" by first drawing a "stretch-out line" and marking off the widths of the faces (distances 1–2, 2–3, 3–4, and so on, from the top view) along it in succession. Through these points light construction lines are then drawn perpendicular to the line 1_D1_D, and the length of the respective edge is set off on each by projecting from the front view. When projecting edge lengths to the development, the points should be taken in a clock-wise order around the perimeter as indicated by the order of the figures in the top view. The outline of the development is completed by joining these points. Thus far, nothing has been said about the lower base or the inclined upper face. These may be joined to the development of the lateral surface, if so desired.

In sheet-metal work, it is usual practice to make the seam on the shortest element in order to save time and conserve solder or rivets.

13.7. To develop an oblique prism. The lateral surface of an oblique prism, such as the one shown in Fig. 13.6, is developed by

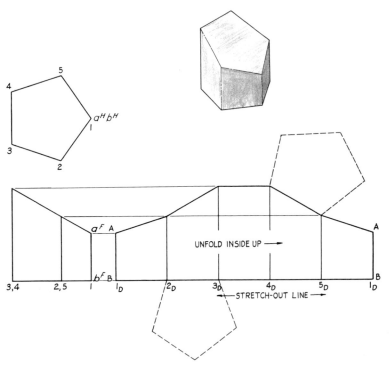

Fig. 13.5. The standard method of developing the lateral surface of a right prism.

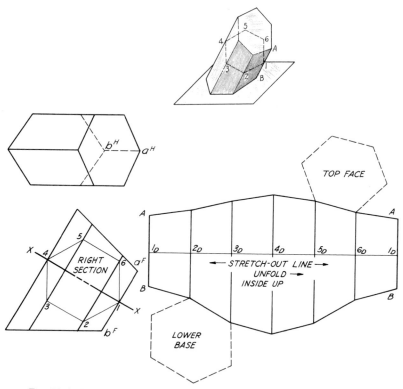

Fig. 13.6. The development of an oblique prism.

the same general method used for a right prism. Similarly, the true lengths of the edges are shown in the front view, but it is necessary to find the true size of the right section by auxiliary plane construction. The widths of the faces, as taken from the auxiliary right section, are set off along the stretch-out line, and perpendicular construction lines representing the edges are drawn through the division points. The lengths of the portions of each respective edge, above and below plane XX, are transferred to the corresponding line in development. Distances above plane XX are laid off above the stretch-out line, and distances below XX are laid off below it. The development of the lateral surface is then completed by joining the end-points of the edges by straight lines. Since an actual fold will be made at each edge line when the prism is formed, it is the usual practice to heavy these edge (fold) lines on the development.

The stretch-out line might well have been drawn in a position perpendicular to the edges of the front view (see Fig. 13.7), so that the length of each edge might be projected to the development (as in the case of the right prism).

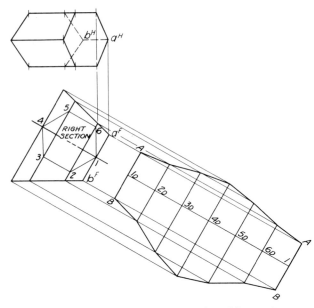

Fig. 13.7. Development of an oblique prism.

13.8. To develop a right cylinder. When the lateral surface of a right cylinder is rolled out upon a plane, the base develops into a straight line (Fig. 13.8). The length of this line, which is equal to the circumference of a right section ($\pi \times$ diam.), may be calculated and laid off as the stretch-out line 1_D1_D.

Since the cylinder can be thought of as being a many-sided prism, the development may be constructed in a manner similar to the method illustrated in Fig. 13.5. The elements drawn on the surface of the cylinder serve as edges of the many-sided prism. Twelve or twenty-four of these elements ordinarily are used, the number depending upon the size of the cylinder. Usually they are spaced by dividing the circumference of the base, as shown by the circle in the top view, into an equal number of parts. The stretch-out line is divided into the same number of equal parts, and perpendicular elements are drawn through each division point. Then the true length of each element is projected to its respective representation on the development, and the development is completed by joining the points with a smooth curve. In joining the points, it is advisable to sketch the curve in lightly, freehand, before using the French curve. Since the surface of the finished cylindrical piece forms a continuous curve, the elements on the development are not heavied. When the development is symmetrical, as in this case, only one-half need be drawn.

A piece of this type might form a part of a two-piece, three-piece,

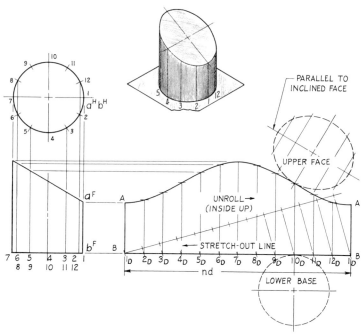

Fig. 13.8. Development of a right circular cylinder.

or four-piece elbow. The pieces are usually developed as illustrated in Fig. 13.9. The stretch-out line of each section is equal in length to the computed perimeter of a right section.

13.9. To develop an oblique cylinder. Since an oblique cylinder theoretically may be thought of as enclosing a regular oblique prism

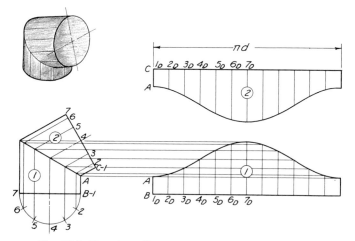

Fig. 13.9. Two-piece elbow.

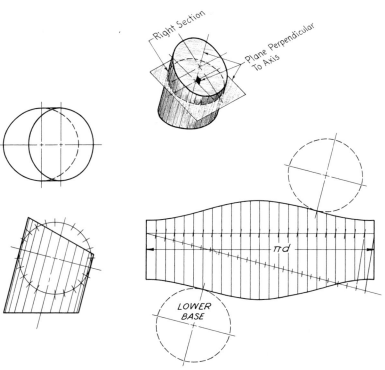

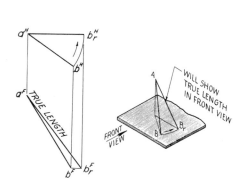

Fig. 13.11. Revolution to position parallel to frontal plane.

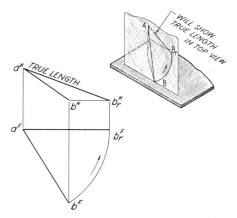

Fig. 13.12. Revolution to position parallel to horizontal plane.

Fig. 13.10. Development of an oblique cylinder.

having an infinite number of sides, the development of the lateral surface of the cylinder shown in Fig. 13.10 may be constructed by using a method similar to the method illustrated in Fig. 13.6. The circumference of the right section becomes stretch-out line 1_D1_D for the development.

13.10. To determine the true length of a line. In order to construct the development of the lateral surface of some objects, it frequently is necessary to determine the true lengths of oblique lines that represent the edges. The general method for determining the true lengths of lines inclined to all of the coordinate planes of projection has been explained in detail in Sec. 12.43. This article should be reviewed before reading the discussion that follows.

If a line is oblique to each of the three planes of projection, none of its principal projections will show its true length. Note in Fig. 13.11 that the principal projections of the line AB are inclined. To determine the true length of AB, it may be revolved into a position parallel to either the H, F, or P coordinate planes, as shown in Figs. 13.11, 13.12, and 13.13. In Fig. 13.11, AB has been revolved into a position parallel to the F (frontal) plane. The view of AB revolved, a^Fb^Fr, shows the true length. In Fig. 13.12, AB was revolved parallel to the H (top) plane, and a^Hb^Hr shows the true length. In Fig. 13.13, the line is shown revolved parallel to the P (profile) coordinate plane.

13.11. True-length diagrams.

When it is necessary, in developing a surface, to find the true lengths of a number of edges or elements, some confusion may be avoided by constructing a true-length diagram adjacent to the orthographic view as shown in Fig. 13.14. The elements were revolved into a position parallel to the F (frontal) plane so that their true lengths show in the diagram. This practice prevents the front view in the illustration from being cluttered with lines, some of which would represent elements and others their true lengths.

Figure 13.15 shows a diagram that gives the true lengths of the edges of the pyramid. Each line representing the true length of an edge is the hypotenuse of a right triangle whose altitude is the altitude of the edge in the front view and whose base is equal to the length of the projection of the edge in the top view. The lengths of the top projections of the edges of the pyramid are laid off horizontally from the vertical line o^FX, which could have been drawn at any distance from the front view. Since all the edges have the same altitude, this line is a common vertical leg for all the right triangles in the diagram. For example, o^FX1' is a true-length triangle having the line o^FX as a vertical leg and $X1'$, which is equal in length to o^H1 in the top view, as a base. Other triangles are o^FX2', o^FX3', o^FX4', and so on. The true-length diagram shown in Fig. 13.14 could very well have been constructed by this method.

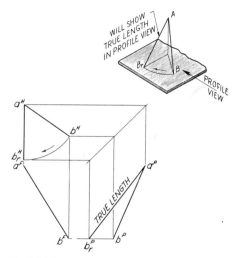

Fig. 13.13. Revolution to position parallel to profile plane.

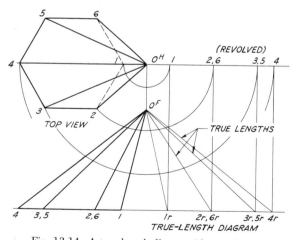

Fig. 13.14. A true-length diagram (the revolution method).

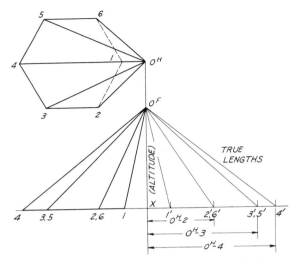

Fig. 13.15. A true-length diagram (right triangle method).

13.12. To develop a right pyramid. To develop (unfold) the lateral surface of a right pyramid, it is first necessary to determine the true lengths of the edges and the true size of the base. With this information, the development can be constructed by laying out the faces in successive order with their common edges joined. If the surface is imagined to be unfolded by turning the pyramid, as shown in Fig. 13.2, each triangular face is revolved into the plane of the paper about the edge that is common to it and the preceding face.

Since the edges of the pyramid shown in Fig. 13.16 are all equal in length, it is necessary only to find the length of the one edge $A1$ by revolving it into the position a^F1r. The edges of the base, 1–2, 2–3, and so on, are parallel to the horizontal plane of projection and consequently show in their true length in the top view. With this information, the development is easily completed by constructing the four triangular surfaces.

13.13. To develop the surface of a frustum of a pyramid. To develop the lateral surface of the frustum of a pyramid (Fig. 13.17), it is necessary to determine the true lengths of edges of the complete pyramid as well as the true lengths of edges of the frustum. The desired development is obtained by first constructing the development of the complete pyramid and then laying off the true lengths of the edges of the frustum on the corresponding lines of the development.

It may be noted with interest that the true length of the edge $B3$ is equal to the length $b'3'$ on the true-length line a^F3', and that the location of point b' can be established by the short-cut method

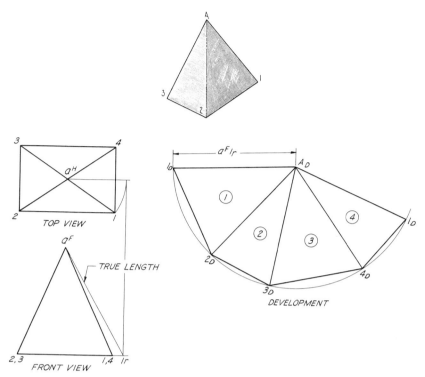

Fig. 13.16. The development of a rectangular right pyramid.

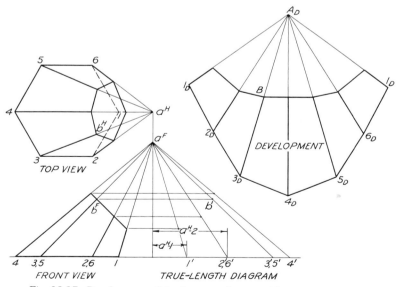

Fig. 13.17. Development of the frustum of a pyramid.

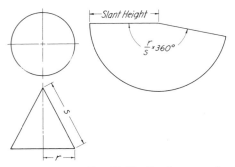

Fig. 13.18. Development of a right cone.

of projecting horizontally from point b^F. Point b' on a^F3' is the true revolved position of point B, because the path of point B is in a horizontal plane that projects as a line in the front view.

13.14. To develop a right cone. As previously explained in Sec. 13.4, the development of a regular right circular cone is a sector of a circle. The development will have a radius equal to the slant height of the cone and an included angle at the center equal to $(r/s) \times 360°$ (Fig. 13.18). In this equation, r is the radius of the base and s is the slant height.

13.15. To develop a right truncated cone. The development of a right truncated cone must be constructed by a modified method of triangulation, in order to develop the outline of the elliptical inclined surface. This commonly used method is based upon the theoretical assumption that a cone is a pyramid having an infinite number of sides. The development of the incomplete right cone shown in Fig. 13.19 is constructed upon a layout of the whole cone by a method similar to the standard method illustrated for the frustum of a pyramid in Fig. 13.17.

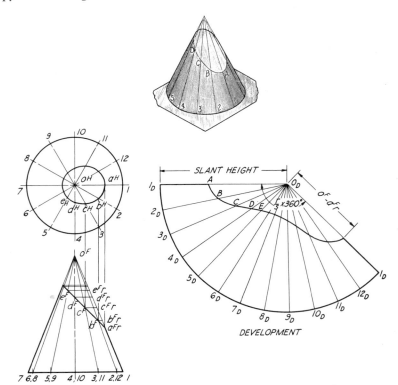

Fig. 13.19. Development of a truncated cone.

Elements are drawn on the surface of the cone to serve as edges of the many-sided pyramid. Either twelve or twenty-four are used, depending upon the size of the cone. Their location is established upon the developed sector by dividing the arc representing the unrolled base into the same number of equal divisions, into which the top view of the base has been divided. At this point in the procedure, it is necessary to determine the true lengths of the elements of the frustum in the same manner that the true lengths of the edges of the frustum of a pyramid were obtained in Fig. 13.17. With this information, the desired development can be completed by setting off the true lengths on the corresponding lines of the development and joining the points thus obtained with a smooth curve.

13.16. The triangulation method of developing approximately developable surfaces. A nondevelopable surface may be developed approximately if the surface is assumed to be composed of a number of small developable surfaces (Fig. 13.21). The particular method ordinarily used for warped surfaces and the surfaces of oblique cones is known as the triangulation method. The procedure consists of completely covering the lateral surface with numerous small triangles that will lie approximately on the surface (Fig. 13.20). These triangles, when laid out in their true size with their common edges joined, produce an approximate development that is accurate enough for most practical purposes.

Although this method of triangulation is sometimes used to develop the lateral surface of a right circular cone, it is not recommended for such a purpose. The resulting development is not as accurate as it would be if constructed by one of the standard methods (see Secs. 13.14 and 13.15).

13.17. To develop an oblique cone using the triangulation method. A development of the lateral surface of an oblique cone is constructed by a method similar to that used for an oblique pyramid. The surface is divided into a number of unequal triangles having sides that are elements on the cone and bases that are the chords of short arcs of the base.

The first step in developing an oblique cone (Fig. 13.22) is to divide the circle representing the base into a convenient number of equal parts and draw elements on the surface of the cone through the division points (1, 2, 3, 4, 5, and so on). To construct the triangles forming the development, it is necessary to know the true lengths of the elements (sides of the triangles) and chords. In the illustration, all the chords are equal. Their true lengths are shown in the top view. The true lengths of the oblique elements may be determined by one of the standard methods explained in Sec. 13.11.

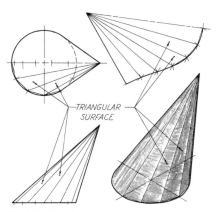

Fig. 13.20. Triangulation of an oblique cone.

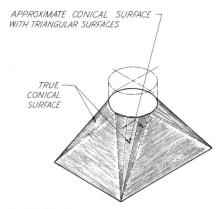

Fig. 13.21. Triangulation of a surface.

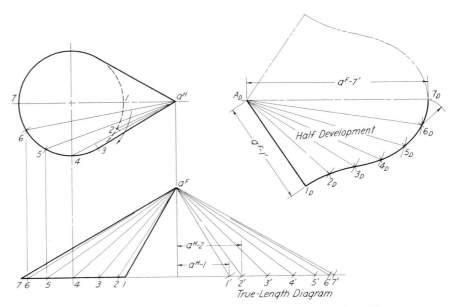

Fig. 13.22. Development of an oblique cone.

Since the seam should be made along the shortest element, $A1$ will lie on the selected starting line for the development and $A7$ will be on the center line. To obtain the development, the triangles are constructed in order, starting with the triangle A–1–2 and proceeding around the cone in a clockwise direction (as shown by the arrow in the top view). The first step in constructing triangle A–1–2 is to set off the true length a^F1' along the starting line. With point A_D of the development as a center, and with a radius equal to a^F2', strike an arc; then, with point 1_D as a center, and with a radius equal to the chord 1–2, strike an arc across the first arc to locate point 2_D. The triangle $A_D2_D3_D$ and the remaining triangles are formed in exactly the same manner. When all the triangles have been laid out, the development of the whole conical surface is completed by drawing a smooth curve through the end-points of the elements.

After the beginner has constructed a few such developments, he will find that much time can be saved by drawing all the long arcs before striking off any of the short ones. To offset any errors in judgment about their approximate correct location, the long arcs may be made fairly long.

13.18. Transition pieces. A few of the many types of transition pieces used for connecting pipes and openings of different shapes and sizes are illustrated pictorially in Fig. 13.23.

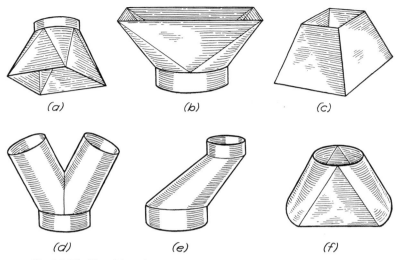

Fig. 13.23. Transition pieces.

13.19. To develop a transition piece connecting rectangular pipes.
The transition piece shown in Fig. 13.24 is designed to connect two
rectangular pipes of different sizes on different axes. Since the piece
is a frustum of a pyramid, it can be accurately developed by the
method explained in Sec. 13.13.

13.20. To develop a transition piece connecting two circular pipes.
The transition piece shown in Fig. 13.25 connects two circular pipes
on different axes. Since the piece is a frustum of an oblique cone,
the surface must be triangulated, as explained in Sec. 13.17, and

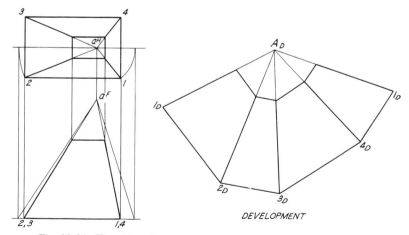

DEVELOPMENT

Fig. 13.24. Transition piece.

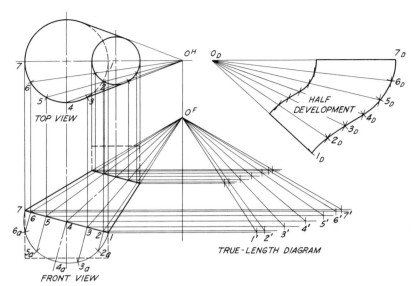

Fig. 13.25. Transition piece connecting two pipes.

the development must be constructed by laying out the triangles in their true size in regular order. The general procedure is the same as that illustrated in Fig. 13.22. In this case, however, since the true size of the base is not shown in the top view, it is necessary to construct a partial auxiliary view to find the true lengths of chords between the end-points of the elements.

13.21. To develop a transition piece connecting a circular and a square pipe. A detailed analysis of the transition piece shown in Fig. 13.26 reveals that it is composed of four isosceles triangles whose bases form the square base of the piece and four conical surfaces that are parts of oblique cones. It is not difficult to develop this type of transition piece because, since the whole surface may be "broken up" into component surfaces, the development may be constructed by developing the first and then each succeeding component surface separately (Fig. 13.21). The surfaces are developed around the piece in a clockwise direction, in such a manner that each successive surface is joined to the preceding surface at their common element. In the illustration, the triangles 1LO, 4LM, 7MN, and 10NO are clearly shown in top view. Two of these, 1LO and 10NO, are visible on the pictorial drawing. The apexes of the conical surfaces are located at the corners of the base.

Before starting the development, it is necessary to determine the true lengths of the elements by constructing a true-length diagram as explained in Sec. 13.11. The true lengths of the edges of the lower base (*LM, MN, NO,* and *OL*) and the true lengths of the chords (1–2, 2–3, 3–4, and so on) of the short arcs of the upper base are shown in the top view. The development is constructed in the following manner: First, the triangle $1_D PL$ is constructed, using the length $p^H l^H$, taken from the top view, and true lengths from the diagram. Next, using the method explained in Sec. 13.17, the conical surface whose apex is at L is developed in an attached position. Triangle $4_D LM$ is then added, and so on, until all component surfaces have been drawn.

13.22. To develop a transition piece having an approximately developable surface by the triangulation method. Figure 13.27 shows a half development of a transition piece that has a warped surface instead of a partially conical one like that discussed in Sec. 13.21. The method of constructing the development is somewhat similar, however, in that it is formed by laying out, in true size, a

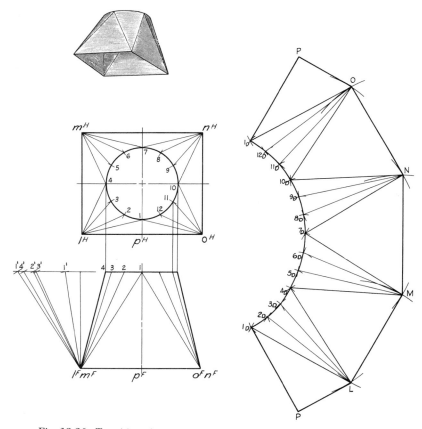

Fig. 13.26. Transition piece connecting a circular and square pipe.

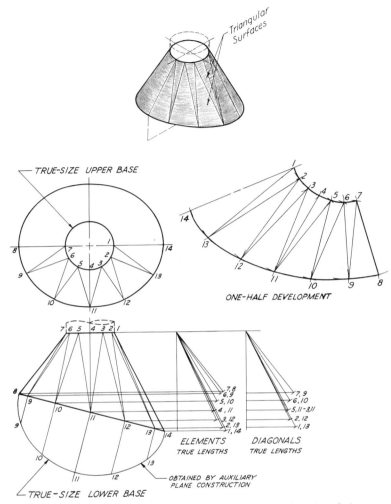

Fig. 13.27. Development of transition piece by triangulation.

number of small triangles that approximate the surface. The true size of the circular intersection is shown in the top view, and the true size of the elliptical intersection is shown in the auxiliary view, which was constructed for that purpose.

The front half of the circle in the top view should be divided into the same number of equal parts as the half-auxiliary view. By joining the division points, the lateral surface may be initially divided into narrow quadrilaterals. These in turn may be subdivided into triangles, by drawing diagonals which, though theoretically they are curved lines, are assumed to be straight. The true lengths of the elements and the diagonals are found by constructing two separate true-length diagrams by the method illustrated in Fig. 13.15.

13.23. To develop a sphere. The surface of a sphere is a double-curved surface that can be developed only by some approximate method. The standard methods commonly used are illustrated in Fig. 13.28.

In (a) the surface is divided into a number of equal meridian sections of cylinders. The developed surfaces of these form an approximate development of the sphere. In drawing the development it is necessary to develop the surface of only one section, for this can be used as a pattern for the developed surface of each of the others.

In (b) the sphere is cut by parallel planes, which divide it into a number of horizontal sections, the surfaces of which approximate the surface of the sphere. Each of these sections may be considered the frustum of a right cone whose apex is located at the intersection of the chords extended.

B: INTERSECTIONS

13.24. Lines of intersection of geometric surfaces. The line of intersection of two surfaces is a line that is common to both. It may

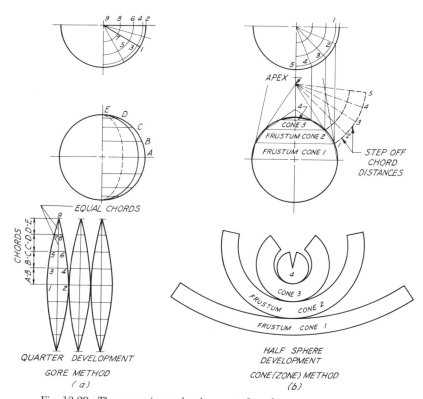

Fig. 13.28. The approximate development of a sphere.

be considered the line that would contain the points in which the elements of one surface would pierce the other. Almost every line on a practical orthographic representation is a line of intersection; therefore, the following discussion may be deemed an extended study of the same subject. The methods presented in this chapter are the recognized easy procedures for finding the more complicated lines of intersection created by intersecting geometric surfaces.

In order to complete a view of a working drawing or a view necessary for developing the surfaces of intersecting geometric shapes, one frequently must find the line of intersection between surfaces. On an ordinary working drawing the line of intersection may be "faked in" through a few critical points. On a sheet-metal drawing, however, a sufficient number of points must be located to obtain an accurate line of intersection and an ultimately accurate development.

The line of intersection of two surfaces is found by determining a number of points common to both surfaces and drawing a line or lines through these points in correct order. The resulting line of intersection may be straight, curved, or straight and curved. The problem of finding such a line may be solved by one of two general methods, depending upon the type of surfaces involved.

For the purpose of simplifying this discussion of intersections, it should be assumed that all problems are divided into these two general groups:

Group I. Problems involving two surfaces, both of which are composed of plane surfaces.

Group II. Problems involving two surfaces which are either single-curved or double-curved.

For instance, the procedure for finding the line of intersection of two prisms is the same as that for finding the line of intersection of a prism and a pyramid; hence, both problems belong in the same group (Group I). Since the problem of finding the line of intersection of two cylinders and the problem of finding the line of intersection of a cylinder and a cone both involve single-curved surfaces, these two also belong in the same group (Group II).

Problems of the first group are solved by locating the points through which the edges of each of two geometric shapes pierce the other. These points are vertices of the line of intersection. Whenever one of two intersecting plane surfaces appears as a line in one view, the points through which the lines of the other surfaces penetrate it usually may be found by inspecting that view.

Problems of the second group may be solved by drawing elements on the lateral surface of one geometric shape in the region of the line of intersection. The points at which these elements intersect the surface of the other geometric shape are points that are common to both surfaces and consequently lie on their line of intersection. A curve, traced through these points with the aid of a French curve, will be a representation of the required intersection. To obtain accurate results, some of the elements must be drawn through certain critical points at which the curve changes sharply in direction. These points usually are located on contour elements. Hence, the usual practice is to space the elements equally around the surface, starting with a contour element.

13.25. Determination of a piercing point by inspection (Fig. 13.29).

It is easy to determine where a given line pierces a surface when the surface appears as an edge view (line) in one of the given views. For example, when the given line AB is extended as shown in (a), the F-view of the piercing point C is observed to be at c^F, where the frontal view of the line AB extended intersects the line view of the surface. With the position of c^F known, the H-view of point C can be quickly found by projecting upward to the H-view of AB extended.

In (b) the H-view (f^H) of the piercing point F is found first by extending $d^H e^H$ to intersect the edge view of the surface pierced by the line. By projecting downward, f^F is located on $d^F e^F$ extended.

In (c) the views of the piercing point K are found in the same manner as in (b), the only difference being that the edge view of

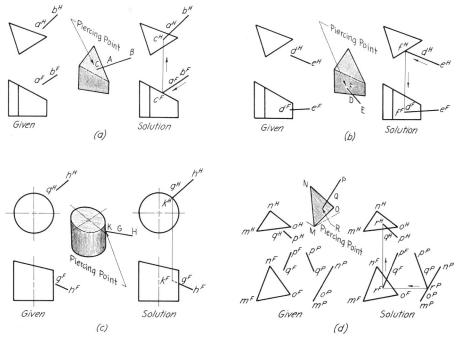

Fig. 13.29. Determination of a piercing point by inspection.

the surface pierced by the line appears as a circle arc in the *H*-view instead of a straight line. It should be noted that a part of the line is invisible in the *F*-view because the piercing point is on the rear side of the cylinder.

The *F*- and *H*-views of the piercing point *R* in (*d*) may be found easily by projection after the *P*-view (r^P) of *R* has been once established by extending $p^P q^P$ to intersect the line view of the surface.

13.26. Determination of a piercing point using a line-projecting plane (Fig. 13.30).

When a line pierces a given oblique plane and an edge view is not given, as in Fig. 13.30, a line-projecting plane (cutting plane) may be used to establish a line of intersection that will contain the piercing point. In the illustration, a vertical projecting plane was selected that would contain the given line *RS* and intersect the given plane *ABC* along line *DE* as illustrated by the pictorial drawing.

Solution: Draw the *H*-view of the projecting plane through $r^H s^H$ to establish $d^H e^H$ as shown in the *H*-view in (*c*). Locate $d^F e^F$ and draw the *F*-view of the line of intersection. Then, complete the line view $r^F s^F$ to establish $p_1{}^F$, at the point of intersection of $r^F s^F$ and $d^F e^F$. Finally, locate $p_1{}^H$ on $r^H s^H$ by projecting upward from $p_1{}^F$ as shown in (*d*).

13.27. To find where a line pierces a geometric solid-cylinder-cone-sphere using projecting planes (Fig. 13.31).

The points where a line pierces a cylinder, cone, or sphere may be found easily through the use of a projecting plane (cutting plane) that contains the given line as illustrated in (*a*), (*b*), and (*c*).

In (*a*) the intersections of the projecting plane and the cylinder

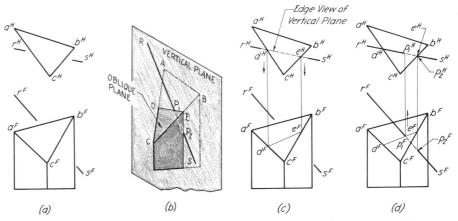

Fig. 13.30. Use of a line-projecting plane.

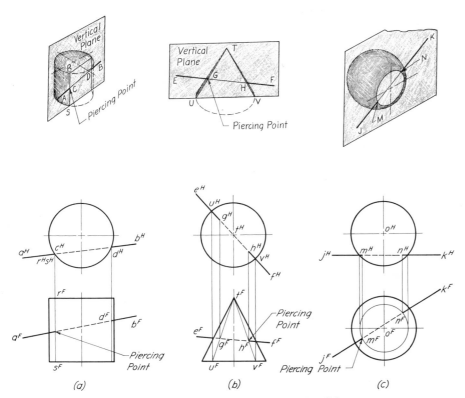

Fig. 13.31. To determine where a line pierces a geometric solid.

are straight line elements because the projecting plane used is parallel to the axis of the cylinder. The use of planes parallel to the axis permits the rapid solution of this type of problem. As shown by the pictorial drawing, the vertical projecting plane employed cuts elements on both the right and left sides of the cylinder. The line *AB* intersects the element *RS* at *C* and the other element at *D*. Points *C* and *D* are the piercing points.

The piercing points of a line and a cone are the points of intersection of the line and the two specific elements of the cone that lie in the projecting plane containing the line as shown in (*b*). The vertex of the cone and the given line fix the position of the projecting plane, the plane of the elements. In the illustration, the vertical projection plane, taken through the line *EF* and the vertex of the cone *T*, cuts the base of cone at *U* and *V*, the points needed to establish the *F*-views of the elements lying in the plane. The points of intersection of the given line *EF* and these elements are points *G* and *H*, the points where the line pierces the cone. If the given line had not been in a position to intersect the axis of the cone, it would have been necessary to use an oblique cutting plane through the apex.

A projecting plane that contains a line piercing a sphere will cut a circle on the surface of the sphere, therefore, points where the given line intersects the circle will be points where the line pierces the sphere. See the pictorial drawing in (c). In the illustrations, a vertical projecting plane was used containing the given line JK. The F-views of the piercing points M and N ($m^F n^F$) were found first at the points of intersection of the line and the circle. The H-views ($m^H n^H$) of the piercing points were found by projecting upward from m^F and n^F in the F-view.

13.28. To find the intersection of two planes—line-projecting plane method. The intersection of two oblique planes may be determined by finding where two of the lines of one plane pierce the other plane as illustrated by the pictorial drawing at the right in Fig. 13.32. The procedure that is illustrated employs line-projecting planes to find the piercing points of the lines XY and XZ and the oblique plane RST. Therefore, it might be said that the solution requires the determination of the piercing point of a line and an oblique plane as explained in Sec. 13.26.

Given: The oblique planes RST and XYZ.

Solution: Since the (vertical) line-projecting plane C_1P_1 is to contain the line XY of the plane XYZ, draw the line view representation of this projecting plane to coincide with $x^H y^H$. Next, project the line of intersection AB between the line-projecting plane

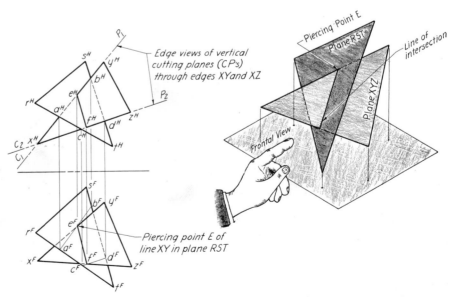

Fig. 13.32. To find the intersection line of two planes.

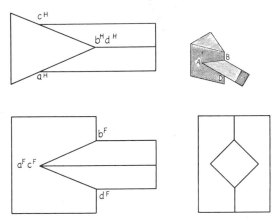

Fig. 13.33. Intersecting prisms.

C_1P_1 and plane RST from the top view where it appears as a^Hb^H in the edge view representation of C_1P_1 to the front view. Then, since it is evident that the line AB is not parallel to XY that lies in the projecting plane (see F-view), the line XY intersects AB. The location of this intersection at E is established first in the F-view where the line view x^Fy^F intersects a^Fb^F at e^F. The H-view of E, that is e^H, is found by projecting upward from e^F in the F-view to the line view x^Hy^H. The other end of the line of intersection between the two given planes at F is found by using the line-projecting plane C_2P_2 and following the same procedure as for determining the location of point E.

13.29. To find the intersection of two prisms. In Fig. 13.33 (see pictorial), points A, B, C, and D, through which the edges of the horizontal prism pierce the faces of the triangular prism, are the critical points or vertices of the closed intersection. The location of these piercing points may be found in the top view by inspection. Then they may be projected to the front view, to establish their location there. For example, the top view shows that the front edge of the horizontal prism pierces the near face of the vertical triangular prism at point a^H. Point a^H, projected downward to the line representing that edge in the front view, locates point a^F in the front view. After the piercing points B, C, and D have been found and projected to the front view in a similar manner, the intersection is completed by joining, in order, the projected points a^F, b^F, c^F, and d^F with straight lines.

13.30. To establish the location of the piercing point of an edge intersecting an inclined surface. In Fig. 13.34, points A, C, and D, through which the edges of the horizontal prism pierce the vertical

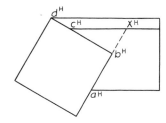

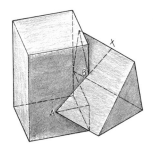

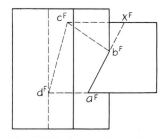

Fig. 13.34. Intersecting prisms.

prism, are first found in the top view and are then projected down-ward to the corresponding edges in the front view. Point *B*, through which the edge of the vertical prism pierces the near face of the triangular prism, cannot be found in this manner because the side view from which it could be projected to the front view is not shown. Its location, however, can be established in the front view without even drawing a partial side view, if some scheme like the one illustrated in the pictorial drawing is used. In this scheme, the intersection line *AB*, whose direction is shown in the top view as line $a^H b^H$, is extended on the triangular face to point *X* on the top edge. Point x^H is projected to the corresponding edge in the front view and a light construction line is drawn between the points a^F and x^F. Since point *B* is located on line *AX* (see pictorial) at the point where the edge of the prism pierces the line, its location in the front view is at point b^F where the edge cuts the line $a^F x^F$.

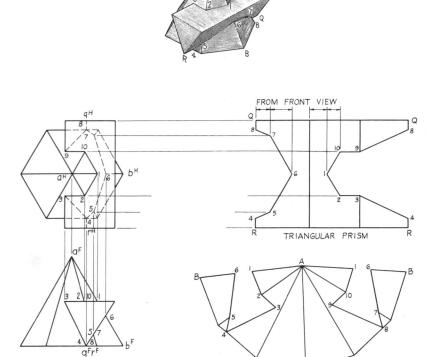

Fig. 13.35. Intersecting pyramid and prism.

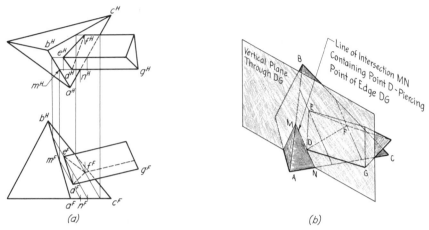

Fig. 13.36. Intersecting pyramid and prism.

13.31. To find the intersection of a pyramid and a prism. The intersection of a right pyramid and a prism (see Fig. 13.35) may be found by the same general method used for finding the intersection of two prisms (Sec. 13.29).

13.32. To determine the intersection of a prism and a pyramid using line-projecting planes. Frequently, it becomes necessary to draw the line of intersection between two geometric shapes so positioned that the piercing points of edges cannot be found by inspection if only the principal views are to be used. In this case, one must resort to the method discussed in Sec. 13.26 to determine where a line, such as the edge line GD of the prism shown in Fig. 13.36, pierces a surface. As illustrated by the pictorial drawing, a vertical plane passed through the edge DG of the prism, intersects the surface ABC of the pyramid along line MN that contains point D, the piercing point of DG. In (a), the H-view ($m^H n^H$) of the line MN lies along $d^H g^H$ extended to m^H on the edge of the pyramid, because the H-view of the cutting plane appears as an edge that coincides with $d^H g^H$. With the F-view of MN established by projecting downward from $m^H n^H$ in the H-view, the frontal view of the piercing point D is at d^F where the view of the edge line DG of the prism intersects $m^F n^F$. The H-view of D is found by projecting upward from d^F. The two other piercing points, at E and F, are found in the same manner using two other line-projecting planes.

13.33. To construct a development using auxiliary views. When one of the components is oblique to the principal planes of projection, as is the prism in Fig. 13.37, the construction work needed

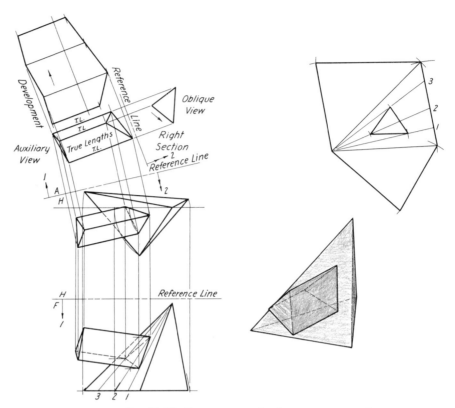

Fig. 13.37. To construct a development using auxiliary views.

for the development can be simplified somewhat through the use of an auxiliary view to find the true lengths of the edges and an oblique (secondary auxiliary) view to show a right section. Since the plane upon which the auxiliary view is projected is a vertical one that is parallel to the edges of the prism, the distances perpendicular to the *AH* reference line are height distances. In making the construction, distances are taken from the *F*-view in the direction of the single-headed arrow for use in the auxiliary view in the direction indicated by a similar arrow. For the oblique view, projected upon an *O*-plane that is perpendicular to both the *A*-plane and the edges of the prism, distances are taken from the *AH* reference line in the direction of the arrow numbered 2 to be laid out from the reference line for the *O*-view. Since this is the second auxiliary, the arrows indicating the direction for equal distances have been given two heads.

If there is sufficient space available, the true length measurements for the edges in the development may be projected directly from the auxiliary view showing the true lengths. The true distances between these edges, taken from the right section in the direction of the arrow, are laid off along the stretch-out line. The arrow on the development indicates the direction in which the successive faces are laid down when the prism is turned so as to unroll the lateral surface inside-up.

13.34. To find the intersection of two cylinders. If a series of elements are drawn on the surface of the small horizontal cylinder, as in Fig. 13.38, the points *A*, *B*, *C*, and *D* in which they intersect the vertical cylinder will be points on the line of intersection (see pictorial). These points, which are shown as a^H, b^H, c^H, and d^H in the top view, may be located in the front view by projecting them downward to the corresponding elements in the front view where they are shown as points a^F, b^F, c^F, and d^F. The desired intersection is represented by a smooth curve drawn through these points.

13.35. To find the intersection of two cylinders oblique to each other. The first step in finding the line of intersection of two cylinders that are oblique to each other (see Fig. 13.39) is to draw a

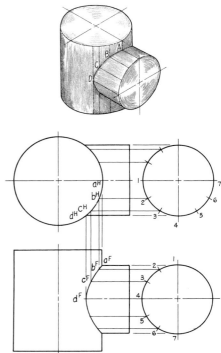

Fig. 13.38. Intersecting cylinders.

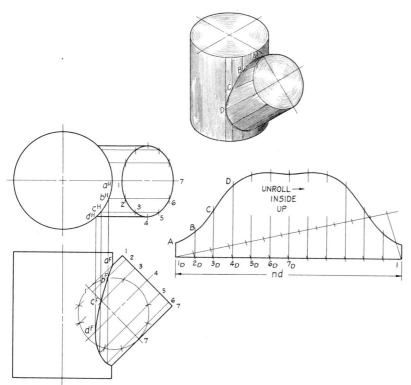

Fig. 13.39. Intersecting cylinders.

revolved right section of the oblique cylinder directly on the front view of that cylinder. If the circumference of the right section then is divided into a number of equal divisions and elements are drawn through the division points, the points *A*, *B*, *C*, and *D* in which the elements intersect the surface of the vertical cylinder will be points on the line of intersection (see pictorial). In the case of the illustration shown, these points are found first in the top view and then are projected downward to the corresponding elements in the front view. The line of intersection in the front view is represented by a smooth curve drawn through these points.

13.36. To find the intersection of two cylinders using line-projecting (cutting) planes. The line of intersection of the two cylinders shown in Fig. 13.39 could have been determined through the use of a series of parallel line-projecting (cutting) planes passed parallel to their axes (see Fig. 13.40). The related straight line elements cut on the cylinders by any one cutting plane, such as *C*, intersect on the line of intersection of the cylinders. As many line-projecting planes as are needed to obtain a smooth curve should be used and they should be placed rather close together where a curve changes sharply.

13.37. To find the intersection of a cylinder and a cone. The intersection of a cylinder and a cone may be found by assuming a number of elements upon the surface of the cone. The points at which these elements cut the cylinder are on the line of intersection (see pictorial drawings in Figs. 13.41 and 13.42). In selecting the elements, it is the usual practice to divide the circumference of the base into a number of equal parts and draw elements through the division points. To obtain needed points at locations where the intersection line will change suddenly in curvature, however, there should be additional elements.

In Fig. 13.41, the points at which the elements pierce the cylinder are first found in the top view and are then projected to the corresponding elements in the front view. A smooth curve through these points forms the figure of the intersection.

In Fig. 13.42, the intersection points are first found in the side view.

An alternate method for finding the line of intersection of a cylinder and a right cone is illustrated in Fig. 13.43. Here horizontal cutting planes are passed through both geometric shapes in the region of their line of intersection. In each cutting plane, the circle cut on the surface of the cone will intersect elements cut on the cylinder at two points common to both surfaces (see pictorial). A curved line traced through a number of such points in different

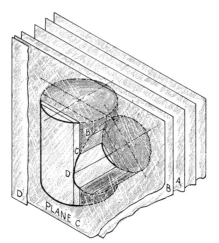

Fig. 13.40. To find the intersection of two cylinders using line-projecting planes.

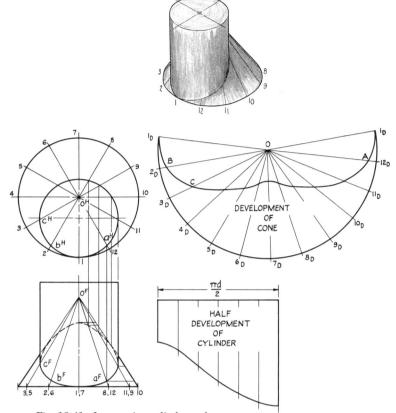

DEVELOPMENT
OF
CONE

$$\frac{\pi d}{2}$$

HALF
DEVELOPMENT
OF
CYLINDER

Fig. 13.41. Intersecting cylinder and cone.

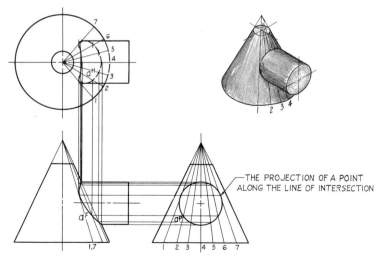

THE PROJECTION OF A POINT
ALONG THE LINE OF INTERSECTION

Fig. 13.42. Intersecting cylinder and cone.

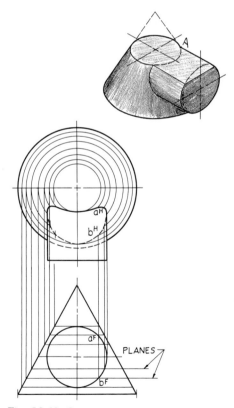

PLANES

Fig. 13.43. Intersecting cylinder
and cone.

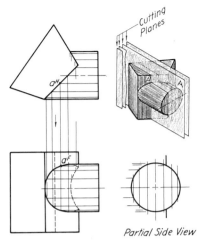

Partial Side View

Fig. 13.44. To find the intersection of a prism and a cylinder.

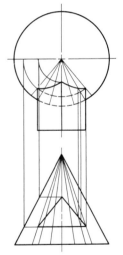

Fig. 13.45. Intersecting cone and prism.

planes is a line common to both surfaces and is therefore the line of intersection.

13.38. To find the intersection of a prism and a cylinder. In Fig. 13.44 it is required to find the intersection between the cylinder and two of the plane surfaces of the prism so that a pattern for the hole can be cut in the prism to match the cylinder. Although the intersection could have been secured merely by determining, through inspection, the piercing points of elements drawn arbitrarily on the cylinder, vertical line-projecting planes were used to illustrate an approach to this type of problem that is used by many people. The cutting planes are located in the view showing the right section of the cylinder. From this first step, the positions for the lines and elements cut on the prism and cylinder respectively, can be determined by projection. Each line-projecting (cutting) plane cuts a line on a plane surface of the prism and a related element on the cylinder that intersect on the line of intersection. A sufficient number of line-projecting planes should be used to enable one to draw a smooth curved-line representation of the intersection. If more points are desired, at a location where a curve changes sharply, additional cutting planes may be added.

13.39. To find the intersection of a prism and a cone. The complete line of intersection may be found by drawing elements on the surface of the cone (see Fig. 13.45) to locate points on the intersection as explained in Sec. 13.37. To obtain an accurate curve, however, some thought must be given to the placing of these elements. For instance, although most of the elements may be equally spaced on the cone to facilitate the construction of its development, additional ones should be drawn through the critical points and in regions where the line of intersection changes sharply in curvature. The elements are drawn on the view that will reveal points on the intersection, then the determined points are projected to the corresponding elements in the other view or views. In this particular illustration a part of the line of intersection in the top view is a portion of the arc of a circle that would be cut by a horizontal plane containing the bottom surface of the prism.

If the surfaces of the prism are parallel to the axis of the cone, as in Fig. 13.46, the line of intersection will be made up of the tips of a series of hyperbolas. The intersection may be found by passing planes that will cut circles on the surface of the cone. The points at which these cutting circles pierce the faces of the prism are points common to the lateral surfaces of both shapes and are therefore points on the required line of intersection. It should be noted that the resulting solution represents a chamfered bolthead.

PROBLEMS

The problems of this chapter have been designed to offer an opportunity to apply the principles of intersections and developments and to provide further drill in projection.

1. (Fig. 13.47.) Develop the lateral surface of one or more of the prisms as assigned.

2. (Fig. 13.48.) Develop the lateral surface of one or more of the prisms as assigned.

3. (Fig. 13.49.) Develop the lateral surface of one or more of the pyramids as assigned. Make construction lines light. Show construction for finding the true lengths of the lines.

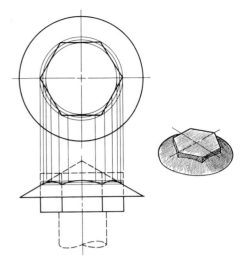

Fig. 13.46. Cone and hexagonal prism.

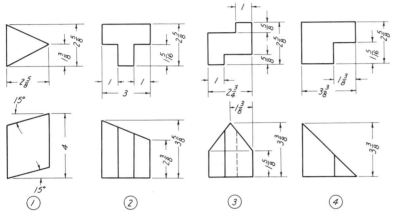

Fig. 13.47. Prisms.

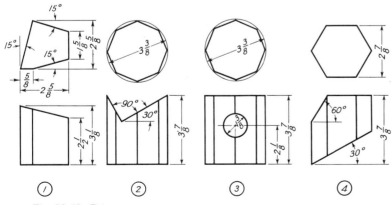

Fig. 13.48. Prisms.

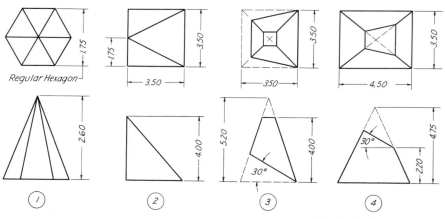

Fig. 13.49. Pyramids.

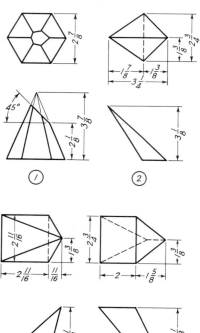

Fig. 13.50. Pyramids.

4. (Fig. 13.50.) Develop the lateral surface of one or more of the pyramids as assigned. With a hard pencil, show the construction for finding the true lengths of the lines.

5. (Fig. 13.51.) Develop the lateral surface of one or more of the cylinders as assigned. Use a hard pencil for construction lines and make them light.

6. (Fig. 13.52.) Develop the lateral surface of one or more of the cones as assigned. Show all construction. Use a hard pencil for construction lines and make them light. In each case start with the shortest element and unroll, inside up. It is suggested that 12 elements be used, in order to secure a reasonably accurate development.

7. (Fig. 13.53.) Develop the lateral surface of one or more of the transition pieces as assigned. Show all construction lines in light, sharp pencil lines. Use a sufficient number of elements on the curved surfaces to assure an accurate development.

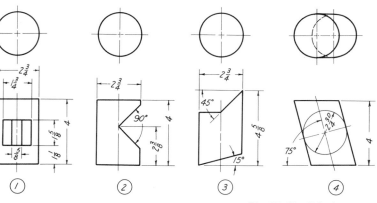

Fig. 13.51. Cylinders.

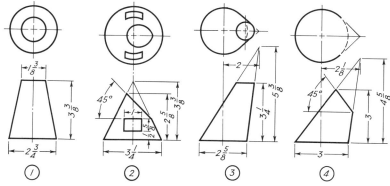

Fig. 13.52. Cones.

8. (Fig. 13.54.) Develop the sheet-metal connections. On pieces 3 and 4, use a sufficient number of elements to obtain a smooth curve and an accurate development.

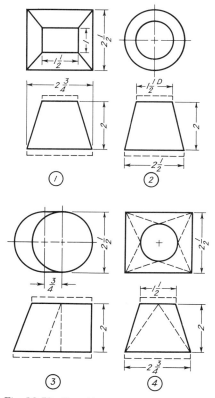

Fig. 13.53. Transition pieces.

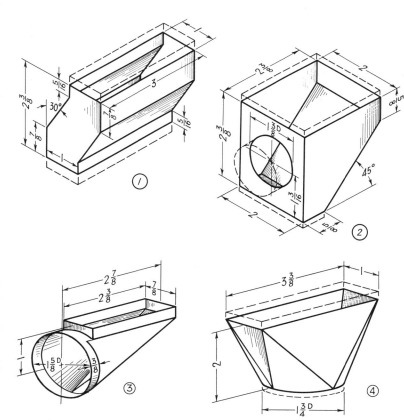

Fig. 13.54. Sheet-metal connections (transitions).

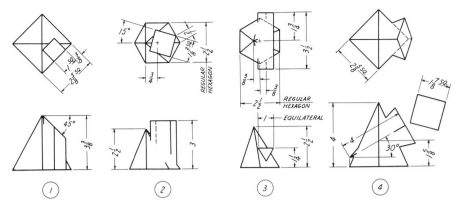

Fig. 13.55. Intersecting surfaces.

9-10. (Figs. 13.55 and 13.56.) Draw the line of intersection of the intersecting geometric shapes as assigned. Show the invisible portions of the lines of intersection as well as the visible. Consider that the interior is open.

11-12. (Figs. 13.57 and 13.58.) Draw the line of intersection of the intersecting geometric shapes as assigned. It is suggested that the elements that are used to find points along the intersection be spaced 15° apart. Do not erase the construction lines. One shape does not pass through the other.

13. (Fig. 13.59.) Draw the line of intersection of the intersecting geometric shapes as assigned. Show the invisible portions of the line of intersection as well as the visible. The interior of the combination is hollow. One shape does not pass through the other. Show construction with light, sharp lines drawn with a hard pencil.

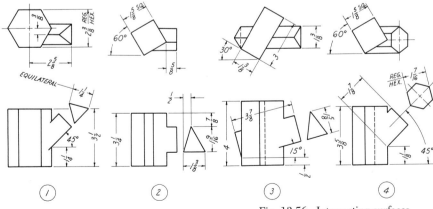

Fig. 13.56. Intersecting surfaces.

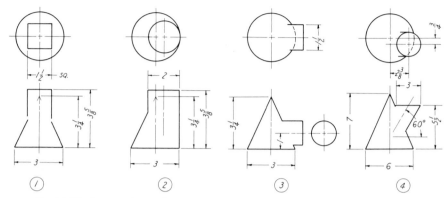

Fig. 13.57. Intersecting surfaces.

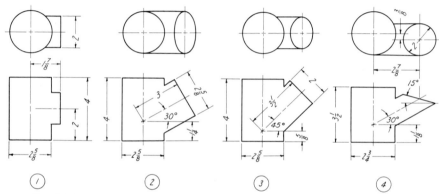

Fig. 13.58. Intersecting surfaces.

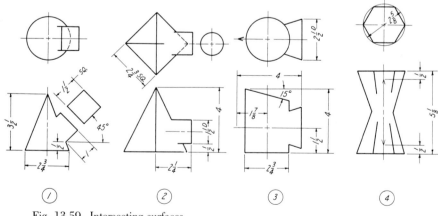

Fig. 13.59. Intersecting surfaces.

14

VECTOR GEOMETRY

14.1. Introduction. In order to be successful in solving some types of problems that arise in design, a well-trained engineer should have a working knowledge of "vector geometry." The methods presented in this chapter should furnish the student with some background knowledge for solving force problems as they appear in the study of mechanics, strength of materials, and design. Through discreet use of the methods of vector geometry, as well as mathematical methods, it is possible to solve engineering problems quickly within a fully acceptable range of accuracy. Since any quantity having both magnitude and direction may be represented by a fixed or rotating vector, vector operations are commonly used for problems in the design of frame structures, problems dealing with velocities in mechanisms, and for problems arising in the study of electrical properties. Because a student in a beginning course in engineering graphics should have basic principles rather than specialized cases presented to him, the methods given in this chapter for solving both two-dimensional and three-dimensional force problems deal mainly with static structures or, in other words, structures with forces acting so as to be in equilibrium. In a study of physics, graphical methods are useful for the composition and resolution of forces.

It is hoped that as a student progresses through his other undergraduate courses, he will desire to learn more about the use of vector methods for solving problems, and that he will become able to recognize the cases where he may have a choice between a graphical and an algebraic method. The graphical method is the better for many cases because it is much quicker and can be checked more easily.

An example of a vector addition is shown in Fig. 14.1. An airplane is flying north with a cross wind from the west. If the speed of the plane is 150 mph (miles per hour) and the wind is blowing toward the east at 60 mph, the plane will be flying NE (northeast) at 161.5 mph. Vectors can be used for problems of this type because forces acting on a body have both magnitude and direction.

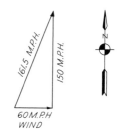

Fig. 14.1. A vector problem.

14.2. A force. In our study of vector methods, a force may be defined as a cause which tends to produce motion in an object.

A force has four characteristics which determine it. First, a force has "magnitude." The value of this magnitude may be expressed in terms of some standard unit. It is usually given in pounds. Second, a force has a "line of action." This is the line along which the force acts. Third, a force has "direction." This is the direction in which it tends to move the object upon which it acts. Fourth, and last, a force has a "point of application." This is the place at which it acts upon the object, often assumed to be a point at the center of gravity.

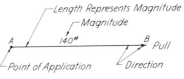

Fig. 14.2. A vector.

14.3. A vector. A force can be represented graphically by a straight line segment with an arrowhead at one end. Such an arrow when used for this purpose is known as a "vector" (Fig. 14.2). The position of the body of the arrow represents the line of action of the force while the arrowhead points out the direction. The magnitude is represented to some selected scale by the over-all length of the arrow itself.

When a force acts in a two-dimensional plane, only one view of the vector is needed. However, if the force is in space, two views of the vector must be given.

Fig. 14.3. A vector addition.

14.4. Addition of vector forces—two forces.

For a thorough understanding of the principles of vector addition, two simple examples will be considered first.

If one of two men who find it necessary to move a supply cabinet pushes on it with 60 lb force while the other pushes in the same direction with 40 lb force, the total force exerted to move the cabinet is 100 lb. The representation of two or more such forces in the manner shown in Fig. 14.3 amounts to a vector addition. Should these men be in a prankish mood and decide to push in opposite directions, as illustrated in Fig. 14.4, the cabinet might move provided the 20 lb resultant force were sufficient to overcome friction. The 20 lb resultant comes from a graphical addition.

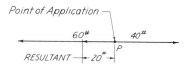

Fig. 14.4. Forces in opposite directions.

Now let it be supposed that force A represented by F_A and force B represented by F_B in Fig. 14.5 act from a point P, the point of application. The resultant force on the body will not now be the sum of forces A and B, but instead will be the graphical addition of these forces as represented by the diagonal of a parallelogram having sides equal to the scaled length of the given forces. This single force R of 105.5 lb would produce an effect upon the body that would be equivalent to the combined forces F_A and F_B. The single force which could replace any given force system, is known as the *resultant* (R) for the force system.

Figure 14.5 shows that the resultant R divides the parallelogram into two equal triangles. Therefore, R could have been found just as well by constructing a single triangle as shown in Fig. 14.6 provided that the vector F_B is drawn so that its tail-end touches the tip-end of F_A, and R is drawn with its arrow-end to the tip-end of F_B. Since either of the triangles shown in Fig. 14.5 could have been drawn to determine R, it should be obvious the resultant is the same regardless of the order in which the vectors are added. However, it is important that they be added tip-end to tail-end and that the vector arrows show the true direction for the action of the concurrent forces in the given system.

To find the resultant of two forces, which are applied as shown in Fig. 14.7, it is first necessary to move the vector arrows along their lines of action to the intersection point P before one can apply the parallelogram method.

Fig. 14.5. Parallelogram of forces.

Fig. 14.6. A vector triangle.

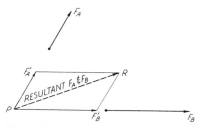

Fig. 14.7. Resultant of two forces.

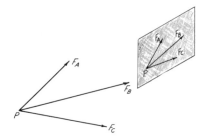

Fig. 14.8. Coplanar, concurrent forces.

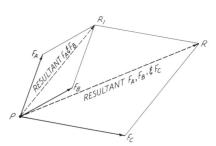

Fig. 14.9. Resultant of three or more forces with a common point of application (parallelogram method).

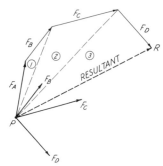

Fig. 14.10. Resultant of forces (polygon of forces).

The forces of a system whose lines of action all lie in one plane are called *coplanar forces.* Should the lines of action pass through a common point, the point of application, the forces are said to be *concurrent.* Figure 14.8 shows a system of forces that are both concurrent and coplanar.

14.5. Addition of vectors—three or more forces. The parallelogram method may be used to determine the resultant for a system of three or more forces that are concurrent and coplanar. In applying this method to three or more forces, it is necessary to draw a series of parallelograms, the number depending upon the number of vector quantities that are to be added graphically. For example, in Fig. 14.9 two parallelograms are required to determine the resultant R for system. The resultant R_1 for forces F_A and F_B is determined by the first parallelogram to be drawn, and then R_1 is combined in turn with F_C by forming the second and larger parallelogram. By combining the forces in this way R becomes the resultant for the complete system.

Where a considerable number of vectors form a system, a somewhat less complicated diagram results, and less work is required when the triangle method is extended and applied to the formation of a vector diagram such as the one shown in Fig. 14.10. In this case the diagram is formed by three vector triangles, one adjacent to the other, and the resultant of forces F_A and F_B is combined with F_C to form the second triangle. Finally, by combining the resultant of the three forces F_A, F_B, and F_C with F_D, the vector R is obtained, which represents the magnitude and direction of the resultant of the four forces. In the construction F_B, F_C, and F_D in the diagram must be drawn so as to be parallel respectively to their lines of action in the system. However, the order in which they are placed in the diagram is optional as long as one vector joins another tip to tail.

14.6. Vector components. A component may be defined as one of two or more forces into which an original force may be resolved. The components, which together have the same action as the single force, are determined by a reversal of the process for vector addition, that is, the original force is resolved using the parallelogram method (see Fig. 14.11). The resolution of a plane vector into two components, horizontal and vertical, is illustrated in (*a*). In (*b*), the resolution of a force into components of specified direction is shown.

14.7. Forces in equilibrium. A body is said to be in equilibrium when the opposing forces acting upon it are in balance. In such a state the resultant of the force system will be zero. The concurrent

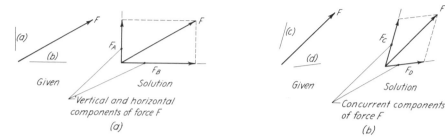

Fig. 14.11. Components.

and coplanar force system shown in Fig. 14.12 is in a state of equilibrium, for the vector triangle closes and each vector follows the other tip to tail.

An "equilibrant" is the force which will balance two or more forces and produce equilibrium. It is a force that would equal the resultant of the system but would necessarily have to act in an opposite direction.

Figure 14.13 shows a weight supported by a short steel cable. The force to be determined is that needed to hold the weight in a state of equilibrium when it is swung from the position indicated by the broken lines into the position shown by solid lines.

This may be done by drawing a vector triangle with the forces in order from tip to tail. The 87.5 lb force vector represents the equilibrant, the force that will balance the 150 lb force and the 173 lb tension force now in the cable. The reader may wonder at the increase in the tension force in the cable from a 150 lb force when hanging straight down to a 173 lb force when the cable is at an angle of 30° with the vertical. It might help to realize that as the weight is swung outward towards a position where the cable will be horizontal, both the tension force and the equilibrant will increase. Theoretically it would require forces infinitely large to hold the system in equilibrium with the cable in a horizontal position.

In solving a force system graphically it is possible to determine two unknowns in a coplanar system.

Now suppose that it is desired to determine the forces acting in the members of a simple truss as shown in Fig. 14.14(a). To determine these forces graphically, one should isolate the joint supporting the weight and draw a diagram, known as a free-body diagram to show the forces acting at the joint (b). Although the lines of this diagram may have any length, they must be parallel to the lines in the space diagram in (a). Since the boom will be in compression, a capital letter C has been placed along the line that represents the boom in the diagram. A letter T has been placed along the line for the cable because it will be in tension. Although the diagram may

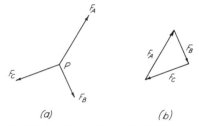

Fig. 14.12. Forces in equilibrium.

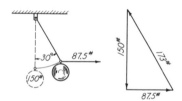

Fig. 14.13. Determination of forces (graphically).

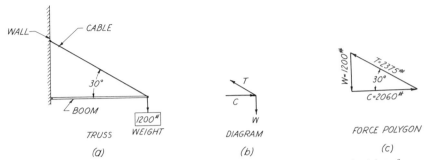

Fig. 14.14. Determination of the forces at the joint of a simple truss.

not have been essential in this particular case, such a diagram does play an important part in solving more complex systems.

In constructing the force polygon, it is necessary to start by drawing the vertical vector, for the load is the only force having a known magnitude and direction. After this vertical vector has been drawn to a length representing 1200 lb, using a selected scale, the force polygon (triangle) may be completed by drawing the remaining lines representing the unknown forces parallel to their known lines of action as shown in (a). The force polygon will close since the force system is in equilibrium.

The magnitude of the unknown forces in the members of the truss can now be determined by measuring the lines of the diagram using the same scale selected to lay out the length of the vertical vector. This method might be used to determine the forces acting in the members at any point in a truss.

It is possible to solve many of the simple force problems of physics graphically by drawing a force polygon. For example, suppose that it should be desirable to determine the least horizontal force necessary to move a wheel over an obstacle. The space dia-

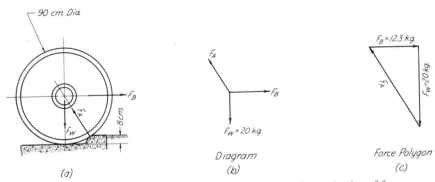

Fig. 14.15. Determination of forces.

gram shown in Fig. 14.15(a) gives the diameter of the wheel as 90 cm and its weight as 20 kg. The height of the obstacle is 8 cm. The forces acting on the wheel are F_W, its weight, which is known, the reaction force F_A, unknown, and F_B the horizontal force that must be applied at the instant the wheel is just at the point of rising over the obstacle. The magnitude of F_B can be found on the force triangle in (c).

14.8. Coplanar, nonconcurrent force systems. Forces in one plane having lines of action that do not pass through a common point are said to be *coplanar, nonconcurrent forces* (Fig. 14.16).

14.9. Two parallel forces. When two forces are parallel and act in the same direction, their resultant will have a line of action that is parallel to the lines of action of the given forces and it will be located between them. The magnitude of the resultant will be equal to the sum of the two forces [Fig. 14.17(a)], and it will act through a point that divides any perpendicular line joining the lines of action of the given forces inversely as the forces.

Should the two forces act in opposite directions, as shown in (b), the resultant will be located outside of them and will have the same direction as the greater force. Its magnitude will be equal to the difference between the two given forces. The proportion shown with the illustration in (b) may be used to determine the location of the point of application of the resultant. Those who prefer to determine graphically the location of the line of action for the resultant may use the method illustrated in Fig. 14.18. This method is based on well known principles of geometry.

With the two forces F_A and F_B given, any line 1–2 is drawn joining their lines of action. From this line two distances must be laid off along the lines of action of the given forces. If the given forces act in the same direction, then the distances are laid off in opposite directions from the line 1–2, (a). If they act in opposite directions, the distances must be laid off on the same side of line 1–2, (b). In Fig. 14.18(a), a length equal by scale to F_A was laid off from point 1 on the line of action of F_B. Then from point 2 a length equal to F_B was marked off in an opposite direction. These measurements located points 3 and 4, the end-points of the line intersecting line 1–2 at point O. Point O is on the line of action of the resultant R. In Fig. 14.18(b) this method has been applied to establish the location of the resultant for two forces acting in opposite directions.

14.10. Moment of a force. The "moment of a force" with respect to a point is the product of the force and the perpendicular distance

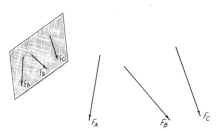

Fig. 14.16. Coplanar, nonconcurrent forces.

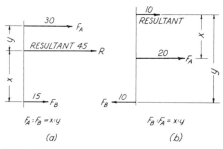

Fig. 14.17. Parallel forces.

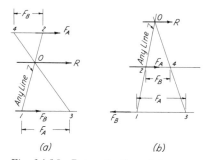

Fig. 14.18. Determination of the position of the resultant of parallel forces (graphical method).

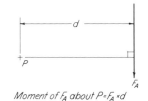

Moment of F_A about $P = F_A \times d$

Fig. 14.19. Moment of a force.

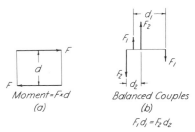

Moment = $F \times d$
(a)

Balanced Couples
(b)

$F_1 d_1 = F_2 d_2$

Fig. 14.20. Force couples.

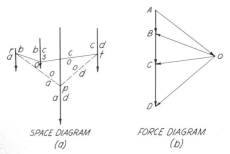

SPACE DIAGRAM
(a)

FORCE DIAGRAM
(b)

Fig. 14.21. Resultant of parallel forces—Bow's notation.

from the given point to the line of action of the force. In the illustration, Fig. 14.19, the moment of the force F_A about point P is Mom. $= F_A \times d$. The perpendicular distance d is known as the lever arm of the force. Should the distance d be measured in inches and the force be given in pounds, the moment of the force will be in inch-pounds.

14.11. Force couples (Fig. 14.20). Two equal forces that act in opposite directions are known as a "couple." A couple does not have a resultant, and no single force can counteract tendency to produce rotation. The measurement of this tendency is the moment of the couple that is the product of one of the forces and the perpendicular distance between them.

To prevent the rotation of a body that is acted upon by a couple, it is necessary to use two other forces that will form a second couple. The body acted upon by these couples will be in equilibrium if each couple tends to rotate the body in opposite directions and the moment of one couple is equal to the other.

14.12. String polygon—Bow's notation. A system for lettering space and force diagrams, known as "Bow's notation," is widely used by technical authors. Its use in this chapter will tend to simplify the discussions which follow.

In the space diagram, shown in Fig. 14.21(a), each space from the line of action of one force to the line of action of the next one is given a lower-case letter such as a, b, c, and d in alphabetical order. Thus the line of action for any particular force can be designated by the letters of the areas on each side of it. For example, in Fig. 14.23 the line of action for the 1080 lb force, acting downward on the beam, would be designated as line of action bc. On the force diagram, corresponding capital letters are used at the ends of the vectors. In Fig. 14.21(b), AB represents the magnitude of ab in the space diagram and BC represents the magnitude of bc.

To find the resultant of three or more parallel forces graphically, the "funicular" or "string polygon" is used. The magnitude and direction of the required resultant for the system shown in Fig. 14.21 are known. The magnitude, representing the algebraic sum of the given forces, appears as the heavy line AD of the force polygon. It is required to determine the location of its line of action. With the forces located in the space diagram and the force polygon drawn, the steps for the solution are as follows:

1. Assume a pole point O and draw the rays OA, OB, OC, and OD. Each of the triangles formed is regarded as a vector triangle with one side representing the resultant of the forces represented by the other two sides. For example: If we consider AB to be a re-

sultant force, then OA and OB are two component forces that could replace AB. For the second vector triangle, OB and BC have OC as their resultant. OC, when combined with CD, will have OD as the resultant. OA and OD combine with AD, the final resultant of the system.

2. Draw directly on the space diagram the corresponding strings of the funicular polygon. The funicular polygon may be started at any selected point r along the line of action ab. The string ob will then be parallel to OB of the force polygon. From point s, where ob intersects bc, draw oc parallel to OC. The line oc extended to cd establishes the location of point t. Line od drawn parallel to OD and line oa drawn parallel to OA intersect at point p. Point p is a point on the line of action of force ad, the resultant force AD for the given force system.

When one or more of a system of parallel forces are directed oppositely from the others, the magnitude and direction of the resultant will be equal to the algebraic sum of the original forces.

14.13. Coplanar, nonconcurrent, nonparallel forces.

In further study of coplanar and nonconcurrent forces it might be supposed that it is necessary to determine the magnitude, direction, and line of action of the one force that will establish a state of equilibrium when combined with the given forces AB, BC, and CD of the force system shown in Fig. 14.22. The direction and line of action of the original forces are given in both the space diagram in (a) and the force polygon in (b). The magnitude and direction of the force that will produce equilibrium is represented by DA, the force needed to close the force polygon. With the force polygon completed, the next step is to assume a pole point O and draw the rays OA, OB, OC, and OD. Now OA and OB are component forces of AB, and AB might be replaced by these forces. To clarify this statement; each of the four triangles may be considered to be a vector triangle, and in the case of vector triangle OAB, AB can be regarded as the resultant for the other two forces OA and OB. It should be noted that component force OB of the vector triangle OBC must be equal and opposite in direction to component force OB of OAB.

All that remains to be done is to determine the line of action of the required force DA by drawing the string diagram as explained in Sec. 14.12, remembering that point r may be any point along the line of action of ab. The intersection point p for strings oa and od is a point along the line of action da of force DA. Although lines of action ab, bc, cd, and da were drawn to a length representing their exact magnitude in Fig. 14.22(a), they could have been drawn to a convenient length to allow for the construction of the string

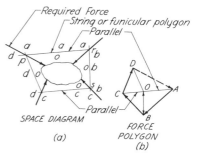

Fig. 14.22. Funicular or string polygon.

polygon, for these lines merely represent lines of action for the forces *AB*, *BC*, *CD*, and *DA*. The lines were presented in scaled length for illustrative purposes.

14.14. Equilibrium of three or more coplanar parallel forces.

When a given system, consisting of three or more coplanar forces, is in equilibrium, both the force polygon and the funicular polygon must close. If the force polygon should close and the funicular polygon not close, the resultant of the given system will be found to be a force couple.

Two unknown forces of a parallel coplanar force system may be determined graphically by drawing the force and funicular polygons as shown in Fig. 14.23, since the forces are known to be in equilibrium, and all are vertical. Although one may be aware that the sum of the two reaction forces R_1 and R_2 is equal to the sum of forces *AB*, *BC*, *CD*, and *DE*, the magnitude of R_1 and R_2 as single forces is unknown. The location of point *F* in the force polygon, which is needed if one is to determine the magnitudes of R_1 and R_2, may be found by fulfilling the requirement that the funicular polygon be closed.

The funicular polygon is started at any convenient point along the known line of action of R_1, and successive strings are drawn parallel to corresponding rays of the force polygon. In area *b* the string will be parallel to *OB*, in area *c* the string will be parallel to *OC* and so on, until the string that is parallel to *OE* has been drawn. String *of* may then be added to close the funicular polygon. This closing line from point *x* to the starting point *y* determines the position of *OF* in the force polygon, for ray *OF* must be parallel to the string *of*. The magnitude of the reaction R_1 is represented to scale by the vector *FA*, and R_2 is represented by the vector *FE*.

The graphical method for determining the values of wind load reactions for a roof truss having both ends fixed is shown in Fig. 14.24. The solution given is practically identical with the solution applied to the beam in Fig. 14.23.

14.15. Concurrent, noncoplanar force systems.

Up to this point in our study of force systems, the student's attention has been directed solely to systems lying in one plane in order that the graphical methods dealing with the composition and resolution of forces could be presented in a clear and simple manner, free from the thinking needed for understanding force systems involving the third dimension.

In dealing with noncoplanar forces it is necessary to use at least two views to represent a structure in space. Although the methods

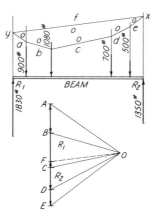

Fig. 14.23. To determine the reaction forces of a loaded beam.

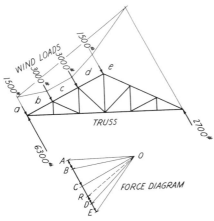

Fig. 14.24. The determination of the reactions for wind loads.

as applied to coplanar force systems for solving problems may be extended to noncoplanar systems, the vector diagram for noncoplanar forces must have two views instead of one view as in the case of coplanar forces. If the student is to understand the discussions that are to follow he must grasp the idea that for the composition and resolution of noncoplanar forces he will work with two distinct and separate space representations, the space diagram for the given structure and the related vector diagram (force polygon). Figure 14.25 shows two views of a concurrent, noncoplanar force system not in equilibrium.

There are a few basic relationships that exist between a space diagram and its related vector diagram, which must be kept in mind when solving noncoplanar force problems. These relationships are: (1) in corresponding views (H-view and H-view, or F-view and F-view), each vector in the vector diagram will be parallel to its corresponding representation in the space diagram, (2) if a system of concurrent, noncoplanar forces is in equilibrium, the force polygon in space closes and the projection on each plane will close, and (3) the true magnitude of a force can be measured only in the vector diagram when it appears in true length or is made to do so.

14.16. Determination of the resultant of a force system of concurrent, noncoplanar forces.

The parallelogram method for determining the resultant of concurrent forces as explained in Sec. 14.5 may be employed to find the resultant of the three forces OA, OB, and OC in Fig. 14.26. Any number of given concurrent, noncoplanar forces can be combined into their resultant by this method. In the illustration, forces OA and OB were combined into their resultant, which is the diagonal of the smaller parallelogram, then this resultant in turn was combined with the third force OC to obtain the final resultant R for the given system. Since the true magnitude of R can be scaled only in a view showing its true length, an auxiliary view was projected from the front view. The true length of R could also have been determined by revolution.

Since the single force needed to hold a force system in balance, known as the *equilibrant,* is equal to the resultant in magnitude but is opposite in direction, this method might be used to determine the equilibrant for a system of concurrent, noncoplanar forces.

In presenting this problem and the two problems that follow, it has been assumed that the student has read the previous sections of this chapter and that his knowledge of the principles of projection is sufficient for him to find the true length of a line, having two views given, and to draw the view of a plane so that it will appear as an edge.

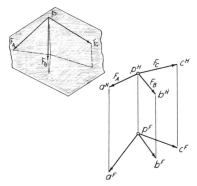

Fig. 14.25. Concurrent, noncoplanar forces.

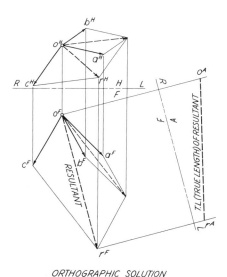

ORTHOGRAPHIC SOLUTION

Fig. 14.26. Determination of the resultant of concurrent, noncoplanar forces.

14.17. To find the three unknown forces of a simple load-bearing frame—special case. In dealing with the simple load-bearing frame in Fig. 14.27, it should be realized that this is a special case rather than a general one, for two of the truss members appear as a single line in the frontal view of the space diagram. This condition considerably simplifies the task of finding the unknown forces acting in the members, and it is this particular spatial situation that makes this a special case. However, it should be pointed out now that this condition must exist or be set up in a projected view when a vector solution is to be applied to any problem involving a system of concurrent, noncoplanar forces. More will be said about the necessity for having two unknown forces coincide in one of the views in the discussion of the problem that is to follow this one.

After the space diagram has been drawn to scale, the steps toward the final solution are as follows:

1. Draw a free-body diagram showing the joint at A, the joint at which the load is applied. The lines of this diagram may be of any length, but each line in it must be parallel respectively to a corresponding line in the view of the space diagram to which the free-body diagram is related. In this case, it is the horizontal (top) view. A modified form of Bow's notation was used for convenience in identifying the forces. The vertical load has been shown pulled to one side in order that this force can be made to fall within the range of the notation. This diagram is important to the solution of this problem, for it enables one to see and note the direction of all of the forces that the members exert upon the joint (note arrowheads). Capital letters were used on the free-body diagram to identify the spaces between the forces, rather than lower-case letters as is customary, so that lower-case letters could be used for the ends of the views of the vectors in the vector diagram.

2. Using a selected scale, start the two views of the vector diagram (b) by laying out vector RS representing the only known force, in this case the 1000 lb load. Since RS is a force acting in a vertical direction $r^F s^F$ will be in true length in the F-view and will appear as point $r^H s^H$ in the H-view.

3. Complete the H- and F-views of the vector diagram. Since each vector line in the top view must be parallel to a corresponding line in the top view of the space diagram, $s^H t^H$ must be drawn parallel to $a^H b^H$, $t^H u^H$ parallel to $a^H c^H$, and $u^H r^H$ parallel to $a^H d^H$. Since the forces acting at joint A are in equilibrium, the vector triangle will close and the vectors will appear tip to tail.

In the frontal view of the vector diagram, $s^F t^F$ will be parallel to $a^F b^F$, and $t^F u^F$ will be parallel to $a^F c^F$ and $r^F u^F$ will be parallel to $d^F a^F$.

4. Determine the magnitude of the forces acting on joint A. Since vector RU shows its true length in the F-view, the true magnitude of the force represented may be determined by scaling $r^F u^F$ using the same scale used to lay out the length of $r^F s^F$. Although it is known that vectors ST and TU are equal in magnitude, it is

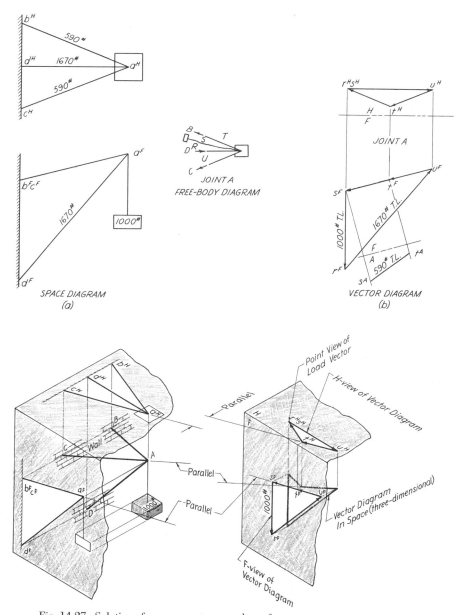

Fig. 14.27. Solution of a concurrent, noncoplanar force system—special case.

necessary to find the true length representation of one or the other of these vectors by some approved method before scaling to determine the true value of the force.

An arrowhead may now be added to the line of action of each force in the free-body diagram to indicate the direction of the action. Since the free-body diagram was related to the top view of the space diagram, the arrowhead for each force will point in the same direction as does the arrowhead on the corresponding vector in the *H*-view of the vector diagram. These arrowheads show that the forces in members *AB* and *AC* are acting away from joint *A* and are therefore *tension forces*. The force in *AD* acts toward *A* and thus is a *compression force*.

14.18. To find the three unknown forces of a simple load-bearing truss—general case. For the general case shown in Fig. 14.28, the known force is in a vertical position as in the previous problem, but no two of the three unknown forces appear coincident in either of

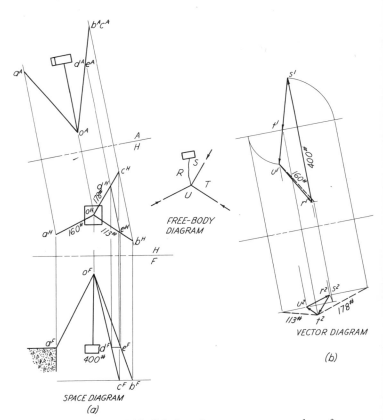

Fig. 14.28. Solution of a concurrent, noncoplanar force system—general case.

the two given views. For this reason, it is necessary at the very start to add a complete auxiliary view to the space diagram that will combine with the existing top view to give a point view of one member and a line view of two of the three unknown forces. To obtain this desired situation, one should start with the following steps, which will transform the general case into the special case with which one should now be familiar.

Step 1. Draw a true length line in the plane of two of the members. In Fig. 14.28(a) this line is DE, which appears in true length (TL) in the H-view.

Step 2. Draw the needed auxiliary view, taken so that DE will appear as a point ($d^A e^A$) and OB and OC will be coincident (line $o^A b^A c^A$). This construction involves finding the edge view of a plane (see Sec. 12.24). In this particular case, the auxiliary view has height in common with the frontal view.

Step 3. Draw the two views of the vector diagram by assuming the H-view and the A-view to be the given views of the special case. Proceed by the steps set forth for the special case in Sec. 14.17.

Step 4. Determine the magnitude of the forces and add arrowheads to the free-body diagram to show the direction of action of the forces acting on point O.

14.19. In practice, engineers find wide use for methods that solve problems through the use of three-dimensional vector diagrams, for any quantity having both magnitude and direction may be represented by a vector. And, although the examples used in the chapter dealt with static structures, which are in the field of the structural engineer, vector diagram methods are used frequently by the electrical engineer for solving problems arising in his field and by the mechanical engineer for problems dealing with bodies in motion. The student will without doubt encounter some of these methods in a textbook for a later course or will have them presented to him by his instructor.

PROBLEMS

The following problems have been selected to emphasize the basic principles underlying vector geometry. By solving a limited number of the problems presented, the student should find that he has a working knowledge of some vector methods that are useful for solving problems in design that involve the determination of the magnitude of forces as well

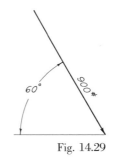

Fig. 14.29

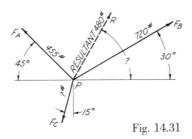

Fig. 14.30

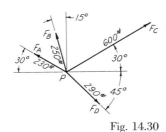

Fig. 14.31

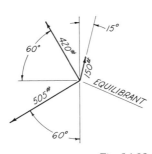

Fig. 14.32

as their composition and resolution. The student is to select his own scale remembering that a drawing made to a large scale usually assures more accurate results.

1. (Fig. 14.29.) A force of 900 lb acts downward at an angle of 60° with the horizontal. Determine the vertical and horizontal components of this force.

2. (Fig. 14.30.) Determine the resultant force for the given coplanar, concurrent force system.

3. (Fig. 14.31.) Determine the magnitude of the force F_C and the angle that the resultant force R makes with the horizontal for the given coplanar, concurrent force system.

4. (Fig. 14.32.) Determine the magnitude and direction of the equilibrant for the given coplanar, concurrent force system.

5. (Fig. 14.33.) A block weighing 45 lb is to be pulled up an inclined plane sloping at an angle of 30° with the horizontal. If the frictional resistance is 16 lb, what is the magnitude of the force F_M that is required to move the block uniformly up the plane?

6. (Fig. 14.34.) Determine the magnitude of the force F needed to start the 800 lb wheel over the obstacle.

7. (Fig. 14.34.) Determine the horizontal force needed to start the wheel over the obstacle (see Problem 6).

8. If the wheel shown in Fig. 14.34 were 2 ft in diameter instead of 3 ft, what is the magnitude of the force needed to start the wheel?

9. (Fig. 14.35.) A horizontal beam AB is hinged at B as shown. The end of the beam at A is connected by a cable to a hook in the wall at C. The load at A is 250 lb. Using the dimensions as given, determine the tension force in the cable and the reaction on the hinge at B. The weight of the beam is to be neglected.

10. (Fig. 14.36.) A 1000 lb load is supported as shown. Determine the magnitude of the tension in the cables.

11. (Fig. 14.37.) A 600 lb load is supported by cables as shown. Determine the magnitude of the tension in the cables.

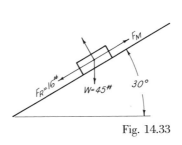

Fig. 14.33

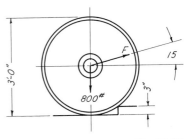

Fig. 14.34

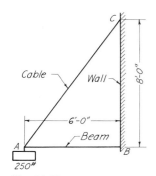

Fig. 14.35

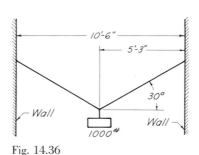

Fig. 14.36

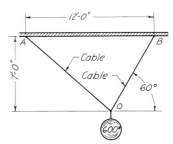

Fig. 14.37

12. (Fig. 14.38.) A 250 lb body hangs vertically as shown by broken lines. If a cable is attached and a side pull is applied in a horizontal direction until the body is drawn to a position with the cable at 30° from the vertical, what will be the magnitude of the applied force F? Determine the magnitude of the tension in the cable with the body in this new position.

13. (Fig. 14.39.) A ship that is being pulled through the entrance of a harbor is headed due east through a cross current moving at 4 knots as shown. If the ship is moving at 12 knots, what is the speed of the tug boat?

14. (Fig. 14.40.) A 170 lb man stands 4 ft to the right of the middle of the wire, which is supported at points 30 ft apart. Determine the magnitude of the tension in the wire if the feet of the man are 5 ft below the platforms.

15. (Fig. 14.41.) Determine the magnitude of the reactions R_1 and R_2 of the beam with loads as shown.

16. (Fig. 14.42.) Determine the magnitude of the reactions R_1 and R_2 of the beam.

17. (Fig. 14.43.) Determine the magnitude of the reactions R_1 and R_2 for the roof truss shown. Each of the six panels is of the same length.

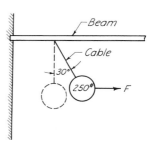

Fig. 14.38

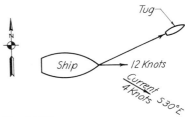

Fig. 14.39

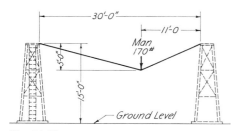

Fig. 14.40

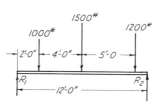

Fig. 14.41

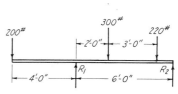

Fig. 14.42

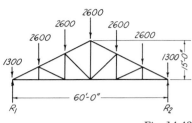

Fig. 14.43

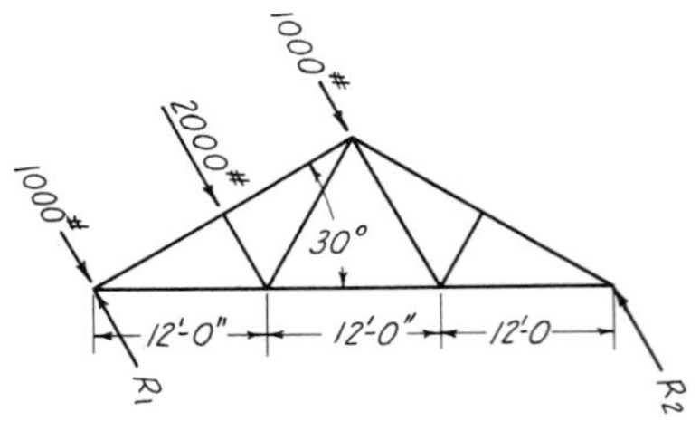

Fig. 14.44

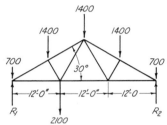

Fig. 14.45

18. (Fig. 14.44.) Determine the magnitude of the reactions R_1 and R_2 to the wind loads acting on the roof truss as shown.

19. (Fig. 14.45.) Determine the magnitude of the reactions R_1 and R_2 for the roof truss acting under loads as shown.

20-21. (Figs. 14.46–14.47.) Using the scale given below the drawing, reproduce the given views of the concurrent, noncoplanar force system shown. Assume the magnitudes of the forces and determine the resultant of the system.

22. (Fig. 14.48.) A tripod with an 85 lb load is set up on a level floor as shown. Determine the stresses in the three legs due to the vertical load on the top.

23-25. (Figs. 14.49–14.51.) Determine the stresses in the members of the space frame shown.

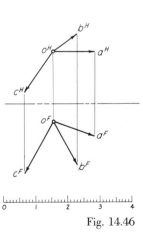

Fig. 14.46

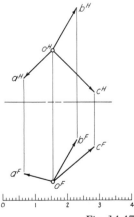

Fig. 14.47

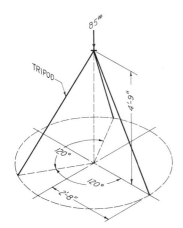

Fig. 14.48

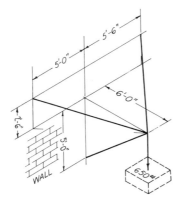

Fig. 14.49

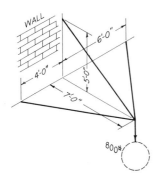

Fig. 14.50

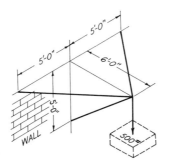

Fig. 14.51

15

SHOP PROCESSES

15.1. Shop processes. An engineering draftsman must be thoroughly familiar with the fundamental shop processes before he is qualified to prepare drawings that will fulfill the requirements of the production shops. In preparing working drawings, he must consider each and every individual process involved in the production of a piece, and then specify the processes in terms that the shopman will understand. All too frequently, drawings that specify impractical methods and impossible operations are sent to the shops. Most of these impractical specifications are the result of a lack of knowledge, on the draftsman's part, of what can or cannot be done by skilled craftsmen using modern machines and tools.

Although an accurate knowledge of the shop processes can be acquired only through actual experience in the various shops, it is possible for an apprentice draftsman to obtain a working knowledge of the fundamental operations through study and observation. This chapter presents and explains the principal operations in the pattern shop, foundry, forge shop, and machine shop.

15.2. Castings. Castings are formed by pouring molten metal into a mold or cavity. In sand molding, the molten metal assumes the shape of the cavity that has been formed in a sand mold by ramming a prepared moist sand around a pattern and then removing the pattern. Although a casting shrinks somewhat in cooling, the metal hardens in the exact shape of the pattern used (Fig. 15.1).

A sand mold consists of at least two sections. The upper section, called the *cope*, and the lower section, called the *drag*, together form a box-shaped structure called a *flask*.

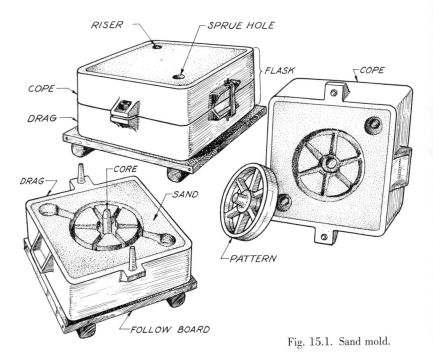

Fig. 15.1. Sand mold.

When large holes (¾ in. and over) or interior passageways and openings are needed in a casting, dry sand cores are placed in the cavity. Cores exclude the metal from the space they occupy and thus form desired openings. Large holes are cored in order to avoid an unnecessary boring operation. A dry sand core is formed by ramming a mixture of sand and a binding material into a core box that has been made in the pattern shop. To make a finished core rigid, the coremaker places it in a core oven where it is baked until it is hard.

The molder when making a mold inserts in the sand a sprue stick that he removes after the cope has been rammed. This resulting hole, known as the *sprue*, conducts the molten metal to the *gate*, which is a passageway cut to the cavity. The adjacent hole, called the *riser*, provides an outlet for excess metal.

15.3. The pattern shop. The pattern shop prepares patterns of all pieces that the foundry is to cast. Although special pattern drawings are frequently submitted, the pattern maker ordinarily uses a drawing of the finished piece that the draftsman has prepared for both the pattern shop and the machine shop. The finish marks on such a drawing are just as important to him as to the machinist, for he must allow, on each surface to be finished, extra metal, the amount of which depends upon the method of machining and the size of the casting. In general, this amount varies from ⅟₁₆ in., on very small castings, to as much as ¾ in., on large castings.

It is not necessary for the draftsman to specify on his drawing the amount to be allowed for shrinkage, for the pattern maker has available a "shrink rule," which is sufficiently oversize (approximately ⅛ in. per ft) to take care of the shrinkage.

A pattern usually is first constructed of light, strong wood, such as white pine or mahogany, which, if only a few castings are required, may be used in making sand molds. In quantity production, however, where a pattern must be used repeatedly, the wooden one will not hold up, so a metal pattern (aluminum, brass, and so on) is made from it and is used in its place.

Every pattern must be constructed in such a way that it can be withdrawn from each section of the sand mold. If the pattern consists of two halves (split), the plane of separation should be so located that it will coincide with the plane of separation of the cope and the drag (Fig. 15.1). Each portion of the pattern must be slightly tapered, so that it can be withdrawn without leaving a damaged cavity. The line of intersection, where the dividing plane cuts the pattern, is called the *parting line*. Although this line is rarely shown on a drawing, the draftsman should make certain that his design will allow the pattern maker to establish it. Ordinarily, it is not necessary to specify the slight taper, known as *draft*, on each side of the parting line, for the pattern maker assumes such responsibility when constructing the pattern.

A "filled-in" interior angle on a casting is called a *fillet*, to distinguish it from a rounded exterior angle, which is known as a *round* (Fig. 6.44). Sharp interior angles are avoided for two reasons: they are difficult to cast; and they are likely to be potential points of failure because the crystals of the cooling metal arrange themselves at a sharp corner in a weak pattern. Fillets are formed by nailing quarter rounds of wood or strips of leather into the sharp angles, or by filling the angles with wax.

15.4. The foundry. Although a draftsman is not directly concerned with the foundry, since the pattern maker takes his drawing and prepares the pattern and core boxes for the molder, it is most important that he be familiar with the operations in making a sand mold and a casting. Otherwise, he will find it difficult to prepare an economical design, the cost of which depends upon how simple it is to mold and cast.

15.5. Die casting. Die casting is an inexpensive method for producing certain types of machine parts, particularly those needing no great strength, in mass production. The castings are made by forcing molten metal or molten alloy into a cavity between metal dies in a die-casting machine. Parts thus produced usually require little or no finishing.

15.6. The forge shop. Many machine parts, especially those that must have strength and yet be light, are forged into shape, the heated metal being forced into dies with a drop hammer. Drop forging, since heated metal is made to conform to the shape of a cavity, might be considered a form of casting. However, because dies are difficult to make and are expensive, this method of production is used principally to make parts having an irregular shape that would be costly to machine and could not be made from casting material. Forgings are made of a high-grade steel. Dies are made by expert craftsmen who are known simply as diemakers.

Generally, special drawings, giving only the dimensions needed, are made for the forge shop.

15.7. Standard stock forms. Many types of metal shapes, along with other materials that are used in the shops for making parts for structures, are purchased from manufacturers in stock sizes. They are made available from the stock department, where rough stock, such as rods, bars, plates, sheet metal, and so on, is cut into sizes desired by the machine shop.

15.8. The machine shop. In general, the draftsman is more concerned with machine-shop processes than with the processes in other shops, as all castings and forgings that have been prepared in accordance with his drawings must receive their final machining in the machine shop. Since all machining operations must be considered in the design and then properly specified, a draftsman must be thoroughly familiar with the limitations as well as the possibilities of such common machines as the lathe, drill press, boring machine, shaper, planer, milling machine, and grinder. An explanation of the operation and capabilities of each machine will be given in the following sections.

15.9. The lathe. Many common operations, such as turning, facing, boring, reaming, knurling, threading, and so on, may be performed with this widely used machine. In general, however, it is used principally for machining (roughing-out) cylindrical surfaces to be finished on a grinding machine. Removing metal from the exterior surfaces of cylindrical objects is known as turning and is accomplished by a sharp cutting tool that removes a thin layer of metal each time it travels the length of a cylindrical surface on the revolving work (Fig. 15.2). The piece, which is supported in the machine between two aligned centers, known as the *dead center* and the *live center,* is caused to rotate about an axis by power transmitted through a lathe dog, chuck, or a face plate. The work revolves against the cutting tool, held in a tool post, as the tool moves parallel to the longitudinal axis of the piece being turned. Cutting an interior surface is known as *boring* (Fig. 15.3). A note is not necessary on a drawing to indicate that a surface is to be turned on a lathe.

When a hole is reamed, it is finished very accurately with a fluted reamer of the exact required diameter. If the operation is performed on a lathe, the work revolves as the nonrotating reamer is fed into

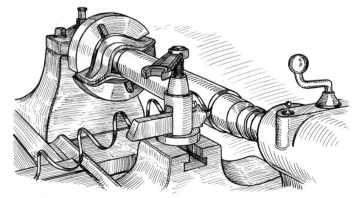

Fig. 15.2. Lathe operation—turning.

Fig. 15.3. Boring on a lathe.

Fig. 15.4. Reaming on a lathe.

the hole by turning the handwheel on the tail stock (see Fig. 15.4).

Screw threads may be cut on a lathe by a cutting tool that has been ground to the shape required for the desired thread. The thread is cut as the tool travels parallel to the axis of the revolving work at a fixed speed (Fig. 15.5).

Knurling is the process of roughening or embossing a cylindrical surface. This is accomplished by means of a knurling tool containing knurl rollers that press into the surface of the work as it is fed across them (Fig. 15.6).

Fig. 15.5. Cutting threads on a lathe.

Fig. 15.6. Knurling.

15.10. The drill press. A drill press is a necessary piece of equipment in any shop because, although it is used principally for drilling, as the name implies (Fig. 15.7), other operations, such as reaming, counterboring, countersinking, and so on, may be performed on it by merely using the proper type of cutting tool. The cutting tool is held in position in a chuck at the end of a vertical spindle that is made to revolve, through power from a motor, at a particular speed suitable for the type of metal being drilled. The most flexible drill press, especially for large work, is the radial type, which is so designed that the spindle is mounted on a movable arm that can be revolved into any desired position for drilling. With this machine, holes may be drilled at various angles and locations without shifting the work, which may be either clamped to the horizontal table or held in a drill vise or drill jig. The ordinary type of drill press without a movable arm is usually found in most shops along with the radial type. A multi-spindle drill is used for drilling a number of holes at the same time.

Figure 15.8 shows a setup on a drill press for performing the operation of counterboring. A counterbore is used to enlarge a hole to a depth that will allow the head of a fastener, such as a fillister-head cap screw, to be brought to the level of the surface of the piece through which it passes. A counterbore has a piloted end having approximately the same diameter as the drilled hole.

Figure 15.9 shows a setup for the operation of countersinking. A countersink is used to form a tapering depression that will fit the head of a flat-head machine screw or cap screw and allow it to be brought to the level of the surface of the piece through which it passes.

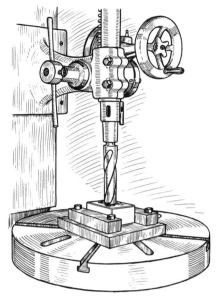

Fig. 15.7. A drill press.

Fig. 15.8. Counterboring on a drill press.

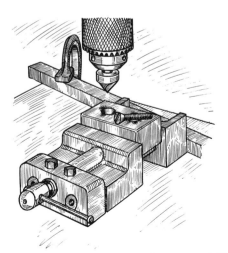

Fig. 15.9. Countersinking on a drill press.

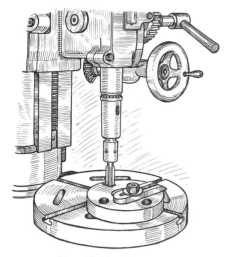

Fig. 15.10. Tapping on a drill press.

A plug tap is used to cut threads in a drilled hole (Fig. 15.10).

A spotfacer is used to finish a round spot that will provide a good seat for the head of a screw or bolt on the unfinished surface of a casting. Figure 15.11 shows various cutting tools commonly used for forming holes and cutting threads.

15.11. Hand reaming. A hole may be finished to an accurate size by hand reaming, as shown in Fig. 15.12. The reamer in this illustration is of a special type known as a *line reamer*.

15.12. Boring (Fig. 15.13). Boring is the operation of enlarging a circular hole for accuracy in roundness or straightness, and may be accomplished on a lathe, drill press, milling machine, or boring mill. When the hole is small and of considerable length, the operation may be performed on a lathe. If the hole is large, the work is usually done on a boring mill, of which there are two types—the vertical and the horizontal. On a vertical boring machine, the work is fastened on a horizontal revolving table, and the cutting tool or tools, which are stationary, advance vertically into it as the table revolves. On a horizontal boring machine, the tool revolves and the work is stationary.

15.13. The milling machine. A milling machine is used for finishing plane surfaces and for milling gear teeth, slots, keyways, and

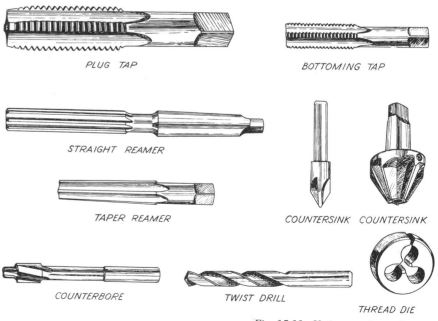

PLUG TAP

BOTTOMING TAP

STRAIGHT REAMER

TAPER REAMER

COUNTERSINK   COUNTERSINK

COUNTERBORE

TWIST DRILL

THREAD DIE

Fig. 15.11. Various cutting tools.

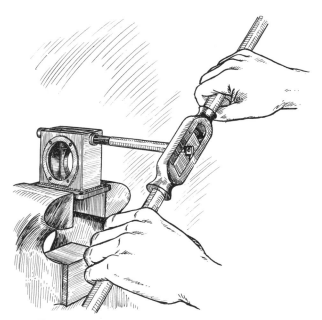

Fig. 15.12. Hand reaming.

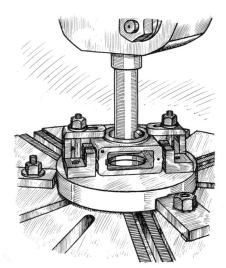

Fig. 15.13. Boring on a boring mill.

so on. In finishing a plane surface, a rotating circular cutter removes the metal for a desired cut as the work, fastened to a moving horizontal bed, is automatically fed against it. Several types of milling cutters are shown in Fig. 15.14.

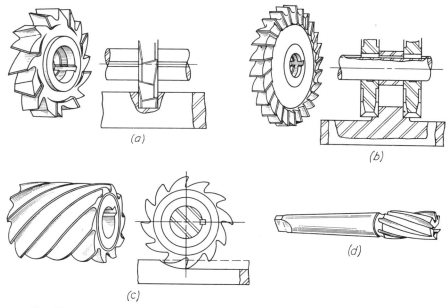

(a)

(b)

(c)

(d)

Fig. 15.14. Milling cutters and operations.

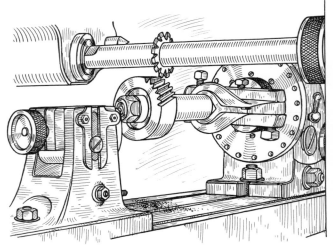

Fig. 15.15. Cutting gear teeth on a milling machine.

Figure 15.15 shows a setup for milling gear teeth in a gear blank. Note the form of this particular type of cutter.

15.14. The shaper (Fig. 15.16). A shaper is used for finishing small plane surfaces and for cutting slots and grooves. In action, a fast-moving reciprocating ram carries a tool across the surface of the work, which is fastened to an adjustable horizontal table. The tool cuts only on the forward stroke.

15.15. The planer. The planer is a machine particularly designed for cutting down and finishing large flat surfaces. The work is fastened to a long horizontal table that moves back and forth under the cutting tool. In action, the tool cuts as the table moves the surface against it. Unlike the cutter on the shaper, it is stationary except for a slight movement laterally for successive cuts.

15.16. The grinding machine. A grinding machine has a rotating grinding wheel that, ordinarily, is either an emery wheel (fine or coarse) or some type of high-speed wheel made of carborundum. Grinding consists of bringing the surface to be ground into contact with the wheel. Although grinding machines are often used for "roughing" and for grinding down projections and surfaces on castings, their principal use, as far as a draftsman is concerned, is for the final finishing operation to bring a piece of work down to accurate dimensions. Internal grinders are available for various purposes.

Fig. 15.16. Shaper.

15.17. Polishing. Polishing consists of bringing a ground surface into contact with a revolving disc of leather or cloth, thus producing a lustrous smoothness that would be impossible to obtain by using even the finest grinding wheel. The operation is specified on a drawing by a note, "polish" or "grind and polish."

15.18. Broaching. A broach is a tool used to cut keyways and to form square, rectangular, hexagonal, or irregular-shaped holes. It is a hard, tempered steel shaft with serrated cutting edges that enlarge a drilled, punched, or cored hole to a required shape. Broaches are either pushed or pulled through the work. A special broaching machine is used for pulling broaches. Some form of press, hydraulic or otherwise, is required for push broaches.

15.19. Jigs and fixtures. Often, when an operation must be performed many times in making a part in quantities on a general machine, one of two devices, a *jig* or a *fixture*, may be used to facilitate production and insure accuracy without making repeated measurements. Although both jigs and fixtures fulfill the same general purpose, there is a distinguishing difference between them. A jig, for example, holds the work as it guides the tool and, ordinarily, is not fixed to the machine. A fixture, on the other hand, is rigidly fastened to a machine and holds the work in position without acting as a guide for the cutting tools.

Since most large manufacturing concerns have special departments for designing jigs and fixtures, the ordinary draftsman is not directly concerned with these auxiliary devices when he is preparing working drawings.

15.20. Special production machines. In large industrial concerns, most mechanical parts are made on specialized machines by semiskilled operators. A discussion of even a few of these, however, is beyond the scope of a general drawing text in which each subject is limited to a few pages. Since most specialized mass-production machines operate on the same general principles as the general-purpose machines, a young engineering draftsman should be able to determine their limitations and capabilities through observation, if he has a general knowledge of such machines as the lathe, shaper, drill press, milling machine, and so on. No prospective designer or draftsman should ever forgo an opportunity to observe special production machines. He must have a thorough understanding of all shop machines and methods, if his drawings are to be satisfactory for the shops.

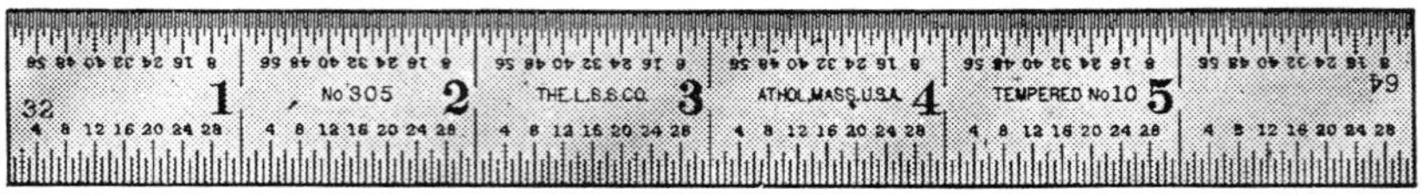

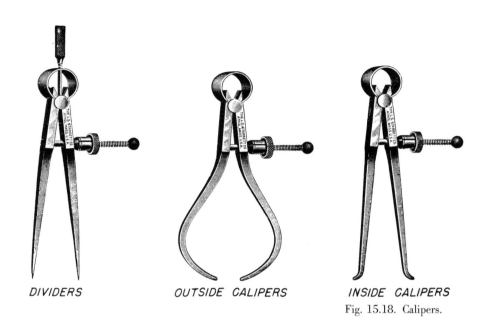

Fig. 15.17. The steel rule.

DIVIDERS   OUTSIDE CALIPERS   INSIDE CALIPERS

Fig. 15.18. Calipers.

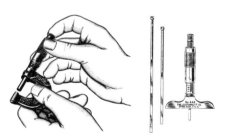

Fig. 15.19. Micrometers.

15.21. Measuring tools. Figures 15.17, 15.18, and 15.19 show a few of the measuring tools commonly available in shops. When great accuracy is not required, calipers are used (Fig. 15.18). The outside calipers are suited for taking external measurements, as for example, from a shaft. They are adjusted to fit the piece, and then the setting is applied to a rule to make a reading. The inside calipers have out-turned toes, which fits them for taking internal measurements, as for example in measuring either a cylindrical or a rectangular hole. When extreme accuracy is required, some form of micrometer calipers may be used (Fig. 15.19).

16

REPRESENTATION AND SPECIFICATION OF THREADS, FASTENERS, AND WELDS

A: SCREW THREADS

16.1. Introduction. In the commercial field, where the practical application of engineering drawing takes the form of working drawings, knowledge of screw threads and fasteners is important. There is always the necessity for assembling parts either with permanent fastenings such as rivets, or with bolts, screws, and so forth, which may be removed easily.

Engineers, detailers, and draftsmen must be completely familiar with the common types of threads and fastenings, as well as with their use and the correct methods of representation, because of the frequency of their occurrence in structures and machines. Information concerning special types of fasteners may be obtained from manufacturers' catalogues.

A young engineer in training should study Fig. 16.1 to acquaint himself with the terms commonly associated with screw threads.

16.2. Threads. The principal uses of threads are: (1) for fastening, (2) for adjusting, and (3) for transmitting power. To satisfy most of the requirements of the engineering profession, the different forms of threads shown in Fig. 16.2 are used.

The American Standard form (National Form N) thread which is being replaced by the new unified thread form is still widely used in the United States. The sharp V is used to some extent where adjustment and holding power are essential.

For the transmission of power and motion, the modified square, Acme, and Brown and Sharpe worm threads have been adopted. The modified square thread, which is now rarely used, transmits power parallel to its axis. A still further modification of the square thread is the stronger Acme, which is easier to cut and more readily disengages split nuts (as lead screws on lathes). The Brown and Sharpe worm thread, with similar proportions but with longer teeth, is used for transmitting power to a worm wheel.

The knuckle thread, commonly found on incandescent lamps, plugs, and so on, can be cast or rolled.

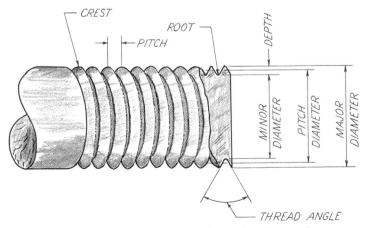

Fig. 16.1. Screw thread nomenclature.

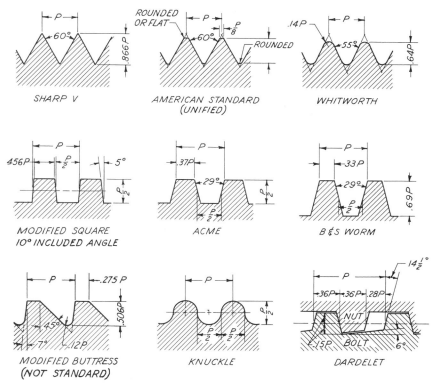

Fig. 16.2. Screw threads.

The Whitworth and buttress threads are not often encountered by the average engineer. The former, which fulfills the same purpose as the American Standard thread, is used in England but is also frequently found in this country. The buttress or breech-block thread, which is designed to take pressure in one direction, is used for breech mechanisms of large guns and for airplane propeller hubs. The thread form has not been standardized and appears in different modified forms.

The Dardelet thread is self-locking in assembly.

16.3. American-British Unified thread. The Unified Thread Standard (ASA B1.1–1949) came into existence after the representatives of the United States, Great Britain, and Canada signed a unification agreement on Nov. 18, 1948 in Washington, D. C. This accord, which made possible the interchangeability of threads for these countries, created a new thread form (Fig. 16.3) that is a compromise between our own American Standard design and the British Whitworth. The external thread of the new form has a rounded root and may have either a flat or rounded crest.

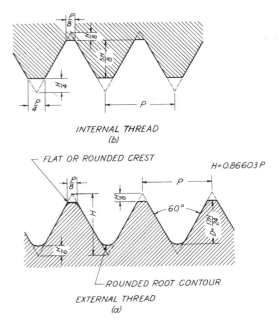

Fig. 16.3. American-British unified thread.

16.4. Multiple threads. Whenever a quick advance is desired, as on fountain pens, valves, and so on, two or more threads are cut side by side. Two threads form a double thread, three a triple thread, and so on. A thread that is not otherwise designated is understood to be a single thread.

In drawing a single, triple, or an odd-number multiple thread, a crest is always diametrically opposite a root; in a double or even-number multiple thread, a crest is opposite a crest and a root opposite a root.

16.5. Right-hand and left-hand threads. A right-hand thread advances into a threaded hole when turned clockwise; a left-hand thread advances when turned counterclockwise. They can be easily distinguished by the thread slant. A right-hand thread on a horizontal shank always slants upward to the left \ and a left-hand upward to the right /. A thread is always considered to be right-hand if it is not otherwise specified. A left-hand thread is always marked L.H. on a drawing.

16.6. Pitch. The pitch of a thread is the distance from any point on a thread to the corresponding point on the adjacent thread, measured parallel to the axis as shown in Fig. 16.1.

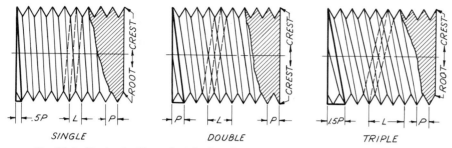

Fig. 16.4. Single, double, and triple threads.

16.7. Lead. The lead of a screw may be defined as the distance advanced parallel to the axis when the screw is turned one revolution (Fig. 16.4). For a single thread, the lead is equal to the pitch; for a double thread, the lead is twice the pitch; for a triple thread, the lead is three times the pitch, and so on.

16.8. Detailed screw-thread representation. The true representation of screw threads by helical curves, requiring unnecessary time and laborious drafting, is rarely used. The detailed representation, closely approximating the actual appearance, is preferred in commercial practice, for it is much easier to represent the helices with slanting lines and the truncated roots and crests with sharp "V's" (Fig. 16.5). Since detailed rendering is also time consuming, its use is justified only in those few cases where appearance and permanency are important factors, and when it is necessary to avoid the possibility that confusion might result from the use of one of the symbolic methods. The preparation of a detailed representation

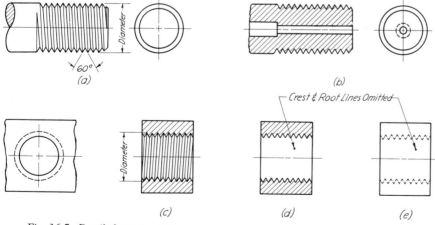

Fig. 16.5. Detailed representation.

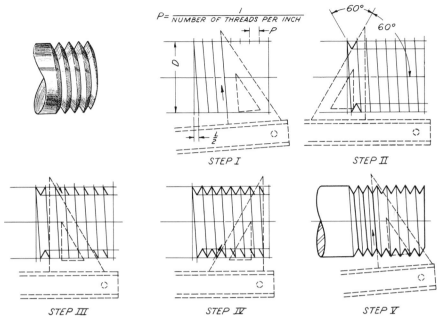

Fig. 16.6. Detailed representation of Unified and American and sharp V-threads (external).

is a task that belongs primarily to a draftsman, the engineer being concerned only with specifying that this form be used.

The steps in drawing a Unified thread are shown in Figs. 16.6 and 16.7.

The stages in drawing the detailed representation of modified square and Acme threads are shown in Figs. 16.8, 16.9, and 16.10. All lines of the finished square thread are made the same weight. The root lines of the Acme thread may be made heavier than the other lines.

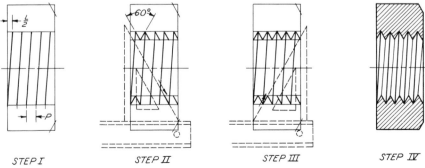

Fig. 16.7. Detailed representation of Unified and American and sharp V-threads (internal).

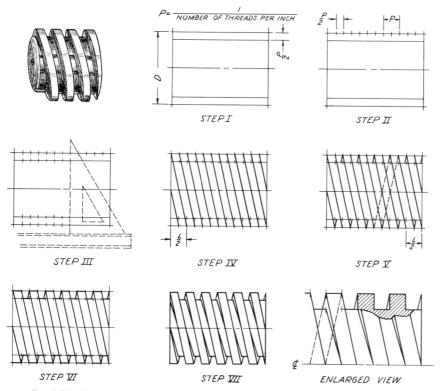

Fig. 16.8. Detailed representation of square threads (modified).

16.9. American Standard conventional thread symbols (Fig. 16.11).

To save valuable time and expense in the preparation of drawings, the American Standards Association has adopted the "schematic" and "simplified" series of thread symbols to represent threads having a diameter of one inch or less.

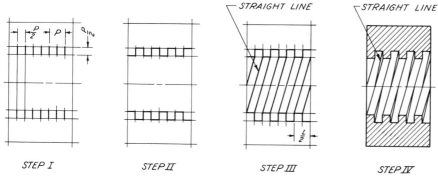

Fig. 16.9. Detailed representation of square threads (internal).

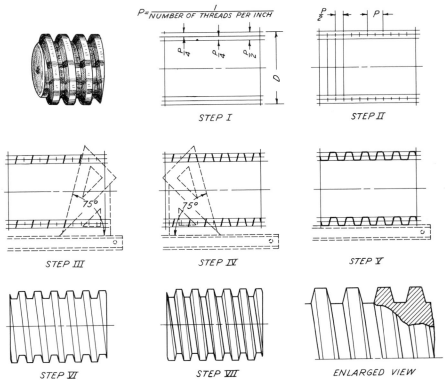

Fig. 16.10. Detailed representation of Acme thread.

The root of the thread for the simplified representation is shown by invisible lines drawn parallel to the axis [Fig. 16.12(a)].

The schematic representation consists of alternate long and short lines perpendicular to the axis. Although these lines, representing the crests and roots of the thread, are not spaced to actual pitch, their spacing should indicate noticeable differences in the number of threads per inch of different threads on the same working drawing or group of drawings (Fig. 16.13). The root lines are made heavier than the crest lines (Fig. 16.14).

Before a hole can be tapped (threaded), it must be drilled to permit the tap to enter. See Table 2 for tap drill sizes for standard threads. Since the last of the thread cut is not well formed or usable,

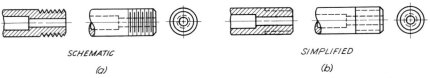

SCHEMATIC

(a)

SIMPLIFIED

(b)

Fig. 16.11. External thread representation.

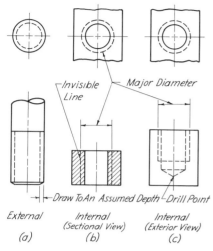

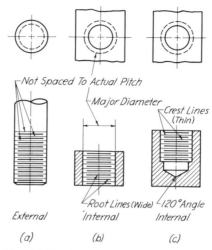

Fig. 16.12. Simplified representation.

Fig. 16.13. Schematic representation.

the hole must be shown drilled and tapped deeper than the screw will enter [see Figs. 16.15(*d*), (*e*), (*f*)]. To show the threaded portion extending to the bottom of the drilled hole indicates the use of a bottoming tap to cut full threads at the bottom. This is an extra and expensive operation not justified except in cases where the depth of the hole and the distance the screw must enter are limited [see Figs. 16.15(*g*), (*h*), (*i*)].

Figure 16.16 shows a simplified method of representation for square threads.

16.10. Threads in section. The detailed representation of threads in section, which is used for large diameters only, is shown in Fig. 16.7. Since the far side of an internal thread in section is visible, the crest and root lines incline in the opposite direction to those of an external thread having the same specifications.

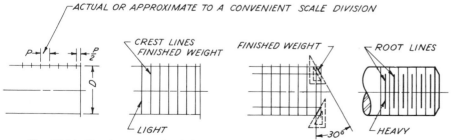

Fig. 16.14. Drawing conventional threads—schematic representation.

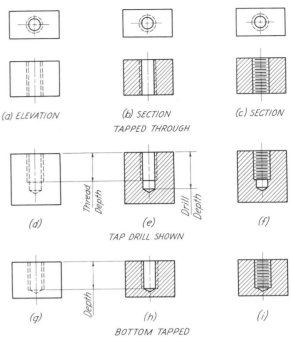

(a) ELEVATION   (b) SECTION   (c) SECTION
TAPPED THROUGH

(d)   (e)   (f)
TAP DRILL SHOWN

(g)   (h)   (i)
BOTTOM TAPPED

Fig. 16.15. Representation of internal threads.

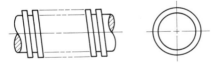

Fig. 16.16. Simplified representation of a square thread.

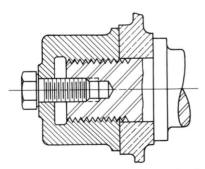

Fig. 16.17. Threads in section.*

* ASA Y14.6–1957.

The schematic and simplified representations for threads of small diameter are shown in Figs. 16.11 and 16.15.

A sectioned assembly drawing is shown in Fig. 16.17. When assembled pieces are both sectioned, the detailed representation is used, and the thread form is drawn. Simplified representation could have been used for the thread on the cap screw instead of the schematic representation shown (see Fig. 17.94).

16.11. Unified and American screw thread series. The Unified and American screw thread series as given in ASA B1.1–1949 consists of six series and a selection of special threads that cover special combinations of diameter and pitch. Each series differs from the other by the number of threads per inch for a specific diameter (see Tables 2 and 3, Appendix).

The coarse thread series (UNC and NC) is designated UNC for sizes above ¼ in. in diameter. This series is recommended for general industrial use.

The fine thread series (UNF and NF) designated UNF for sizes above ¼ in., was prepared for use when a fine thread is required and for general use in the automotive and aircraft fields.

The extra-fine thread series, designated NEF, is used for automotive and aircraft work when a maximum number of threads is required for a given length. A few specific sizes of this series are designated UN.

The 8 thread series (8N) is a uniform pitch series for large diameters. It is sometimes used in place of the coarse thread series for diameters greater than 1 in. This series was originally intended for high-pressure joints.

The 12 thread series (12UN or 12N) is a uniform pitch series intended for use with large diameters requiring threads of medium-fine pitch. This series is used as a continuation of the fine thread series for diameters greater than 1½ in.

The 16 thread series (16UN or 16N) is a uniform pitch series for large diameters requiring a fine pitch thread. This series is used as a continuation of the extra-fine thread series for diameters greater than 2 in.

16.12. Unified and American screw thread classes. Classes of thread are determined by the amounts of tolerance and allowance specified. Under the new unified system, classes 1A, 2A, and 3A apply only to external threads; classes 1B, 2B, and 3B apply to internal threads. Classes 2 and 3 from the former American Standard have been retained without change in the new Unified and American Thread Standard for use in the United States only, but they are not among the Unified classes even though the thread forms are identical. These classes are used with the American thread series (NC, NF, and N series) which covers sizes from size 0 (.060) to 6 in.

Class 1A and class 1B replace class 1 of the old American Standard.

Class 2A and class 2B were adopted as the recognized standards for screws, bolts, and nuts.

Class 3A and class 3B invoke new classes of tolerance. These classes along with class 2A and class 2B should eventually replace class 2 and class 3 now retained from the American Standard. Class 2 and class 3 are defined in the former standard ASA B1.1–1935 as follows:

Class 2 fit. Represents a high quality of commercial thread product and is recommended for the great bulk of interchangeable screw-thread work.

Class 3 fit. Represents an exceptionally high quality of commercially threaded product and is recommended only in cases where the high cost of precision tools and continual checking is warranted.

16.13. Identification symbols for Unified screw threads. Threads are specified under the new unified system by giving the diameter, number of threads per inch, initial letters (UNC, UNF, etc.), and class of thread (1A, 2A, and 3A; or 1B, 2B, and 3B) (see Fig. 16.18).

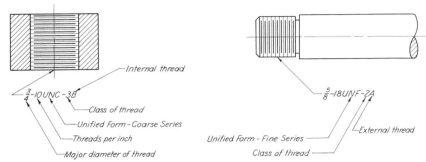

Fig. 16.18. Unified thread identification symbols.

16.14. Identification symbols for American Standard, Square, and Acme threads. American Standard, Square, and Acme threads are specified on drawings, in specifications, and in stock lists by thread information given as shown in Fig. 16.19.

16.15. American Standard pipe thread. The American Standard pipe taper thread, illustrated in Fig. 16.20, is similar to the ordinary American Standard thread and has the same thread angle; but it is tapered 1/16 in. per in., to insure a tight joint at a fitting. The crest is flattened and the root is filled in so that the depth of the thread is 0.80P. The number of threads per inch for any given

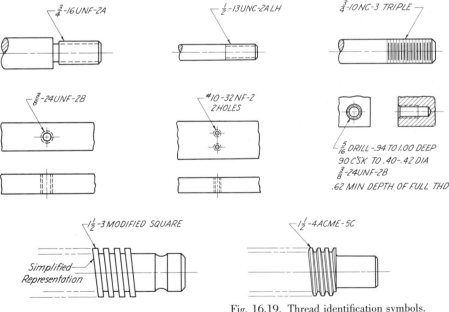

Fig. 16.19. Thread identification symbols.

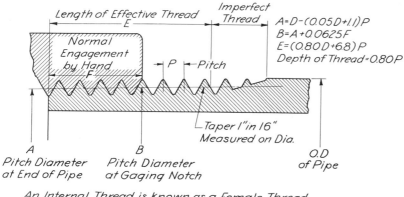

$A = D - (0.05D + 1.1)P$
$B = A + 0.0625F$
$E = (0.80D + 6.8)P$
Depth of Thread $= 0.80P$

An Internal Thread is known as a Female Thread
An External Thread is known as a Male Thread

Fig. 16.20. American Standard pipe thread.

nominal diameter can be obtained from Table 19 in the Appendix.

An American National straight pipe thread, having the same number of threads per inch as the taper thread, is in use for pressure-tight joints for couplings, for pressure-tight joints for grease and oil fittings, and for hose couplings and nipples. This thread may also be used for free-fitting mechanical joints. Usually a taper external thread is used with a straight internal thread, as pipe material is sufficiently ductile for an adjustment of the threads.

In specifying pipe threads, the ASA recommends that the note be formulated using symbolic letters as illustrated in Fig. 16.21. For example, the specification for a 1 in. standard pipe thread

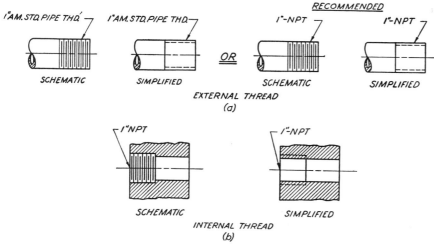

Fig. 16.21. American Standard representation of pipe threads.

should read, 1″-*NPT*. The letters *NPT*, following the nominal diameter, indicate that the thread is American National (*N*), pipe (*P*), taper (*T*) thread. Continuing with the same scheme of using letters, the specification for a 1 in. straight pipe thread would read, 1″-*NPS* [National (*N*)—pipe (*P*)—straight (*S*)]. The form of note given in Fig. 16.21(*a*), reading *1″ AM. STD. PIPE THD.*, is quite commonly used in practice. Identification symbols and dimensions of American National pipe threads are given in the American Standard for Pipe Threads (ASA B2.1–1945).

16.16. Drawing pipe threads. The taper on a pipe thread is so slight that it will not attract attention on a drawing unless it is exaggerated. If it is shown at all, it is usually magnified to ⅛ in. per in.

Pipe threads are generally represented by the same conventional symbols used for ordinary American Standard thread (Fig. 16.21).

B: FASTENERS

16.17. American Standard bolts and nuts (Fig. 16.22). Commercial producers of bolts and fasteners manufacture their products in accordance with the standard specifications given in the American Standard entitled "Square and Hexagon Bolts and Nuts" (Revised 1955).* See Table 5 in Appendix.

The ASA has approved the specification for three series of bolts and nuts:

1. *Regular series.* The regular series was adopted for general use.
2. *Heavy series.* Heavy boltheads and nuts are designed to satisfy the special commercial need for greater bearing surface.
3. *Light series nuts.* Light nuts are used under conditions requiring a substantial savings in weight and material. They are usually supplied with a fine thread.

The amount of machining is the basis for further classification of hexagonal bolts and nuts in both the regular and heavy series as unfinished and semifinished.

Square-head bolts and nuts are standardized as unfinished only.

Unfinished heads and nuts are not washer-faced, nor are they machined on any surface.

Semifinished boltheads and nuts are machined or treated on the bearing surface so as to provide a washer face for boltheads and

* ASA B18.2–1955.

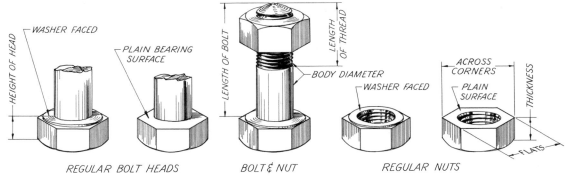

Fig. 16.22. American Standard bolts and nuts.

either a washer face or a circular bearing surface for nuts. Nuts, not washer-faced, have the circular bearing surface formed by chamfering the edges.

Bolts and nuts are *always* drawn across corners in all views. This recognized commercial practice, which violates the principles of true projection, prevents confusion of square and hexagonal forms on drawings.

The chamfer angle on the tops of heads and nuts is 30° on hexagons and 25° on squares, but both are drawn at 30° on bolts greater than 1 in. in diameter.

Bolts are specified in parts lists and elsewhere by giving the diameter, number of threads per inch, series, class of thread, length, finish, and type of head.

EXAMPLE: ½-13UNC-2A × 1¾ SEMI-FIN. HEX. HD. BOLT.

Frequently it is advantageous and practical to abbreviate the specification thus:

EXAMPLE: ½ × 1¾ UNC SEMI-FIN. HEX. HD. BOLT.

Although bolt lengths have not been standardized in construction practice, because of the varied requirements in engineering design, length increments for length under the head to the end of a hexagonal bolt can be considered as: ⅛ in. for bolts ¼ in. to ¾ in. in length, ¼ in. for bolts ¾ in. to 3 in. in length, and ½ in. for bolts 3 in. to 6 in. in length. Length increments for square head bolts are: ⅛ in. for bolts ¼ in. to ¾ in. in length, and ¼ in. for bolts ¾ in. to 4¾ in. in length.

The minimum thread length for bolts up to and including 6 in. in length shall be twice the diameter plus ¼ in. For lengths over 6 in. the minimum thread length shall be twice the diameter of the bolt plus ½ in. (ASA B18.2–1955).

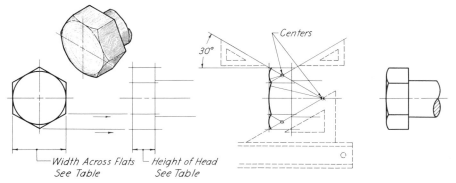

Fig. 16.23. Steps in drawing a hexagonal bolt head.

16.18. To draw boltheads and nuts. Using the dimension taken from the tables, draw the lines representing the top and contact surfaces of the head or nut and the diameter of the bolt. Lay out a hexagon about an inscribed chamfer circle having a diameter equal to the distance across the flats (Fig. 16.23) and project the necessary lines to block in the view. Draw in the arcs after finding the centers as shown in Fig. 16.23.

A square-head bolt or nut may be drawn by following the steps indicated in Fig. 16.24.

The engineer and experienced draftsman wisely resort to some form of template for drawing the views of a bolthead or nut (see Fig. 3.51). To draw the views as shown in Figs. 16.23 and 16.24 consumes valuable time needlessly.

16.19. Studs. Studs, or stud bolts, which are threaded on both ends, as shown in Fig. 16.25, are used where bolts would be impractical and for parts that must be removed frequently (cylinder heads, steam chest covers, pumps, and so on). They are first screwed permanently into the tapped holes in one part before the removable

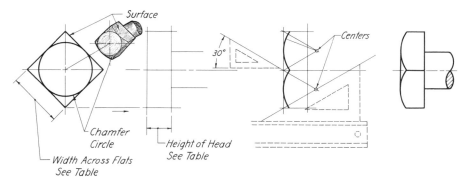

Fig. 16.24. Steps in drawing a square bolt head.

member with its corresponding clearance holes is placed in position. Nuts are used on the projecting ends to hold the parts together.

Since studs are not standard they must be produced from specifications given on a detail drawing. In dimensioning a stud, the length of thread must be given for both the stud end and nut end along with an over-all dimension. The thread information is given by note.

In a bill of material, studs may be specified as follows:

EXAMPLE: ½-13UNC-2A × 2¾ STUD.

It is good practice to abbreviate the specification thus:

EXAMPLE: ½ × 2¾ STUD.

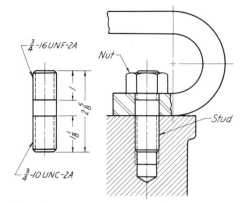

Fig. 16.25. Stud bolt.

16.20. Cap screws (Fig. 16.26). Cap screws are similar to machine screws. They are available in four standard heads, usually in finished form. When parts are assembled, the cap screws pass through clear holes in one member and screw into threaded holes in the other (Fig. 16.26). Hexagonal cap screws have a washer face ¹⁄₆₄ in. thick with a diameter equal to the distance across flats. All cap screws 1 in. or less in length are threaded very nearly to the head.

Cap screws are specified by giving the diameter, number of threads per inch, series, class of thread, length, and type of head.

EXAMPLE: ⅝-11UNC-2A × 2 FIL. HD. CAP SC.

It is good practice to abbreviate the specification thus:

EXAMPLE: ⅝ × 2 UNC FIL. HD. CAP SC.

16.21. Machine screws. Machine screws, which fulfill the same purpose as cap screws, are used chiefly for small work having thin sections (Fig. 16.27). Under the approved American Standard they range from No. 0 (0.060 in. diam.) to ¾ in. (0.750 in. diam.) and are available in either the American Standard Coarse or Fine-

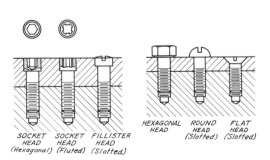

Fig. 16.26. Cap screws.

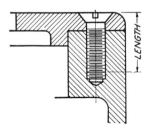

Fig. 16.27. Use of a machine screw.

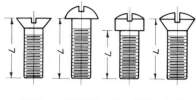

FLAT   ROUND   FILLISTER OVAL
HD.   HD.   HD.   HD.

Fig. 16.28. Types of machine screws.

Threaded Series. The four forms of heads shown in Fig. 16.28 have been standardized.

To specify machine screws, give the diameter, threads per inch, thread series, class of thread, length, and type of head.

EXAMPLE: No. 12–24NC–3 × ¾″ FIL. HD. MACH. SC.

It is good practice to abbreviate by omitting the thread series and class of fit.

EXAMPLE: No. 12–24 × ¾″ FIL. HD. MACH. SC.

16.22. Commercial lengths: studs, cap screws, machine screws. Unless a fastening of any of these types carries a constant and appreciable fatigue stress, the usual practice is to have it enter a distance related to its nominal diameter. If the depth of the hole is not limited, it should be drilled to a depth of 1 diameter beyond the end of the fastener to permit tapping to a distance of ½ diameter below the fastener.

The length of the fastening should be determined to the nearest commercial length that will allow it to fulfill minimum conditions. In the case of a stud, care should be taken that the length allows for a full engagement of the nut. Commercial lengths for fasteners increase by the following increments:

Standard length increments:
For fastener lengths ¼ in. to 1 in. = ⅛ in.
For fastener lengths 1 in. to 4 in. = ¼ in.

For fastenings and other general-purpose applications, the engagement length should be equal to the nominal diameter (D) of the thread when both components are of steel. For steel external threads in cast iron, brass, or bronze, the engagement length should be 1½D. When assembled into aluminum, zinc, or plastic the engagement should be 2D.

16.23. Set screws. Set screws are used principally to prevent rotary motion between two parts, such as that which tends to occur in the case of a rotating member mounted on a shaft. A set screw is screwed through one part until the point presses firmly against the other part (Fig. 16.29).

The several forms of safety heads shown in Fig. 16.30 are available in combination with any of the points. Headless set screws comply with safety codes and should be used on all revolving parts. The many serious injuries that have been caused by the projecting heads of square-head set screws have led to legislation prohibiting their use in some states (Fig. 16.29).

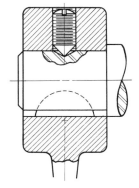 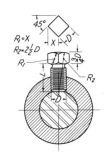

Fig. 16.29. Use of set screws.

Set screws are specified by giving the diameter, number of threads per inch, series, class of thread, length, type of head, and type of point.

EXAMPLE: ¼-20 UNC-2A × ½ SLOTTED CONE PT. SET SC.

The preferred abbreviated form gives the diameter, number of threads per inch, length, type of head, and type of point.

EXAMPLE: ¼-20 × ½ HEX. SOCKET CONE PT. SET SC.

16.24. Keys. Keys are used in the assembling of machine parts to secure them against relative motion, generally rotary, as is the case between shafts, cranks, wheels, and so on. When the relative forces are not great, a round key, saddle key, or flat key is used (Fig. 16.31). For heavier duty, rectangular keys are more suitable.

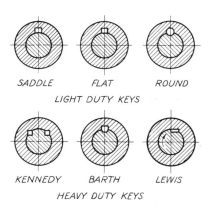

Fig. 16.31. Special light- and heavy-duty keys.

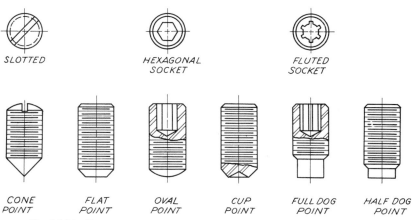

Fig. 16.30. Set screws.

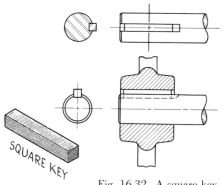

Fig. 16.32. A square key.

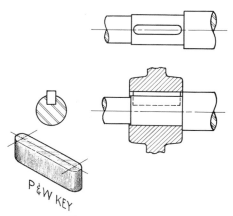

Fig. 16.33. A Pratt and Whitney key.

The square key (Fig. 16.32) and the Pratt and Whitney key (Fig. 16.33) are the two keys most frequently used in machine design. A plain milling cutter is used to cut the keyway for the square key, and an end mill is used for the Pratt and Whitney keyway. Both keys fit tightly in the shaft and in the part mounted upon it.

The gib-head key (Fig. 16.34) is designed so that the head remains far enough from the hub to allow a drift pin to be driven to remove the key. The hub side of the key is tapered ⅛ in. per ft to insure a fit tight enough to prevent both axial and rotary motion. For this type of key, the keyway must be cut to one end of the shaft.

16.25. Woodruff keys. A Woodruff key is a flat segmental disc with either a flat or a round bottom (Fig. 16.35). It is always specified by a number, the last two digits of which indicate the nominal diameter in eighths of an inch, while the digits preceding the last two give the nominal width in thirty-seconds of an inch.

A practical rule for selecting a Woodruff key for a given shaft is: Choose a standard key that has a width approximately equal to one-fourth of the diameter of the shaft, and a radius nearly equal (plus or minus) to the radius of the shaft. Table 16 in the Appendix gives the dimensions for American Standard Woodruff keys.

When Woodruff keys are drawn, it should be remembered that the center of the arc is placed above the top of the key at a distance shown in column E in the table.

16.26. Locking devices. A few of the many types of locking devices that prevent nuts from becoming loose under vibration are shown in Figs. 16.36–16.40.

Figure 16.36 shows six forms of patented spring washers. The ones shown in D, E, and F have internal and external teeth.

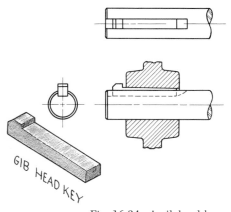

Fig. 16.34. A gib-head key.

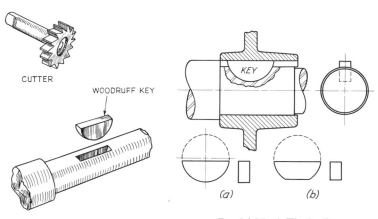

Fig. 16.35. A Woodruff key.

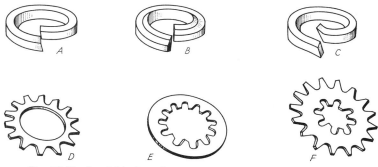

Fig. 16.36. Special lock washers.

Fig. 16.37. Shakeproof preassembled nut and lock washer.

Figure 16.37 shows a preassembled nut and washer combination.

Secured in the top of the elastic stop nut shown in Fig. 16.38 is a red fiber locking collar slightly smaller than the diameter of the bolt. Because this collar is plastic in character, it forms to the bolt thread and grips securely enough to prevent the nut from coming loose under strong vibration.

In common use is the castellated nut [Figs. 16.39 and 16.40(a)] with a spring cotter pin that passes through the shaft and the slots in the top. This type is used extensively in automotive and aeronautical work.

Fig. 16.38. Elastic stop nut.

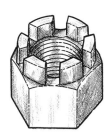

Fig. 16.39. Castellated nut.

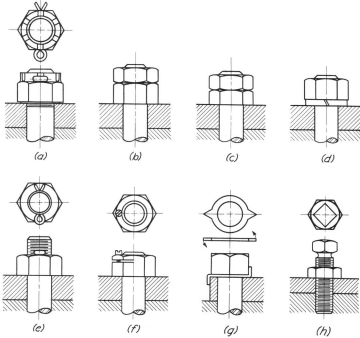

Fig. 16.40. Locking schemes.

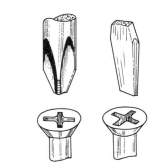

Fig. 16.41. Phillips head screw.

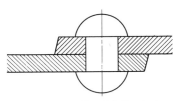

Fig. 16.42. A rivet.

Figure 16.40(*b*) shows a regular nut that is prevented from loosening by an American Standard jam nut.

In Fig. 16.40(*c*) the use of two jam nuts is illustrated.

A regular nut with a spring-lock washer is shown in Fig. 16.40(*d*). The reaction provided by the lock washer tends to prevent the nut from turning.

A regular nut with a spring cotter pin through the shaft, to prevent the nut from backing off, is shown in Fig. 16.40(*e*).

Special devices for locking nuts are illustrated in Fig. 16.40(*f*) and (*g*). A set screw may be held in position with a jam nut as in (*h*).

16.27. Phillips head. The Phillips head, shown in Fig. 16.41 for a wood screw, is one of various types of recessed heads. Although special drivers are usually employed for installation, an ordinary screw driver can be used. Machine screws, capscrews, and many special types of fasteners are available with Phillips heads.

16.28. Rivets. Rivets are permanent fasteners used chiefly for connecting members in such structures as buildings and bridges and for assembling steel sheets and plates for tanks, boilers, and ships. They are cylindrical rods of wrought iron or soft steel, with one head formed when manufactured. A head is formed on the other end after the rivet has been put in place through the drilled or punched holes of the mating parts. A hole for a rivet is generally drilled, punched, or punched and reamed $\frac{1}{16}$ in. larger than the diameter of the shank of the rivet. Figure 16.42 illustrates a rivet in position. Small rivets, less than $\frac{1}{2}$ in. in diameter, may be driven cold, but the larger sizes are driven hot. For specialized types of engineering work, rivets are manufactured of chrome-iron, aluminum, brass, copper, and so on. Standard dimensions for small rivets are given in Table 13 in the Appendix.

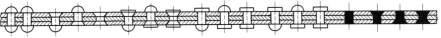

SHOP RIVETS					FIELD RIVETS	
BUTTON HEADS	COUNTERSUNK AND CHIPPED	COUNTERSUNK NOT CHIPPED	FLATTENED TO $\frac{1}{4}$ HIGH FOR $\frac{1}{2}$" AND $\frac{5}{8}$ RIVETS	FLATTENED TO $\frac{3}{8}$ HIGH FOR $\frac{3}{4}$" TO 1" RIVETS	FULL HEADS	COUNTERSUNK AND CHIPPED

Fig. 16.43. Conventional symbols for rivets.

The type of rivets and their treatment are indicated on drawings by the American Standard conventional symbols shown in Fig. 16.43.

The holes for field rivets are indicated in solid black on a drawing, and shop rivets are shown by open circles with the same diameter as the rivet head. Rivets should be drawn with either a drop pen or a bow pencil. In practice, the circles representing rivets are often drawn freehand on pencil drawings.

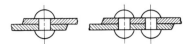

Fig. 16.44. Lap joints.

16.29. Riveted joints. Joints on boilers, tanks, and so on, are classified as either lap joints or butt joints. Lap joints are generally used for seams around the circumference (Fig. 16.44). Butt joints are used for longitudinal seams, except on small tanks where the pressure is to be less than 100 lb per sq in. (Fig. 16.45).

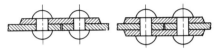

Fig. 16.45. Butt joints.

16.30. Springs. In production work, a spring is largely a matter of mathematical calculation rather than drawing, and it is usually purchased from a spring manufacturer, with the understanding that it will fulfill specified conditions. For experimental work, and when only one is needed, it may be formed by winding oil-tempered spring wire or music wire around a cylindrical bar. As it is wound, the wire follows the helical path of the screw thread. For this reason the steps in the layout of the representation for a spring are similar to the screw thread. Pitch distances are marked off, and the coils are given a slope of one-half of the pitch. Figure 16.46(*a*) shows a partial layout of a tension spring. Other types of ends are shown in (*b*). A compression spring layout, with various types of ends, is illustrated in Fig. 16.47.

When making a detail working drawing of a spring, it should be shown to its free length. On either an assembly or detail drawing, a fairly accurate representation, neatly drawn, will satisfy all requirements.

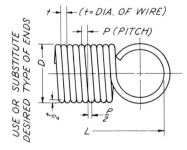

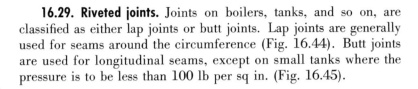

SPRING LAYOUT – FULL LOOP- CLOSED

(a)

OTHER TYPES OF ENDS

(b)

Fig. 16.46. Tension springs.

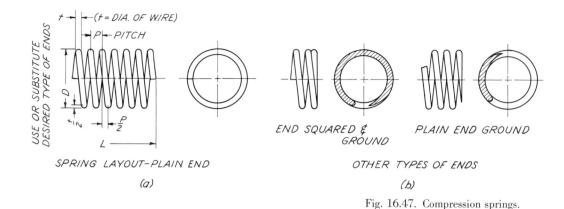

Fig. 16.47. Compression springs.

Single line symbols for the representation of springs are shown in Fig. 16.48.

C: WELDING

16.31. Welding processes. For convenience, the various welding processes used in commercial production may be classified into three types: pressure processes, nonpressure processes, and casting processes. The nonpressure processes are arc welding and gas welding. Metallic arc welding is the joining of two pieces of metal through the use of a sustained arc formed between the work and a metal rod held in a holder. The intense heat melts the metal of the work and at the same time heats the end of the electrode, causing small globules to form and cross the arc to the weld. In gas welding, the heat is produced by a burning mixture of two gases, which ordinarily are oxygen and acetylene. The weld is formed by melting a filler rod with the torch flame, along the line of contact, after the metal of the work has been preheated to a molten state. This method is essentially a puddling process, in that the weld is produced by a small moving molten pool that is maintained by the flame constantly directed upon it. Resistance welding is a pressure process, the fusion being made through heat and mechanical pressure. The work is heated by a strong electrical current that passes through it

Fig. 16.48. Single line representation of springs.*

* ASA Z14.1–1946.

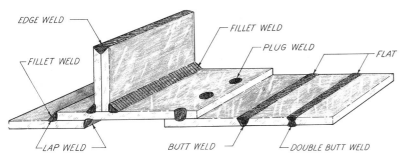

Fig. 16.49. Types of welds.

until fusion temperature is reached; then pressure is applied to create the weld.

The forms of resistance welding are: projection welding, seam welding, spot welding, and flash welding. In spot welding, the parts are overlapped and welds are made at successive single spots. A seam weld is similar to a spot weld, except that a continuous weld is produced. In projection welding, one part is embossed and welds are made at the successive projections. In making a flash weld, the two pieces to be joined are held end to end in jaws and act as electrodes. At the right instant, after the facing metal has been heated by the arc across the gap, the power is shut off and the two ends are forced together to cool in a fused position.

16.32. Types of welded joints. Figure 16.49 shows the ordinary types of welded joints.

16.33. Working drawings of welded parts. Figure 16.50 shows a part that is to be constructed by welding rolled shapes. It should

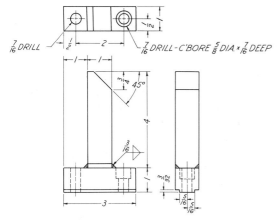

Fig. 16.50. A welding drawing (*Courtesy Lincoln Electric Co.*).

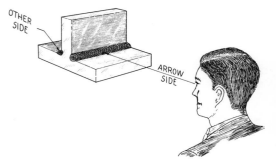

Fig. 16.51. Arrow-side and other-side welds.

be noted that the joint is completely specified through the use of a welding symbol. A careful study will show that the drawing, except for the absence of fillets and rounds, is very much like a casting drawing.

16.34. Arrow-side and other-side welds (Fig. 16.51). "The use of the words 'far side' and 'near side' in the past has led to confusion, because when joints are shown in section, all welds are equally distant from the reader, and the words 'near' and 'far' are meaningless. In the present system the joint is the basis of reference. Any joint whose welding is indicated by a symbol will always have an 'arrow-side' and an 'other-side.'"*

16.35. Welding symbols. An enlarged drawing of the approved welding symbol is shown in Fig. 16.52, along with explanatory notes that indicate the proper locations of the marks and size dimensions necessary for a complete description of a weld.

The arrow is the basic portion of the symbol. It points toward the joint where the required weld is to be made, as in Fig. 16.50.

If the weld is on the arrow-side, the symbol indicating the type of weld is placed below or to the right of the base line, depending upon whether that line is horizontal or vertical (Fig. 16.52). If the weld is located on the other-side, the symbol should be above or to the left.

To indicate that a weld is to be made all around a connection, as is necessary when a piece of tubing must be welded to a plate, a weld all-around symbol, a circle, is placed as shown in Fig. 16.53.

The size of a weld is given along the base of the arrow, at the side of the symbol, as shown in Fig. 16.53. If the welds on the arrow-side and the other-side of a lap joint are the same size, only one dimension should be given. If they are not the same size, each dimension should be placed beside its associated symbol.

* Extracted from ASA Z32.2.1–1949.

16.36. Gas and arc welding symbols. In order to satisfy the need for a standard group of symbols that could be understood in all manufacturing plants, the American Welding Society recommended in 1940 a set of conventional symbols so designed that each symbol resembled in a general way the type of weld it represented. Figure 16.53 shows a condensed table of symbols taken from ASA Z32.2.1– 1949. The symbols shown are the same as those first proposed by the American Welding Society.

16.37. Resistance welding. Figure 16.54 shows the symbols for the four principal types of resistance welding. The method of specifying resistance welds differs from the methods used for arc and gas welds. In the former, the strength of a weld is given in units instead of size, and the symbols do not show the form of the weld. The strength of spot and projection welds is given in units of pounds per weld. The strength for seam welds is given in units of pounds per linear inch.

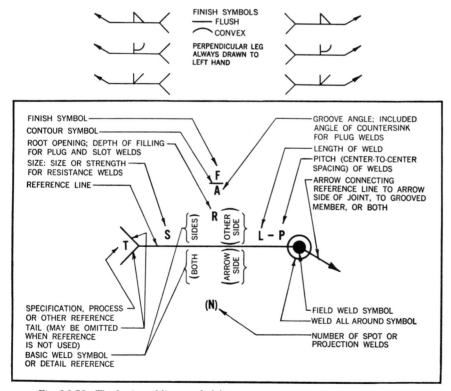

Fig. 16.52. The basic welding symbol.*

* ASA Z32.2.1–1949.

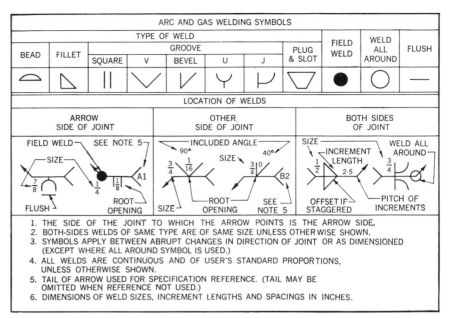

Fig. 16.53. American Standard arc and gas welding symbols.

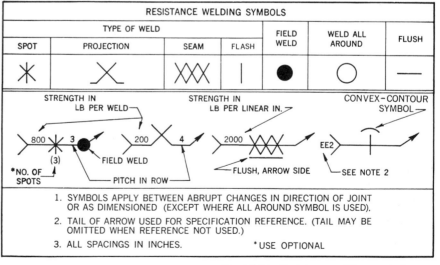

Fig. 16.54. Resistance welding symbols.

PROBLEMS

Excellent practice in drawing (or sketching) the representations of threads, threaded fasteners, keys, and rivets is provided by the problems of this chapter.

1. Draw or sketch the layout shown in Fig. 16.55, and on it show the following fasteners: (1) On center line *AA* draw a ¾ in. unfinished hexagonal-head bolt and nut. (2) On center line *BB* draw a ⅞ in. square-head bolt and nut. (3) On center line *CC* draw a ¾ in. fillister-head cap screw. (4) On center line *DD* draw a ⅝ in. hexagonal head cap screw. Determine the measurements for the layout by using the given scale. Make each fastener a standard length. Use the schematic symbol for the representation of the threads.

2. Draw or sketch the three layouts shown in Fig. 16.56 to full size, using the given scale to determine the measurements. On layout (1) complete the drawing to show a suitable fastener on center line *AA*. On layout (2) show a ½ in. hexagonal-head cap screw on center line *BB*. On layout (3) show a ⅜ in. button-head rivet on center line *CC* and a No. 608 Woodruff key on center line *DD*. Use the schematic symbol for the representation of threads.

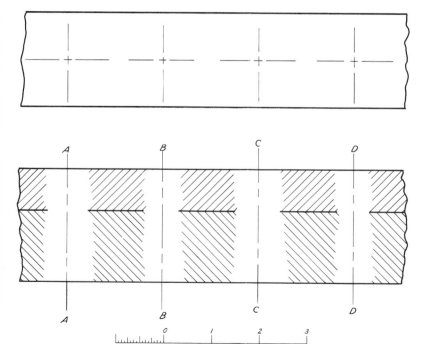

Fig. 16.55

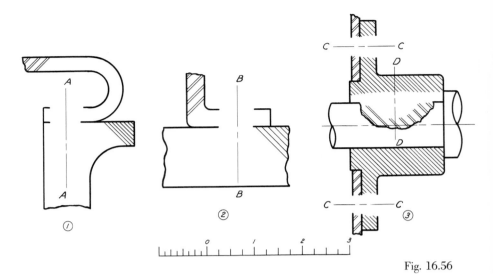

Fig. 16.56

3. (Fig. 16.57.) Reproduce the views of the assembly of the alignment bearing. On C. L's. *A* show ¼ in. button-head rivets (4 required). On C. L. *B* show a ⁵⁄₁₆″ × ½″ Am. Std. square-head set screw. Do not dimension the views.

4. (Fig. 16.58.) Reproduce the views of the assembly of the impeller drive. On C. L's. *A* show ¼″-20 UNC × ½″ round-head machine screws and regular lock washers. On C. L. *B* show a No. 406 Woodruff key. On C. L. *C* show a standard No. 2 × 1½″ taper pin.

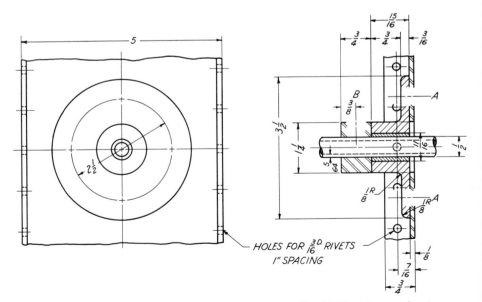

Fig. 16.57. Alignment bearing.

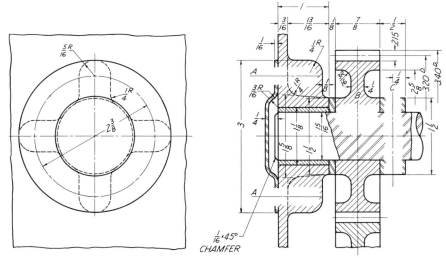

Fig. 16.58. Impeller drive.

5. (Fig. 16.59.) Reproduce the views of the assembly of the bearing head. On C. L.'s. *A* show ½″-UNC studs with regular lock washers and regular semifinished hexagonal nuts (4 required). On C. L.'s. *B* show ⅜″-UNC × 1¼″ hexagonal-head cap screws (2 required). On C. L. *C* drill through and tap ⅛ in. pipe thread.

6. (Fig. 16.60.) Reproduce the views of the assembly of the air cylinder. On C. L. *AA* at the left end of the shaft show a 1″-UNF

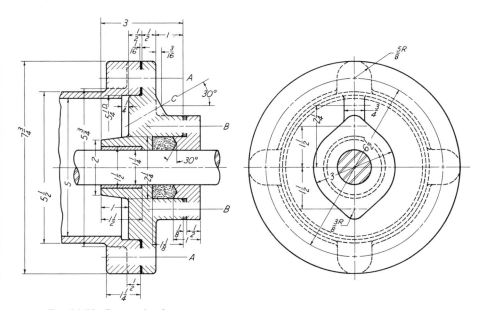

Fig. 16.59. Bearing head.

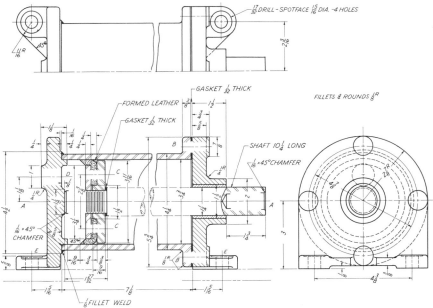

Fig. 16.60. Air cylinder.

semifinished hexagonal nut. At the right end show a hole tapped ¾″-UNF × 1½″ deep. Between the piston and the (right) end plate draw a spring 3 in. O.D., 5 full coils, ¼ in. wire. On C. L.'s. *B* show ⅜″-UNC × 1¼″ hexagonal-head cap screws. On C. L.'s. *C* draw ¼″-UNC × ¾″ flat-head cap screws with heads to the left. On C. L.

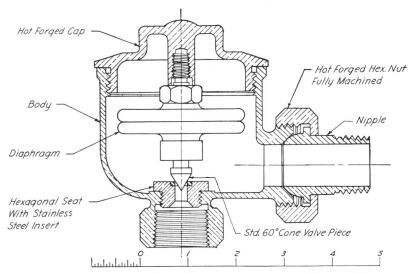

Fig. 16.61. Thermostatic radiator trap (*Courtesy Warren Webster & Company*).

D show a ¼ in. standard pipe thread. On C. L's. *E* show ½″-UNC × 1¾″ semifinished hexagonal-head bolts. Use semifinished hexagonal nuts. Show visible fasteners on the end view.

7. (Fig. 16.61.) Make a sketch or drawing of an assigned part of the thermostatic radiator trap. Prepare correct specifications for threads.

8. (Figs. 16.62–16.63.) Make a drawing of an assigned part of the air cleaner. Determine the dimensions by transferring them from the drawing to the accompanying scale by means of the dividers (study Fig. 16.63).

9. (Fig. 16.64.) Make a sketch or drawing of an assigned part of the check valve. Prepare correct specifications for threads.

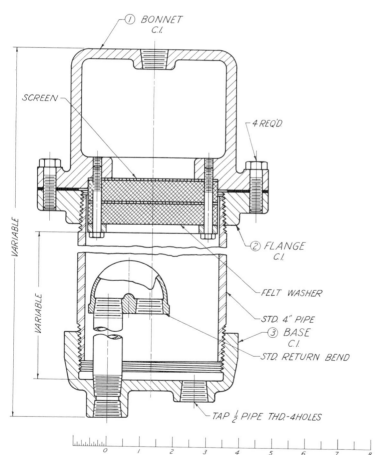

Fig. 16.62. Air cleaner (*Courtesy A. Schrader's Son Mfg. Co.*).

Fig. 16.63. Air cleaner (*Courtesy A. Schrader's Son Mfg. Co.*).

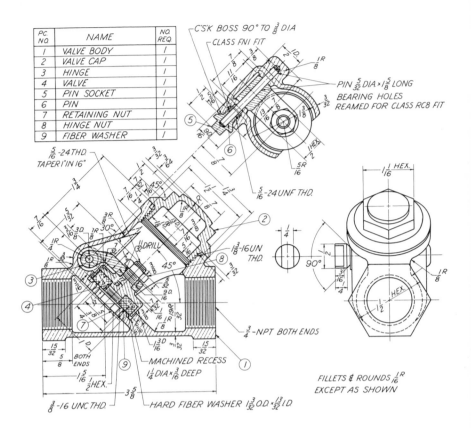

PC. NO.	NAME	NO. REQ
1	VALVE BODY	1
2	VALVE CAP	1
3	HINGE	1
4	VALVE	1
5	PIN SOCKET	1
6	PIN	1
7	RETAINING NUT	1
8	HINGE NUT	1
9	FIBER WASHER	1

Fig. 16.64. Check valve.

10. Prepare a welding drawing of the bracket shown in Fig. 16.65.

11. Prepare a welding drawing of the caster bracket shown in Fig. 16.66. The length of the tubing is $2^{11}/_{16}$ in.

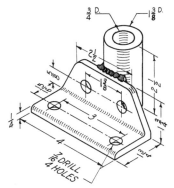

Fig. 16.65. Bracket.

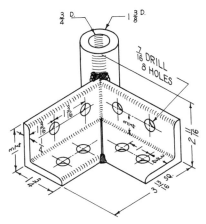

Fig. 16.66. Caster bracket.

17

SIZE DESCRIPTION: DIMENSIONS AND SPECIFICATIONS

A: FUNDAMENTALS AND TECHNIQUES

17.1. Introduction. A detail drawing, in addition to giving the shape of a part, must furnish information such as the distances between surfaces, locations of holes, kind of finish, type of material, number required, and so forth. The expression of this information on a drawing by the use of lines, symbols, figures, and notes is known as *dimensioning*.

Intelligent dimensioning requires engineering judgment and a thorough knowledge of the practices of pattern making, forging, and machining.

17.2. Theory of dimensioning. Any part may be dimensioned easily and systematically by dividing it into simple geometric solids. Even complicated parts, when analyzed, usually are found to be composed principally of cylinders and prisms and, frequently, frustums of pyramids and cones. The dimensioning of an object may be accomplished by dimensioning each elemental form to indicate its size and relative location from a center line, base line, or finished surface. A machine drawing requires two types of dimensions: *size dimensions* and *location dimensions*.

17.3. Size dimensions (Fig. 17.2). Size dimensions give the size of a piece, component part, hole, or slot.

Figure 17.1 should be carefully analyzed, as the placement of dimensions shown is applicable to the elemental parts of almost every piece.

The rule for placing the three principal dimensions (width, height, and depth) on the drawing of a prism or modification of a prism is: *Give two dimensions on the principal view and one dimension on one of the other views.*

The circular cylinder, which appears as a boss or shaft, requires only *the diameter and length, both of which are shown preferably on the rectangular view.* It is better practice to dimension a hole (negative cylinder) by giving the diameter and operation as a note on the contour view with a leader to the circle (Figs. 17.2 and 17.57).

Cones are dimensioned by giving *the diameter of the base and*

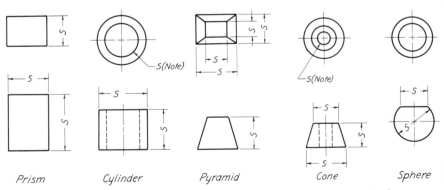

Prism   Cylinder   Pyramid   Cone   Sphere

Fig. 17.1. Dimensioning geometric shapes.

the altitude on the same view. A taper is one example of a conical shape found on machine parts (Fig. 17.54).

Pyramids, which frequently form a part of a structure, are dimensioned by giving *two dimensions on the view showing the shape of the base.*

A sphere requires only the diameter.

17.4. Location dimensions. Location dimensions fix the relationship of the component parts (projections, holes, slots, and other significant forms) of a piece or structure (Fig. 17.3). Particular care must be exercised in the selection and placing of location dimensions because upon them depends the accuracy of the operations in making a piece and the proper mating of the piece with other parts. To select location dimensions intelligently, one must first determine the contact surfaces, finished surfaces, and center lines of the elementary geometric forms and, with the accuracy demanded and the method of production in mind, decide from what other surface or center line each should be located. Mating location dimensions must be given from the same center line or finished surface on both pieces.

Location dimensions may be from center to center, surface to center, or surface to surface (Fig. 17.4).

17.5. Procedure in dimensioning. The theory of dimensioning may be applied in six steps, as follows:

1. Mentally divide the object into its component geometric shapes (Fig. 17.5).

2. Place the size dimensions on each form.

3. Select the locating center lines and surfaces after giving

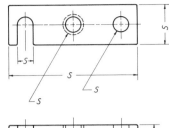

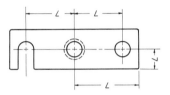

Fig. 17.2. Size dimensions.

Fig. 17.3. Location dimensions.

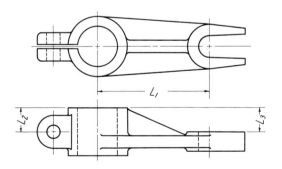

L_1 – CENTER TO CENTER
L_2 – SURFACE TO CENTER
L_3 – SURFACE TO SURFACE

Fig. 17.4. Types of location dimensions.

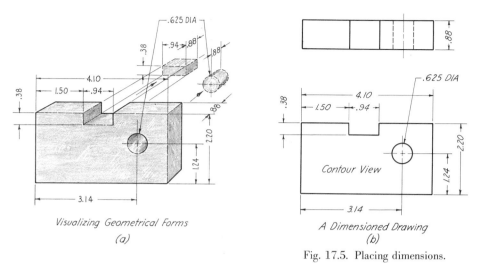

Visualizing Geometrical Forms
(a)

A Dimensioned Drawing
(b)

Fig. 17.5. Placing dimensions.

careful consideration to mating parts and to the processes of manufacture.

4. Place the location dimensions so that each geometric form is located from a center line or finished surface.

5. Add the over-all dimensions. (These are usually the summation of the included dimensions in the direction of the width, height, and depth.)

6. Complete the dimensioning by adding the necessary notes.

17.6. Placing dimensions. Dimensions must be placed where they will be most easily understood—in the locations where the reader will expect to find them. They generally are attached to the view that shows the contour of the features to which they apply, and a majority of them usually will appear on the principal view (Fig. 17.5). Except in cases where special convenience and ease in reading are desired, or when a dimension would be so far from the form to which it referred that it might be misinterpreted, dimensions should be placed outside a view. They should appear directly on a view only when clarity demands.

All extensions and dimension lines should be drawn before the arrowheads have been filled in or the dimensions, notes, and titles have been lettered. Placing dimension lines not less than ½ in. from the view and at least ⅜ in. from each other will provide spacing ample to satisfy the one rule to which there is no exception: *Never crowd dimensions.* If the location of a dimension forces a poor location on other dimensions, its shifting may allow all to be placed more advantageously without sacrificing clearness. Important loca-

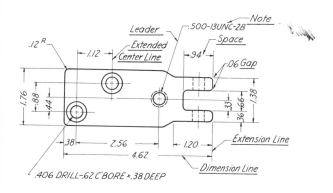

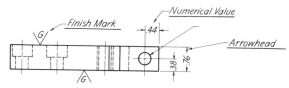

Fig. 17.6. Terms and dimensioning notation.

tion dimensions should be given where they will be conspicuous, even if a size dimension must be moved.

17.7. Dimensioning practices. A generally recognized system of lines, symbols, figures, and notes is used to indicate size and location. Figure 17.6 illustrates dimensioning terms and notation.

A *dimension line* is a light-weight line that is terminated at each end by an arrowhead. A numerical value, given along the dimension line, specifies the number of units for the measurement that is indicated (Fig. 17.7). When the numerals are in a single line, the dimension line is broken near the center as shown in (*a*) and (*b*). Under no circumstances should the line pass through the numerals. When the numerals are in two lines the dimension line is not broken and one line of numerals is placed above the dimension line and the other below as in (*c*).

Extension lines are light continuous lines extending from a view to indicate the extent of a measurement given by a dimension line

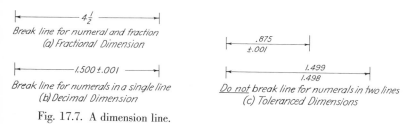

Fig. 17.7. A dimension line.

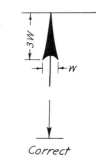

Fig. 17.8. Arrowheads.

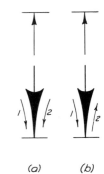

(a)   (b)

Fig. 17.9. Formation of arrowheads.

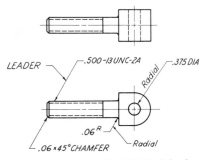

Fig. 17.10. A leader.

that is located outside of a view. They start $\frac{1}{16}$ in. from the view and extend $\frac{1}{8}$ in. beyond the dimension line (Fig. 17.6).

Arrowheads are drawn for each dimension line, before the figures are lettered. They are made with the same pen or pencil used for the lettering. The size of an arrowhead, although it may vary with the size of a drawing, should be uniform on any one drawing. To have the proper proportions, the length of an arrowhead must be approximately three times its spread (American Standard). This length for average work is usually $\frac{1}{8}$ in. Figure 17.8 shows an enlarged drawing of an arrowhead of correct proportions. Although many draftsmen draw an arrowhead with one stroke, the beginner will get better results by using two slightly concaved strokes drawn toward the point [Fig. 17.9(a)] or, as shown in Fig. 17.9(b), one stroke drawn to the point and one away from it.

A *leader* or *pointer* is a light continuous line (terminated by an arrowhead) that extends from a note to the feature of a piece to which the note applies (Fig. 17.10). It should be made with a straightedge and should not be curved or made freehand (American Standard's recommendation).

A leader pointing to a curve should be radial, and the first $\frac{1}{8}$ in. of it should be in a line with the note (Fig. 17.10).

Finish marks indicate the particular surfaces of a rough casting or forging that are to be machined or "finished." They are placed in all views, across the visible or invisible lines that are the edge views of surfaces to be machined (Fig. 17.12).

The modified italic *f*, shown in Fig. 17.11(a), is the form of finish mark that is preferred for general use. The student will find that careful adherence to the dimensions shown will improve the appearance of the *f* marks on his drawing.

Figure 17.11(b) shows the 60° **V** style of mark with its point touching the line view of the surface to be machined. In commercial practice a code letter oftentimes is used to indicate the type of machining required. The code letter or letters are placed in the **V** as shown in (c).

It is not necessary to show finish marks on drilled or reamed holes, when the finish is specified as an operation in a note, such as ¾″ Drill or 1″ Ream. They are also omitted, and a title note, "finish all over," is substituted, if the piece is to be completely machined. Finish marks are not required when limit dimensions are used.

Dimension figures should be lettered either horizontally or vertically with the whole numbers equal in height to the capital letters in the notes and guide lines and slope lines must be used. The numerals must be legible; otherwise, they might be misinterpreted in the shop and cause errors which would be embarrassing to the draftsman.

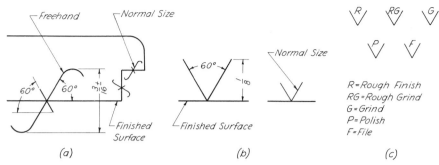

R = Rough Finish
RG = Rough Grind
G = Grind
P = Polish
F = File

Fig. 17.11. Finish marks.

17.8. Fractional dimensioning. For ordinary work, where accuracy is relatively unimportant, shopmen work to nominal dimensions given as common fractions of an inch, as ½, ¼, ⅛, ¹⁄₁₆, ¹⁄₃₂, ¹⁄₆₄. When dimensions are given in this way, many large corporations specify the required accuracy through a note on the drawing that reads as follows: *Permissible variations on common fraction dimensions to machined surfaces to be plus or minus .010 unless otherwise specified.* It should be understood that the allowable variations will differ among manufacturing concerns because of the varying degrees of accuracy required for different types of work.

17.9. Decimal system. Since the use of the decimal system for expressing dimensional values has made rapid gains in American industry and is now accepted in the aircraft and automotive fields, many of the examples in this chapter will show decimal dimensions (read Sec. 3.15). At present, the fractional system, which dominated the whole of American industry until the Ford Motor Company adopted the decimal-inch some 25 years ago, is still used widely in those fields that are not under the direct influence of the automotive and aircraft companies. How long the present coexistence of the two systems will last cannot be foretold. It could be only a few years or it could be many years before the decimal system completely replaces the fractional system.

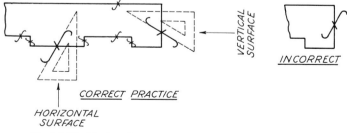

CORRECT PRACTICE

VERTICAL SURFACE

INCORRECT

HORIZONTAL SURFACE

Fig. 17.12. Placing *f* marks.

However, this need not be of great concern to the student, for he should be primarily interested in the selection and placement of dimensions. At a later time he will find it easy to use either the fractional or decimal systems as is required in his field of employment. To assist one to use either system, a Standard Conversion Table has been provided in the Appendix (Table 1).

In Fig. 17.13 a drawing is shown that illustrates decimal dimensioning.

The ASA recommendation for decimal dimensioning, as given in the standard ASA Y14.5–1957, reads as follows:

> Optionally, decimals may be used to replace common fractions altogether. The elimination of common fractions simplifies computations; decimals can be added, subtracted, multiplied or divided more easily than fractions. . . . The following conventions are generally observed by those who have adopted the decimal system. However, the advantages of using decimals can be gained, whether or not all of these rules are followed.
>
> (a) Two-place decimals are used for dimensions where tolerance limits of $\pm.01$ or more can be allowed (see Fig. 17.13).
>
> (b) Decimals to three or more places must be used for tolerance limits less than $\pm.010$ [see Fig. 17.7(b) and (c)].
>
> (c) The second decimal place in a two-place decimal should preferably be an even digit (.02, .04, .06 are preferred to .01, .03, .05, etc.), so that when divided by two, as in obtaining a radius from a diameter, the result will remain a two-place decimal. Odd two-place decimals are used where necessary for design reasons; as, to provide clearance, strength, smooth curves, etc.

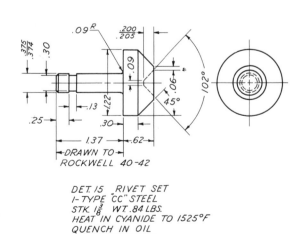

Fig. 17.13. Decimal dimensioning (*Courtesy Ford Motor Co.*).

(d) Common fractions may be used to indicate standard nominal sizes of materials, punched holes, drilled holes, threads, keyways and other features produced by tools that are so designated.

EXAMPLE: ¼-20UNC-2A; ⁵⁄₁₆ Drill; Stock ⅝ × ⅞.

(e) Where it is desired to use decimals exclusively, nominal sizes of materials, threads and other features produced by commercial tools may be expressed in decimal equivalents of commercial sizes; as, .625 HEX.

B: *GENERAL DIMENSIONING PRACTICES*

17.10. Selection and placement of dimensions and notes. The reasonable application of the selected dimensioning practices that follow should enable a student to dimension acceptably. The practices in boldface type should never be violated. In fact, these have been so definitely established by practice that they might be called rules.

1. Place dimensions using either of two recognized methods—aligned or unidirectional.

(a) *Aligned method.* Place the numerals for the dimension values so that they are readable from the bottom and right side of the drawing. An aligned expression is placed along and in the direction of the dimension line (see Fig. 17.14). Make the values for oblique dimensions readable from the directions shown in Fig. 17.15.

(b) *Unidirectional method.* Place the numerals for the dimension values so that they can be read from the bottom of the drawing (see Fig. 17.16). The fraction bar for a common fraction should be parallel to the bottom of the drawing (Fig. 17.20).

2. Place dimensions outside a view, unless they will be more easily and quickly understood if shown on the view (see Figs. 17.16 and 17.17).

3. Place dimensions between views unless the rules, such as the contour rule, the rule against crowding, and so forth, prevent their being so placed.

4. Do not use an object line or a center line as a dimension line.

5. Locate dimension lines so that they will not cross extension lines.

6. If possible, avoid crossing two dimension lines.

7. A center line may be extended to serve as an extension line (Fig. 17.18).

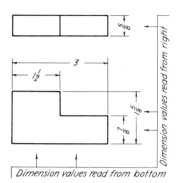

Fig. 17.14. Reading dimensions aligned.

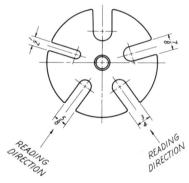

Fig. 17.15. Reading oblique dimensions—aligned.

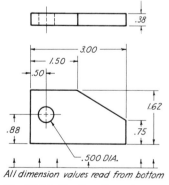

Fig. 17.16. Reading dimensions—unidirectional.

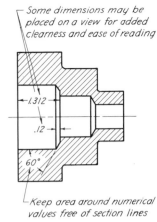

Some dimensions may be placed on a view for added clearness and ease of reading

1.312

.12

60°

Keep area around numerical values free of section lines

Fig. 17.17. Dimensions on the view.

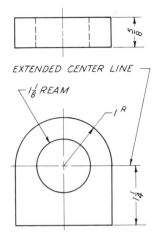

EXTENDED CENTER LINE

$1\frac{1}{8}$ REAM

1^R

Fig. 17.18. Extended center line.

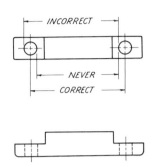

INCORRECT

NEVER

CORRECT

Fig. 17.19. Locating holes.

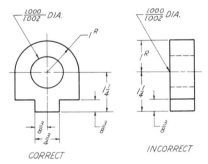

$\frac{1.000}{1.002}$ DIA.

$\frac{1.000}{1.002}$ DIA.

1^R

$1\frac{1}{4}$

1^R

$1\frac{1}{4}$

$\frac{3}{8}$

$\frac{3}{8}$

$\frac{3}{4}$

$\frac{3}{8}$

CORRECT   INCORRECT

Fig. 17.20. Contour principle of dimensioning.

8. Keep parallel dimensions equally spaced (usually ⅜ in. apart) and the figures staggered (see Fig. 17.23).

9. Always give locating dimensions to the centers of circles that represent holes, cylindrical projections, or bosses (Fig. 17.19).

10. If possible, attach the location dimensions for holes to the view upon which they appear as circles (Fig. 17.20).

11. Group related dimensions on the view showing the contour of a feature (Fig. 17.20).

12. Arrange a series of dimensions in a continuous line (Fig. 17.21).

13. Dimension from a finished surface, center line, or base line that can be readily established (Fig. 17.22).

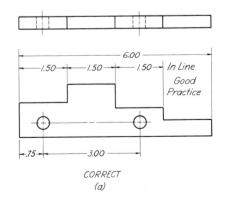

6.00

1.50   1.50   1.50   In Line Good Practice

.75   3.00

CORRECT
(a)

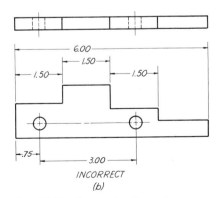

6.00

1.50

1.50   1.50

.75   3.00

INCORRECT
(b)

Fig. 17.21. Consecutive dimensions.

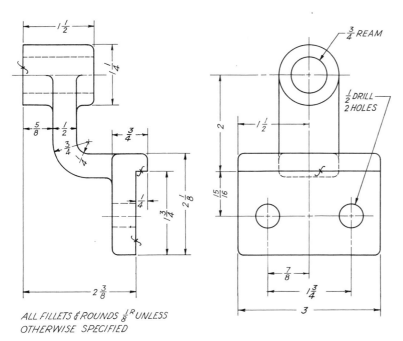

ALL FILLETS & ROUNDS $\frac{1}{8}$R UNLESS
OTHERWISE SPECIFIED

Fig. 17.22. Dimensioning a bracket.

14. Stagger the figures in a series of parallel dimension lines to allow sufficient space for the figures and to prevent confusion (Fig. 17.23).

15. Place longer dimensions outside shorter ones so that extension lines will not cross dimension lines.

16. Give three over-all dimensions located outside any other dimensions (unless the piece has cylindrical ends).

17. When an over-all is given, one intermediate distance should be omitted unless noted (REF.) as being given for reference (Fig. 17.24).

18. Do not repeat a dimension. One of the duplicated dimensions may be missed if a change is made. Give only those dimensions that are necessary to produce or inspect the part.

19. Make decimal points of a sufficient size so that dimensions cannot be misread.

20. When dimension figures appear on a sectional view, show them in a small uncrosshatched portion so that they may be easily read. This may be accomplished by doing the section lining after the dimensioning has been completed (Fig. 17.25).

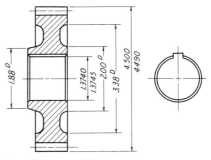

Fig. 17.23. Parallel dimensions.

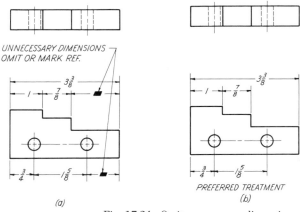

UNNECESSARY DIMENSIONS
OMIT OR MARK REF.

(a)

PREFERRED TREATMENT

(b)

Fig. 17.24. Omit unnecessary dimensions.

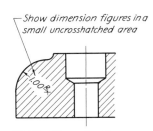

Show dimension figures in a
small uncrosshatched area

Fig. 17.25. Dimension figures on
a section view.

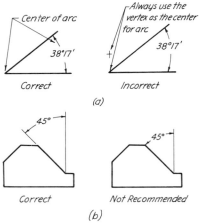

Center of arc

Correct

Always use the
vertex as the center
for arc

38°17'

38°17'

Incorrect

(a)

45°

Correct

45°

Not Recommended

(b)

Fig. 17.26. To dimension an angle.

21. When an arc is used as a dimension line for an angular measurement, use the vertex of the angle as the center [Fig. 17.26(a)]. It is usually undesirable to terminate the dimension line for an angle at lines that represent surfaces. It is better practice to use an extension line [Fig. 17.26(b)].

22. Place the figures of angular dimensions so they will read from the bottom of a drawing, except in the case of large angles (Fig. 17.27).

23. Always dimension an arc by giving its radius followed by the abbreviation R, and indicate the center with a small cross. [Note that the arrowhead is omitted at the center (Fig. 17.28).]

24. Show the diameter of a circle, never the radius. If it is not clear that the dimension is a diameter, the figures should be followed by the abbreviation D or DIA (Figs. 17.29 and 17.31). Often this will allow the elimination of one view.

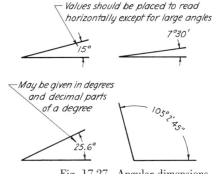

Values should be placed to read
horizontally except for large angles

7°30'

15°

May be given in degrees
and decimal parts
of a degree

25.6°

105°2'45"

Fig. 17.27. Angular dimensions.

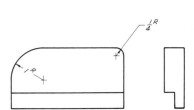

$\frac{1}{4}$R

1 R

Fig. 17.28. Dimensioning radii.

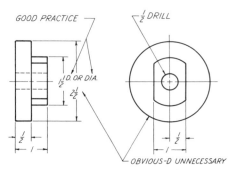

Fig. 17.29. Dimensioning a cylindrical piece.

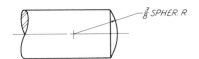

Fig. 17.30. Dimensioning a piece with a spherical end.

25. When dimensioning a portion of a sphere with a radius the term SPHER. R is added (Fig. 17.30).

26. Letter all notes horizontally.

27. Make dimensioning complete, so that it will not be necessary for a workman to add or subtract to obtain a desired dimension or to scale the drawing.

28. Letter the word *bore* or *core* with the diameter of bored or cored holes (Fig. 17.32).

29. Give the diameter of a circular hole, never the radius, because all hole-forming tools are specified by diameter. If the hole does not go through the piece, the depth may be given as a note (Fig. 17.33).

30. Never crowd dimensions into small spaces. Use the practical methods suggested in Fig. 17.34.

31. Avoid placing inclined dimensions in the shaded areas shown in Fig. 17.35. Place them so that they may be conven-

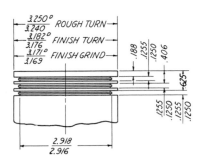

Fig. 17.31. Dimensioning machined cylinders.

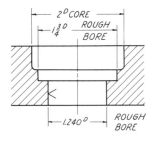

Fig. 17.32. Dimensioning cored and bored holes.

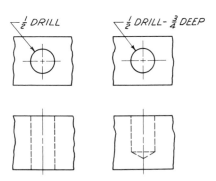

Fig. 17.33. Dimensioning holes.

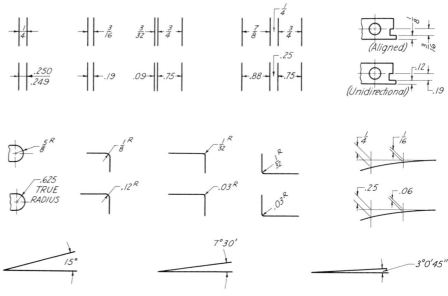

Fig. 17.34. Dimensioning in limited spaces.

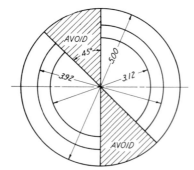

Fig. 17.35. Areas to avoid.

iently read from the right side of the drawing. If this is not desirable, make the figures read from the left in the direction of the dimension line [Fig. 17.36(a)]. The unidirectional method is shown in (b).

32. Omit superfluous dimensions. Do not supply dimensional information for the same feature in two different ways.

33. Give dimensions up to 72″ in inches, except on structural

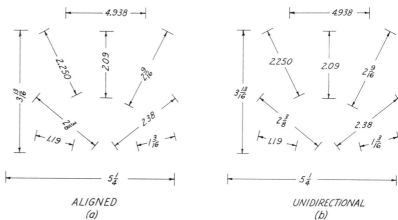

ALIGNED
(a)

UNIDIRECTIONAL
(b)

Fig. 17.36. Reading horizontal, vertical, and oblique dimensions.

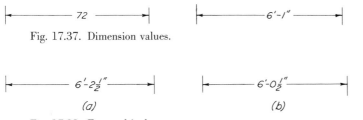

Fig. 17.37. Dimension values.

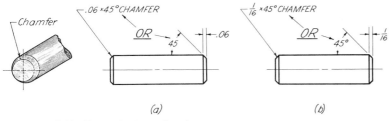

(a)   *(b)*

Fig. 17.38. Feet and inches.

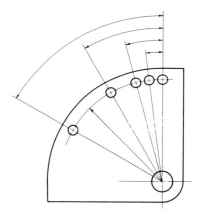

(a)   *(b)*

Fig. 17.39. Dimensioning a chamfer.

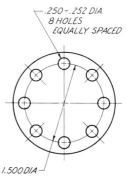

Fig. 17.40. Equally spaced holes.*

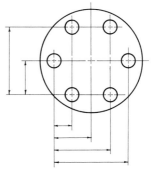

Fig. 17.41. Locating holes on a circle by polar coordinates.*

and architectural drawings (Fig. 17.37). Omit the inch marks when all dimensions are in inches.

34. Show dimensions in feet and inches as illustrated in Fig. 17.38. Note that the use of the hyphen in (*a*) and (*b*), and the cipher in (*b*), eliminates any chance of uncertainty and misinterpretation.

35. If feasible, design a piece and its elemental parts to such dimensions as ⅜″, ½″, ⅝″ or .40 and .50. Avoid such fractions as ¹⁷⁄₃₂″ and ¹⁹⁄₆₄″ and decimals as .19 and .53.

36. Dimension a chamfer by giving the angle and length as shown in Fig. 17.39. For a 45° angle only, it is permissible to give the needed information as a note. The word chamfer may be omitted in the note form.

37. Equally spaced holes in a circular flange may be dimensioned by giving the diameter of the bolt circle, across the circular center line, and the size and number of holes, in a note (Fig. 17.40).

38. When holes are unequally spaced on a circular center line, give the angles as illustrated in Fig. 17.41.

39. Holes that must be accurately located should have their location established by the coordinate method. Holes arranged in a circle may be located as shown in Fig. 17.42 rather than through the use of angular measurements. Figure 17.43 shows

Fig. 17.42. Accurate location dimensioning of holes.*

* ASA Y14.5–1957.

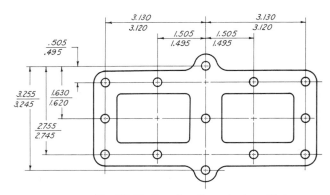

Fig. 17.43. Location dimensioning of holes.

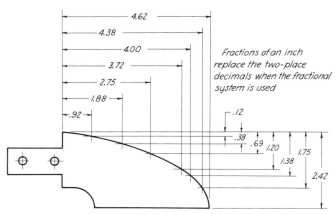

Fractions of an inch replace the two-place decimals when the fractional system is used

Fig. 17.44. Dimensioning curves by offsets.

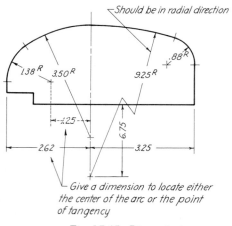

Should be in radial direction

Give a dimension to locate either the center of the arc or the point of tangency

Fig. 17.45. Dimensioning curves by radii.

the application of the coordinate method to the location of holes arranged in a general rectangular form. The method with all dimensions referred to datum lines is sometimes called *baseline dimensioning*.

40. Dimension a curved line by giving offsets or radii.

(a) A noncircular curve may be dimensioned by the coordinate method illustrated in Fig. 17.44. Offset measurements are given from datum lines.

(b) A curved line, which is composed of circular arcs, should be dimensioned by giving the radii and locations of either the centers or points of tangency (see Fig. 17.45).

41. Show an offset dimension line for an arc having an inaccessible center (Fig. 17.45). Locate with true dimensions the point placed in a convenient location that represents the true center.

42. Dimension, as required by the method of production, a piece with rounded ends (see Figs. 17.46–17.49).

(a) Give radii and center-to-center distance on parts that would be laid out by using centers and radii. Do not show an over-all dimension. It is not required (see Fig. 17.46).

(b) Slots that are to provide for adjustment are dimensioned by over-all length and width dimensions and are located by dimensions given to their center lines (see Fig. 17.47).

(c) Slots that are to perform a mechanical function are dimensioned from center-to-center as two partial holes. The R is given to indicate a true radius. Slots of this type are subject to gage inspection (see Fig. 17.48).

(d) Give the width and over-all length for Pratt and Whitney keyways because this is the manner in which the keys are specified.

43. A keyway on a shaft or hub should be dimensioned as shown in Fig. 17.50. Woodruff keyslots are dimensioned as shown in (b).

44. When knurls are to provide a rough surface for better grip, it is necessary to specify the pitch and kind of knurl as shown in Fig. 17.51(a) and (b). When specifying knurling for a press fit, it is the best practice to give the diameter before knurling with a tolerance and include the minimum diameter after knurling in the note that gives the pitch and type of knurl as shown in (c).

45. Snug fitting dovetailed parts should be dimensioned with tolerances as shown in Fig. 17.52. Dimensions are given to sharp corners. Flats may be substituted for rounded corners if desired.

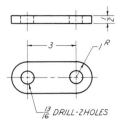

Fig. 17.46. Dimensioning a piece with rounded ends.

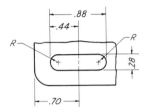

Fig. 17.47. Slot to provide for adjustment.

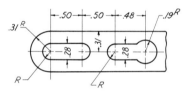

Fig. 17.48. Slots performing a mechanical function.

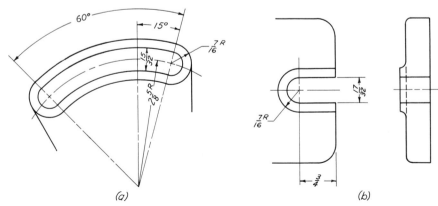

(a)   (b)

Fig. 17.49. Dimensioning semicircular features.

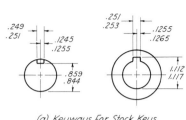

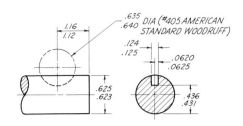

(a) Keyways for Stock Keys

(b) Woodruff Keyslots

Fig. 17.50. Dimensioning keyways and keyslots.*

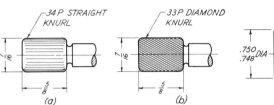

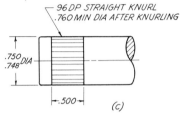

Fig. 17.51. Dimensioning knurls.

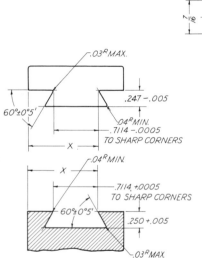

Fig. 17.52. Dimensioning a dove-tail slot and tongue.

46. In sheet-metal work mold lines are used in dimensioning instead of the centers of the arcs (see Fig. 17.53). A mold line (construction line) is the line at the intersection of the plane surfaces adjoining a bend. The formula for bend allowance is given in Fig. 6.41.

47. Dimension standard and special tapers as illustrated in Fig. 17.54. Standard tapers require one diameter, the length, and a

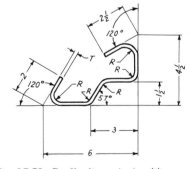

Fig. 17.53. Profile dimensioning.**

* ASA Y14.5–1957.
** ASA Z14.1–1946.

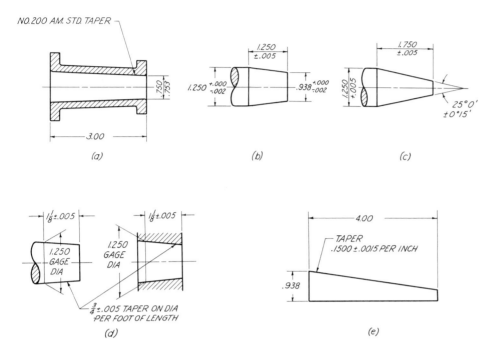

Fig. 17.54. Dimensioning tapers.

note specifying the taper by number. The usual practice is to give the diameter at the large end.

Special conical tapers may be dimensioned in different ways, as illustrated in (b), (c), and (d). The recommendation given in ASA Y14.5–1957, reads as follows:

> Conical tapers. The following dimensions may be given in different combinations, to specify the size and form of tapered conical surfaces:
>   (a) the diameter at each end of the taper;
>   (b) the length of the taper;
>   (c) the diameter at a selected cross-sectional plane; this plane may or may not be within the length of the tapered piece;
>   (d) the distance locating a cross-sectional plane at which a diameter is specified;
>   (e) the rate of taper;
>   (f) the included angle.

The dimensioning of noncritical tapers is shown in Fig. 17.54(b) and (c). The dimensions and notes given in (d) are considered adequate for tapers which engage one another permanently or intermittently.

Flat tapers may be dimensioned as shown in (e).

When given in a note, taper may be specified either in inches per foot or inches per inch [see (*d*) and (*e*)].

48. A half section may be dimensioned through the use of hidden lines on the external portion of the view (Fig. 17.55).

49. The fact that a dimension is out of scale may be indicated by a wavy line placed underneath the dimension value.

17.11. Dimensions from datum. When it is necessary to locate the holes and surfaces of a part with a considerable degree of accuracy, it is the usual practice to specify their position by dimen-

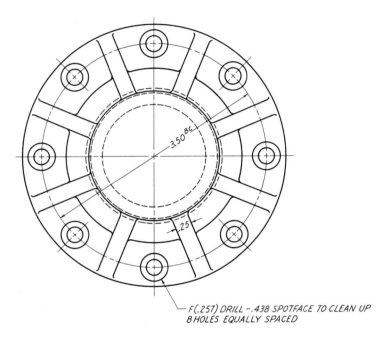

F(.257) DRILL –.438 SPOTFACE TO CLEAN UP
8 HOLES EQUALLY SPACED

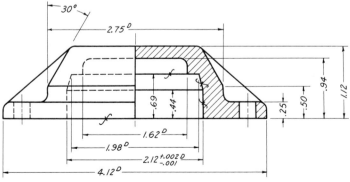

Fig. 17.55. Dimensioning a half-section.

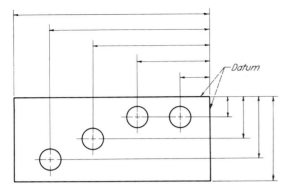

Fig. 17.56. Dimensions from datum lines.*

sions given from a datum (Fig. 17.56) in order to avoid cumulative tolerances. By this method the different features of a part are located with respect to carefully selected datums and not with respect to each other (Fig. 17.43). Lines and surfaces that are selected to serve as datums must be easily recognizable and accessible during production. Corresponding datum points, lines, or surfaces must be used as datums on mating parts.

17.12. Notes (Fig. 17.57). The use of properly composed notes often adds clarity to the presentation of dimensional information involving specific operations. Notes also are used to convey supplementary instructions about the kind of material, kind of fit, degree of finish, and so forth. It is good practice to specify a dimension representing a tool operation or a series of tool operations by a note rather than by figured dimensions. Brevity in form is desirable for notes of general information or specific instruction.

Rules for the Formulation and Placement of Shop Notes

1. Give the size first, then the machining operation.
   EXAMPLE: $^{17}/_{32}$ *Drill.*

2. In the case of threaded parts, use the terminology recommended by the ASA for the American-British unified thread.
   EXAMPLE: ½-13 UNC-2A.

3. Where there are several holes alike in a group, use one note and indicate the number of holes.
   EXAMPLE: ½ *Drill-4 Holes.*

4. Where there are two or more similar groups, repeat the entire note for each group.

* ASA Y14.5–1957.

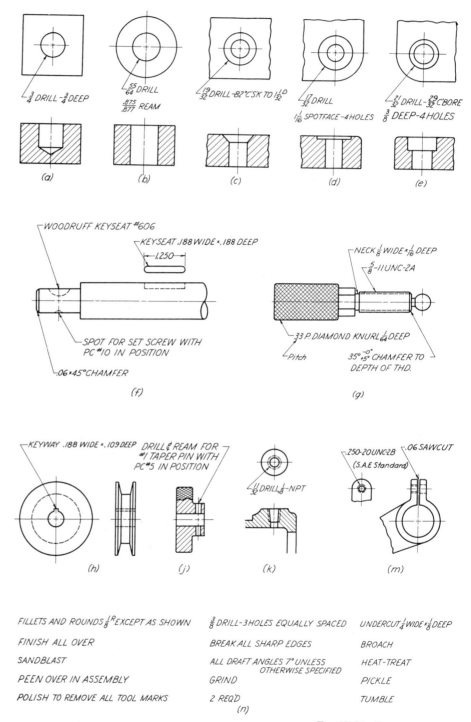

Fig. 17.57. Shop notes.

5. For drilled holes and reamed holes, give the diameter, the operation required, and the depth. If the hole goes all the way through the piece, the depth should be omitted.

6. For a tapped (threaded) hole, give the tap-drill size, the diameter of the screw, the number of threads per inch, the kind of thread, and the thread class (see Fig. 16.18). The depth is omitted if the hole goes all the way through the piece. Depth measurements for drilled and tapped holes are shown in Figs. 6.37(*b*) and 16.15.

7. Locate the notes for a piece in such a way that they will not overlap the adjacent views of another piece on the same drawing.

8. Notes should not be placed on views or near the lines of a drawing. Use leaders to clarify their purpose.

9. When putting a shop note for a hole on a drawing, if possible, make the leader point to the circular view.

10. If a single note is applicable to similar holes on two adjacent pieces on the same drawing, it should not be used as a common reference but should be repeated for each piece.

11. *Good practice.* In the formulation of shop notes, it is good practice to supply all necessary information. For example, although 5-40NC-2 is considered by many to be a satisfactory note, it is much better to add the tap-drill size thus: #38(.1015) DRILL, 5-40NC-2.

In the case of reamed holes, the drill should accompany the note, as for example:

$$\frac{31}{64} \text{ DRILL } \frac{.5000}{.5010} \text{ REAM.}$$

This will relieve the engineering department of any responsibility in case the wrong drill should be used.

When dimensioning a gear, it is recommended that the cutting data be incorporated in an accompanying table (Fig. 17.58).*

C: LIMIT DIMENSIONING
AND GEOMETRIC TOLERANCING

17.13. Limit dimensions. Present-day competitive manufacturing requires quantity production and interchangeability for many closely mating parts. The production of each of these mating parts to an exact decimal dimension, although theoretically possible, is eco-

---

* Additional information covering gears and cams may be obtained from the author's text, *Fundamentals of Engineering Drawing*, 4th ed., Englewood Cliffs, N.J.: Prentice-Hall, Inc. (1959).

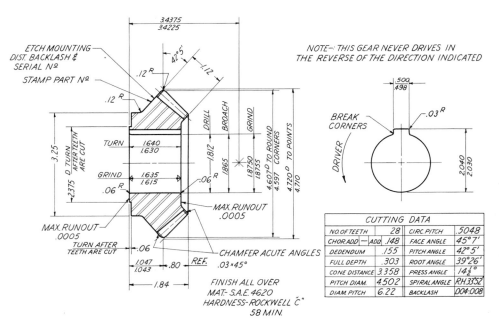

Fig. 17.58. Notes and specifications for a spiral bevel gear
(*Courtesy Fairfield Mfg. Co.*).

nomically unfeasible, since the cost of a part rapidly increases as an absolute correct size is approached. For this reason, the commercial draftsman specifies an allowable error (tolerance) between decimal limits (Fig. 17.59). The determination of these limits depends upon the accuracy and clearance required for the moving parts to function satisfactorily in the machine. Although manufacturing experience is often used to determine the proper limits for the parts of a mechanism, it is better and safer practice to adhere to the fits

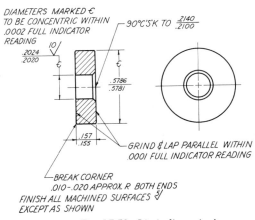

Fig. 17.59. Limit dimensioning.

recommended by the American Standards Association in ASA B4.1–1955. This standard applies to fits between plain cylindrical parts. Recommendations are made for preferred sizes, allowances, toler-ances, and fits for use where applicable. Up to a diameter of 20 in. the standard is in accordance with ABC (American-British-Canadian) conference agreements.

There are many factors that a designer must take into considera-tion when selecting fits for a particular application. These factors might be the bearing load, speed, lubrication, materials, and length of engagement. Frequently temperature and humidity must be taken into account. Considerable practical experience is necessary to make a selection of fits or to make the subsequent adjustments that might be needed to satisfy critical functional requirements. In addition, manufacturing economy must never be overlooked.

Those interested in the selection of fits should consult texts on machine design and technical publications, for coverage of this phase of the dimensioning of cylindrical parts is not within the scope of this book. However, since it is desirable to be able to determine limits of size following the selection of a fit, attention in this section will be directed to the use of Table 24 (Appendix). Whenever the fit to be used for a particular application has not been specified in the instructions for a problem or has not been given on the draw-ing, the student should consult his instructor after a tentative choice has been made based on the brief descriptions of fits as given in this section.

To compute limit dimensions it is necessary to understand the following associated terms.*

Nominal size. The nominal size is the designation which is used for the purpose of general identification.

Basic size. The basic size is that size from which the limits of size are derived by the application of allowances and tolerances.

Allowance. An allowance is an intentional difference between the maximum material limits of mating parts. It is a minimum clearance (positive allowance) or maximum interference (negative allowance) between mating parts.

Tolerance. A tolerance is the total permissible variation of a size. The tolerance is the difference between the limits of size.

Limits of size. The limits of size are the applicable maximum and minimum sizes.

Fit. Fit is the general term used to signify the range of tight-ness which may result from the application of a specific combination of allowances and tolerances in the design of mating parts.

---

* Extracted from American Standard Preferred Limits and Fits for Cylindrical Parts (ASA B4.1–1955) with permission of the publisher, The American Society of Mechanical Engineers, 29 W. 39th St., New York 18, N.Y.

Clearance fit. A clearance fit is one having limits of size so prescribed that a clearance always results when mating parts are assembled.

Interference fit. An interference fit is one having limits of size so prescribed that an interference always results when mating parts are assembled.

Transition fit. A transition fit is one having limits of size so prescribed that either a clearance or an interference may result when mating parts are assembled.

Basic hole system. A basic hole system is a system of fits in which the design size of the hole is the basic size and the allowance is applied to the shaft.

Basic shaft system. A basic shaft system is a system of fits in which the design size of the shaft is the basic size and the allowance is applied to the hole.

Tables 24A, B, C, D, and E cover three general types of fits: running fits, locational fits, and force fits. For educational purposes standard fits may be designated by means of letter symbols as follows:

RC   Running or Sliding fit
LC   Locational clearance fit
LT   Transition fit
LN   Locational interference fit
FN   Force or Shrink fit

It should be understood that these letters are not to appear on working drawings. Only the limits for sizes are shown.

When a number is added to these letter symbols a complete fit is represented. For example FN4 specifies, symbolically a class 4, force fit for which the limits of size for mating parts may be determined from use of Table 24E. The minimum and maximum limits of clearance or interference for a particular application may be read directly from this table.

Classes of fits as given in these tables are as follows:

Running and Sliding fits—Classes RC1 through RC9
Clearance locational fits—Classes LC1 through LC11
Transition locational fits—Classes LT1 through LT7
Interference locational fits—Classes LN2 and LN3
Force and Shrink fits—Classes FN1 through FN5

*Running and Sliding fits.** Running and Sliding fits are intended to provide a similar running performance, with suitable lubrication allowance, throughout the range of sizes. The clearances for the first two classes, used chiefy as slide fits, increase more slowly with diameter than

* Extracted from American Standard Preferred Limits and Fits for Cylindrical Parts (ASA B4.1–1955).

the other classes, so that accurate location is maintained even at the expense of free relative motion.

A brief description of the fits is given here. For a more complete understanding one should read and study the standard.

RC1 Close sliding fits are intended for accurate location of parts which must assemble without perceptible play.

RC2 Sliding fits are intended for accurate location but with greater maximum clearance than Class RC1.

RC3 Precision running fits are about the closest fits which can be expected to run freely and are intended for precision work at slow speeds and light journal pressures, ...

RC4 Close running fits are intended chiefly for running fits on accurate machinery with moderate surface speeds and journal pressures, ...

RC5⎱
RC6⎰ Medium running fits are intended for higher running speeds, or heavy journal pressures, or both.

RC7 Free running fits are intended for use where accuracy is not essential or where large temperature variations are likely to be encountered, ...

RC8⎱
RC9⎰ Loose running fits are intended for use where materials such as cold-rolled shafting and tubing, made to commercial tolerances, are involved.

*Locational fits.** Locational fits are divided into three groups: clearance fits (LC), transition fits (LT), and interference fits (LN).

LC. Locational clearance fits are intended for parts which are normally stationary, but which can be freely assembled or disassembled. They run from snug fits for parts requiring accuracy of location, through the medium clearance fits for parts such as spigots, to the closer fastener fits where freedom of assembly is of prime importance.

LT. Transition fits are a compromise between clearance and interference fits, for application where accuracy of location is important, but either a small amount of clearance or interference is permissible.

LN. Locational interference fits are used where accuracy of location is of prime importance, and for parts requiring rigidity and alignment with no special requirements for bore pressure.

*Force fits.** Force or shrink fits constitute a special type of interference fit, normally characterized by maintenance of constant bore pressures throughout the range of sizes.

FN1 Light drive fits are those requiring light assembly pressures, and produce more or less permanent assemblies.

FN2 Medium drive fits are suitable for ordinary steel parts, or for shrink fits on light sections.

* Extracted from American Standard Preferred Limits and Fits for Cylindrical Parts (ASA B4.1–1955).

FN3   Heavy drive fits are suitable for heavier steel parts, or for shrink fits in medium sections.

FN4 } Force fits are suitable for parts which can be highly stressed,
FN5 } or for shrink fits where the heavy pressing forces required are impractical.

17.14. Computation of limits of size for cylindrical parts. To obtain the correct fit between two engaging parts, compute limit dimensions that modify the nominal size of both. Numerical values of the modifications necessary to obtain the proper allowance and tolerances for various diameters for all fits mentioned previously are given in Tables 24A, B, C, D, and E in the Appendix.

The two systems in common use for computing limit dimensions are (1) the basic hole system, and (2) the basic shaft system. The same American Standard tables may be used conveniently for both systems.

17.15. Basic hole system. Because most limit dimensions are computed on the basic hole system, the illustrated example shown in Fig. 17.60 involves the use of this system. If, as is the usual case, the

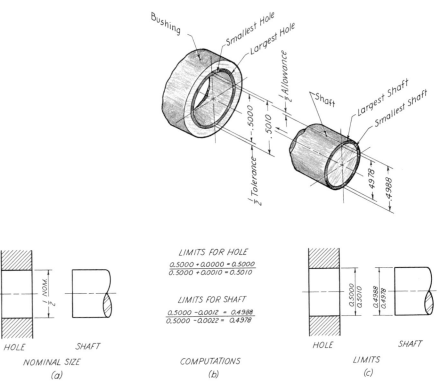

LIMITS FOR HOLE

$$\frac{0.5000 + 0.0000 = 0.5000}{0.5000 + 0.0010 = 0.5010}$$

LIMITS FOR SHAFT

$$\frac{0.5000 - 0.0012 = 0.4988}{0.5000 - 0.0022 = 0.4978}$$

HOLE   SHAFT   COMPUTATIONS   HOLE   SHAFT
NOMINAL SIZE   (b)   LIMITS
(a)   (c)

Fig. 17.60. Computation of limits (basic hole system).

nominal size is known, all that is necessary to determine the limits is to convert the nominal size to the basic hole size and apply the figures given under "standard limits," adding or subtracting (according to their signs) to or from the basic size to obtain the limits for both the hole and the shaft.

EXAMPLE:

Suppose that a ½ in. shaft is to have a class RC6 fit in a ½ in. hole [Fig. 17.60(a)]. The nominal size of the hole is ½ in. The basic hole size is the exact theoretical size 0.5000.

From Table 24A it is found that the hole may vary between plus 0.0000 and plus 0.0010, and the shaft between −0.0012 and −0.0022. The tolerance on both mating parts is 0.0010, and the allowance (minimum clearance) is 0.0012 as given in the table.

The limits on the hole are: $\dfrac{(0.5000 \text{ plus } 0.0000)}{(0.5000 \text{ plus } 0.0010)} = \dfrac{0.5000}{0.5010}$

The limits on the shaft are: $\dfrac{(0.5000 - 0.0012)}{(0.5000 - 0.0022)} = \dfrac{0.4988}{0.4978}$

The limits are placed in the order in which they will be approached when the part is machined [Fig. 17.60(c)]. The minimum limit should appear above the line for an internal dimension, and the maximum limit above for an external dimension.

17.16. Basic shaft system. When a number of parts requiring different fits but having the same nominal size must be mounted upon a shaft, the basic shaft system is used because it is much easier to adjust the limits for the holes than to machine a shaft of one nominal diameter to a number of different sets of limits required by different fits.

For basic shaft fits the maximum size of the shaft is basic. The limits of clearance or interference are the same as those shown in Tables 24A, B, C, D, and E for the corresponding fits. The symbols for basic shaft fits are identical with those used for the standard fits with a letter S added. For example, LC4S specifies a clearance locational fit, class 4, as determined on a basic shaft basis.

To determine the limits for size under this system, the limits for hole and shaft as given in Tables 24A–E are increased for clearance fits, or decreased for transition or interference fits by the value shown for the upper shaft limit which is the amount required to change the maximum shaft to basic size.

17.17. Tolerances. Necessary tolerances may be expressed by general notes printed on a drawing form or they may be given with definite values for specific dimensions (Fig. 17.59). When expressed

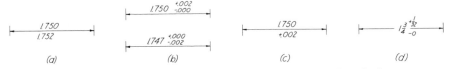

Fig. 17.61. Unilateral tolerances.

in the form of a printed note, the wording might be as follows: ALLOWABLE VARIATION ON ALL FRACTIONAL DIMENSIONS IS ±.010 UNLESS OTHERWISE SPECIFIED. A general note for tolerance on decimal dimensions might read: ALLOWABLE VARIATION ON DECIMAL DIMENSIONS IS ±.001. This general note would apply to all decimal dimensions where limits were not given.

The general notes on tolerances should be allowed to apply to all dimensions where it is not necessary to use specific tolerances.

17.18. Unilateral tolerances. Unilateral tolerances may be expressed in any one of several ways as shown in Fig. 17.61.

Two limits may be given as in (*a*) or the basic size can be shown to the required number of decimal places, followed by a plus tolerance above a minus tolerance as in (*b*). Another method illustrated in (*c*) gives the preferred dimension with a tolerance that may be plus or minus but not both. When the dimension is given as a fraction the zero tolerance is expressed by a 0 (cipher).

17.19. Bilateral tolerances. Bilateral tolerances are expressed with a divided tolerance (Fig. 17.62). Whenever the plus and minus values are unequal as in (*c*) the plus value is placed above the dimension line.

17.20. Cumulative tolerances. An undesirable condition may result when either the location of a surface or an over-all dimension is affected by more than one tolerance dimension. When this condition exists as illustrated in Fig. 17.63(*a*) the tolerances are said to be cumulative. It can be noted in (*a*) where the dimensions are continuous from surface-to-surface that there is a permissible variation of only 0.005 in the over-all length of the piece while at the same time it is not unreasonable to expect all dimensions to vary between either the extreme high or low limits. If minimum toler-

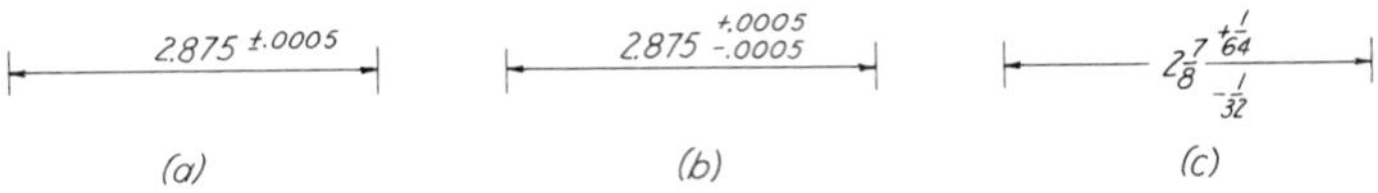

2.875 ±.0005	2.875 $^{+.0005}_{-.0005}$	$2\frac{7}{8}\,^{+\frac{1}{64}}_{-\frac{1}{32}}$
(*a*)	(*b*)	(*c*)

Fig. 17.62. Bilateral tolerances.

ances are obtained between all surfaces, the length of the part could be 3.980 as against a minimum specified length of 3.995. If it is necessary to maintain the over-all dimension within the specified limits, the allowable variation of 0.005 must be distributed among the four dimensions. This would increase manufacturing costs because the machinist would find it necessary to work to limits closer than those specified. In order to avoid this situation, it is the preferred practice to locate the surfaces from a datum plane as shown in (b), so that each surface is affected by only one dimension. The use of a datum plane makes it possible to take full advantage of permissible variations in size and still satisfy all requirements for the proper functioning of the part.

17.21. Production tolerances. Whenever extreme accuracy is required for the production of parts it becomes necessary to specify tolerances for concentricity, squareness, parallelism, and flatness. The tolerances for these features are usually expressed in notes (see Figs. 17.59 and 17.64).

17.22. Specification of angular tolerances. Angular tolerances may be expressed in degrees, minutes, or seconds (see Fig. 17.65). If desired, an angle may be given in degrees and decimal parts of a degree with the tolerance in decimal parts of a degree.

17.23. Geometric tolerancing. Geometric tolerances specify the maximum variation that can be allowed in form or position from true geometry. Actually, a geometrical tolerance is either the width or diameter of a tolerance zone within which a surface or axis of a

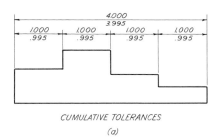

CUMULATIVE TOLERANCES
(a)

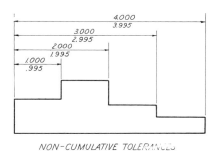

NON-CUMULATIVE TOLERANCES
(b)

Fig. 17.63. Cumulative tolerances.

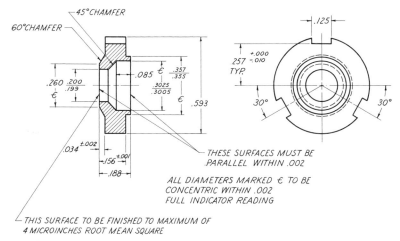

Fig. 17.64. Tolerance of concentricity and parallelism.

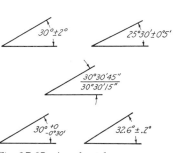

Fig. 17.65. Angular tolerances.

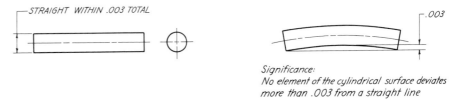

Significance:
No element of the cylindrical surface deviates
more than .003 from a straight line

Fig. 17.66. Specification for straightness.

hole or cylinder can lie with the resulting part satisfying the necessary standards of accuracy for proper functioning and interchangeability. Whenever tolerances of form are not specified on a drawing
for a part, it is understood that the part as produced will be acceptable regardless of form variations. Expressions of tolerances of form
control straightness, flatness, parallelism, squareness, concentricity,
roundness, angular displacement, and so forth.

17.24. Tolerance specification for straightness. Straightness is
specified by a note that is lettered on the drawing in the form
shown on the left in Fig. 17.66. The significance of the note is illustrated by the drawing on the right.

17.25. Tolerance specification for flatness. The note used to control flatness requires that all points of the actual surface must lie
between two parallel planes that are a distance apart equal to the
specified tolerance (see Fig. 17.67). The expressions MUST NOT
BE CONCAVE or MUST NOT BE CONVEX may be added to the
specification note if desired.

17.26. Tolerance specification for squareness. The notes used to
govern squareness and their significance are shown in Figs. 17.68
and 17.69. It should be noted that for the condition illustrated in
Fig. 17.68, the tolerance zone is cylindrical.

17.27. Tolerance specification for parallelism. The form of note to
be used to control parallelism is shown in Fig. 17.70. In using this
method, the datum is considered as a plane established by the high

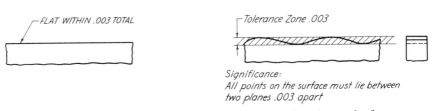

Significance:
All points on the surface must lie between
two planes .003 apart

Fig. 17.67. Specification for flatness.

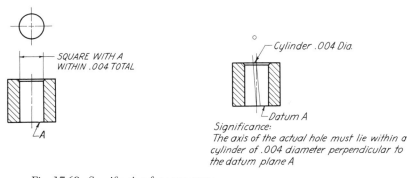

Fig. 17.68. Specification for squareness.

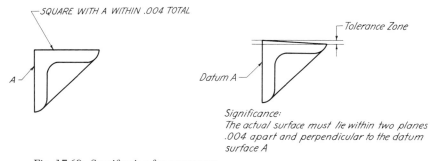

Fig. 17.69. Specification for squareness.

points of surface *A*. All points of the other surface must lie between two planes that are parallel to the datum.

17.28. Tolerance specification for concentricity. When the cylindrical or conical features of a part must be basically concentric, it is the usual practice to specify the permissible eccentricity in terms of the maximum permissible deviation from concentricity. The form of note that is commonly used is shown in Fig. 17.71.

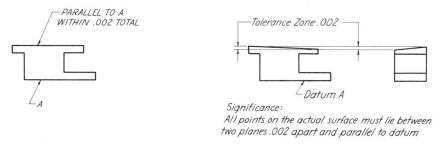

Fig. 17.70. Specification for parallelism.

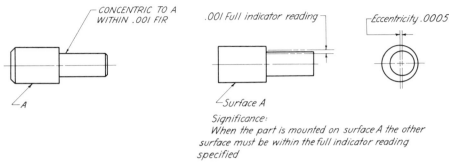

CONCENTRIC TO A
WITHIN .OOI FIR

A

.OOI Full indicator reading

Surface A

Eccentricity .0005

Significance:
When the part is mounted on surface A the other
surface must be within the full indicator reading
specified

Fig. 17.71. Specification for concentricity.

17.29. Tolerance specification for angularity. The note that is commonly used to specify the tolerance for control of angularity is shown in Fig. 17.72. The term angularity is used to define the relation of such features as surfaces, axes, and so forth, to each other when they are not perpendicular.

17.30. True position dimensioning. In the past, it has been the usual practice to locate points by means of rectangular dimensions given with tolerances. A point located in this manner lies within a square or rectangular area. However, this method frequently does not convey the engineering intent nor does it take full account of the relations that must be maintained for the interchangeable assembly of mating parts. True position dimensioning locates the point within a circular area.

Positional tolerancing can be used for specific features of a machine part. When the part contains a number of features arranged in groups, positional tolerances can be used to relate each of the groups to one another as necessary and to tolerance the position of the features within a group independently of the features of the other groups.

The term "true position" denotes the theoretically exact position for a feature. In practice, the basic (exact) location is given with

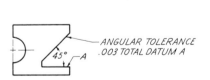

ANGULAR TOLERANCE
.003 TOTAL DATUM A

45°   A

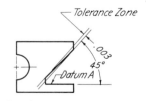

Tolerance Zone

.003
45°
Datum A

Significance:
Actual surface must lie between two
planes .003 apart at specified
angle to datum

Fig. 17.72. Specification for angularity.

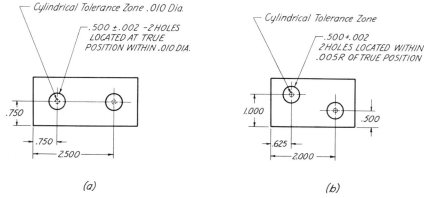

Fig. 17.73. True position dimensioning.

untoleranced dimensions as shown in Fig. 17.73. Then, an expression such as LOCATED AT TRUE POSITION WITHIN .XXX DIA. or LOCATED WITHIN .XXXR OF TRUE POSITION is added to the normal note specifying the size of the feature to be located. When the alignment between mating parts depends upon some functional feature, this feature is selected as a datum, and the datum is identified in the note. Such a note might read: XX HOLES LOCATED WITHIN .XXXR OF TRUE POSITION IN RELATION TO DATUM *A*.

The requirement of true position dimensioning for a cylindrical feature is illustrated in Fig. 17.74(*a*). As must be understood, the axis of the hole at all points must lie within the specified cylindrical tolerance zone having its center located at true position. This cylindrical tolerance zone also defines the limits within which variations in the squareness of the axis of the hole in relation to the flat surface must be confined.

In applying true position dimensioning to noncylindrical features, such as slots, dovetails, serrations, and so forth, it will be found that

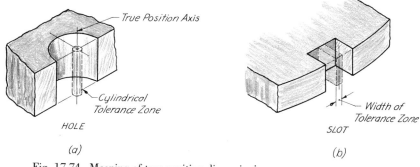

Fig. 17.74. Meaning of true position dimensioning.

the principal difference is in the geometric form of the tolerance zone. The note specifying slots might read: 6 SLOTS EQUALLY SPACED AND LOCATED WITHIN .005 EACH SIDE OF TRUE POSITION. The expression .005 EACH SIDE OF TRUE POSI-TION specifies that the axis of the slot must fall within a rectangular tolerance zone as shown in Fig. 17.74(*b*). The tolerance zone must be symmetrically disposed on each side of true position by the amount of the true position tolerance.

The illustrations used with this discussion have been presented with the sole idea of showing briefly what is meant by true position dimensioning. They are not to be thought of as being practical examples. Dotted circles have been added to each illustration to call attention to the imaginary tolerance zones. Those who may have the need for the use of this method of tolerancing should consult Sec. 5, American Drafting Standards Manual (ASA Y14.5–1957) so as to acquire a full understanding of true position dimensioning.

17.31. Maximum material condition. Although, in general, tolerances of position are determined by the maximum metal condition of mating features, and limits of location must be strictly observed at times regardless of the actual finished size of mating components, there are situations in which the limits of center distance may be exceeded and acceptable parts produced when the finished sizes of mating features are away from maximum material conditions. With this latter condition permissible, it is desirable to indicate the fact that limits of center distance need be observed only under maximum material conditions. This is accomplished by a note reading as follows: $\frac{.500}{.502}$ 2 HOLES LOCATED AT TRUE POSITION WITHIN .010 DIA AT MMC. The letters MMC denote maximum material condition.

When maximum material condition is not used, and the exact positional tolerance applies regardless of the size of the feature, this fact should be indicated by a note. Such a note might read: 6 HOLES LOCATED AT TRUE POSITION WITHIN .010 DIA REGARDLESS OF HOLE SIZE or 6 HOLES LOCATED WITHIN .005R OF TRUE POSITION REGARDLESS OF HOLE SIZE.

Additional information concerning the meaning of MMC as related to positional tolerances may be found in the Appendix of ASA Y14.5–1957.

17.32. Surface quality. The improvement in machining methods within recent years coupled with a strong demand for increased life for machined parts has caused engineers to give more attention to

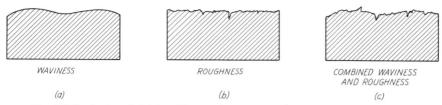

Fig. 17.75. Surface definitions illustrated.

the quality of the surface finish. Not only the service life but also the proper functioning of the part as well may depend upon obtaining the needed smoothness quality for contact surfaces.

On an engineering drawing a surface may be represented by line if shown in profile or it may appear as a bounded area in a related view. Machined and ground surfaces, however, do not have the perfect smoothness represented on a drawing. Actually a surface has three dimensions, namely, length, breadth, and curvature (waviness) as illustrated in Fig. 17.75(*a*). In addition there will be innumerable peaks and valleys of differing lengths, widths, and heights. An exaggerated profile of surface roughness is shown in (*b*). Combined waviness and roughness is illustrated in (*c*).

The following terms must be understood before the surface symbol shown in Fig. 17.76(*a*) can be properly applied:

Roughness. Roughness is the relatively finely spaced surface irregularities that are produced by the cutting action of tool edges and abrasive grains on surfaces that are machined.

Waviness. Waviness is the surface undulations that are of much greater magnitude than the roughness irregularities. Waviness may result from machine or work deflections, vibrations, warping, strains, or similar causes.

Lay. Lay is the predominate direction of the tool marks of the surface pattern [see Fig. 17.76(*b*)].

Microinch. A microinch is one millionth (0.000001) of an inch.

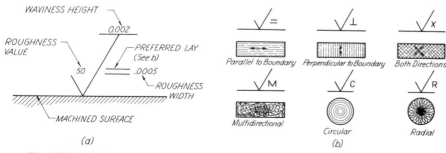

Fig. 17.76. Surface quality symbols.

The following was abstracted from the American Standard Publication "Drawings and Drafting Room Practice" (ASA Z14.1–1946):

A surface whose finish is to be specified should be marked with the finish mark having the general form of a check mark (√) so that the point of the symbol is

(a) On the line indicating the surface,

(b) On a leader pointing to the surface (Fig. 17.77).

Where it is desired to specify only the surface roughness height, and the width of roughness or direction of tool marks is not important, the simplest form of the symbol should be used (see Fig. 17.59). This height may be either maximum peak to valley height, average peak to valley height, or average deviation from the mean (RMS or arithmetical). The numerical value is placed in the √ as shown.

Where it is desired to specify waviness height in addition to roughness height a straight horizontal line should be added to the top of the simple symbol [see Fig. 17.76(a)]. The numerical value of height of waviness would be shown above this line.

Then, if the nature of the preferred lay is to be shown in addition to these two characteristics, it will be indicated by the addition of a combination of lines as shown in Fig. 17.76(a) and (b). The parallel and perpendicular part of the symbol indicates that the dominant lines on the surface are parallel or perpendicular to the boundary line of the surface in contact with the symbol.

The complete symbol, including the roughness width placed to the right of the lay symbol, is shown in Fig. 17.76(a).

The use of only one number to specify the height or width of roughness or waviness shall indicate the maximum value. Any lesser degree of roughness will be satisfactory. When two numbers are used separated by a dash, they indicate the maximum and minimum permissible values.

Surface finish should be specified only by experienced persons because the function of many parts does not depend upon the smoothness quality of a surface or surfaces. In addition, surface quality need not be necessarily indicated for many parts that are produced to close dimensional tolerances because a satisfactory surface finish may result from the required machining processes. It

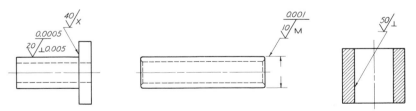

Fig. 17.77. Application of surface finish symbols.

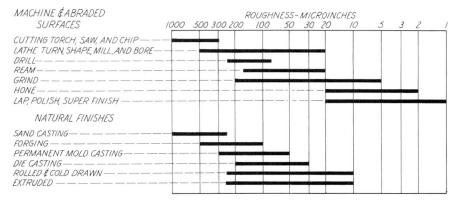

Fig. 17.78. Surface finishes expected from common production methods.

should be remembered that the cost of producing a part will generally become progressively greater as the specification of surface finish becomes more exacting.

The chart in Fig. 17.78 shows the expected surface roughness in microinches for surfaces produced by common production methods.

The surface-quality symbol, which is used only when it is desirable to specify surface smoothness, should not be confused with a finish mark that indicates the removal of material. A surface-quality symbol might be used for a surface on a die-casting, forging, or extruded shape where the surface is to have a natural finish and no material is to be removed.

D: STRUCTURAL DIMENSIONING

17.33. Location of dimension lines. All dimensions must be placed in such a manner that they will be easily understood. Principal dimensions are generally obtained from the design sheets; other dimensions necessary for detailing are found in tables or are determined by the detailer.

Dimensions for rivet spacing, short location and size dimensions, and so on, are placed close to the view, whereas the longer dimensions such as over-all lengths are placed farther away so that extension lines will not cross dimension lines (Fig. 17.79).

Dimension figures are placed above or at the side of continuous (unbroken) dimension lines. These lines generally should be placed off the view, but usually added clearness may be obtained by putting some dimensions in an open area on the view itself. Dimension lines ordinarily should not be placed less than ⅜ in. apart or closer to the view than ½ in.

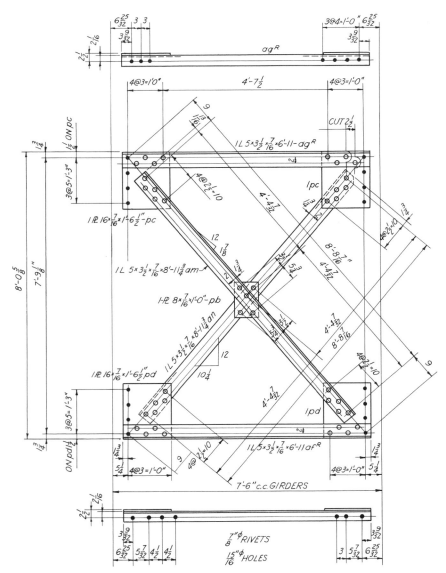

Fig. 17.79. Detail drawing of a cross frame.

17.34. Dimensions and notes in structural detailing (Fig. 17.79).

1. Figures can be placed to one side, with a leader to the dimension line, if the available space is very small.

2. Figures and notes must read from the bottom and the right side of the sheet because shopmen are familiar with reading from these positions.

3. For dimensions less than one foot, the inch marks ($''$) may be omitted.

4. With the exception of widths of plates and depths of sections, all dimensions of one foot or more are expressed in feet and inches.

Correct	Incorrect
¼	0¼
9	0′–9″
10	10″
1′–0″	12″
2′–3¼″	2′–03½″
4′–0¼″	4′¼″

5. Usually, dimensions are given in multiples of ⅛ in. or, preferably, ¼ in. It is not desirable to use multiples of 1⁄16 in. or 1⁄32 in., except in rare cases.

6. Decimals found in tables should be converted into fractions to the nearest 1⁄16 in.

7. Rivets and holes are located by dimensions from center to center.

8. Dimensions *always* should be given to the center lines of I-beams and to the backs of angles and channels.

9. When three or more rivet spaces for a line of rivets are equal, they should be dimensioned as a group (4 @ 3″ = 1′–0″). Staggered rivets are dimensioned as if they were on one gage line.

10. Since a workman must use a rule or tape to lay off angles, a slope triangle should be shown to give the inclination of a working line.

11. A general note is usually placed on a detail drawing giving the edge distances, painting instructions, size of rivets, size of open holes, and so on.

12. The size of a member is indicated by a specification (in the form of a note) parallel to it.

13. The width of a plate is always given in inches.

PROBLEMS

The following problems offer the student the opportunity to apply the rules of dimensioning given in this chapter. If it is desired, decimals of an inch may be used in place of fractions. Use Table 1 in the Appendix.

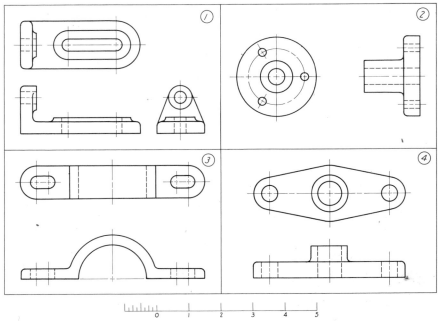

Fig. 17.80. Dimensioning problems.

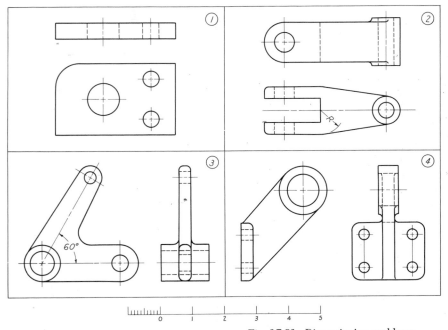

Fig. 17.81. Dimensioning problems.

1-2. (Figs. 17.80–17.81.) Reproduce the given views of an assigned part. Determine the dimensions by transferring them from the drawing to the open-divided scale by means of the dividers. Decimal-inch dimensioning is to be used for the parts given in Fig. 17.81.

3-13. (Figs. 17.82–17.92.) Make a fully dimensioned multiview sketch or drawing of an assigned part. Draw all necessary views. Give a detail title with suitable notes concerning material, number required, etc. These parts have been selected from different fields of industry—automotive, aeronautical, chemical, electrical, etc.

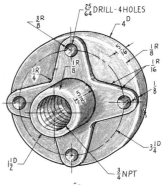

Fig. 17.82. Flange.

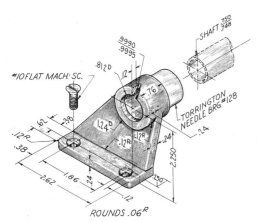

Fig. 17.83. Bearing bracket—airplane control system.

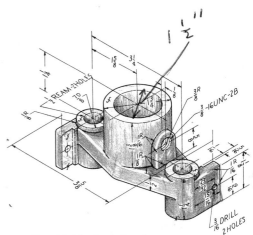

Fig. 17.84. Guide bracket.

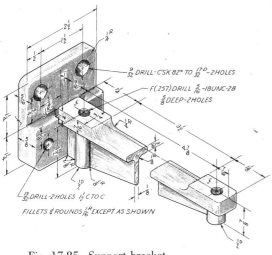

Fig. 17.85. Support bracket.

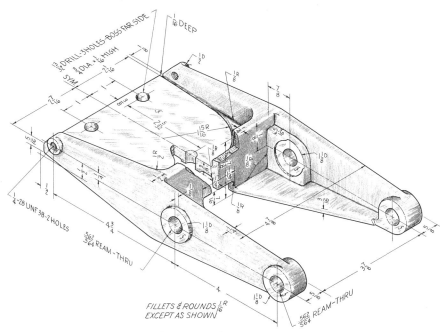

Fig. 17.86. Control pedal—airplane control system.

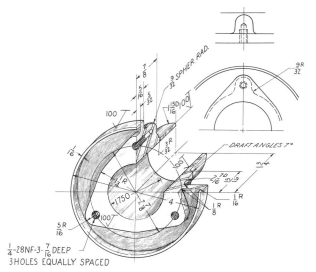

Fig. 17.87. Inlet flange—airplane cooling system.

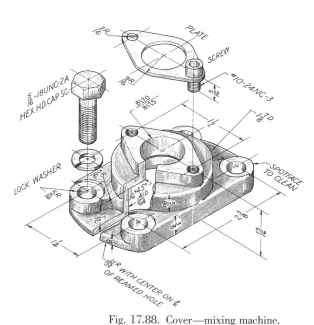

Fig. 17.88. Cover—mixing machine.

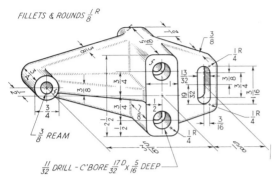

FILLETS & ROUNDS $\frac{1}{8}R$

Fig. 17.89. Elevator bracket.

$\frac{11}{32}$ DRILL - C'BORE $\frac{17}{32}D \times \frac{5}{16}$ DEEP

$\frac{3}{8}$ REAM

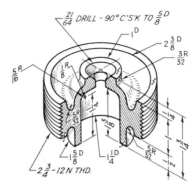

$\frac{21}{64}$ DRILL - 90° C'S'K TO $\frac{5}{8}D$

$2\frac{3}{4}$ -12 N THD.

Fig. 17.90. Valve seat.

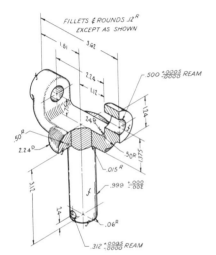

FILLETS & ROUNDS .12^R
EXCEPT AS SHOWN

.500 $^{+.0005}_{-.0000}$ REAM

.999 $^{+.000}_{-.002}$

.312 $^{+.0005}_{-.0000}$ REAM

Fig. 17.91. Yoke.

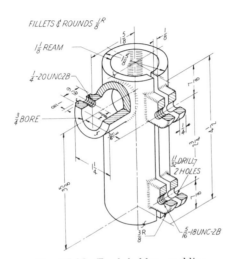

FILLETS & ROUNDS $\frac{1}{8}R$

$1\frac{1}{8}$ REAM

$\frac{1}{4}$-20 UNC2B

$\frac{3}{4}$ BORE

$\frac{11}{32}$ DRILL
2 HOLES

$\frac{5}{16}$-18 UNC-2B

$\frac{3}{8}R$

Fig. 17.92. Torch holder—welding.

14. (Fig. 17.93.) Make a fully dimensioned multiview sketch or drawing of the rocker arm. Show a detail section taken through the ribs. *Supplementary information:* (1) The distance from the center of the shaft to the center of the hole for the pin is 4.00 in. The distance from the shaft to the threaded hole is 4.50 in. (2) The nominal diameter of the hole for the shaft is 1.875 in. The hole in the rocker arm is to be reamed for a definite fit. Consult your instructor, but *do not* use a limit dimension for either the shaft or the pin. The diameter of the pin is .969 in. (3) The diameter of the threaded boss is 2.00 in. (4) The diameter of the roller is 2.25 in., and its length 1.46 in. Total clearance between the roller and finished faces is to be .03 in. (5) The inside faces of the arms are to be milled in towards the hub far enough to accommodate the roller. (6) The rib is .62 in. thick. (7) The lock nut has 1¼–12 UNF thread. (8) Fillets and rounds .12 in. R except where otherwise noted.

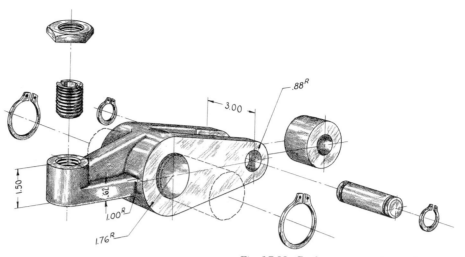

Fig. 17.93. Rocker arm—marine engine.

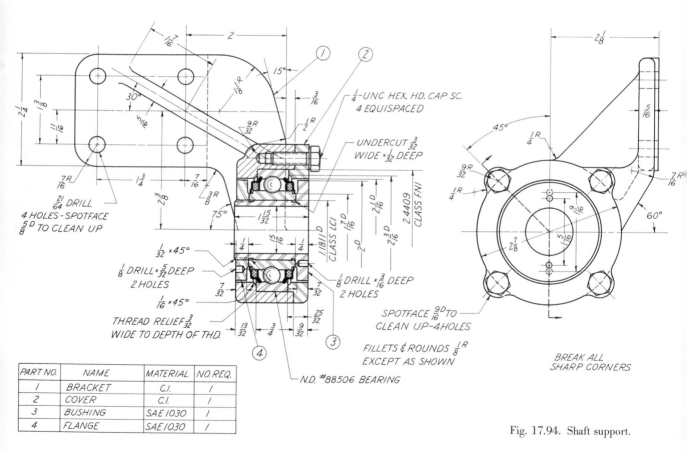

PART NO.	NAME	MATERIAL	NO. REQ.
1	BRACKET	C.I.	1
2	COVER	C.I.	1
3	BUSHING	SAE 1030	1
4	FLANGE	SAE 1030	1

Fig. 17.94. Shaft support.

15. (Fig. 17.94.) Make a fully dimensioned drawing of an assigned part of the shaft support.

16. (See Fig. 18.36.) Make a fully dimensioned drawing of an assigned part of the tool holder.

17. (Fig. 17.95.) Make a fully dimensioned drawing of an assigned part of the bearing bracket. Compose a suitable detail title, giving the name of the part, the material, etc.

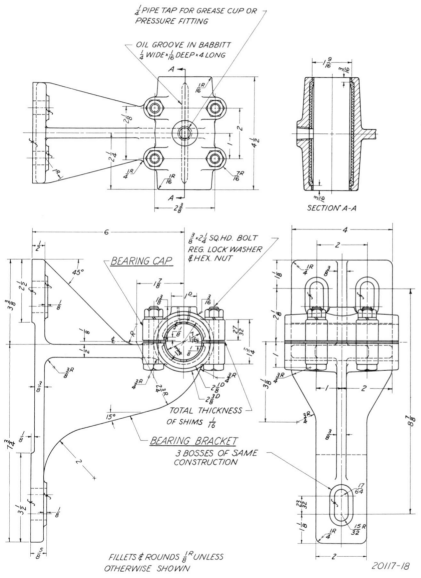

Fig. 17.95. Bearing bracket.

18

DESIGN AND COMMUNICATION DRAWINGS

18.1. Communication drawings. These varied types of engineering drawings, ranging from design drawings to exploded pictorial drawings, have one thing in common, and that is that they are prepared to convey needed ideas and facts to others. Since all serve the same purpose, they may be classed together as "communication drawings," this term being almost all inclusive.

In this chapter we will be concerned mainly with the types of drawings that are prepared by draftsmen under an engineer's supervision, and which are to serve as communications to others beyond the engineering department. The preparation of idea sketches, both multiview and pictorial, has been discussed in detail in Chapters 7 and 11. Charts and graphs, which may also be thought of as communication drawings, are presented in Chapter 19. Charts and graphs are used by engineers to supplement written reports and technical papers.

18.2. Sketches and design drawings. The first stage in the development of an idea for a structure or machine is to prepare freehand sketches and to make the calculations required to determine the feasibility of the design. From these sketches the designer prepares a layout, on which an accurate analysis of the design is worked out. It is usually drawn full size and is executed with instruments in pencil (Fig. 18.1). The layout should be complete enough to allow a survey of the location of parts (to avoid interference), the accessibility for maintenance, the requirements for lubrication, and the method of assembly.

Usually, only center distances and certain fixed dimensions are given. The general dimensioning, as well as the determination of material and degree of finish of individual parts, is left for the draftsman who makes the detail drawings while using the layout drawing as a guide.

Design layouts require both empirical and scientific design. Empirical design involves the use of charts, formulas, tables, and so forth, which have been derived from experimental studies and scientific computations. Scientific design, which requires a broad knowledge of the allied fields such as mechanics, metallurgy, and mathematics, is used when a new machine is designed to operate under special specified conditions for which data are not available in any handbook.

A: MACHINE DRAWINGS

18.3. Classes of machine drawings. There are two recognized classes of machine drawings: detail drawings and assembly drawings.

18.4. Set of working drawings. A complete set of working drawings for a machine consists of detail sheets, giving all necessary shop information for the production of individual pieces, and an assembly drawing showing the location of each piece in the finished machine.

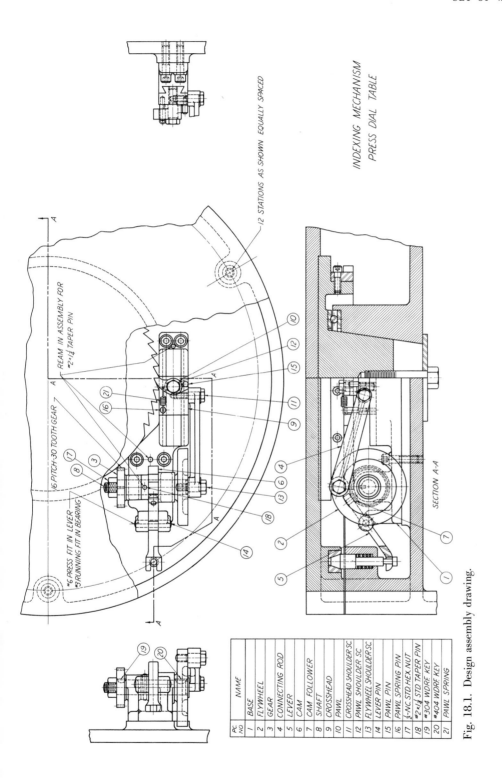

INDEXING MECHANISM
PRESS DIAL TABLE

12 STATIONS AS SHOWN EQUALLY SPACED

REAM IN ASSEMBLY FOR
*2·1¼ TAPER PIN

16 PITCH–30 TOOTH GEAR

*6 PRESS FIT IN LEVER
*3 RUNNING FIT IN BEARING

SECTION A–A

PC NO	NAME
1	BASE
2	FLYWHEEL
3	GEAR
4	CONNECTING ROD
5	LEVER
6	CAM
7	CAM FOLLOWER
8	SHAFT
9	CROSSHEAD
10	PAWL
11	CROSSHEAD SHOULDER SC.
12	PAWL SHOULDER SC.
13	FLYWHEEL SHOULDER SC.
14	LEVER PIN
15	PAWL PIN
16	PAWL SPRING PIN
17	½-NC. STD.HEX.NUT
18	*2×1¼ STD TAPER PIN
19	*304 WDRF. KEY
20	*404 WDRF. KEY
21	PAWL SPRING

Fig. 18.1. Design assembly drawing.

In addition, the set may include drawings showing a foundation plan, piping diagram, oiling diagram, and so on.

18.5. Detail drawings. A detail drawing should give complete information for the manufacture of a part, describing with adequate dimensions the part's size. Finished surfaces should be indicated and all necessary shop operations shown. The title should give the material of which the part is to be made and should state the number of the parts that are required for the production of an assembled unit of which the part is a member. Commercial examples of detail workings are shown in Figs. 18.2 and 18.3.

Since a machinist will ordinarily make one part at a time, it is advisable to detail each piece, regardless of its size, on a separate individual sheet. In some shops, however, custom dictates that related parts be grouped on the same sheet, particularly when the parts form a unit in themselves. Other concerns sometimes group small parts of the same material together thus: castings on one sheet, forgings on another, special fasteners on still another, and so on.

18.6. Making a detail drawing. With a design layout or original sketches as a guide, the procedure for making a detail drawing is as follows:

1. Select the views, remembering that, aside from the view showing the characteristic shape of the object, there should

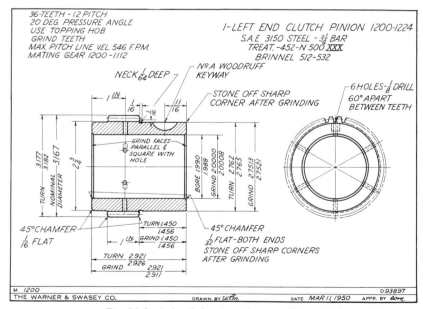

Fig. 18.2. A detail drawing (*Courtesy Warner & Swasey Co.*).

be as many additional views as are necessary to complete the shape description. These may be sectional views that reveal a complicated interior construction, or auxiliary views of surfaces not fully described in any of the principal views.

2. Decide upon a scale that will allow, without crowding, a balanced arrangement of all necessary views and the location of dimensions and notes. Although very small parts should be drawn double size or larger, to show detail and to allow for dimensions, a full-size scale should be used when possible. In general, the same scale should be used for pieces of the same size.

3. Draw the main center lines and block in the general outline of the views with light, sharp 6H pencil lines.

4. Draw main circles and arcs in finished weight.

5. Starting with the characteristic view, work back and forth from view to view until the shape of the object is completed. Lines whose definite location and length are known may be drawn in their finished weight.

6. Put in fillets and rounds.

7. Complete the views by darkening the object lines.

8. Draw extension and dimension lines.

9. Add arrowheads, dimensions, and notes.

10. Complete the title.

11. Check the entire drawing carefully.

18.7. One-view drawings. Many parts, such as shafts, bolts, studs, and washers, may require only one properly dimensioned view. In the case of each of these parts, a note can imply the complete shape of the piece without sacrificing clearness. Most engineering departments, however, deem it better practice to show two views.

18.8. Detail titles. Every detail drawing must give information not conveyed by the notes and dimensions, such as the name of the part, part number, material, number required, and so on. The method of recording and the location of this information on the drawing varies somewhat in different drafting rooms. It may be lettered either in the record strip or directly below the views (see Figs. 18.3 and 18.4).

If all surfaces on a part are machined, finish marks are omitted and a title note, "Finish all over," is added to the detail title.

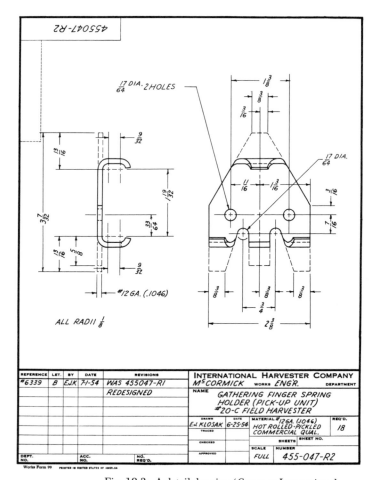

Fig. 18.3. A detail drawing (*Courtesy International Harvester Co.*).

18.9. Title blocks and record strips. The purpose of a title or record strip is to present in an orderly manner the name of the machine, name of the manufacturer, date, scale, drawing number, and other drafting-room information.

Every commercial drafting room has developed its own standard title forms, whose features depend upon the processes of manufacture, the peculiarities of the plant organization, and the established customs of particular types of manufacturing. In large organizations, the blank form, along with the border line, is printed on standard sizes of drawing or tracing paper.

A record strip is a form of title extending almost the entire distance across the bottom of the sheet. In addition to the usual title information, it may contain a section for recording revisions, changes, and so on, with the dates on which they were adopted.

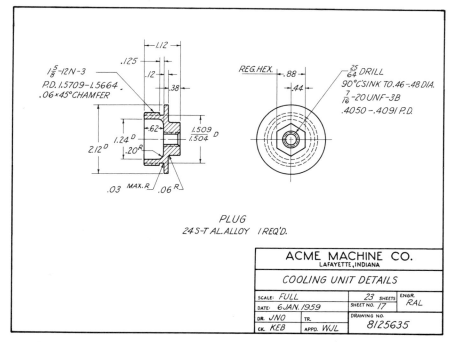

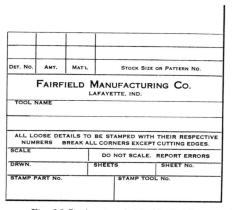

Fig. 18.4. A working drawing.

18.10. Contents of the title (Figs. 18.3 and 18.10). The title on a machine drawing generally contains the following information:

1. Name of the part.
2. Name of the machine or structure. (This is given in the main title and is usually followed by one of two words: *details* or *assembly*.)
3. Name and location of the manufacturing firm.

Fig. 18.5. A printed title block (*Courtesy Fairfield Mfg. Co.*).

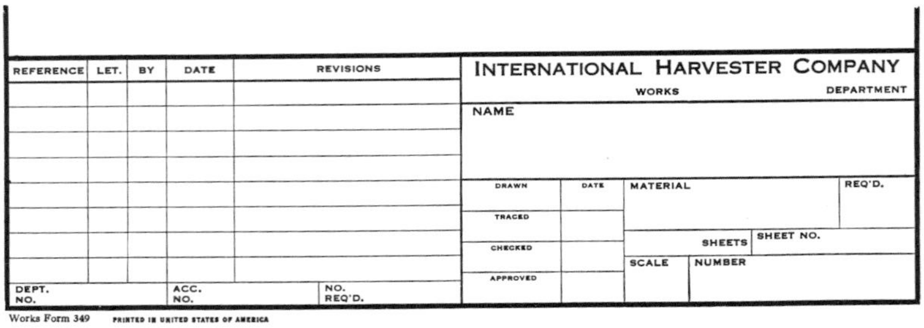

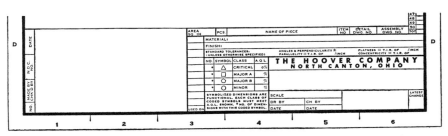

Fig. 18.6. A printed record strip (*Courtesy International Harvester Co.*).

4. Name and address of the purchasing firm, if the structure has been designed for a particular company.

5. Scale.

6. Date. (Often spaces are provided for the date of completion of each operation in the preparation of the drawing. If only one date is given, it is usually the date of completion of the drawing.)

7. Initials or name of the draftsman who made the pencil drawing.

8. Initials of the checker.

9. Initials or signature of the chief draftsman, chief engineer, or another in authority who approved the drawing.

10. Initials of the tracer (if drawing has been traced).

11. Drawing number. This generally serves as a filing number and may furnish information in code form. Letters and numbers may be so combined to indicate departments, plants, model, type, order number, filing number, and so on. The drawing number is sometimes repeated in the upper left-hand corner (in an upside-down position), so that the drawing may be quickly identified if it should become reversed in the file.

Fig. 18.7. A record strip (*Courtesy The Hoover Co.*).

Some titles furnish information such as material, part number, pattern number, finish, treatment, estimated weight, superseded drawing number, and so on.

18.11. Corrections and alterations. Alterations on working drawings are made either by cancellation or by erasure. Cancellations are indicated by parallel inclined lines drawn through the views, lines, notes, or dimensions to be changed.

Superseding dimensions should be placed above or near the original ones. If alterations are made by erasure, the changed dimensions are often underlined.

All changes on a completed or approved drawing should be recorded in a revision record that may be located either adjacent to the title block (Fig. 18.10) or at one corner of the drawing (Fig. 18.8). This note should contain the identification symbol, date, authorization number, character of the revision, and the initials of the draftsman and checker who made the change. The identification symbol is a letter or numeral placed in a small circle near the alteration on the body of the drawing (see Fig. 18.8).

If changes are made by complete erasure, record prints should be made for the file before the original is altered. Many companies make record prints whenever changes are extensive.

Since revisions on completed drawings are usually necessitated by unsatisfactory methods of production or by a customer's request, they should never be made by a draftsman unless an order has been issued with the approval of the chief engineer's office.

18.12. Pattern-shop drawings. Sometimes special pattern-shop drawings, giving information needed for making a pattern, are required for large and complicated castings. If the pattern maker receives a drawing that shows finished dimensions, he provides for the draft necessary to draw the pattern and for the extra metal for machining. He allows for shrinkage by making the pattern oversize. When, however, the draft and allowances for finish are determined by the engineering department, no finish marks appear on the drawing. The allowances are included in the dimensions.

18.13. Forge-shop drawings. If a forging is to be machined, separate detail drawings usually are made for the forge and machine shops. A forging drawing gives all the nominal dimensions required by the forge shop for a completed rough forging.

18.14. Machine-shop drawings. Rough castings and forgings are sent to the machine shop to be finished. Since the machinist is not interested in the dimensions and information for the previous stages,

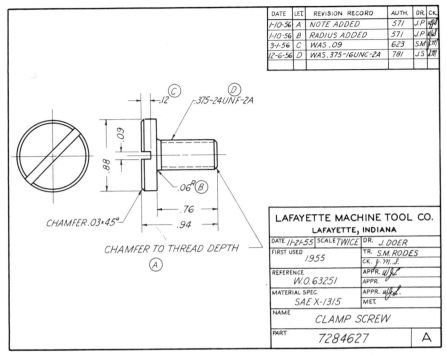

DATE	LET.	REVISION RECORD	AUTH.	DR.	CK.
1-10-56	A	NOTE ADDED	571	J.P.	
1-10-56	B	RADIUS ADDED	571	J.P.	
3-1-56	C	WAS .09	623	S.M.	
12-6-56	D	WAS .375-16UNC-2A	781	J.S.	

CHAMFER .03×45°

CHAMFER TO THREAD DEPTH

LAFAYETTE MACHINE TOOL CO.
LAFAYETTE, INDIANA

DATE 11-21-55	SCALE TWICE	DR. J. DOER
FIRST USED 1955		TR. S.M. RODES
		CK.
REFERENCE W.O. 63251		APPR.
		APPR.
MATERIAL SPEC. SAE X-1315		APPR.
		MET

NAME *CLAMP SCREW*

PART *7284627* | A

Fig. 18.8. Alterations.

a machine-shop drawing frequently gives only the information necessary for machining.

18.15. Assembly drawings. A drawing that shows the parts of a machine or machine unit assembled in their relative working positions is an assembly drawing. There are several types of such drawings: design assembly drawings, working assembly drawings, unit assembly drawings, installation diagrams, and so on, each of which will be described separately (Figs. 18.9–18.10 and 18.12–18.14).

18.16. Working assembly drawings. A working assembly drawing, showing each piece completely dimensioned, is sometimes made for a simple mechanism or unit of related parts. No additional detail drawings of parts are required.

18.17. Sub-assembly (unit) drawings. A unit assembly is an assembly drawing of a group of related parts that form a unit in a more complicated machine. Such a drawing would be made for the tail stock of a lathe, the clutch of an automobile, or the carburetor of an airplane. A set of assembly drawings thus takes the place of a complete assembly of a complex machine (Fig. 18.10).

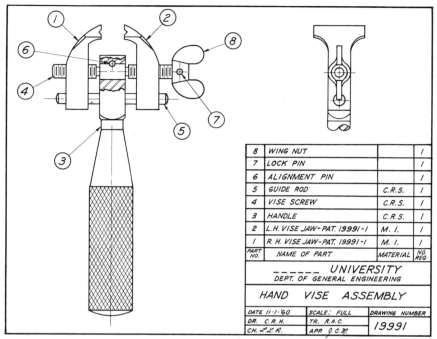

8	WING NUT		1
7	LOCK PIN		1
6	ALIGNMENT PIN		1
5	GUIDE ROD	C.R.S.	1
4	VISE SCREW	C.R.S.	1
3	HANDLE	C.R.S.	1
2	L.H. VISE JAW – PAT. 19991–1	M. I.	1
1	R.H. VISE JAW – PAT. 19991–1	M. I.	1
PART NO.	NAME OF PART	MATERIAL	NO. REQ.

_____ UNIVERSITY
DEPT. OF GENERAL ENGINEERING

HAND   VISE   ASSEMBLY

DATE 11·1·'60	SCALE: FULL	DRAWING NUMBER
DR. C.R.H.	TR. R.A.C.	
CH. L.L.R.	APP. J.C.M.	19991

Fig. 18.9. An assembly drawing.

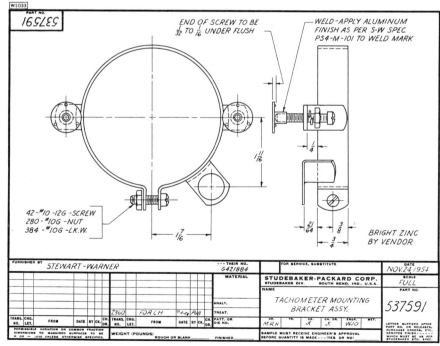

Fig. 18.10. A unit assembly drawing (*Courtesy Studebaker-Packard Corp.*).

18.18. Bill of material. A bill of material is a list of parts placed on an assembly drawing just above the title block, or, in the case of quantity production, on a separte sheet. The bill contains the part number, descriptive name, material, quantity (number) required, and so on, of each piece. Additional information, such as stock size, pattern number (castings), and so forth, is sometimes listed.

Suggested dimensions for ruling are shown in Fig. 18.11. For ⅛ in. letters, the lines should never be spaced closer than ⁵⁄₁₆ in. Fractions are made slightly less than full height and are centered between the lines.

When listing standard parts in a bill of material, the general practice is to omit the name of the materials and to use abbreviated descriptive titles. A pattern number may be composed of the commercial job number followed by the assigned number one, two, three, and so on. It is suggested that parts be listed in the following order: (a) castings, (b) forgings, (c) parts made from bar stock, (d) standard parts.

Sometimes bills of material are first typed on thin paper and then blueprinted. The form may be ruled or printed.

18.19. Title. The title strip on an assembly drawing usually is the same as that used on a detail drawing. It will be noted, when lettering in the block, that the title of the drawing is generally composed of the name of the machine followed by the word *assembly* (see Figs. 18.9 and 18.10).

18.20. Making the assembly drawing. The final assembly may be traced from the design assembly drawing, but more often it is redrawn to a smaller scale on a separate sheet. Since the redrawing, being done from both the design and detail drawings, furnishes a check that frequently reveals errors, the assembly always should be

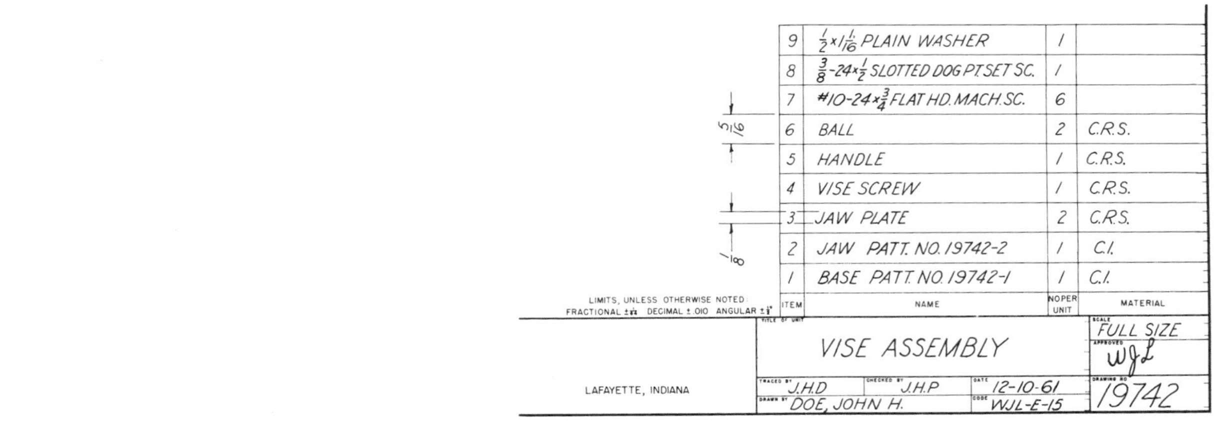

ITEM	NAME	NO PER UNIT	MATERIAL
9	$\frac{1}{2} \times 1\frac{1}{16}$ PLAIN WASHER	1	
8	$\frac{3}{8}$-24×$\frac{1}{2}$ SLOTTED DOG PT. SET SC.	1	
7	#10-24×$\frac{3}{4}$ FLAT HD. MACH. SC.	6	
6	BALL	2	C.R.S.
5	HANDLE	1	C.R.S.
4	VISE SCREW	1	C.R.S.
3	JAW PLATE	2	C.R.S.
2	JAW PATT. NO. 19742-2	1	C.I.
1	BASE PATT. NO. 19742-1	1	C.I.

LIMITS, UNLESS OTHERWISE NOTED
FRACTIONAL ±¹⁄₆₄ DECIMAL ±.010 ANGULAR ±½°

TITLE OF UNIT

VISE ASSEMBLY

SCALE FULL SIZE
APPROVED WJL

LAFAYETTE, INDIANA

TRACED BY J.H.D.   CHECKED BY J.H.P   DATE 12-10-61
DRAWN BY DOE, JOHN H.   CODE WJL-E-15   DRAWING NO. 19742

Fig. 18.11. A bill of material.

drawn before the details are accepted as finished and the blueprints are made. The assembly of a simple machine or unit is sometimes shown on the same sheet with the details.

Accepted practices to be observed on assemblies are:

1. *Sectioning.* Parts should be sectioned using the American Standard symbols shown in Fig. 9.32. The practices of sectioning apply to assemblies.

2. *Views.* The main view, which is usually in full section, should show to the best advantage nearly all the individual parts and their locations. Additional views are shown only when they add necessary information that should be conveyed by the drawing.

3. *Hidden lines.* Hidden lines should be omitted from an assembly drawing, for they tend merely to overload it and create confusion. Complete shape description is unnecessary, since parts are either standard or are shown on detail drawings.

4. *Dimensions.* Over-all dimensions and center-to-center distances indicating the relationship of parts in the machine as a whole are sometimes given. Detail dimensions are omitted, except on working assembly drawings.

5. *Identification of parts.* Parts in a machine or structure are identified on the assembly drawing by numbers that are used on the details and in the bill of material (Fig. 18.9). These should be made at least ³⁄₁₆ in. high and enclosed in a ⅜ in. circle. The centers of the circles are located not less than ¾ in. from the nearest line of the drawing. Leaders, terminated by arrowheads touching the parts, are drawn radial with a straightedge. The numbers, in order to be centered in the circles, should be made first and the circles drawn around them. An alternate method used in commercial practice is to letter the name and descriptive information for each part and draw a leader pointing to it in the main view.

18.21. Checking drawings. Checking, the final assurance that the machine is correctly designed, should be done by a person (checker or squad foreman) who has not prepared the drawings but who is thoroughly familiar with the principles of the design. He must have a broad knowledge of shop practices and assembly methods. In commercial drafting rooms, the most experienced men are assigned to this type of work. The assembly drawing is checked against the detail drawings and corrections are indicated with either a soft or colored pencil. The checker should:

1. Survey the machine as a whole from the standpoint of operation, ease of assembly, and accessibility for repair

work. He should consider the type, strength, and suitability of the materials.

2. Check each part with the parts adjacent to it, to make certain that proper clearances are maintained. (To determine whether or not all positions are free of interference, it may be necessary to lay out the extreme travel of moving parts to an enlarged scale.)

3. Study the drawing to see that each piece has been illustrated correctly and that all necessary views, types of views, treatments of views, and scales have been shown.

4. Check dimensions by scaling; calculate and check size and location dimensions that affect mating parts; determine the suitability of dimensions from the standpoint of the various departments' needs, such as pattern, forge, machine, assembly shop, and so on; examine views for proper dimensioning and mark unnecessary, repeated, or omitted dimensions.

5. Check tolerances, making sure the computations are correct and that proper fits have been used, so that there will be no unnecessary production costs.

6. See that finishes and such operations as drilling, reaming, boring, tapping, and grinding are properly specified.

7. Check specifications for material.

8. Examine notes for correctness and location.

9. See that stock sizes have been used for standard parts such as bolts, screws, keys, and so on. (Stock sizes may be determined from catalogs.)

10. Add any additional explanatory notes that should supply necessary information.

11. Check the bill of material to see that each part is completely and correctly specified.

12. Check items in the title block.

13. Make a final survey of the drawing in its entirety, making certain there is either a check or correction for each dimension, note, and specification.

B: DRAWINGS FOR CATALOGS, INSTRUCTION MANUALS, AND TECHNICAL PUBLICATIONS

18.22. Installation assembly drawings. An installation drawing gives useful information for putting a machine or structure together. The names of parts, order of assembling parts, location dimensions, and special instructions for operating may also be shown.

18.23. Outline assembly drawings. Outline assembly drawings are most frequently made for illustrative purposes in catalogs. Usually they show merely over-all and principal dimensions (Fig. 18.12). Their appearance may be improved by the use of line shading.

18.24. Exploded pictorial assembly drawings for parts lists and instruction manuals. Exploded pictorial assembly drawings are used frequently in the parts lists sections of company catalogs and in instruction manuals. Drawings of this type are easily understood by those with very little experience in reading multiview drawings. Figure 18.13 shows a commercial example of an exploded pictorial assembly drawing.

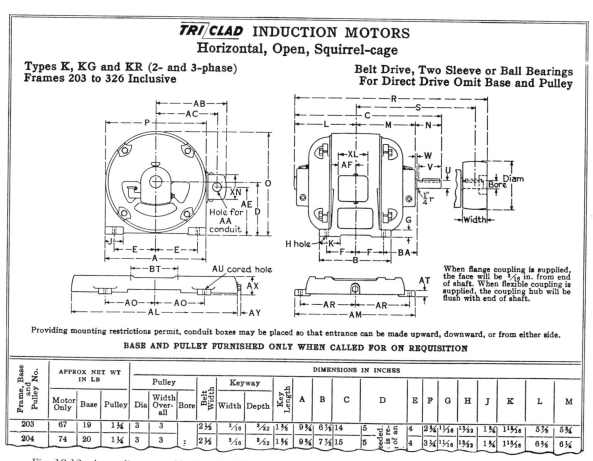

Fig. 18.12. An outline assembly drawing (*Courtesy General Electric Co.*).

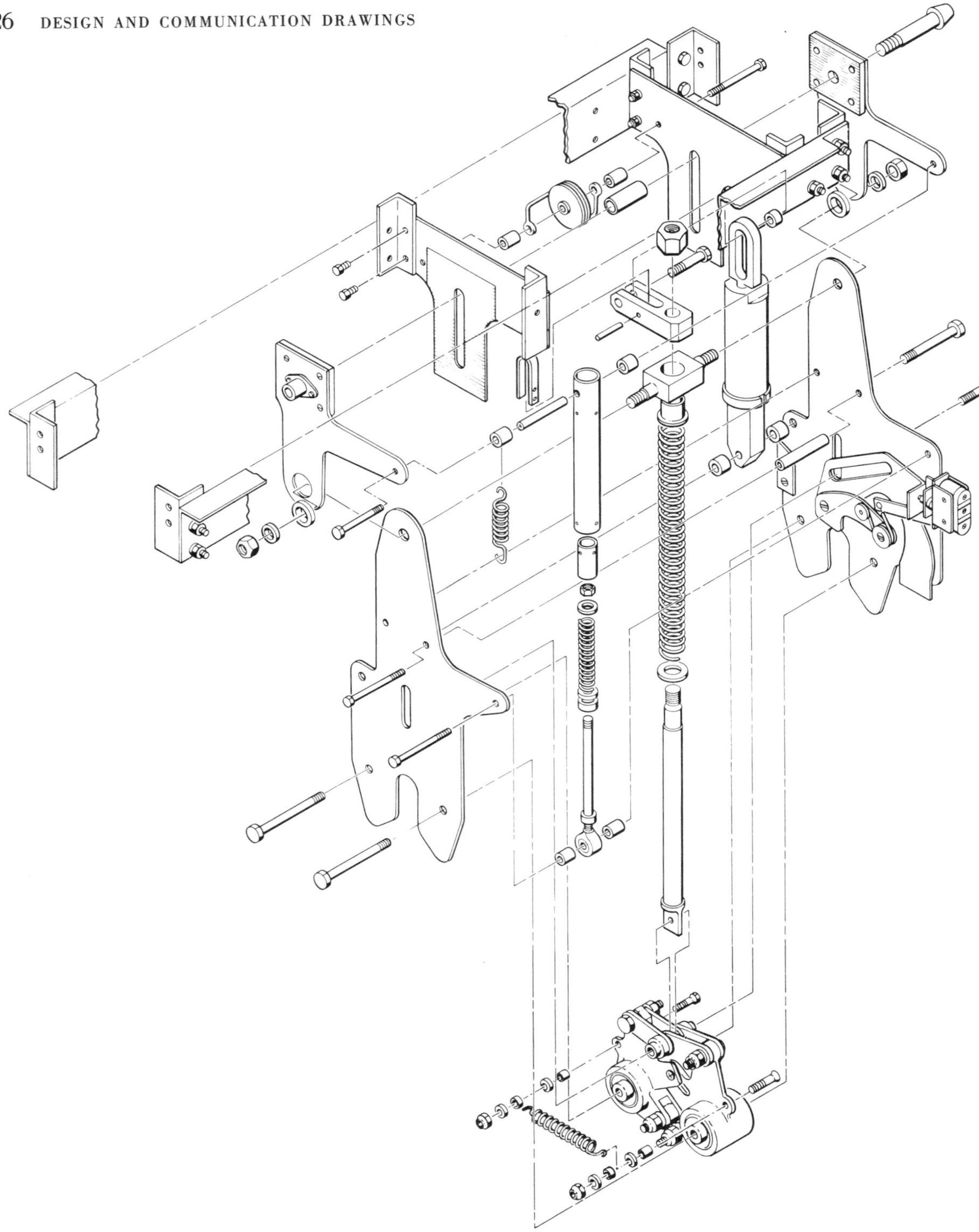

Fig. 18.13. An exploded pictorial assembly drawing (*Courtesy Lockheed Aircraft Corp.*).

18.25. Diagram assembly drawings. Diagram drawings may be grouped into two general classes: (1) those composed of single lines and conventional symbols, such as piping diagrams, wiring diagrams, and so on (Fig. 18.14), and (2) those drawn in regular projection, such as an erection drawing, which may be shown in either orthographic or pictorial projection.

Piping diagrams give the size of pipe, location of fittings, and so on. To draw an assembly of a piping system in true orthographic projection would add no information and merely entail needless work.

A large portion of electrical drawing is composed of diagrammatic sketches using conventional electrical symbols. Electrical engineers therefore need to know the American Standard wiring symbols given in the Appendix.

C: CHEMICAL ENGINEERING DRAWINGS

18.26. Chemical engineering drawings. In general, the chemical engineer is concerned with plant layouts and equipment design. He must be well informed on the types of machinery used in grinding, drying, mixing, evaporation, sedimentation, and distillation, and must be able to design or select conveying machinery.

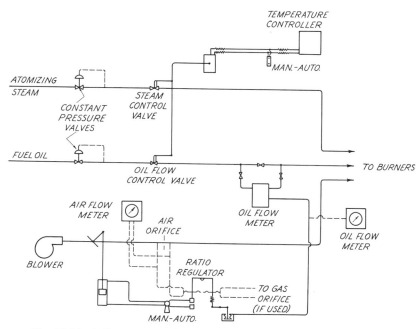

Fig. 18.14. A diagram assembly drawing (*Courtesy "Instruments Magazine"*).

It is obvious that the determining of the sequence of operations, selecting of machinery, arranging of piping, and so on, must be done by a trained chemical engineer who can speak the basic language of the mechanical, electrical, or civil engineer with whom he must cooperate. To be able to do this, he must have a thorough knowledge of the principles of engineering drawing.

Plant layout drawings, the satisfactory development of which requires numerous preliminary sketches (layouts, scale diagram, flow sheets, and so on), show the location of machines, equipment, and the like. Often, if the machinery and apparatus are used in the manufacturing of chemicals and are of a specialized nature, a chemical engineer is called upon to do the designing. It even may be necessary for him to build experimental apparatus.

D: ELECTRICAL ENGINEERING DRAWINGS

18.27. Electrical engineering drawings. Electrical engineering drawings are of two types, machine drawings and diagrammatic assemblies (Fig. 18.15). Working drawings, which are made for electrical machinery, involve all of the principles and conventions of the working drawings of the mechanical engineer. Diagrammatic drawings have been discussed in Sec. 18.25.

E: PLANT LAYOUT DRAWINGS

18.28. Floor-plan drawings. An engineer usually is not an architect nor is an architect usually an engineer; therefore, when a new factory is to be built or an addition is to be added to an existing one, both architect and engineer are needed and both must cooperate in the design. In this partnership it becomes the job of the engineer to prepare the floor plans so that the highest possible production efficiency can be obtained. He must study carefully the necessary steps of production and then decide upon the locations for the offices, supply rooms, storage rooms, shops, and finally the production machines. The design becomes a recorded study of the flow of materials and parts through the plant. Frequently it may be necessary to show a conveyor system or a piping system on the plan. In the case of small plants, circumstances may be such that the engineer must assume full responsibility for the design of the entire building.

F: CIVIL ENGINEERING DRAWINGS

18.29. Civil engineering drawings. The civil engineer is concerned with a broad field of construction and with civic planning.

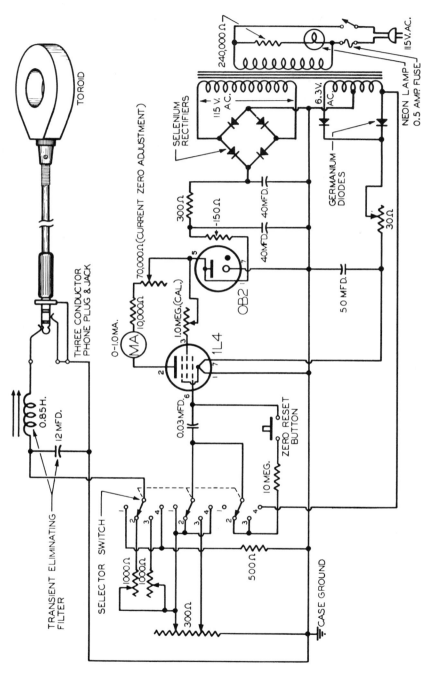

Fig. 18.15. A schematic diagram (*Courtesy General Motors Corp.*).

The drawings prepared by civil engineers may be in the nature of maps for city, state, and nationwide planning for streets, water systems, sewerage systems, airports, highways, railroads, harbor and waterways or they may be design, fabrication, and erection drawings for concrete and steel structures as in the case of buildings and bridges.

18.30. Engineering maps. * A map is a drawing that represents a portion of the earth's surface area. Since it usually represents a relatively small part, and the third dimension (the height) is not shown except in some cases by contour lines, a map may be thought of as a one-view orthographic projection. Various forms of maps have been devised to satisfy different requirements. Land maps, plats, and so on, which fulfill their purpose by revealing only the natural and man-made features along with imaginary division lines and geometric measurements, show only two dimensions. Others, such as topographical maps, show three dimensions, by representing height by means of contours (Fig. 18.16).

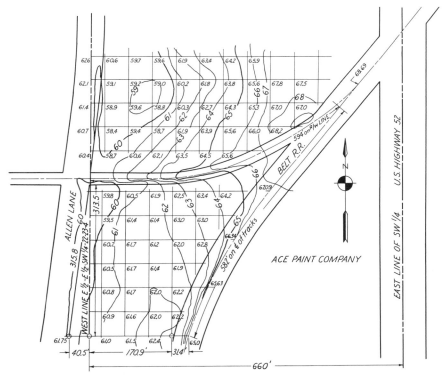

Fig. 18.16. A contour map of a small area.

* Additional information covering engineering maps may be obtained from the author's text, *Fundamentals of Engineering Drawing*, 4th ed., Englewood Cliffs, N. J.: Prentice-Hall, Inc. (1959).

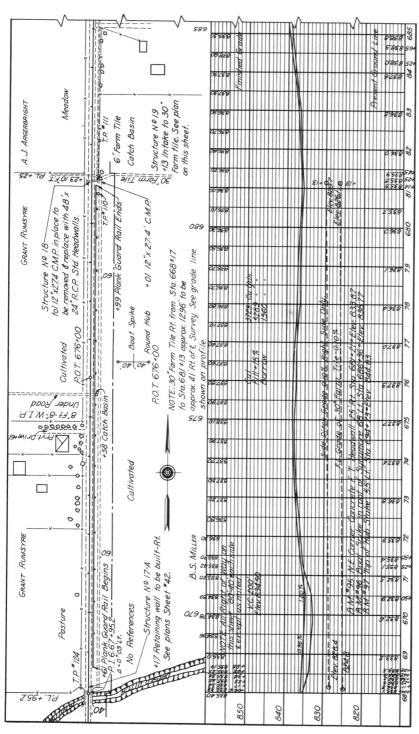

Fig. 18.17. A plan and profile sheet of a proposed highway project.

Working maps prepared for engineering projects are known as *engineering maps*. They may be drawn for either reconnaissance or construction purposes (Fig. 18.17). They usually are made to a large scale and accurately show the location of all property lines and important features. On maps of a topographic nature, practically all natural and man-made features along a right-of-way or on a site are shown, and the form of the surface of the ground is indicated by means of contours.

18.31. Classes of structural drawings.* Most of the large steel fabricators maintain a design office and a detailing office. The former prepares design drawings and estimates costs in the preparation of bids and frequently serves in a consulting capacity on designs

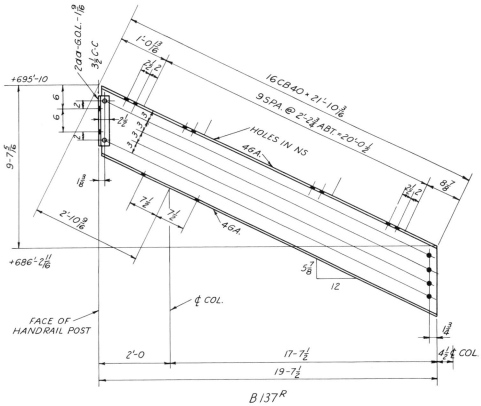

Fig. 18.18. Structural detail drawing (*Courtesy American Bridge Co.*).

* Additional information covering structural drawing may be obtained from the author's text, *Fundamentals of Engineering Drawing*, 4th ed., Englewood Cliffs, N. J.: Prentice-Hall, Inc. (1959).

furnished by a customer. The detailing office, which is usually located at the fabricating plant, orders material and prepares shop and erection plans from the design sheets.

Design drawings usually are line diagrams showing the shape of a structure, the principal dimensions, structural sections, and in some cases the stresses to be used in detailing the connections.

For the use of the layout man a set of design drawings may contain elaborate design details, showing the type of connections, thickness of gusset plates, and the number of rivets.

A set of specifications covering special conditions, unit stresses, materials to be used, and so forth, is considered as part of the design information.

Shop detail drawings show all of the information necessary for shop fabrication (Fig. 18.18).

Erection plans, which are prepared primarily for use in the field, consist of line diagrams giving dimensions, shipping marks, and notes in sufficient detail to guide the erector in assembling the parts to complete the finished structure.

PROBLEMS

The four general types of problems presented in this chapter have been designed to furnish practice in the preparation of working drawings or sketches. The first type is composed of dimensioned pictorial drawings of individual pieces taken from a variety of mechanisms. The student should prepare complete working detail drawings of these pieces as they may be assigned by his instructor. It should be recognized that dimensions are not necessarily placed the same on orthographic views as they are on pictorial drawings. In order to make it possible for the student to apply the principles presented in Chapter 17, no special effort has been made to place dimensions in accordance with the rules of good practice.

The second type of problem is that which shows in pictorial all the parts of a unit mechanism. This gives the student an opportunity to prepare a complete set of working drawings of a simple unit. It is suggested that the detail drawings be prepared before the assembly is drawn.

The third and fourth types provide practice in both reading and preparing drawings, the third requiring the preparation of detail drawings from given assembly drawings, the fourth requiring the making of assembly drawings from the details.

1-14. (Figs. 18.19–18.32.) Make a detail drawing of an assigned machine part. Draw all necessary views. Give a detail title with suitable notes concerning material, number required, etc.

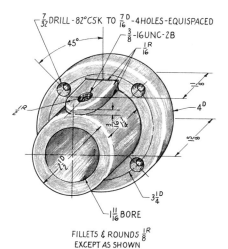

Fig. 18.19. Pipe support.

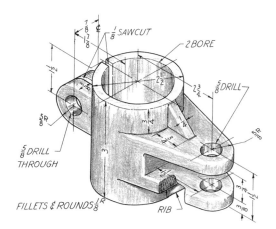

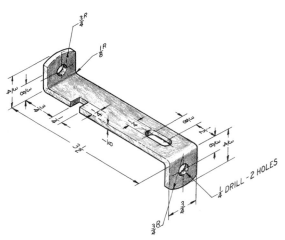

Fig. 18.20. Guide bracket.

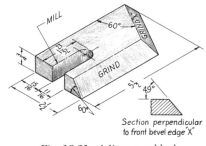

Fig. 18.21. Adjustment block.

Fig. 18.22. Bent angle.

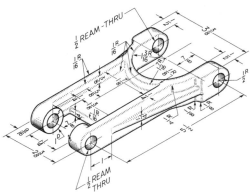

Fig. 18.23. Link.

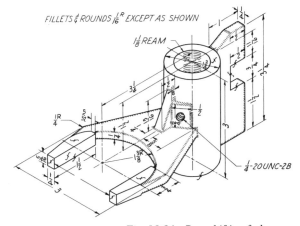

Fig. 18.24. Gear shifting fork.

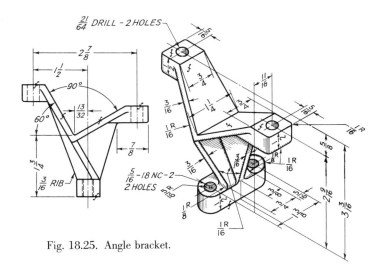

Fig. 18.25. Angle bracket.

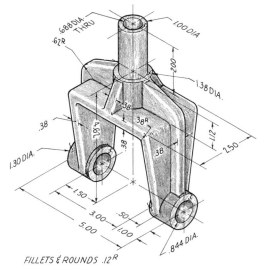

FILLETS & ROUNDS .12 R

Fig. 18.26. Caster frame.

FILLETS & ROUNDS 1/8 R

Fig. 18.27. Slide bracket.

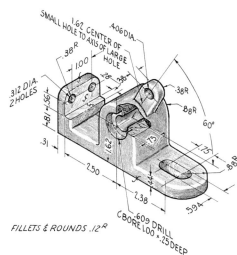

FILLETS & ROUNDS .12 R

Fig. 18.28. Stabilizer bracket.

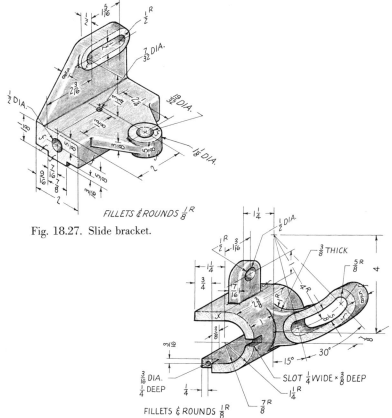

FILLETS & ROUNDS 1/8 R

Fig. 18.29. Gear-shifter link.

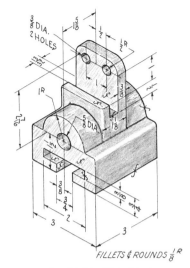

FILLETS & ROUNDS $\frac{1}{8}$ R

Fig. 18.30. Slide block.

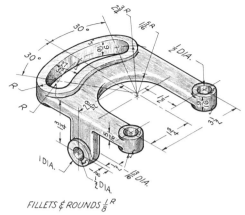

FILLETS & ROUNDS $\frac{1}{8}$ R

Fig. 18.31. Shifter arm.

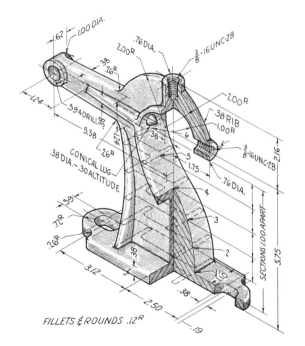

FILLETS & ROUNDS .12 R

SECTION NUMBER	A	B	C	D	E
1	1.00	2.00	3.00	1.88	1.62
2	.94	1.88	2.82	1.75	1.38
3	.62	1.82	2.44	1.62	1.12
4	0.00	1.88	1.88	1.50	.88
5	.68	2.12	1.44	1.38	.62
6	1.00	—	—	1.25	—

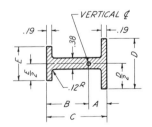

Fig. 18.32. Shaft hanger.

15. (Fig. 18.33.) Make a detail working drawing of the bracket or its mating part that clamps around the 1¾ in. shaft.

The given pictorial drawing shows the adjustment bracket assembly of a positioning mechanism on a cartridge type core blower. The bracket when attached to the vertical column supports a positioning clamp that may be tilted into different positions. The clamp screw keeps the positioning clamp in a desired position when it is tightened down against the clamp plate.

16. (Fig. 18.34.) Make a two-view freehand detail sketch of the fan spindle. Determine dimensions by transferring them from the drawing to the open-divided scale, by means of the dividers. The material is SAE 1045, CRS. Shaft limits for the bearings are

$$\frac{.7874}{.7867} \text{ and } \frac{.9840}{.9836}.$$

Use an RC7 fit between spindle and felt retainer, spindle and felt-retaining washer, spindle and cone-clamp washer.

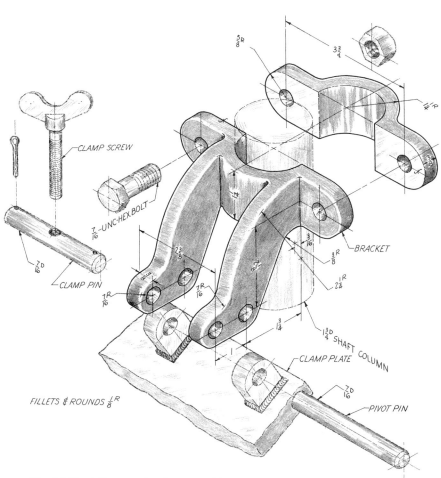

Fig. 18.33. Adjustment bracket—core blower.

17. (Fig. 18.34.) Make a complete two-view detail drawing of the fan pulley. It is suggested that a half-circular view and a full-sectional view be shown. Determine the dimensions as suggested in Problem 16. Housing limits for the given bearings are

$$\frac{1.8497}{1.8503} \text{ and } \frac{2.4401}{2.4409}.$$

18. (Fig. 18.35.) Make a detail drawing of an assigned part of the motorcycle clutch. Determine the dimensions by transferring them from the drawing to the accompanying scale, by means of the dividers. Compose a suitable detail title.

19. (Fig. 18.36.) Make a detail drawing of an assigned part of the tool holder.

20. (Fig. 18.37.) Make a detail drawing of an assigned part of the Simplex ball-bearing screw jack.

21. (Fig. 18.38.) Make a detail drawing of an assigned part of the roller-bearing stud unit.

22. (Fig. 18.39.) Make a detail drawing of an assigned part of the boring fixture.

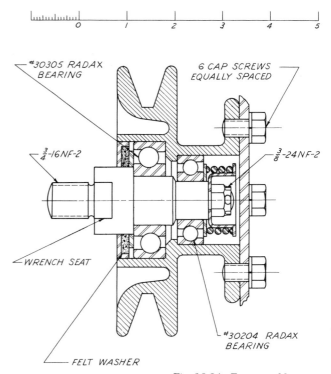

Fig. 18.34. Fan assembly.

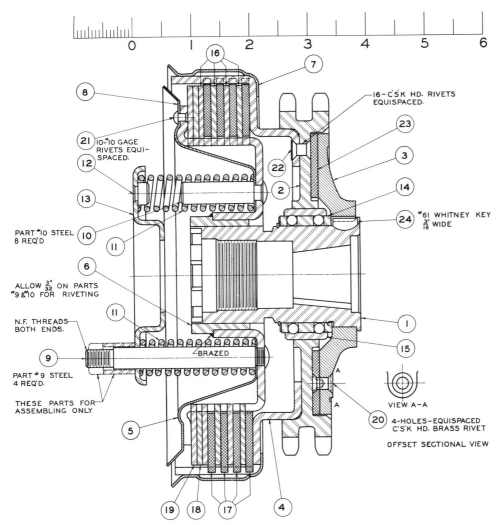

Fig. 18.35. Motorcycle clutch assembly (*Courtesy Harley-Davidson Motor Co.*).

23. (Fig. 18.40.) Make a detail drawing of an assigned part of the conveyor take-up unit.

24. (Fig. 18.41.) Make a detail drawing of an assigned part of the handle.

25. (Fig. 18.42.) Make a detail drawing of an assigned part of the gear pump.

26. (Fig. 18.43.) Make a detail drawing of an assigned part of the bench arbor press.

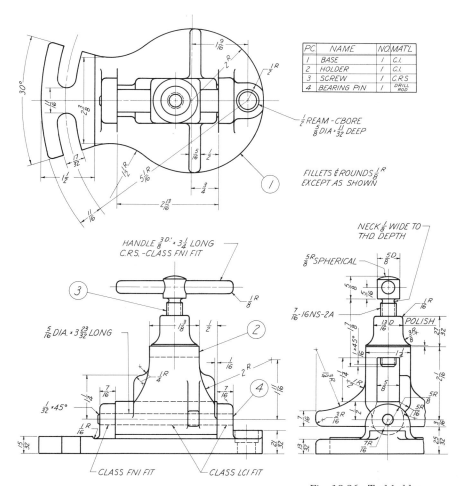

PC	NAME	NO.	MAT'L
1	BASE	1	C.I.
2	HOLDER	1	C.I.
3	SCREW	1	C.R.S
4	BEARING PIN	1	DRILL ROD

Fig. 18.36. Tool holder.

27. (Fig. 18.44.) Make a detail drawing of an assigned part of the compensating collet chuck.

28. (Fig. 18.45.) Make a detail working drawing of an assigned part of the bench grinder.

29. (Fig. 18.46.) Make a complete set of working drawings of the flexible coupling. The complete set should include detail drawings of the individual parts and an assembly drawing complete with bill of material.

PC.NO.	NAME	QUAN.	MATERIAL	PC.NO.	NAME	QUAN.	MATERIAL
1	STANDARD	1	MALL. IRON	5	GROOVE PIN	3	$\frac{7}{32}D \times \frac{5}{8}$ STEEL ROD
2	SCREW	1	S.A.E.1120 FORGING	6	LEVER BAR	1	REROLLED RAIL STK.
3	CAP	1	S.A.E.1045 FORGING	7	$\frac{7}{8}$ DIA. BALL BEARING	1	STD.
4	THRUST WASHER	1	S.A.E. 2315				

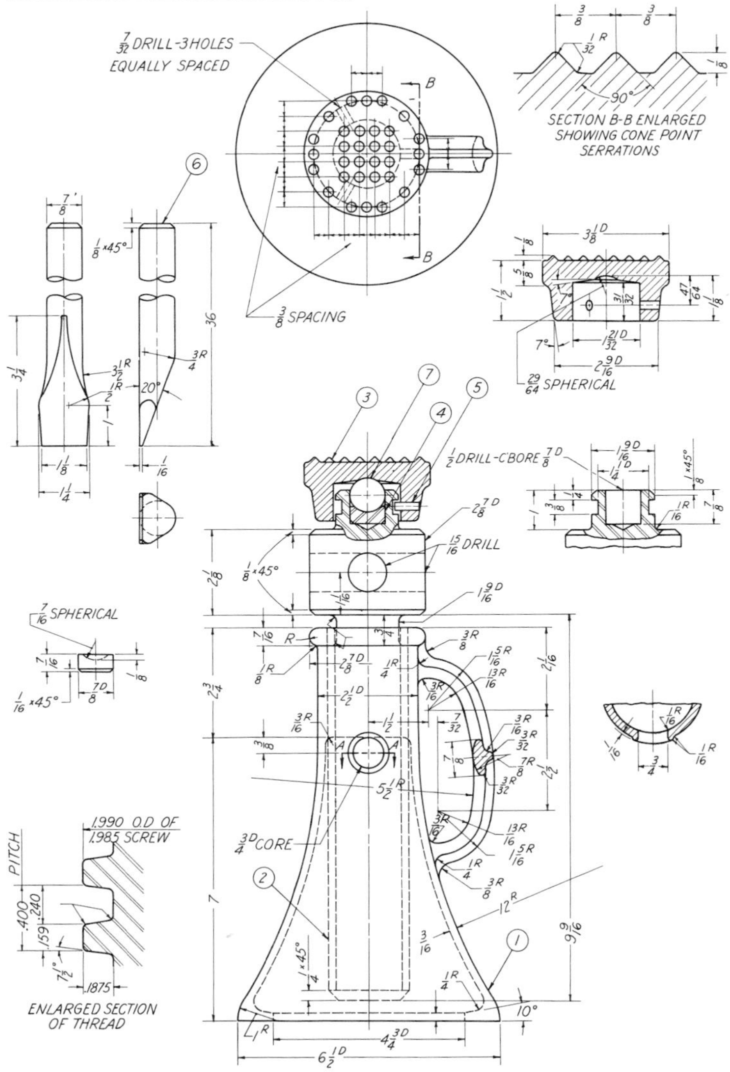

Fig. 18.37. Simplex ball-bearing screw jack (*Courtesy Templeton, Kenly & Co.*).

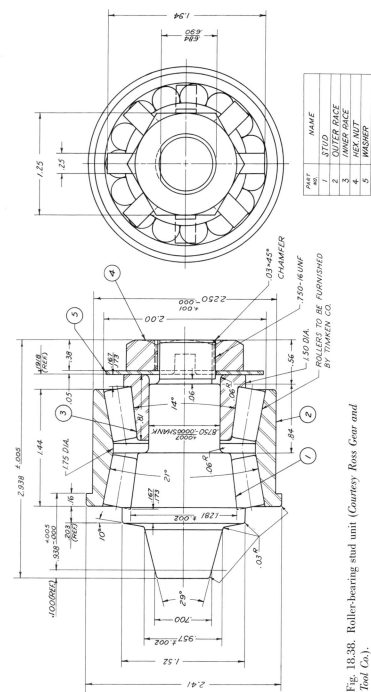

PART NO.	NAME
1	STUD
2	OUTER RACE
3	INNER RACE
4	HEX. NUT
5	WASHER

Fig. 18.38. Roller-bearing stud unit (*Courtesy Ross Gear and Tool Co.*).

PART NO.	NAME	MATERIAL	NO. REQ'D
1	HOLDER	C.R.S.	1
2	CLAMP STRAP	C.R.S.	1
3	CLAMP	C.R.S.	1
4	CLAMP SCREW	C.R.S.	1
5	PLUG	BRASS	1
6	THUMB SCREW	C.R.S.	1
7	REST BUTTON	TOOL STEEL	2
8	BUSHING	TOOL STEEL	1
9	PIN	DRILL ROD	1

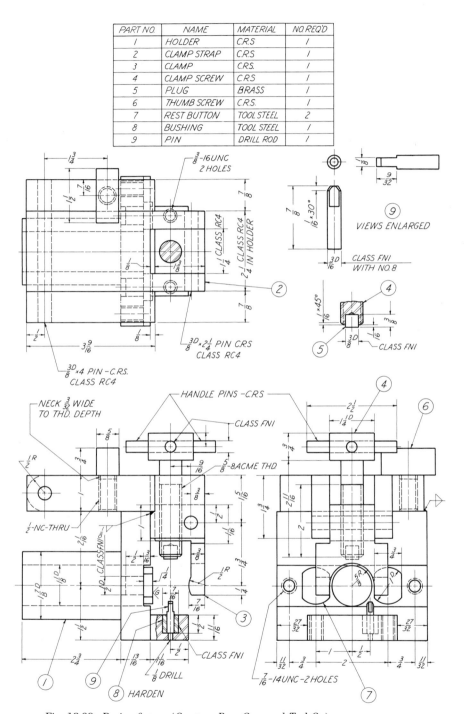

Fig. 18.39. Boring fixture (*Courtesy Ross Gear and Tool Co.*).

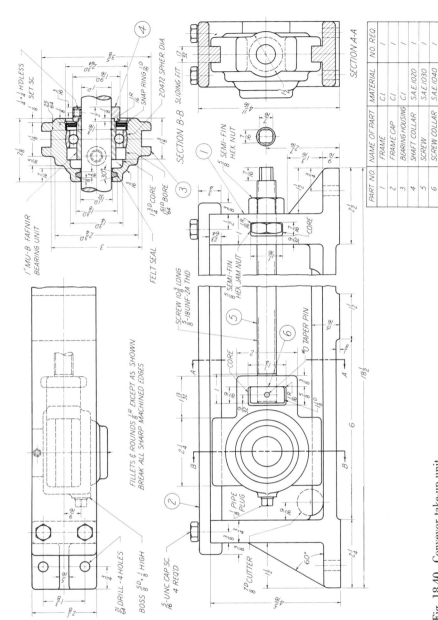

Fig. 18.40. Conveyor take-up unit.

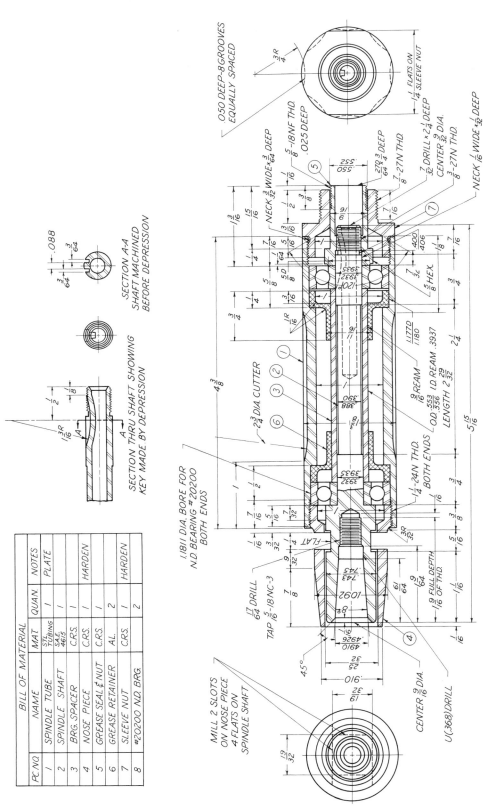

Fig. 18.41. Handle (*Courtesy R. C. Haskins Co.*).

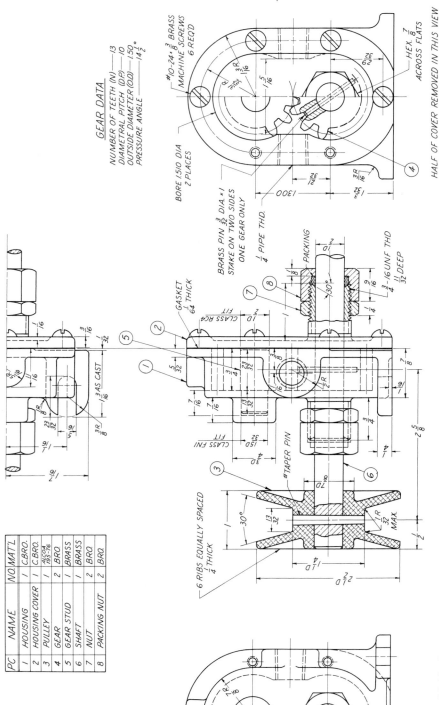

Fig. 18.42. Gear pump.

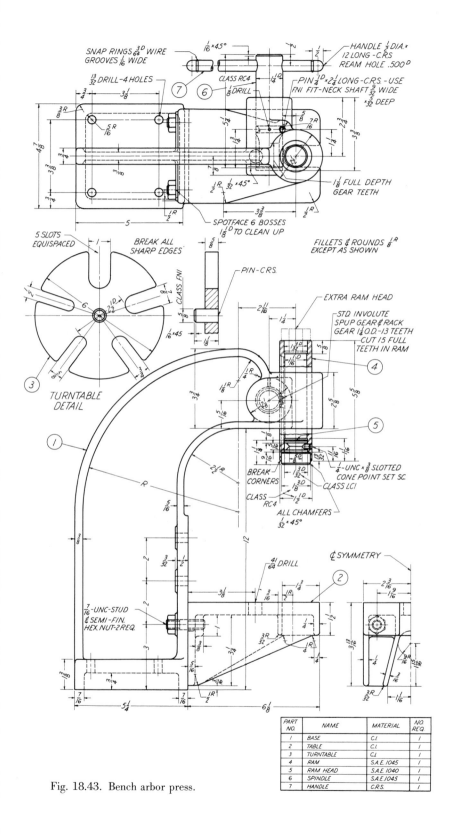

Fig. 18.43. Bench arbor press.

PART NO.	NAME	MATERIAL	NO. REQ.
1	BASE	C.I.	1
2	TABLE	C.I.	1
3	TURNTABLE	C.I.	1
4	RAM	S.A.E. 1045	1
5	RAM HEAD	S.A.E. 1040	1
6	SPINDLE	S.A.E. 1045	1
7	HANDLE	C.R.S.	1

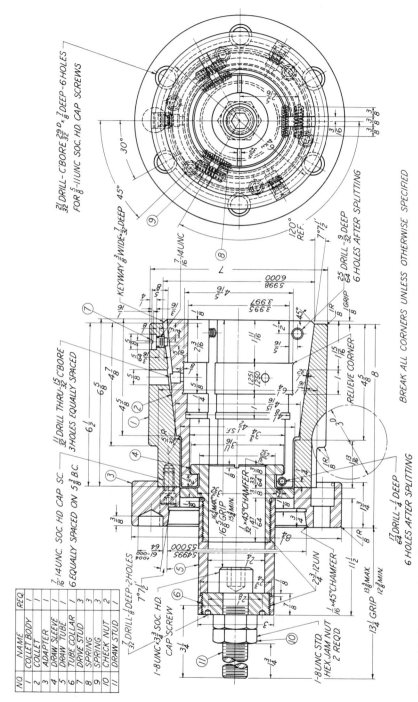

Fig. 18.44. Compensating collet chuck (*Courtesy Logansport Machine Co.*).

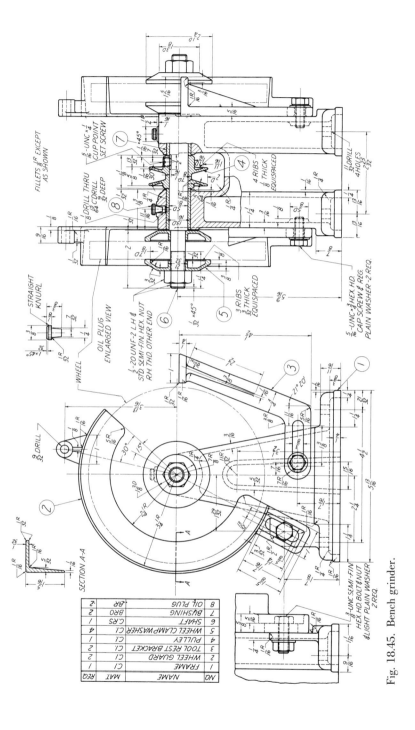

Fig. 18.45. Bench grinder.

NO	NAME	MAT	REQ
8	OIL PLUG	BR	2
7	BUSHING	BRO	2
6	SHAFT	C.R.S.	1
5	WHEEL CLAMP WASHER	C.I.	4
4	PULLEY	C.I.	1
3	TOOL REST BRACKET	C.I.	2
2	WHEEL GUARD	C.I.	1
1	FRAME	C.I.	1

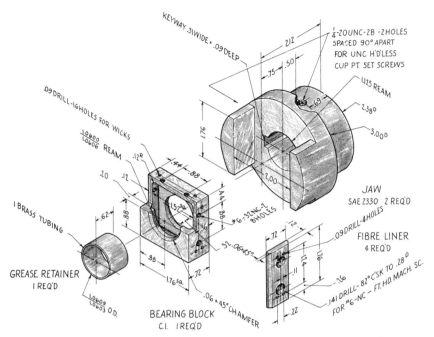

Fig. 18.46. Flexible coupling.

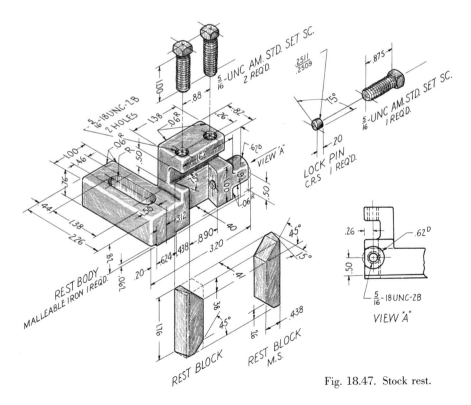

Fig. 18.47. Stock rest.

30. (Fig. 18.47.) Make detail drawings of the rest body and the rest block. Make an assembly drawing showing the parts of the stock rest assembled in their relative positions.

31. (Fig. 18.48.) Make detail drawings of the carrier and the holder. Make an assembly drawing showing all of the parts in their relative positions.

32. (Fig. 18.49.) Make a complete set of working drawings of the adjustable attachment. The complete set should consist of detail drawings of the individual parts and an assembly drawing complete with a bill of material.

33. (Fig. 18.50.) Make a complete set of working drawings of the vise. The complete set of drawings should be composed of detail drawings of the parts (except standard parts) and an assembly drawing.

34. (Fig. 18.51.) Make a complete set of working drawings of the tumble jig. The complete set should consist of detail drawings of the individual parts (except standard parts) and an assembly drawing complete with a bill of material.

35. (Figs. 18.52 and 18.53.) Make an assembly drawing of the idler pulley, using the given details. Use the schematic symbol for screw threads.

36. (Fig. 18.54.) Make a two-view assembly drawing of the cup center using the given details. Use the schematic symbol for screw threads. Study the pictorial drawing carefully before starting the views.

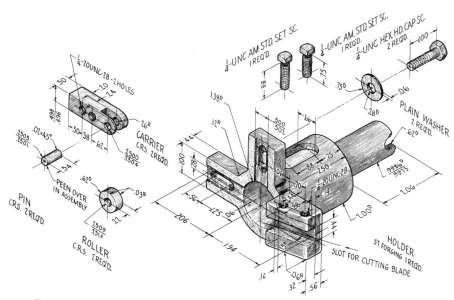

Fig. 18.48. Tool holder.

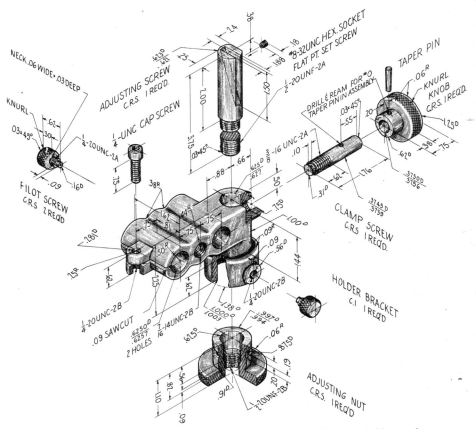

Fig. 18.49. Adjustable attachment.

37. (Fig. 18.55.) Make an assembly drawing of the radial engine unit, using the given details. It is suggested that one piston be shown in full section so that the relative positions of the parts will be revealed.

38. (Figs. 18.56, 18.57, and 18.58.) Make detail drawings and an assembly drawing of the speed reducer.

39. (Figs. 18.59, 18.60, and 18.61.) Make an assembly drawing of the hand clamp, vise, using the given details. Use the schematic symbol for screw threads.

40. (Figs. 18.62, 18.63, and 18.64.) Make an assembly drawing of the blow gun.

41. (Figs. 18.65, 18.66, and 18.67.) Make an assembly drawing of the hand grinder.

42. (Figs. 18.68, 18.69, and 18.70.) Make an assembly drawing of the right-angle head using the given details.

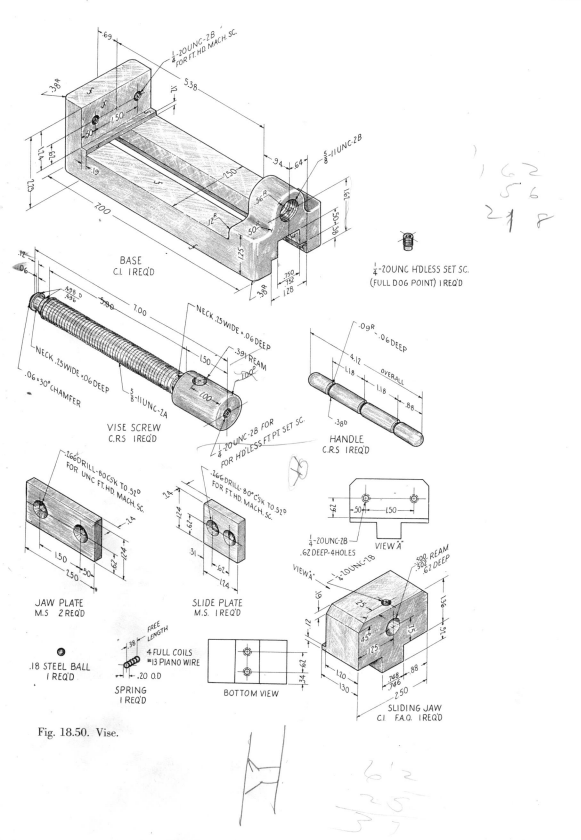

Fig. 18.50. Vise.

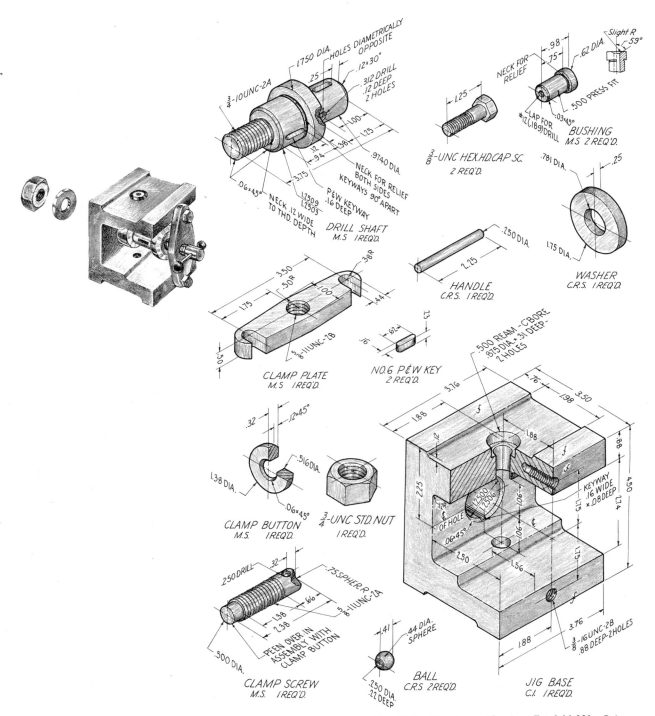

Fig. 18.51. Tumble jig (*Courtesy Fairfield Mfg. Co.*).

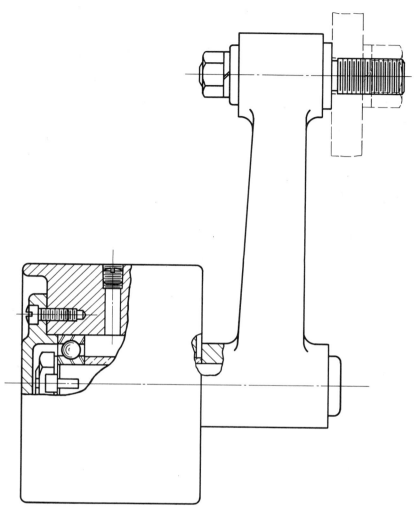

Fig. 18.52. Idler pulley.

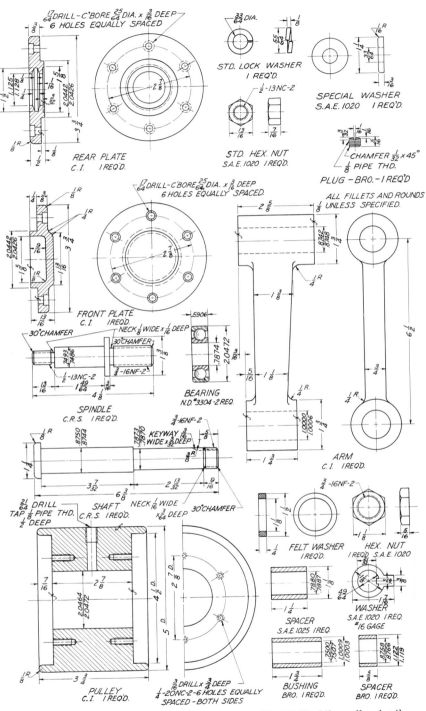

Fig. 18.53. Idler pulley details.

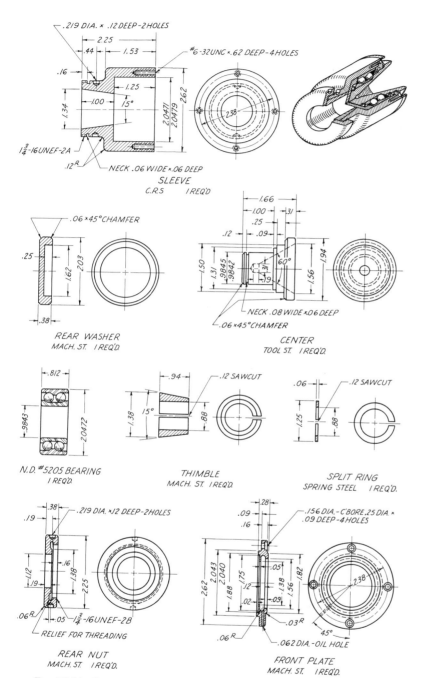

.219 DIA. × .12 DEEP-2HOLES

2.25

.44 1.53

#6-32UNC×.62 DEEP-4HOLES

.16

1.25

1.34

1.00   15°

2.0471
2.0479
262

2.38

1¾-16UNEF-2A

.12R

NECK .06 WIDE×.06 DEEP

SLEEVE
C.R.S   1 REQ'D

.06×45°CHAMFER

.25

.62
.203

.38

REAR WASHER
MACH. ST. 1 REQ'D.

1.66

1.00   .31

.25

.12   .09

1.50

1.31

.9845
.9842

.31

.19

60°

1.94

1.56

NECK .08 WIDE×.06 DEEP

.06×45°CHAMFER

CENTER
TOOL ST. 1 REQ'D.

.812

.9843

2.0472

N.D. #5205 BEARING
1 REQ'D.

.94   .12 SAWCUT

1.38   15°

.88

THIMBLE
MACH. ST. 1 REQ'D.

.06   .12 SAWCUT

1.25

.88

SPLIT RING
SPRING STEEL   1 REQ'D.

.38   .219 DIA. ×.12 DEEP-2HOLES

.19

.112

.16

.19

1.38

2.25

.06R

.05   1¾-16UNEF-2B

RELIEF FOR THREADING

REAR NUT
MACH. ST. 1 REQ'D.

.28

.09

.16

.156 DIA.-C'BORE.25 DIA.×
.09 DEEP-4HOLES

2.262
2.043
2.040

.175

.188

.12

.02

.05

1.38

.09

1.56

1.82

2.38

.06R

.03R

45°

.062 DIA.-OIL HOLE

FRONT PLATE
MACH. ST.   1 REQ'D.

Fig. 18.54. Cup center details.

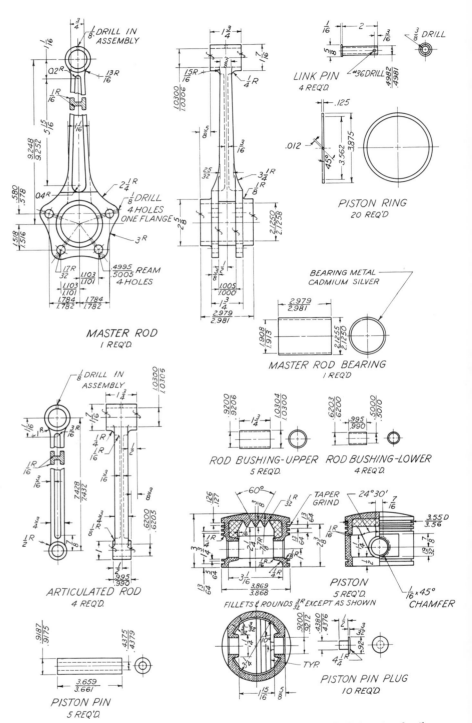

Fig. 18.55. Radial engine details.

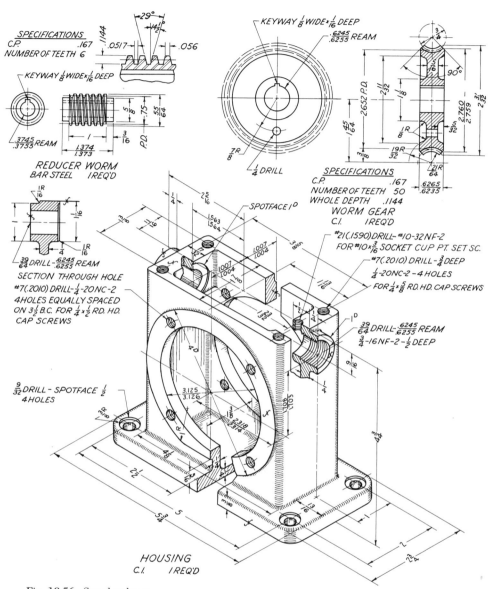

SPECIFICATIONS
C.P. .167
NUMBER OF TEETH 6

KEYWAY ⅛ WIDE × 1/16 DEEP

REDUCER WORM
BAR STEEL 1 REQ'D

KEYWAY ⅛ WIDE × 1/16 DEEP
.6245/.6255 REAM

SPECIFICATIONS
C.P. .167
NUMBER OF TEETH 50
WHOLE DEPTH .1144

WORM GEAR
C.I. 1 REQ'D

¼ DRILL

SECTION THROUGH HOLE

#7(.2010) DRILL-¼-20NC-2
4 HOLES EQUALLY SPACED
ON 3½ B.C. FOR ¼ × ½ RD. HD.
CAP SCREWS

9/32 DRILL - SPOTFACE ½
4 HOLES

SPOTFACE 1

#21(.1590) DRILL-#10-32NF-2
FOR #10 × 3/16 SOCKET CUP PT. SET SC.

#7(.2010) DRILL-¾ DEEP
¼-20NC-2 - 4 HOLES
FOR ¼ × 5/8 RD. HD. CAP SCREWS

39/64 DRILL-.6245/.6255 REAM
¾-16NF-2-½ DEEP

HOUSING
C.I. 1 REQ'D

Fig. 18.56. Speed reducer.

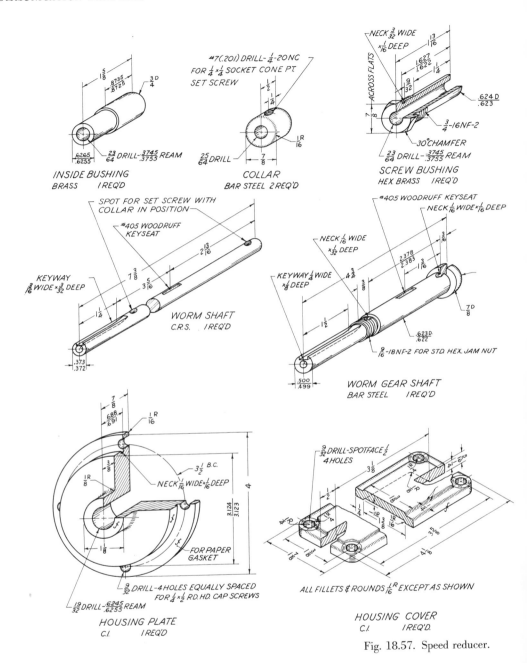

INSIDE BUSHING
BRASS   1 REQ'D

COLLAR
BAR STEEL 2 REQ'D

SCREW BUSHING
HEX. BRASS   1 REQ'D

WORM SHAFT
C.R.S.   1 REQ'D

WORM GEAR SHAFT
BAR STEEL   1 REQ'D

HOUSING PLATE
C.I.   1 REQ'D

HOUSING COVER
C.I.   1 REQ'D.

Fig. 18.57. Speed reducer.

Fig. 18.58. Speed reducer.

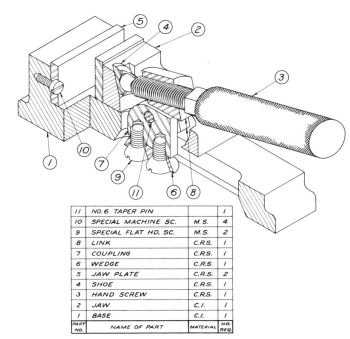

11	NO. 6 TAPER PIN		1
10	SPECIAL MACHINE SC.	M.S.	4
9	SPECIAL FLAT HD. SC.	M.S.	2
8	LINK	C.R.S.	1
7	COUPLING	C.R.S.	1
6	WEDGE	C.R.S.	1
5	JAW PLATE	C.R.S.	2
4	SHOE	C.R.S.	1
3	HAND SCREW	C.R.S.	1
2	JAW	C.I.	1
1	BASE	C.I.	1
PART NO.	NAME OF PART	MATERIAL	NO. REQ.

Fig. 18.59. Hand clamp vise.

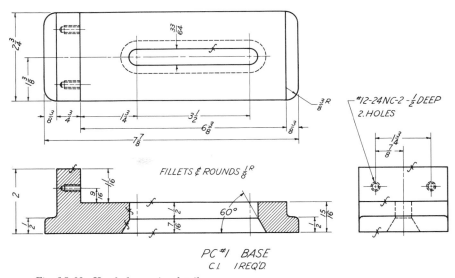

FILLETS & ROUNDS $\frac{1}{8}$ R

#12-24NC-2 - $\frac{1}{2}$ DEEP
2. HOLES

PC #1 BASE
C.I. 1 REQ'D.

Fig. 18.60. Hand clamp vise details.

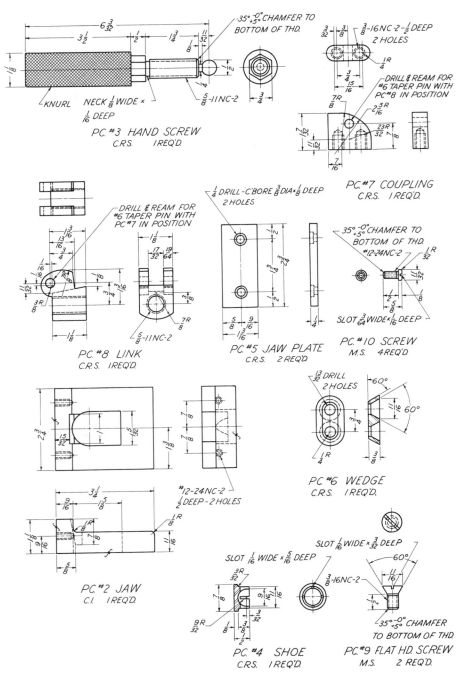

Fig. 18.61. Hand clamp vise details.

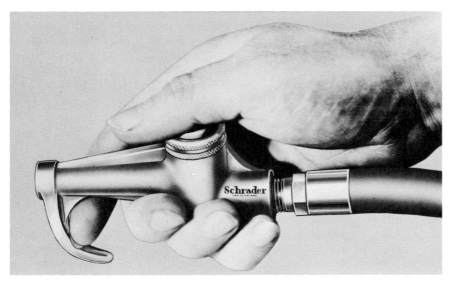

Fig. 18.62. Blow gun (*Courtesy A. Schrader's Son Mfg. Co.*).

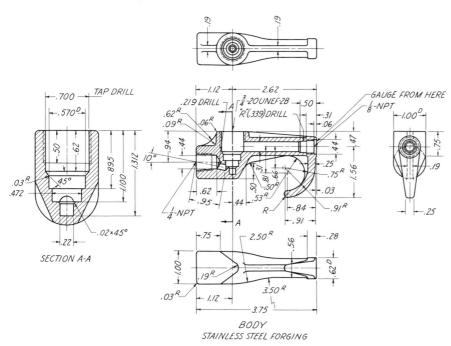

Fig. 18.63. Blow gun details.

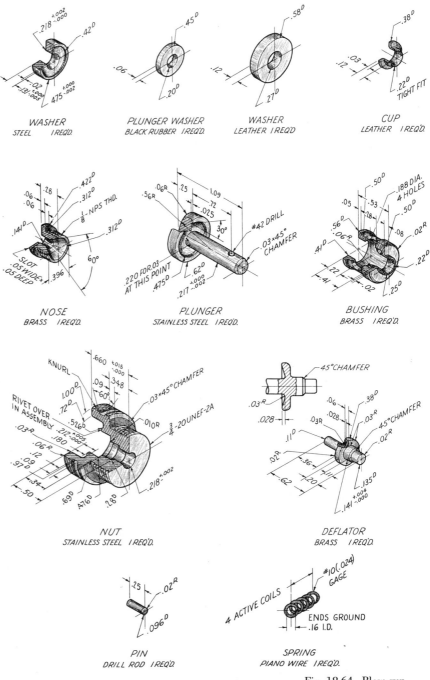

WASHER
STEEL   1 REQ'D.

PLUNGER WASHER
BLACK RUBBER 1 REQ'D.

WASHER
LEATHER 1 REQ'D

CUP
LEATHER 1 REQ'D.

NOSE
BRASS 1 REQ'D.

PLUNGER
STAINLESS STEEL 1 REQ'D.

BUSHING
BRASS 1 REQ'D.

NUT
STAINLESS STEEL 1 REQ'D.

DEFLATOR
BRASS   1 REQ'D.

PIN
DRILL ROD 1 REQ'D.

SPRING
PIANO WIRE 1 REQ'D.

Fig. 18.64. Blow gun.

Fig. 18.65. Hand grinder.

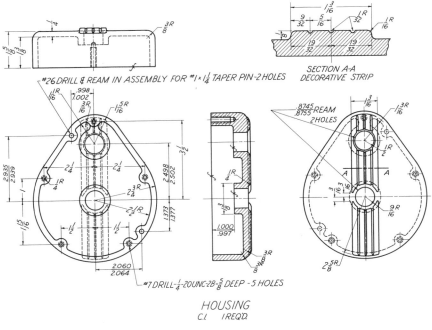

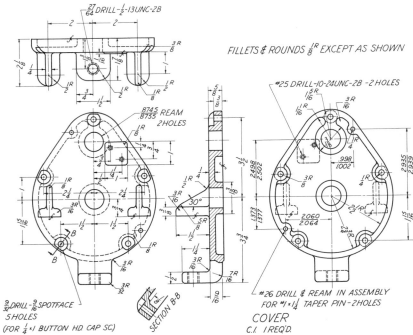

Fig. 18.66. Hand grinder details.

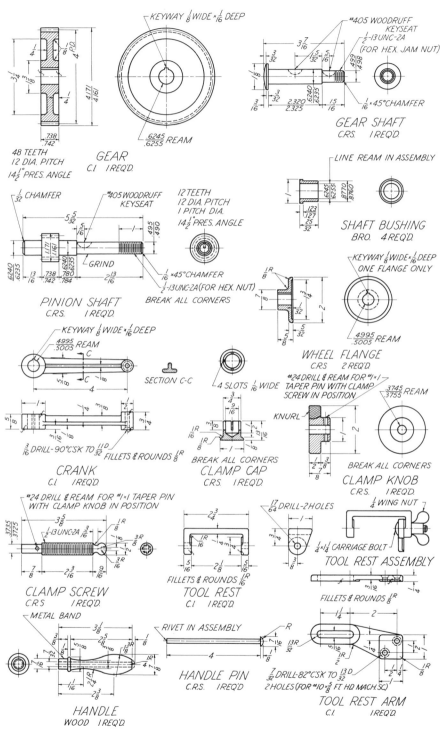

Fig. 18.67. Hand grinder details.

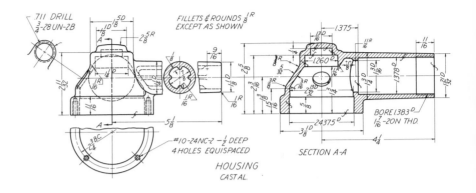

HOUSING
CAST AL.

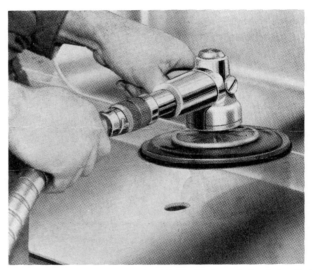

Fig. 18.68. Right-angle head details (*Courtesy R. C. Haskins Co.*).

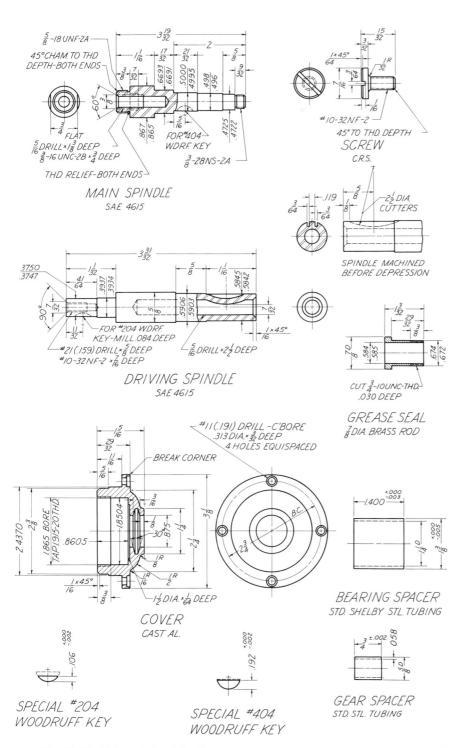

$\frac{5}{8}$-18 UNF-2A

45° CHAM. TO THD
DEPTH-BOTH ENDS

$\frac{3}{4}$ FLAT

$\frac{5}{16}$ DRILL $\times 1\frac{3}{8}$ DEEP
$\frac{3}{8}$-16 UNC-2B $\times \frac{3}{4}$ DEEP

THD. RELIEF-BOTH ENDS

FOR #404
WDRF. KEY

$\frac{3}{8}$-28NS-2A

MAIN SPINDLE
SAE 4615

#10-32NF-2
45° TO THD. DEPTH
SCREW
C.R.S.

$2\frac{1}{2}$ DIA.
CUTTERS

SPINDLE MACHINED
BEFORE DEPRESSION

FOR #204 WDRF.
KEY-MILL .084 DEEP

#21 (.159) DRILL $\times \frac{5}{8}$ DEEP
#10-32NF-2 $\times \frac{7}{16}$ DEEP

$\frac{5}{16}$ DRILL $\times 2\frac{1}{2}$ DEEP

DRIVING SPINDLE
SAE 4615

CUT $\frac{3}{4}$-10UNC-THD.
.030 DEEP

GREASE SEAL
$\frac{7}{8}$ DIA. BRASS ROD

#11 (.191) DRILL -C'BORE
.313 DIA. $\times \frac{3}{32}$ DEEP
4 HOLES EQUISPACED

BREAK CORNER

1.8504
1.8605
1.865 BORE
TAP 1.95-20 THD.

B.C.

1×45°

$1\frac{1}{2}$ DIA. $\times \frac{1}{64}$ DEEP

COVER
CAST AL.

$\frac{1.400}{\substack{+.000 \\ -.003}}$

BEARING SPACER
STD. SHELBY STL. TUBING

**SPECIAL #204
WOODRUFF KEY**

**SPECIAL #404
WOODRUFF KEY**

GEAR SPACER
STD. STL. TUBING

Fig. 18.69. Right-angle head details.

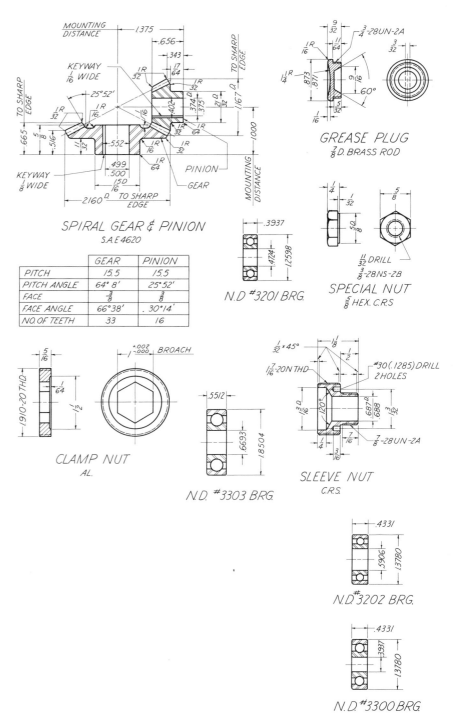

Fig. 18.70. Right-angle head details.

19

ENGINEERING GRAPHS AND CHARTS

19.1. Introduction. A properly designed graphical representation will convey correlated data and facts to an average individual more rapidly and effectively than a verbal, written, or tabulated description, because a visual impression is easily comprehended and requires less mental effort than would be necessary to ascertain the facts from complex tables and reports (Figs. 19.1 and 19.22). It is because of this that diverse kinds of graphs and charts have been developed to present scientific, statistical, and technical information. Note how quickly the relationship presented by the line graph in Fig. 19.2 can be interpreted.

Engineers, even though they are concerned mainly with technical graphs, should be familiar also with the popular forms, for every industrial concern frequently must prepare popular types of graphs in order to strengthen their relationship with the public.

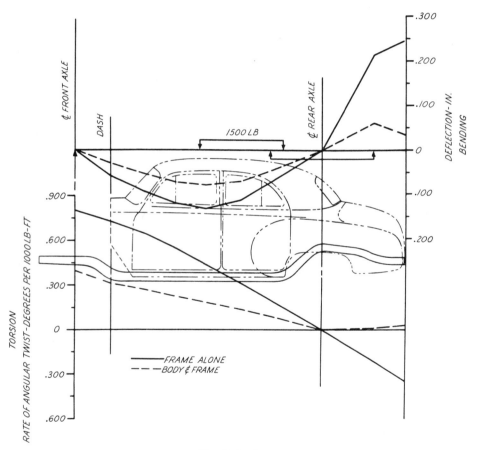

Fig. 19.1. An engineering graph* (*Courtesy General Motors Corp.*).

* Reprinted from the General Motors Engineering Journal with permission.

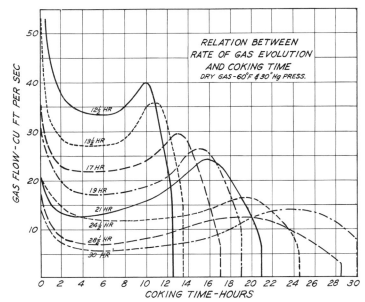

Fig. 19.2. An engineering graph prepared for publication (*Courtesy Blast Furnace and Steel Plant Magazine*).

It is impossible to treat exhaustively the subject of graphical representation in a single chapter. Only a few of the most common forms used to analyze economic, scientific, and technical data can be discussed in detail. Many of the principles followed in the construction of engineering graphs, however, apply to the other types.

As much drafting skill is required in the execution of a graph as in making any other type of technical drawing. Good appearance is important and can be achieved only with the help of good lettering and smooth, uniform, and properly contrasted lines.

19.2. Classification of charts, graphs, and diagrams. Graphs, charts, and diagrams may be divided into two classes in accordance with their use, and then further subdivided according to type. When classified according to use, the two divisions are, first, those used for strictly scientific and technical purposes and, second, those used for the purpose of popular appeal. The classification according to type is as follows:

1. Rectilinear charts
2. Semilogarithmic charts
3. Logarithmic charts
4. Barographs, area, and volume charts

5. Percentage charts
6. Polar charts
7. Trilinear charts
8. Alignment charts (nomographs)
9. Pictorial charts

19.3. Quantitative and qualitative charts and graphs. In general, charts and diagrams are used for one of two purposes, either to read values or to present a comparative picture relationship between variables. If a chart or graph is prepared for reading values, it is called a *quantitative* graph; if prepared for presenting a comparative relationship, it is called *qualitative*. Obviously, some charts serve both purposes and cannot be classified strictly as either type. One of these purposes, however, must be predominant. Since a number of features in the preparation depend upon the predominant purpose, such purpose must be determined before attempting to construct a graph.

19.4. Ordinary rectangular coordinate graphs. Most engineering graphs, prepared for laboratory and office use, are drawn on ruled, rectangular graph paper and are plotted in the first quadrant (upper right-hand), with the intersection of the X (horizontal) axis and Y (vertical) axis at the lower left used as the zero point or origin of coordinates. The paper is ruled with equispaced horizontal and vertical lines, forming small rectangles. The type most commonly used for chart work in experimental engineering is 8½″ × 11″ and is ruled to form one-twentieth-inch squares [Fig. 19.3(a)], every fifth line being heavy. Another type of paper frequently used, which is suitable for most laboratory reports in technical schools, has rulings that form one-millimeter and one-centimeter squares [Fig. 19.3(b)]. Other rulings run ¹⁄₁₀ in., ⅛ in., or ¼ in. apart. Ordinarily the ruled lines are spaced well apart on charts prepared for

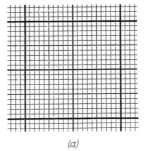

(a)

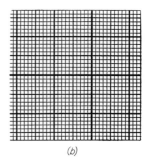

(b)

Fig. 19.3. Types of graph paper.

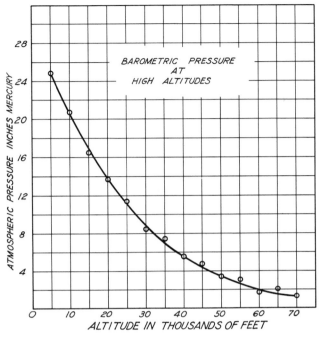

Fig. 19.4. Rectangular graph.

reproduction in popular and technical literature (Fig. 19.2). The principal advantage of having greater spacing between the lines is that large squares or rectangles tend to make the graph easier to read. Ready printed graph papers are available with various rulings in several colors.

Ordinary coordinate line graphs are used extensively because they are easily constructed and easily read. The known relationship between the variables is expressed by one or more continuous lines, which may be straight, broken, or curved.

The graph in Fig. 19.4 shows the approximate barometric pressure at different heights above sea level.

A graphical representation may be drawn easily and correctly if, after the required data have been assembled, careful consideration is given to the principles of curve drawing discussed in the following articles.

19.5. The determination of the variables for ordinate and abscissa.
The independent variable, the quantity arbitrarily varied during the experiment, usually is chosen for the abscissa (Fig. 19.5). Certain kinds of experimental data, however, such as a stress-strain diagram

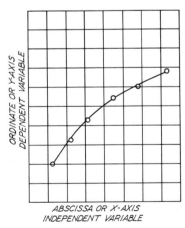

Fig. 19.5. Independent and dependent variables.

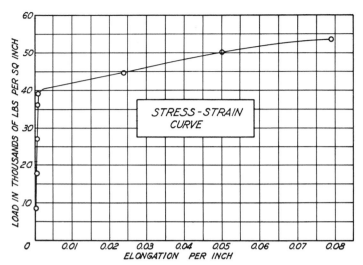

Fig. 19.6. Stress-strain diagram.

(Fig. 19.6), are plotted with the independent variable along the ordinate.

19.6. The selection of suitable scales.* The American Society of Mechanical Engineers in a standard for engineering and scientific graphs recommends:

(a) Very careful consideration should be given to the choice of scales since this has a controlling influence on the slope of the curve. The slope of the curve, as a whole and also at intermediate points, provides a visual impression of the degree of change in the dependent variable for a given increment in the independent variable. Creating the right impression of the relationship to be shown by a line graph is, therefore, probably controlled more critically by the relative stretching of the vertical and horizontal scales than by any other feature involved in the design of the graph.

(b) The range of scales should be chosen to insure effective and efficient use of the coordinate area in attaining the objective of the chart.

(c) The zero line should be included, if visual comparison of plotted magnitudes is desired.

(If the chart is quantitative, the intersection of the axes need not be at the origin of coordinates. If it is qualitative, however, both the ordinate and abscissa generally should have zero value at the intersection of the axes, as in Fig. 19.2.)

* These statements were abstracted from the American Standard for Engineering and Scientific Graphs for Publication (ASA Z15.3–1943).

(d) For arithmetic scales, the scale numbers shown on the graph and space between coordinate rulings should preferably correspond to 1, 2, or 5 units of measurement, multiplied or divided by 1, 10, 100, etc.

(Other units could be used except for the fact that they create situations where it becomes difficult to interpolate values. For example, one square should equal one of the following.)

0.01	0.1	1	10	100	etc.
0.02	0.2	2	20	200	etc.
0.04	0.4	4	40	400	etc.
0.05	0.5	5	50	500	etc.
etc.	etc.	etc.	etc.	etc.	etc.

(e) The horizontal (independent variable) scale values should usually increase from left to right and the vertical (dependent variable) from bottom to top.

19.7. Locating the axes and marking the values of the variables.
On graphs prepared for laboratory reports and not for publication, the axes should be located 1 in. or more inside the border of the coordinate ruling (see Fig. 19.7). When selecting the scale units and locating the axes, it should be remembered that the abscissa may be taken either the long way or short way of the coordinate paper, depending upon the range of the scales.

Concerning the numbers, the ASME standard recommends:

The use of many digits in scale numbers should be avoided. This can usually be accomplished by a suitable designation in the scale caption.

EXAMPLE: PRESSURE, MM. OF HG. $\times$ 10^{-5}; RESISTANCE, THOUSANDS OF OHMS.

The numbers should read from the bottom when possible (Fig. 19.7). For the sake of good appearance, they never should be crowded. Always place a cipher to the left of the decimal point when the quantity is less than one.

Usually, only the heavy coordinate lines are marked to indicate their values or distance from the origin, and, even then, the values may be shown only at a regular selected interval (see Fig. 19.7). These numbers should be placed to the left of the Y-axis and just below the X-axis.

When several curves representing different variables are to appear on the same graph, a separate axis generally is required for each variable (see Fig. 19.8). In this case, a corresponding description should be given along each axis. The axes should be grouped at the left or at the bottom of the graph, unless it is desirable to place some at the right or along the top.

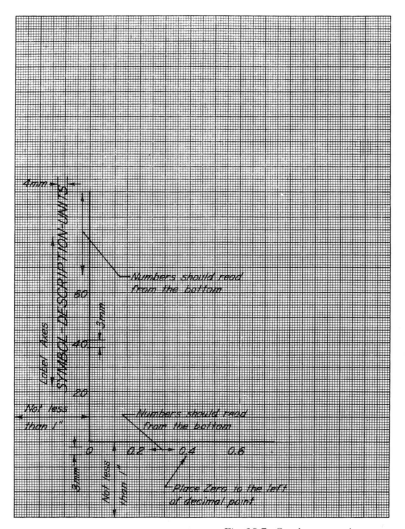

Fig. 19.7. Graph construction.

19.8. Indicating plotted points representing the data. If the data represent a set of experimental observations, the plotted points of a single-curve graph should be marked by small circles approximately 0.1 in. in diameter (see Fig. 19.9). The following practice is recommended: open circles, filled-in circles, and partially filled-in circles (○ ● ◒) rather than crosses, squares, and triangles should be used to differentiate observed points of several curves on a graph. Filled-in symbols may be made smaller than those not filled in.

Mathematical curves are frequently drawn without distinguishing marks at computed positions.

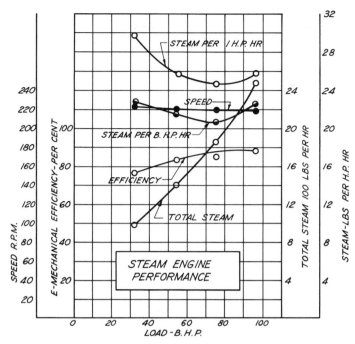

Fig. 19.8. Representation of several curves on a graph.

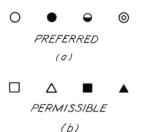

PREFERRED
(a)

PERMISSIBLE
(b)

Fig. 19.9. Identification symbols.

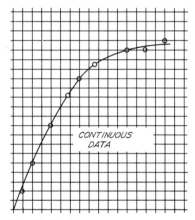

CONTINUOUS DATA

Fig. 19.10. Continuous curve.

19.9. Drawing a curve. Since most physical phenomena are continuous, curves on engineering graphs usually represent an average of plotted points (see Fig. 19.10). Discontinuous data should be plotted with a broken line, as shown in Fig. 19.11.

It is preferable to represent curves by solid lines. If more than one curve appears on a graph, differentiation may be secured by varied types of lines; but the most important curve should be represented by a solid one. A very fine line should be used for a quantitative curve if values are to be read accurately. A heavy line (¼₀ in. width) is recommended for a qualitative curve. It should be observed in Figs. 19.10 and 19.11 that the curve line does not pass through open circles.

For ordinary qualitative graphs, the ASME standard proposes:

(a) When more than one curve is presented on a graph, relative emphasis or differentiation of the curves may be secured by using different types of line, i.e., solid, dashed, dotted, etc. A solid line is recommended for the most important curve.

(b) When more than one curve is presented on a graph, each should bear a suitable designation.

(c) Curves should, if practicable, be designated by brief labels placed close to the curves (horizontally or along the curves) rather than by letters, numbers or other devices requiring a key (see Fig. 19.8).

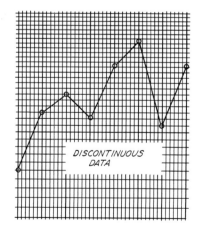

DISCONTINUOUS DATA

Fig. 19.11. Discontinuous data.

19.10. The labeling of the scales. Each scale caption should give a description of the variable represented and the unit of measurement. The captions on engineering graphs frequently contain an added identifying symbol such as "N-EFFICIENCY-PER CENT" or "P-OUTPUT-H.P."

All lettering should be readable from the bottom and right side of the graph (not the left side). When space is limited, standard abbreviations should be used, particularly for designating the unit of measurement. To avoid confusing the reader, the draftsman should use only recognized word contractions.

19.11. Titles, legends, notes, and so on. The title of a graph should be clear, concise, complete, and symmetrical. It should give the name of the curve, the source of the data, the date, and other important information (Fig. 19.12). It should be so placed that it gives a balanced effect to the completed drawing (see Fig. 19.2). In addition to the title, a wiring diagram, pictorial diagram, formula, or explanatory note is often necessary to give a clear picture of the nature of the experiment. For example, if there is any great irregularity in the plotted points or a condition that may have affected the values as shown by the data, a note of explanation should be given. A legend or key is sometimes included to explain a set of curves in greater detail.

In commercial practice, alcohol is often used to clear a rectangular area of coordinate lines in order that the title may be printed in an open space.

19.12. Procedure for making a graphical representation in ink.

1. Select the type of coordinate paper.
2. Determine the variables for ordinate and abscissa.
3. Determine the scale units.
4. Locate the axes and mark the scale values in pencil.
5. Plot the points representing the data. [Many draftsmen ink the symbol (○ ◖) indicating the points at this stage.]
6. Draw the curve. If the curve is to strike an average among the plotted points, a trial curve should be drawn in pencil. If the curve consists of a broken line, as is the case with discontinuous data, the curve need not be drawn until the graph is traced in ink.
7. Label the axes directly in ink.
8. Letter the title, notes, and so on. The title should be lettered on a trial sheet that can be used as a guide for lettering directly in ink on the graph.
9. Check the work and complete the diagram by tracing the curve in ink.

STRESS - STRAIN DIAGRAM
FOR
COMPRESSION
IN
CAST IRON

Fig. 19.12. A title.

19.13. Logarithmic graphs. Logarithmic coordinate graphs are constructed on prepared paper on which the parallel horizontal and parallel vertical rulings are spaced proportional to the logarithms of numbers (Fig. 19.13). This type of graph has two principal advantages over the ordinary coordinate type. First, the error in plotting or reading values is a constant percentage, and, second, an algebraic equation of the form $y = ax^b$ appears as a straight line if x has a value other than 0. The exponent b may be either plus or minus.

The equation for a falling body, $D = \frac{1}{2}gt^2$, is represented in Figs. 19.13 and 19.14. A practical application of interest to engineers is in the design of drop hammers. In this equation, based on uniform accelerated motion, t represents time in seconds and D the distance traveled in t seconds by a freely falling body with no initial velocity. Observe that the plotted points form a parabolic curve on ordinary coordinate graph paper, and a straight line on logarithmic paper. To draw the line on the graph in Fig. 19.13, it is necessary to calculate and locate only two points, while in Fig. 19.14 several points must be plotted to establish the location of the corresponding curved-line representation. The line on Fig. 19.13 has a slope of 2 to 1, because the exponent of t is 2. Therefore, the line could

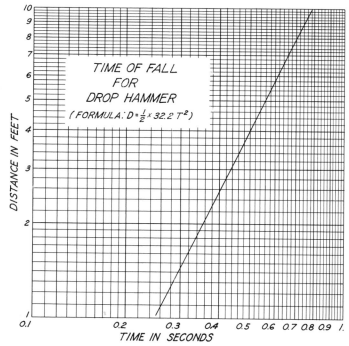

Fig. 19.13. Logarithmic graph.

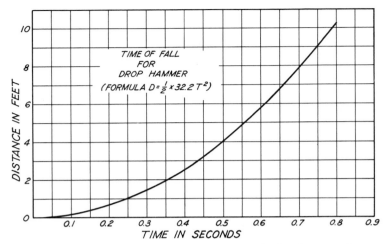

Fig. 19.14. Coordinate graph.

be drawn by utilizing one point and the slope, instead of plotting two points and joining them with a straight line.

Log paper is available with rulings in one or more cycles for any range of values to be plotted. Part-cycle and split-cycle papers may also be purchased.

19.14. Semilogarithmic graphs.

Semilogarithmic paper has ruled lines that are spaced to a uniform scale in one direction and to a logarithmic scale in the other direction (Fig. 19.15). Charts drawn on this form of paper are used extensively in scientific studies, because functions having values in the form of geometric progressions are represented by straight lines. In any case, the main reason for the use of semilogarithmic paper is that the slope of the resulting curve indicates rate of change rather than amount of change, the opposite being true in the case of curves on ordinary coordinate graph paper. Persons who are interested may determine the rate of increase or decrease at any point by measuring the slope. A straight line indicates a constant rate of change. In commercial work this form of paper is generally called "ratio paper," and the charts are known as "rate-of-change charts."

As previously stated, the choice of a type of graph paper depends upon the information to be revealed. Curves drawn on uniform coordinate graph paper to illustrate the percentage of expansion or contraction of sales, and so on, present a misleading picture. The same data plotted on semilogarithmic paper would reveal the true rate of change to the business management. For this reason, semilogarithmic paper should be used whenever percentage of change rather than quantity change is to be shown. In scientific work, when

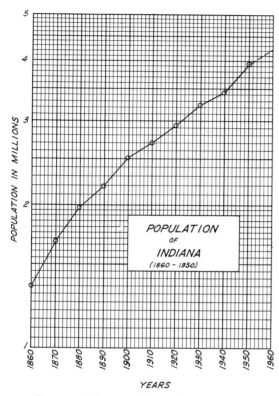

Fig. 19.15. Semilogarithmic chart.

the value of one variable increases in a geometric progression and the other in an arithmetic progression, this form is valuable.

19.15. Bar charts. Bar charts or barographs are used principally in popular literature covering economic and industrial surveys. They are a simple diagrammatic form giving a pictorial summary of statistical data and can be easily understood by the average person. Logarithmic and uniform coordinate graphs are less suited for this purpose, because few people know the procedure for reading curves or understand their picture qualities.

Whenever values or quantities are illustrated, as in Fig. 19.16, by consecutive heavy bars whose lengths are proportional to the amounts they represent, the resulting representation is called a *bar chart*.

The bars on this type of diagram may be drawn either horizontally or vertically, but all should start at the same zero line. Their lengths should be to some fixed scale, the division values of which may be given in the margin along the bottom or left side of the graph. When it is necessary to give the exact values represented,

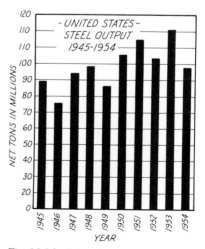

Fig. 19.16. A bar chart.

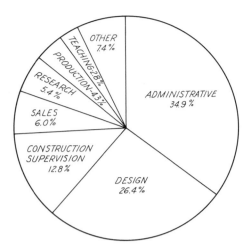

PROFESSIONAL ENGINEERS
THE KIND OF WORK THEY DO

Fig. 19.17. A pie chart.

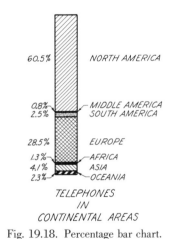

TELEPHONES
IN
CONTINENTAL AREAS

Fig. 19.18. Percentage bar chart.

the figures should be placed along each bar in a direction parallel to it. To place the values at the end gives the illusion of increasing the length of the bars. Usually, the names of the items are lettered to the left of the vertical starting line on a horizontal chart and below the starting line on a vertical chart.

19.16. Area (percentage) charts. An area diagram can be used profitably when it is desirable to present pictorially a comparison of related quantities in percentage. This form of representation illustrates the relative magnitudes of the component divisions of a total of the distribution of income, the composition of the population, and so on. Two common types of the various forms of area diagrams used in informative literature are illustrated in Figs. 19.17 and 19.18. Percentages, when represented by sectors of a circle or subdivisions of a bar, are easy to interpolate.

The pie chart (Fig. 19.17) is the most popular form of area diagram, as well as the easiest to construct. The area of the circle represents 100 per cent and the sectors represent percentages of the total. In order to make the chart effective, a description of each quantity and its corresponding percentage should be lettered in its individual sector. All lettering should be completed before the areas are crosshatched or colored if this is to be done. The percentage bar chart shown in Fig. 19.18 fulfills the same purpose as the pie chart. The all-over area of the bar represents 100 per cent. Note that each percentage division is crosshatched in a different direction. The descriptions may be placed on either side of the bar; the percentages should be on the bar or at the side.

19.17. Polar charts. Certain types of technical data can be more easily plotted and better represented on polar coordinate paper. Polar charts drawn by self-recording instruments, polar diagrams, and plotted polar curves representing various kinds of scientific data are very common. Polar curves are used to represent the intensity of diffused light, intensity of heat, and so on. The polar chart in Fig. 19.19 gives, in terms of candle power, the intensity of light in two planes.

19.18. Trilinear charts. Trilinear charts are used principally in the study of the properties of chemical compounds, mixtures, solutions, and alloys (Fig. 19.20). Basically this is a 100 per cent chart the use of which, owing to its geometric form, is limited to the investigation of that which is composed of three constituents or variables. Its use depends upon the geometric principle that the sum of the three perpendiculars from any point is equal to the altitude. If the altitude represents 100 per cent, the perpendiculars will represent the percentages of the three variables composing the whole.

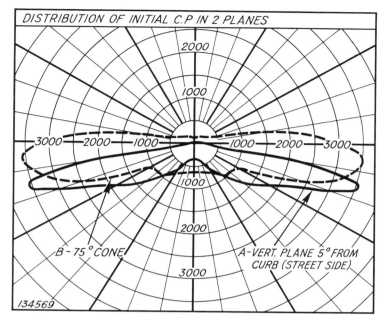

Fig. 19.19. Polar chart (*Courtesy General Electric Co.*).

The ruling can be accomplished conveniently by dividing any two sides of the triangle into the number of equal percentage divisions desired and drawing through these points lines parallel to the sides of the triangle.

19.19. Chemical engineering charts. Figure 19.21 shows a type of flow chart that must be prepared frequently by chemical engineers in industrial practice.

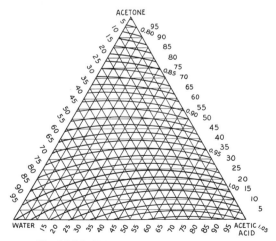

Fig. 19.20. Trilinear chart (*Courtesy American Chemical Society*).

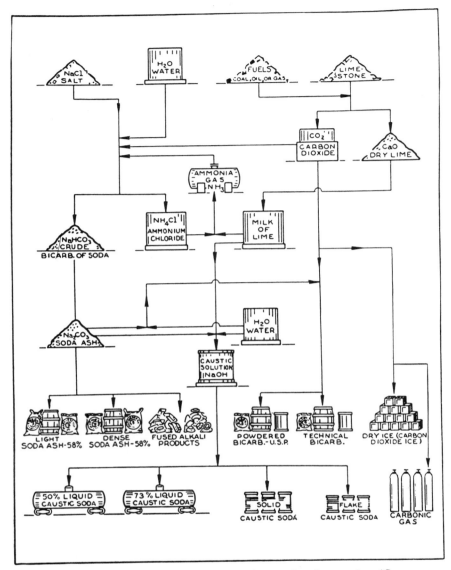

Fig. 19.21. Flow chart of ammonia-soda operations (*Courtesy Chemical Industries Magazine*).

19.20. Pictorial charts. Pictorial charts are quite generally used to present data in reports prepared for nontechnical readers. Usually, such charts present comparisons of populations (Fig. 19.22), expenditures, costs, and so forth. Stacks of silver dollars may represent expenditures; size of animals can represent livestock production; and human figures can present employment data.

PROBLEMS

The following problems have been designed to emphasize the fundamental principles underlying the preparation and use of technical graphs and charts.

1. Determine the values for the following equations, as assigned, and plot the curve in each case for quantitative purposes.

Parabola	$Y = 4x^2$, x from 0 to 5
Ellipse	$Y^2 = 100 - 2x^2$
Sines	$Y = \sin x$, x from $0°$ to $360°$
Cosines	$Y = \cos x$, x from $0°$ to $360°$
Logarithms	$Y = \log x$, x from 1 to 10
Reciprocals	$Y = \dfrac{1}{x}$, x from 1 to 10

2. The freezing temperatures for two common antifreeze solutions for various compositions are given below.

PRESTONE		DENATURED ALCOHOL	
% by vol.	Temp. °F	% by vol.	Temp. °F
10	25	10	25
20	16.5	20	17.5
25	11	25	14
30	5	30	5
35	−3	35	−1
40	−12	40	−11
45	−25	45	−18
50	−38	50	−25
55	−47	55	−32
		65	−45

Prepare a chart for these data, mainly quantitative in character, from which the required per cent volume can be read for any desired freezing temperature. Use the type of paper shown in Fig. 19.3(b).

3. Approximate barometric pressures at different heights above sea level are given below. Prepare a qualitative chart for the given data on rectangular coordinate paper.

Note that the curve would be straight on semilogarithmic paper.

H—Altitude in miles

0	1	2	3	4	5	6	7	8	9	10
29.92	24.5	20.0	16.2	13.45	11.0	8.9	7.28	5.95	4.87	4.0

B—Barometric pressure, in. of Hg

4. Data on rate of growth are frequently plotted on semilogarithmic paper, because the slope of the curve then represents the rate of

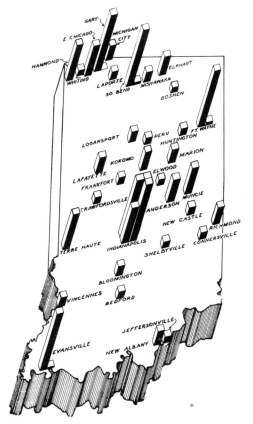

Fig. 19.22. Population chart. (*Courtesy Indiana State Planning Board*).

growth. On semilogarithmic paper, plot the data for the enrollment in a university.

Year	Enrollment	Year	Enrollment	Year	Enrollment
1930	5,745	1940	8,231	1950	12,122
1931	5,273	1941	8,457	1951	9,018
1932	4,564	1942	6,013	1952	8,976
1933	4,278	1943	4,376	1953	9,451
1934	4,534	1944	4,122	1954	10,313
1935	5,364	1945	4,451	1955	11,287
1936	6,332	1946	10,698	1956	12,111
1937	7,125	1947	14,291	1957	12,809
1938	7,613	1948	14,012	1958	13,761
1939	7,923	1949	13,287	1959	14,621

Place the vertical axis one unit in from the left edge and the horizontal axis at the extreme bottom of the page ruling. Letter in an appropriate title.

Also draw the curve of the general trend and enter on the chart, just below the title, what the enrollment would be in 1965 if the same rate of growth is maintained.

5. In a hydraulics laboratory, the construction of a quantitative curve that would give the weight of water contained in tubes of various diameters and lengths was desired. This was accomplished by filling tubes of known diameters with water to a depth of one foot and observing the weight of water thus added. The water was kept at a temperature for maximum density and the following data were obtained:

D = Diam. of tube in inches	W = Weight of 1 ft col. of water	D = Diam. of tube in inches	W = Weight of 1 ft col. of water
2	1.362	5	8.512
2½	2.128	5½	10.299
3	3.064	6	12.257
3½	4.171	6½	14.385
4	5.448	7	16.683
4½	6.895	7½	19.152
		8	21.790

On a sheet of graph paper [Fig. 19.3(b)], plot the above data. Place the axes 3 cm in from the edges. Letter the title in any convenient open space.

6. Owing to uncontrollable factors, such as lack of absolute uniformity of material or test procedure, repeated tests of samples of material do not give identical results. Also, it has been observed in many practical situations that:

1. Large departures from the average seldom occur.
2. Small variations from average occur quite often.
3. The variations are equally likely to be above average and below average.

The foregoing statements are borne out by the accompanying data showing the results of 4000 measurements of tensile strength of malleable iron.

On a sheet of coordinate graph paper [Fig. 19.3(a) or (b)] prepare a graph showing frequency of occurrence of various strength values as ordinates, and tensile strength as abscissa. Draw a smooth symmetrical curve approximating the given data.

Range of tensile strength values in lb per sq in.	No. of observations
Under 45,000	0
45,000–45,999	1
46,000–46,999	2
47,000–47,999	3
48,000–48,999	6
49,000–49,999	20
50,000–50,999	232
51,000–51,999	376
52,000–52,999	590
53,000–53,999	740
54,000–54,999	771
55,000–55,999	604
56,000–56,999	383
57,000–57,999	184
58,000–58,999	60
59,000–59,999	20
Over 60,000	8
	4000

7. On a sheet of paper, of the type shown in Fig. 19.3(b), using India ink, plot a curve to represent the data given below. *Note:* For *stress-strain diagrams*, although the load is the independent variable, it is plotted as ordinate, contrary to the general rule as given in Sec. 19.5. Figure 19.6 shows a similar chart. In performing tests of this nature, some load is imposed before any readings of elongation are taken.

It is suggested that the label along the abscissa be marked "Strain, 0.00001 in. per in.," then fewer figures will be required along the axis.

Stress, lb per sq in.	Strain, in. per in.	Stress, lb per sq in.	Strain, in. per in.
3,000	0.0001	25,000	0.00090
5,000	0.0002	30,000	0.00106
10,000	0.00035	32,000	0.00112
15,000	0.00054	33,000	0.00130
20,000	0.00070	34,000	0.00140

8. Make a vertical multiple bar chart showing the enrollment at _____ University from 1950–1959. Obtain data from Problem 4.

9. Make a semilogarithmic graph showing the enrollment of your school for the last twenty years.

20

GRAPHICAL ARITHMETIC AND ALGEBRA

20.1. Introduction. Persons who have a thorough understanding of the many graphical methods at hand frequently find it more desirable to use a graphical procedure for making a calculation than to resort to an algebraic approach, particularly when repeated calculations of the same nature are required. These people, no matter in what phase of engineering endeavor they may be found (research, design, development or production) have discovered that a graphical method can be used to present a needed visual relationship of the variables, save valuable time, minimize the possibility of error, and provide a sure way to explain the given calculation. Furthermore, a technical aide who is unskilled in the symbolic language of pure mathematics, can rapidly learn graphical methods, and he can then accomplish, or have explained to him, computations that otherwise would be too difficult for him to perform.

The student must realize that graphical methods, while theoretically precise, give only approximate solutions. The accuracy is limited by the size of the paper, the tools available, and the skill of the "graphician." However, in many problems the initial data is also approximate in that it is dependent upon the visual reading of instruments provided with graphical scales. With careful construction, a graphical solution can often be more accurate than the initial data, particularly if one has made a proper choice of the scale and a wise selection of tools. On certain occasions, where extreme accuracy is needed, a magnifying glass and pricker may be used for laying out measurements with a scale. A magnifying glass is also helpful in establishing the exact intersection of lines.

As stated before, when the solution has been accomplished by certain graphical methods, that solution may often be used for subsequent problems at a great saving in time. Furthermore, in most cases the solution by graphical methods can be arrived at in a shorter time than through the use of pure mathematical methods.

It is desirable for an engineer to be well versed in both the graphical and mathematical sciences and he should be aware of the limitations of both so that he can exercise sound judgement as to which method to use for any given situation.

20.2. Addition and subtraction. The graphical methods used for the addition and/or subtraction of definite numbers are the same as those used for the addition or subtraction of vector quantities as discussed in Sec. 14.4. The solution of the problem $y = 5 + 3$ is shown in Fig. 20.1. In (a), using a selected scale, five units were laid off along a line, starting at point O, to locate point A. Then, as shown in (b), three units were added to the right of A along the same line, using the same scale. The over-all distance O to B represents the solution, that is, the sum of the given numbers [see (c)].

The solution of the problem $y = 5 - 3$ is shown in Fig. 20.2. Point A was located as in the previous problem. However, in this case the minus sign dictates that while the value -3 must start at A, it must be laid off back towards O. The distance O to B is the solution, the answer being read directly from the scale.

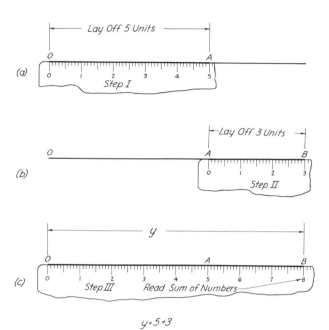

Fig. 20.1. Addition.

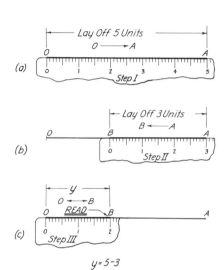

Fig. 20.2. Subtraction.

These methods can be expanded or combined for the solution of any quantity of values. Figure 20.3 shows such a solution.

In some cases, one may wish to represent the addition or subtraction of variable quantities. This can be done with a rectangular chart that gives, through interpolation, the solution when any set of definite numbers is substituted in the equation. Figure 20.4 shows the solution for $y = a + b$. This type of chart, known as a network chart, is used for repeated calculations. In the illustration, the lines have been heavied for reading; $y = 20 + 10$, where a has a value of 20. This same chart (Fig. 20.4) will also give the solution for $a = y - b$. The method can be extended to cover the addition and/or subtraction of any quantity of unknowns. Figure

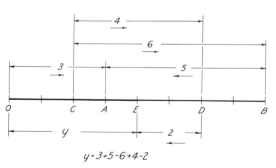

Fig. 20.3. Addition and subtraction.

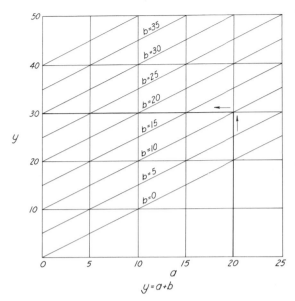

Fig. 20.4. A network chart for addition and subtraction.

20.5 shows a chart that has been designed to give the solution for $y = a + b - c$.

20.3. Multiplication. The multiplication of two numbers may be accomplished through the use of similar triangles. Figure 20.6

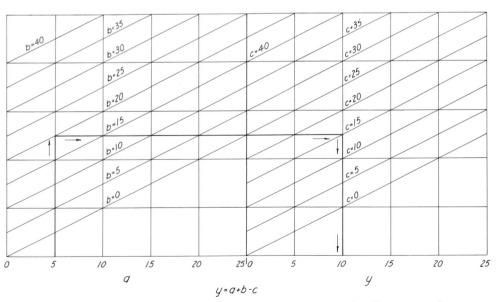

Fig. 20.5. A network chart for $y = a + b - c$.

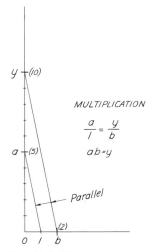

Fig. 20.6. Multiplication, $ab = y$.

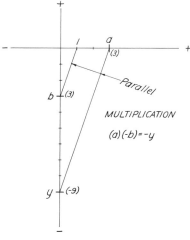

Fig. 20.7. Multiplication, $(a)(-b) = -y$.

shows the solution for $ab = y$. The steps in the procedure for laying out the triangles are: First, draw two perpendicular lines and lay off a and b along these lines as shown using some convenient scale. Next, along the b-scale mark off one unit and connect this point by a straight line to a. Finally, through b draw a line parallel to the line from a to 1. The value of y is found where the line through b crosses the vertical scale. The proof for this construction is simple. Triangle $aO1$ is similar to triangle yOb. Therefore, $a:1 = y:b$, and by cross multiplication, $y = ab$. This method provides the solution, regardless of sign, as shown in Figs. 20.7, 20.8, and 20.9.

In some cases, it may be deemed desirable to construct a chart

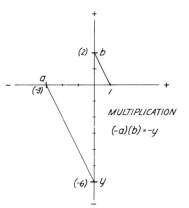

Fig. 20.8. Multiplication, $(-a)(b) = -y$.

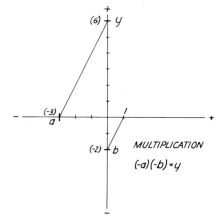

Fig. 20.9. Multiplication, $(-a)(-b) = y$.

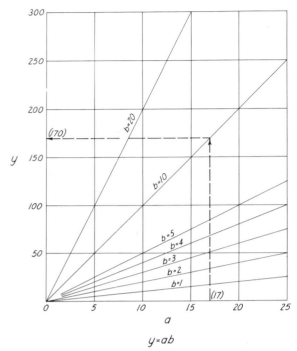

Fig. 20.10. Multiplication, $y = ab$.

for the multiplication of two variables that will be suitable for repeated use such as the one shown in Fig. 20.10 for $y = ab$. The heavy broken lines with arrows are to show how the chart would be used when a has a value of 17 and b is 10. This form may be combined with one for the addition and subtraction of numbers when the equation is in the form $y = ab + c$. With a little experience and some experimentation the student should discover that there are unlimited combinations that will satisfy most equations involving multiplication, division, addition, and subtraction.

Another graphical method for the solution of this type of problem will be discussed in Chapter 21.

20.4. Division. The division of two numbers is based upon the same principle as the multiplication of numbers, that is, the construction is based upon the relationship of similar triangles. Figure 20.11 shows the solution for $y = b/a$. The steps to be followed in making the needed construction are: First, construct two perpendicular lines as axes and lay off b along the vertical axis and a along the horizontal axis. Next, join a and b with a straight line. Then, through a point along the horizontal axis that is one unit from the vertical axis, draw a line that is parallel to the line ab. The

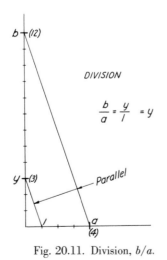

Fig. 20.11. Division, b/a.

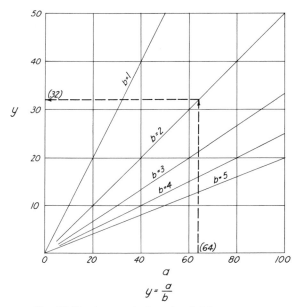

$$y = \frac{a}{b}$$

Fig. 20.12. A network chart for division.

point at which this last line crosses the vertical axis gives the value of y. The proof, as in the case of multiplication, is based on similar triangles (see Sec. 20.3).

The division of variable numbers is accomplished in the same manner as for multiplication. Figure 20.12 shows a network chart that has been prepared for this purpose. The heavy broken lines with arrows were added to illustrate how the chart would be used for $^{64}\!/_{2}$.

20.5. The square of a number. As should be expected, the determination of the square of a number is based on multiplication. However, the best graphical method of finding the square utilizes a slightly different construction than that discussed in Sec. 20.3.

Figure 20.13 shows a construction for $y = ab$ that serves as a proof for the simplified construction given in Fig. 20.14. In Fig. 20.13, the steps in preparing the drawing for the solution for $y = ab$ are: (1) Starting with two perpendicular lines as before, lay off both a and b on the horizontal axis, starting both from point O. (2) Lay off one unit along the vertical axis and connect this point to b with a straight line. (3) Through a draw a line perpendicular to the line from point 1 to b. The value of y is found where the line through a crosses the vertical axis.

Now, if $a = b$, then y would be the square of a and the construction would be as shown in Fig. 20.14.

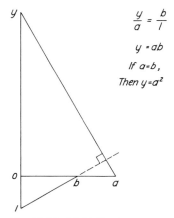

$$\frac{y}{a} = \frac{b}{l}$$

$$y = ab$$

If $a = b$,
Then $y = a^2$

Fig. 20.13. Multiplication.

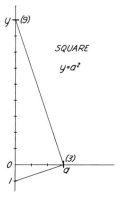

SQUARE
$y = a^2$

Fig. 20.14. To determine the square of a number.

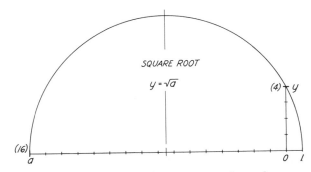

Fig. 20.15. To determine the square root of a number.

20.6. The square root of a number. The drawing in Fig. 20.15 shows a geometric construction that yields the square root of a number. To understand this construction, the reader should turn back to Fig. 20.14 and note that, since triangle $y1a$ is a right triangle with the right angle at a, point a would lie on the circumference of a circle drawn with line $y1$ as a diameter if such a circle were drawn. This fact is the basis for the construction shown for $y = \sqrt{a}$, when a is 16. The steps to be followed to determine the square root of a number graphically are: First, from a point O on a straight line using a selected scale, lay off a on one side of O and one unit on the other side. Next, draw the circle arc that has line $a1$ for a diameter. Finally, erect a perpendicular to the straight line at point O. The length of this perpendicular from point O to its intersection with the circle arc gives the value of y, the square root of a.

20.7. Other powers and roots of numbers. When it is necessary to determine powers and roots of numbers, a network chart, such as the one shown in Fig. 20.16, may be prepared and used repeatedly. Those who construct a chart for this purpose know that, since the equation $y = a^n$ can be rewritten as $\log y = n \log a$, the equation, when represented on logarithmic graph paper, is the same as a multiplication network chart.

20.8. Simultaneous equations. Since simultaneous equations are frequently encountered in engineering work and there are times when the algebraic solution of a pair of simultaneous equations is complicated and difficult, if not almost impossible, it is necessary for an engineer to know how to find the solution by graphical means. Situations that make a graphical approach desirable arise when the data has been obtained as the result of an experiment and when the equations, although known, are so complicated that the algebraic solution would be too time-consuming. In some cases, the graphical

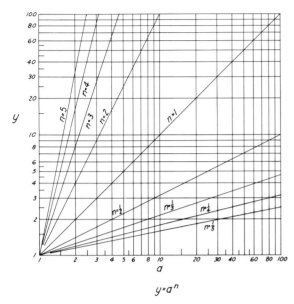

Fig. 20.16. Powers and roots of numbers.

solution may, by giving the roots to the desired accuracy or by showing where the roots are located, permit a saving of time in the
mathematical solution. Figure 20.17 shows the solution of two
linear simultaneous equations. Figure 20.18 shows the solution of
two higher-order equations. The pair of equations are:

$$y = x^2 + x + 3$$
$$y = x^3 - x^2 - 2x + 5$$

The mathematical solution of this pair of equations would be
very time-consuming. The graphical solution is largely a matter of
plotting. It should be noted that there are three roots which satisfy
both equations.

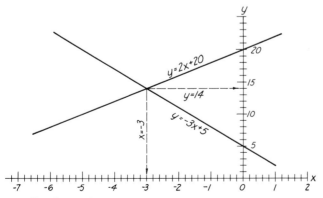

Fig. 20.17. Solution of linear simultaneous equations.

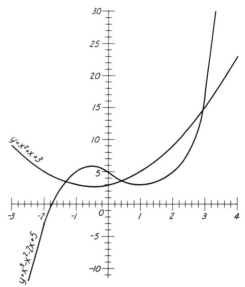

Fig. 20.18. Solution of higher-order equations.

20.9. Determination of the roots of quadratic equations. There are three methods of solution that can be used for the determination of the roots (points where $y = O$) of quadratic equations, each method having its own advantages. First, the equation can be plotted directly as illustrated in Fig. 20.19. The roots are the points where the curve crosses the x-axis. If the curve crosses the x-axis, there are two real and different roots; if the curve is tangent to the x-axis, there are two real but equal roots; and finally, if the curve does not cross the x-axis, there are two imaginary roots. Imaginary roots are always in pairs, equal but opposite in sign. The advantage of this method is that an immediate picture of the conditions of the equation is obtained. This method is applicable for any order equation. However, a new curve must be drawn for each equation.

Secondly, the equation can be rewritten as two simultaneous equations, one being the equation of a straight line. For example, the equation:

$$y = x^2 + Ax - C$$

can be rewritten as:

$$y = x^2$$
$$y = -Ax + C$$

This pair of equations can be solved as explained in Sec. 20.8 and the x-values of their solution will be the roots of the original quadratic equation. Figure 20.20 shows this method applied to the

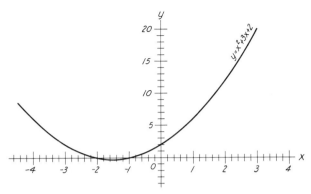

Fig. 20.19. Graphical determination of roots of the equation
$y = x^2 + 3x + 2$.

same quadratic equation as represented in Fig. 20.19. If the straight line cuts the curve, there are two real and different roots; if the straight line is tangent to the curve there are two real but equal roots; and finally, if the straight line does not cut the curve, there are two imaginary roots. The advantage of this method is that the curve representing $y = x^2$ need be drawn only once. Each subsequent quadratic is solved by drawing a different straight line.

For the third method, based on geometric construction, the quadratic must be written in the form:

$$y = x^2 + Ax + C$$

The steps to be followed in making the construction shown in Fig. 20.21 are: (1) Draw a set of x- and y-axes and lay off A along

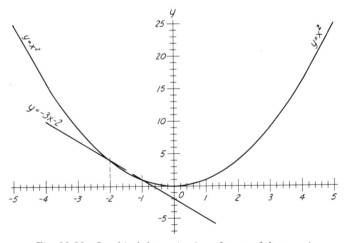

Fig. 20.20. Graphical determination of roots of the equation
$y = x^2 + 3x + 2$.

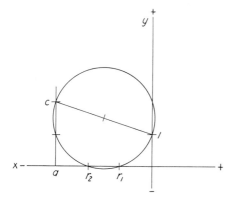

Fig. 20.21. Graphical determination of roots of the equation $y = x^2 + 3x + 2$.

the x-axis, with opposite sign, to locate point a. (2) At a erect a perpendicular and lay off C with the same sign to locate c. Finally, (3) Connect c to a point at plus one unit on the y-axis with a straight line and draw the circle that has this line as a diameter. The points where this circle cuts the x-axis are the roots that are sought. Again there is the possibility of real and different; real but equal; and imaginary roots. The existing condition would be revealed by the position of the circle. The advantage of this method is that all construction is done with a straightedge, scale, and compass. No irregular curves need be drawn with the likelihood of errors in construction. However, a completely new construction is required for each equation.

PROBLEMS

All problems are to be solved by graphical methods only.

1. Solve $y = 5 + 8 + 4 - 6 - 3 + 2$.

2. Set up a network chart for $y = a + b$; a to vary from 0 to 30 and y to vary from 0 to 60.

3. Set up a network chart for $y = a - b + c$; a to vary from 0 to 50, b to vary from 0 to 40, and y to vary from 0 to 50.

4. Multiply:
(a) 5×10 (b) 3×6 (c) -5×4 (d) -4×-7

5. Set up a network chart for $y = ab$; a to vary from 0 to 20, and b to vary from 0 to 10 in steps of one.

6. Divide:
(a) $20/4$ (b) $15/5$ (c) $-8/2$ (d) $-14/-3$

7. Set up a network chart for $y = a/b$; a to vary from 0 to 80, and b to vary from 1 to 6 in steps of one.

8. Set up a network chart for $y = ab + c$; a to vary from 0 to 25, b to vary from 1 to 10 in steps of two, and c to vary from 0 to 30.

9. Determine the square of:
(a) $2\frac{1}{4}$ (b) 3.6 (c) 1.9 (d) $4\frac{1}{2}$

10. Determine the square roots of:
(a) 15 (b) 23 (c) 30 (d) 7

11. Find the roots of the simultaneous equations:
$$y = 2x^2 - x + 4$$
$$y = x^2 + 3x + 9$$

12. Find the roots of the equation by the method shown in Fig. 20.20.
$$y = x^2 + 2x - 3$$

13. Find the roots of the equation by the method shown in Fig. 20.21.
$$y = 3x^2 + 6x + 3$$

14. Find the roots of the equation by the method shown in Fig. 20.20.
$$y = 3x^2 + 12x + 12$$

21

EMPIRICAL EQUATIONS

21.1. Introduction. In all phases of engineering work considerable experimentation is done with physical quantities, and the engineer in his work is usually the one person most concerned with the behavior of quantities in relation to one another. Often it is known that the subject of the experiment obeys some physical law which can be expressed by a mathematical equation, but the exact equation is unknown. Then, the person performing the experiment is faced with the task of finding an equation to fit the data that has been obtained. The three articles that follow discuss means of arriving at an equation from a graphical study of the data. An equation determined in this manner is an *empirical equation*. Since the unknown law may be quite complex, a single empirical equation to fit the whole range of data may not exist. However, in the majority of such cases a series of the various empirical equations with limited coverage (parameters) can be found.

21.2. Equations of the form: $y = a + bx$. If the plotted points, representing the data, lie in what appears to be a straight line when plotted on rectangular coordinate paper, the equation of the data is a linear or first degree equation of the form: $y = a + bx$, where b is the slope of the line and a is the y-intercept ($x = 0$).

After it has been decided that the relationship between quantities is linear, the next step is to draw the best average straight line that will be representative of the data (see Fig. 21.1). This line, extended if necessary to the y-axis, establishes the y-intercept ($x = 0$) which will be the value of a in the equation. The slope can be determined from any two points along the line. However, for accuracy the points should be selected as far apart as possible. The value of b is expressed as

$$b = \frac{y_2 - y_1}{x_2 - x_1}$$

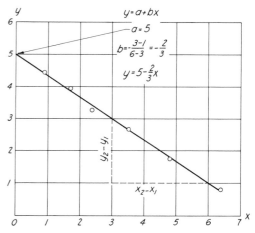

Fig. 21.1. Determination of empirical equations of the form $y = a + bx$ (first degree).

Thus, for the line in Fig. 21.1, having selected two points as illustrated,

$$b = -\frac{3-1}{6-3} = -\frac{2}{3} \quad \text{(slope)}$$

With the slope now known and the value of a having been read directly on the y-axis as 5, the equation of the line can be written as

$$y = 5 - \frac{2}{3}x$$

If it is not reasonable to include $x = 0$ in the plot of the data, then a pair of simultaneous equations are set up using two points on the line:

$$y_1 = a + bx_1$$
$$y_2 = a + bx_2$$

This system can then be solved for a and b.

21.3. Equations of the form: $y = ax^b$. If the data plots very nearly in a straight line on logarithmic graph paper, the equation of the data is a power equation of the form: $y = ax^b$. Power equations of this type, where one quantity varies directly as some power of another, appear as either parabolic or hyperbolic curves when plotted on rectangular coordinate paper, depending upon whether the exponent is positive or negative. For positive values of b (except for unity) the curves are parabolic; negative values produce hyperbolic curves.

When the equation is placed in logarithmic form and rewritten as: $\log y = \log a + b \log x$, it is now in the same form as the equation of a straight line. In this case, when $x = 1$ then $y = a$ because $\log 1 = 0$.

Hence, after the data has been plotted (y vs. x) on logarithmic paper as in Fig. 21.2, a representative (average) straight line should be drawn. The line extended to the y-axis establishes a at the y intercept ($x = 1$). The value of a can be read directly, since the spacing is logarithmic. As before, two points along the line are used in the equation that follows to determine b:

$$b = \frac{\log y_2 - \log y_1}{\log x_2 - \log x_1}$$

For the two points selected along the line in Fig. 21.2,

$$b = \frac{1.477 - 0.699}{1.772 - 0.398} = .57$$

Thus, the equation is $y = 3x^{.57}$.

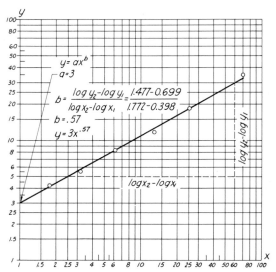

Fig. 21.2. Determination of empirical equations of the form $y = ax^b$ (power).

If $x = 1$ is not included in the plot of the data, then one may resort to a pair of simultaneous equations

$$\log y_1 = \log a + b \log x_1$$
$$\log y_2 = \log a + b \log x_2$$

In solving for a (also b) the solution gives the value for $\log a$. The real value of a (and b) must be found in the log tables.

21.4. Equations of the form: $y = ab^x$. If the data plots as a nearly straight line on semilogarithmic graph paper, the equation of the data is an exponential equation of the form: $y = ab^x$. This equation may be rewritten as: $\log y = \log a + x \log b$, which once again is in the same form as the equation of a straight line. In this case, when $x = 0$ then $y = a$.

With the data for the exponential equation plotted directly on semilogarithmic graph paper, one must again draw the most representative line along the path of the plotted points. This line extended to the y-axis ($x = 0$) determines the value of a. Again, two points must be selected along the line and their coordinates substituted in the equation

$$\log b = \frac{\log y_2 - \log y_1}{x_2 - x_1}$$

Then, with the logarithm of the value of b known, the real value of b as needed for the equation can be determined from log tables.

For the two points selected for the line in Fig. 21.3

$$\log b = \frac{1.778 - 1.176}{5 - 2} = \frac{0.602}{3} = .201$$

Hence,

$$b = 1.59$$

With the value of a read on the y-axis as 6, the formula for the data may be written as: $y = 6\,(1.59)^x$.

If $x = 0$ is not included in the plot of the data, then one must solve the simultaneous equations

$$\log y_1 = \log a + x_1 \log b$$
$$\log y_2 = \log a + x_2 \log b$$

Then, since the solution gives both a and b in terms of logarithms, log tables must be used to determine the real values of a and b.

When natural logarithms are available, the equation $y = ab^x$ may be changed to $y = Ae^{mx}$. This latter equation, in turn, may be written as: $\ln y = \ln A + mx$, which is still the equation of a straight line. The value of A can be determined as before at $x = 0$, and

$$m = \frac{\ln y_2 - \ln y_1}{x_2 - x_1}$$

where the value of m is found directly.

When $x = 0$ is not included, the equations to be used are

$$\ln y_1 = \ln A + mx_1$$
$$\ln y_2 = \ln A + mx_2$$

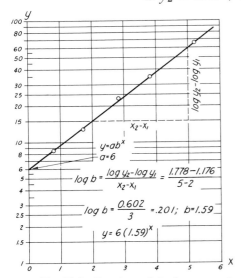

Fig. 21.3. Equations of the form $y = ab^x$.

22

GRAPHICAL CALCULUS

22.1. Graphical calculus. In solving engineering problems, it is frequently desirable and often necessary to present a graphical analysis of empirical data. Even though it is often possible to make an evaluation through the use of analytical calculus, a graphical representa-

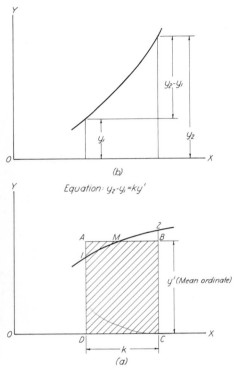

Equation: $y_2 - y_1 = ky'$

$y' $ (Mean ordinate)

(b)

(a)

Fig. 22.1. Illustration of the principle of integration.

tion is more meaningful because it is pictorial in character. Graphical integration and differentiation are particularly desirable for problems for which only a set of values are known, or for curves that have been produced mechanically, as in the case of steam engine indicator diagrams, or if the results cannot be determined by the analytical methods of calculus.

The following sections are devoted to the graphical rules and methods for determining derived curves. Discussion of the interpretation of results has been intentionally omitted since interpretation is not usually graphical and, therefore, not within the scope of this text.

22.2. Graphical integration. In deriving curves of a higher order, the principle is applied that the area bounded by two successive ordinates, the curve, and the axis is equal to the difference in magnitude of the corresponding ordinates of the integral curve. Figure 22.1 illustrates this principle of graphical integration. In (a) an increment of a curve is shown enlarged. The area under the curve will be approximately equal to the area of the shaded rectangle $ABCD$ when the line AB is drawn so that the area $AM1$ above the curve is approximately equal to the area $MB2$ below the curve. With a little practice one will find it easy to establish a line such as AB quite accurately by eye if a strip of celluloid or a triangle is used through which the curve can be seen.

By applying the principle of graphical integration to a series of increments, an integral curve may be drawn as shown in Fig. 22.2. At this point, it should be recognized that since the difference between successive ordinates represents increase in area, the difference between the final ordinate and the initial ordinate represents the total area between these ordinates that is bounded by the curve and the X-axis.

The scale selected for the Y-axis of the integral curve need not be the same as the scale for the given curve.

Portions of a lower-order curve that are above the X-axis are considered to be positive whereas areas below with negative ordinates are recognized as negative [see Fig. 22.3(a)]. Since the negative area between any two ordinates on the lower-order curve represents only the difference in the length of the corresponding ordinates on the integral curve, the length of y_7 is less than the length of y_6 by an amount equal to the negative area. Also, because areas represent only differences in length of successive ordinates of the integral curve, the initial point on the integral curve might have any value and still fulfill its purpose. For example, either integral curve shown in Fig. 22.3(b) is a satisfactory solution for the curve in (a).

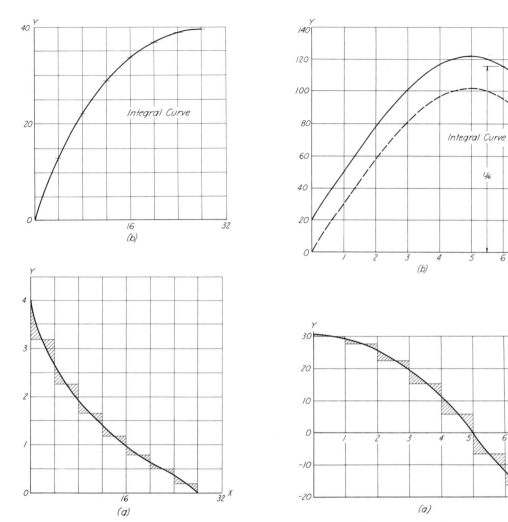

Fig. 22.2. The integration of a curve.   Fig. 22.3. The integration of a curve.

Figure 22.4 shows the derived curves for a falling drop hammer. It is common practice, when drawing related curves, to place them in descending order as shown, that is, the lower-order curve is placed below.

In (a) the straight line represents a uniform acceleration of 32.2 ft per sec per sec, which is the acceleration for a freely falling body. The initial velocity is 0. The units along the X-axis represent time in seconds and the units along the Y-axis represent acceleration in feet per second per second.

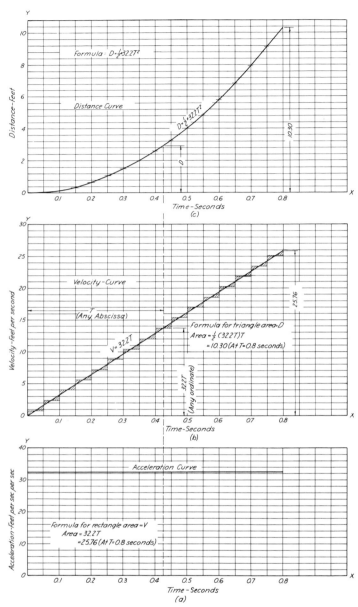

Fig. 22.4. Derived curves for a falling drop hammer.

Since the acceleration is uniform, the velocity curve will be a straight line of constant slope, (b). The length of the last ordinate is equal to the total area under the acceleration curve, namely 25.76 ft per sec (fps).

The distance curve, which is obtained by integrating the velocity time curve, is shown in (c). The length of the ordinate at any interval point is equal to the total area below the velocity curve between the origin and the point $[D = A = \frac{1}{2}(32.2T)T]$. See Figs. 22.1, 22.2, and 22.3.

22.3. To integrate a curve by the ray polygon method. An integral curve may be drawn by a purely graphical process known as the ray polygon method.

This method of integrating the area under a curve is illustrated in Fig. 22.5.

Divide the X-axis into intervals and draw ordinates at the division points. Then, select the pole point P at some convenient location that will make the distance d equal to any number of the full units assigned to the X-axis. The selection of the number of units for the distance d determines the length of the scale along a Y-axis for the integral curve. To establish relationship between y_1 and y_0 the following equation based on similar right triangles can be written:

$$y_1 : k = y_0 : d$$
$$y_1 \cdot d = k \cdot y_0$$
$$y_1 = \frac{k \cdot y_0}{d} = \frac{k}{d} \cdot y_0$$

Determine the mean ordinate for each strip and transfer its height to the Y-axis as length OA, OB, OC, and so forth. Draw rays from P to points A, B, C, D, E, and F.

To construct the integral curve, start at O and draw a line parallel to PA cutting the first vertical through R at R'. Through

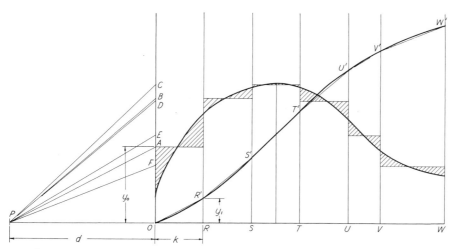

Fig. 22.5. Use of ray polygon.

R' draw a line parallel to PB until it cuts the second vertical through S at S'. Repeat this procedure to obtain points T', U', and so on. Points R', S', T', U', V', and W' are points on the required integral curve. In Fig. 22.5 the integral curve is constructed on the same coordinate axes as the lower-order curve.

22.4. Pole method applied to the construction of an integral curve. The first of the several examples that have been selected to illustrate the use of the so-called pole method for the construction of an integral graph, has a sloping straight line, plotted on rectangular coordinates, as the given curve of lower order (see Fig. 22.6). It should be noted in this case that the integral graph has been placed directly above the lower graph and in projection with it so that the same intervals may be used for both. As shown, ordinates were first drawn to divide the chart area into vertical strips. With this done the horizontal lines were drawn next, one for each of the strips at mean-ordinate height, to form the five rectangular areas that are assumed to approximate the area under the curve (sloping straight line). Then, these mean-ordinate heights must be projected horizontally to the y-axis. With the pole distance k determined and the pole point P located along the x-axis extended, ray lines are drawn from P to the points on the y-axis representing the heights of the mean ordinates. The manner in which the distance k affects the steepness of the integral curve, as illustrated in Fig. 22.8, will be discussed

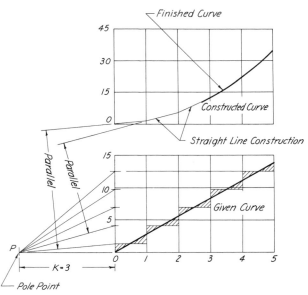

Fig. 22.6. Pole method.

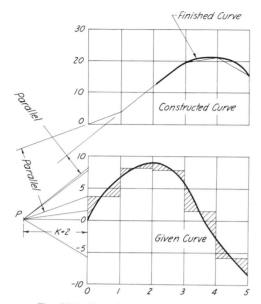

Fig. 22.7. Use of pole point.

later. The first point on the integral curve was found by drawing a
line through the origin parallel to the ray for the corresponding
interval below, in this case the lowest ray. The second segment is
then drawn parallel to the ray for the second interval through the
end of the first segment. Other intervals are treated similarly and
then the smooth curve, that is, the integral curve, is drawn through
the points obtained. Since the finished curve has in reality been
drawn through the end-points of chords by this method, most persons identify this construction procedure by calling it the "chordal
method."

In Fig. 22.7, the so-called "chordal method" using a pole, has
been applied to the integration of an irregular curve. The intervals
between the ordinates need not be equal as shown. In fact, the number and spacing of the ordinates will usually be determined by the
shape of the curve and one soon discovers that it is wise to space
ordinates closer together where there is a sharp change or a reversal
of curvature and farther apart where the curve is flat. For this illustration, an example was purposely selected that would have a portion of the curve below the x-axis. This area below represents
negative area that must be subtracted from the positive area above
the x-axis. When a pole is used, this subtraction is taken care of
graphically by the negative slope of the rays for the intervals at the
location where the curve lies below the x-axis.

Ordinarily, the modulus of the ordinate (y-axis) scale of the integral curve must be smaller than the modulus of the given (lower-order) curve if the graph for the integral curve is to be of reasonable size. When the height of the derived curve is somewhat near the same as the height of the given curve, the general over-all appearance of the graphs will be satisfactory and the scales will ordinarily be large enough to be read with reasonable accuracy. At the very beginning when it becomes necessary to determine the maximum value to be read on the ordinate scale for the integral curve, one must first remember that the value will be equal numerically to the value for the total area under the given curve. This value may be found either by adding the areas of the individual rectangles or by calculating the area of a single large rectangle that is estimated to be equal to the total area under the curve. Once this maximum value is known it is relatively easy to select a value for k that will give good proportion to the integral curve and at the same time permit one to make accurate readings.

When the pole distance used is equal to the length of one abscissa unit as shown in Fig. 22.8(a), the same distance represents the same number of units on both scales. In (b), where a pole distance of 2 has been used, ten units are represented on the scale of the constructed curve by the same distance that represents 5 units on the scale of the curve below. As can be easily seen, a three-unit pole distance reduces the height of the constructed curve still more

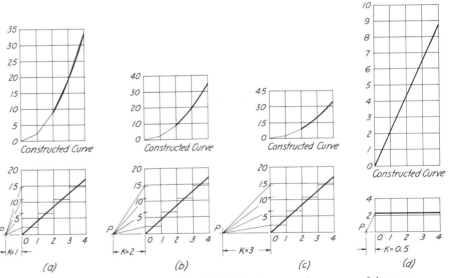

Fig. 22.8. Pole distance and steepness of the curve.

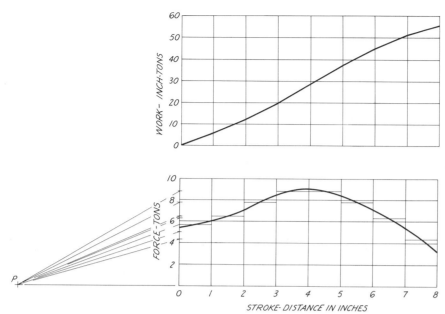

Fig. 22.9. Example of graphical integration.

(*c*). When the pole distance is one-half unit, the constructed graph becomes very high, too high to be appropriate in the case shown in (*d*). However, there may be conditions encountered now and then when the use of a pole distance of one-half unit is desirable. An area graph is shown in Fig. 22.9, where a five-unit pole distance was used to construct the work (integral) curve.

An interesting application of graphical integration is shown in Fig. 22.10. Let it be supposed that an irregularly shaped plot of land, lying along a lake shore and a road, is to be divided into three equal lots. The area to be divided was first plotted (feet against feet) on the lower graph. Its boundary lines in addition to the shore line at the north, are the *x* and *y* axes, representing property lines, and the right-of-way line of S.R. 60. It was decided that the division lines were to run due north and south, perpendicular to the south property line. With the lower curve drawn, the integral curve was constructed by the pole-and-ray method as shown and the total area was found to be 180,000 sq ft, an area that, in this particular case, can be divided evenly into three lots, each having 60,000 sq ft. Horizontal lines, drawn through points representing 60,000 and 120,000 values on the scale of the area graph to the area curve and thence downward to the shore line, located the end-points of the division lines for the lots.

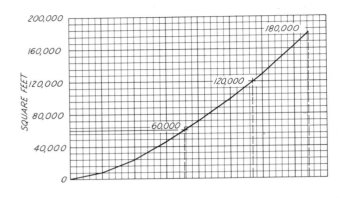

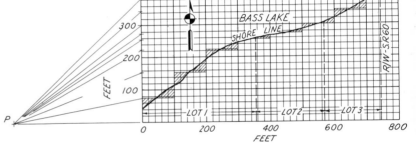

Fig. 22.10. Example of graphical integration.

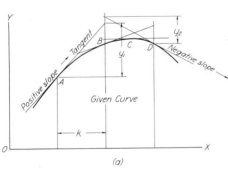

(a)

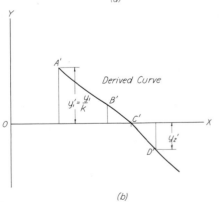

(b)

Fig. 22.11. Illustration of the principle of differentiation.

22.5. Graphical differentiation. Curves of a lower order are derived through the application of the principle that the ordinate at any point on the derived curve is equal to the slope of a tangent line at the corresponding point on the given curve. The slope of a curve at a point is the tangent of the angle with the X-axis formed by the tangent to the curve at the point. For all practical purposes, when constructing a derivative curve, the slope may be taken as the rise of the tangent line parallel to the Y-axis in one unit of distance along the X-axis, or the slope of the tangent equals y_1/k as shown in Fig. 22.11.

Figure 22.11 illustrates the application of this principle of graphical differentiation. The length of the ordinate y_1' at point A' on the derived curve is equal to the slope y_1/k at point A on the given curve as shown in (a). When the slope is zero as at point C, the length of the ordinate is zero and point C' lies on the X-axis for the derived curve. When the slope is negative, as shown at D, the ordinate is negative and lies below the X-axis.

The graph shown in Fig. 22.12 is composed of segments of straight lines. Since the slope is constant for the interval 0–1, the derivative curve in the interval is a horizontal line. In the interval 1–2, the slope is also constant but of a lesser magnitude. Thus, the derivative curve is composed of straight line segments as shown in (b).

At this point in the discussion of graphical calculus it becomes possible to determine the relationship between the principles of integration and differentiation and to show that one is derived from the other.

From inspection of the graphs shown in Fig. 22.12, equations may be formulated as follows:

By the principle of differentiation

$$y_2' = \frac{y_2 - y_1}{k_2}$$

in the interval 1–2 where

$$\frac{y_2 - y_1}{k_2}$$

represents the slope of AB. The area under the curve in (b) in the interval 1–2 is equal to

$$y_2' \cdot k_2 = \frac{y_2 - y_1}{k_2} \cdot k_2 = y_2 - y_1 \quad \text{(integral curve)}$$

and

$$y_2' = \frac{y_2 - y_1}{k_2} \quad \text{(differential curve)}$$

In constructing a derivative curve, the determination of the tangent lines is often difficult because the direction of a tangent at a particular point is usually not well defined by the curvature of the graph. Two related schemes that may be used for constructing tangents are shown in Fig. 22.13(a) and (b). In (a) the tangent is drawn parallel to a chord of the curve, the arc of which is assumed to approximate the arc of a parabola. A sufficiently accurate location for the point of tangency T_1 may be determined by drawing a line from the mid-point of the chord to the arc, parallel to an assumed direction for the diameter of the parabola. When working with small segments of the curve, one may assume the diameter to be either horizontal or vertical.

A more accurate construction is shown in (b) where the tangent is drawn parallel to two parallel chords. The point of tangency T_2

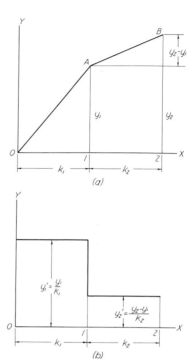

Fig. 22.12. Graphical differentiation.

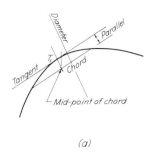

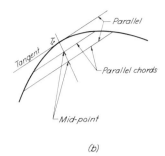

(a)   (b)

Fig. 22.13. Construction of a tangent line.

is determined by connecting the mid-points of the chords and extending this line to the curve. This line determines the direction of the diameter.

The construction in (b) using two chords to establish a tangent is applicable to any curve that may be approximated by a portion of a circle, ellipse, parabola, or hyperbola.

Since a tangent is assumed to be parallel to a chord, it is common practice to use chords instead of tangents for constructing a derivative curve, as shown in Fig. 22.14(a). The slope is plotted on an ordinate located midway in the corresponding interval of the derived curve.

A derivative curve can also be drawn using the ray polygon method as explained in Sec. 22.3 in reverse (see Fig. 22.15). The lines PA, PB, and PC of the ray polygon are drawn parallel to the tangents at points T_1, T_2, and T_3. Point Q is found by drawing a line horizontally from point A to the ordinate through the point of contact of the tangent parallel to PA. Points R and S are found similarly.

22.6. Drawing a derivative curve by the pole method. Before attempting to construct a derivative curve by the pole method, the beginner must have a clear understanding of the "slope law" as it applies to the differentiation and he must be able to think of the derived curve being sought as the curve of slopes (slope locus) for the given curve. If deemed necessary, the first part of the discussion given in the previous section should be reviewed before continuing. In making a start, the given curve should first be analyzed and certain facts noted concerning the slope at specific points along the curve. For example, in Fig. 22.16, it should be recognized that the slope for the first and second intervals is constant and positive, a fact indicated by the single straight line sloping upward across both strips. In the third interval (2 to 3), the curve has a constant zero

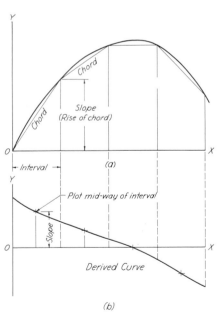

Fig. 22.14. Use of chords in place of tangents.

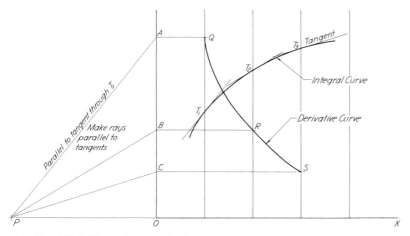

Fig. 22.15. Ray polygon method.

slope; while again, for the fourth and fifth intervals, the slope is constant and positive. Finally, the curve for the last three intervals has a constant negative slope, because the straight line, this time downward, indicates decreasing values.

A pole distance must now be selected, remembering that the distance in abscissa units determines the ordinate scale ratio for both curves. Then, with the location of the pole point *P* established,

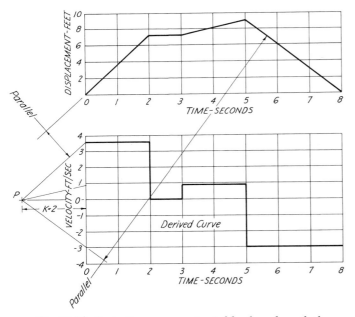

Fig. 22.16. Derivative curve constructed by the pole method.

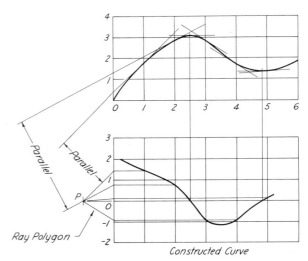

Fig. 22.17. Use of tangents.

rays are drawn, parallel to the straight lines of the given curve until they intersect the Y-axis for the derived curve. These points of intersection, projected horizontally, determine the derived curve that is composed of straight lines in this particular case.

In Fig. 22.17, the derived curve (slope locus) was obtained from the given (upper) curve by using tangents. Through the pole point P, a ray was drawn parallel to each of the several tangent lines. Then, the intersection point of each ray with the Y-axis was projected horizontally across to the corresponding ordinate as shown. The drawing of a smooth curve through these points completed the graph.

Chords were used instead of tangent lines in Fig. 22.18. The procedure that is followed here may be thought of as being the reverse of the chordal method illustrated in Fig. 22.6. As the initial step for the construction, chords of the given curve were drawn as shown. In selecting these chords, an effort was made in every case to see that the curve would be nearly symmetrical about a perpendicular bisector of the subtended chord. Also, as is appropriate and desirable, shorter chords were used where the curvature is sharper. After the pole point P had been located and the axes established for the derivative curve, rays were drawn through point P, parallel to the chords, to an intersection with the Y-axis. Next, the tangent point (such as T_1) was located for each of the subtended arcs of the given curve, using the method shown at the right in (b). In doing this it was assumed that the chords would be parallel to tangents at points, such as T_1, where the perpendicular bisector of the chord would cut the subtended arc. These tangent points, when projected downward to corresponding horizontal lines drawn from the points along the Y-axis, at the rays, determine the derivative curve. For example, in (b) point U_1 in interval A is found by projecting T_1 downward to a horizontal line drawn through the point of intersection of the Y-axis and the related ray through P. The related ray in this case being the one that is parallel to the chord of the arc of the given curve in interval A. The desired derivative curve was completed by drawing a smooth curve through U_1 and the several other points shown, all of which were located in the same manner.

When using the chordal method to determine a derivative curve, some people frequently prefer to use equally spaced ordinates and then confine each chord to a single interval. Although this procedure proves to be quite satisfactory in many cases, there are times when desired results cannot be obtained for there are either no points or too few points given to draw a smooth curve at critical locations. In such cases, some extra construction will be needed. However, the easiest and best solution would have resulted from a careful choice of chords of the given curve at the start.

Figure 22.19 shows the differentiation of a curve using chords instead of tangents. The given distance-time curve was plotted from data obtained for a passenger train leaving a small station near a large city. The velocity and acceleration curves reveal that the train moves with a constant acceleration for approximately 100 sec until it reaches a velocity of 55 mph. From this point it travels with a constant velocity toward its destination.

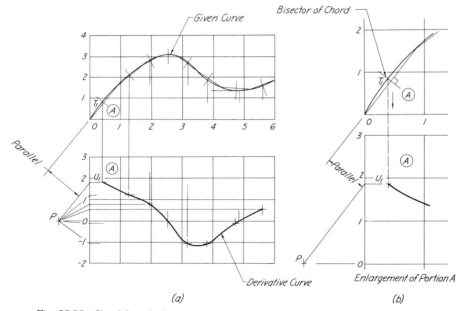

Fig. 22.18. Chordal method.

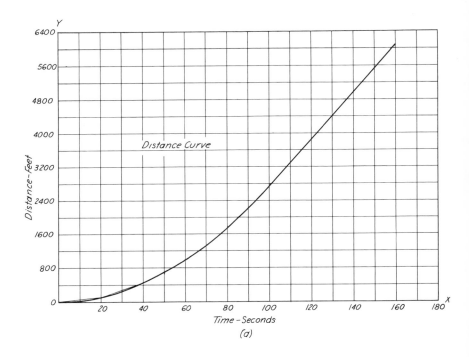

(a)

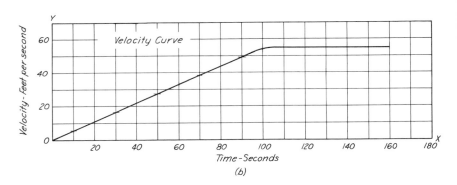

(b)

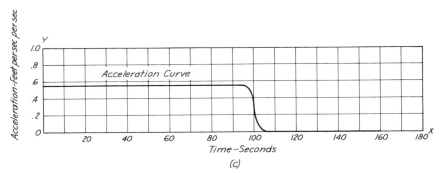

(c)

Fig. 22.19. Graphical differentiation.

PROBLEMS

The following problems have been designed to emphasize the fundamental principles underlying graphical integration and differentiation and to offer the student an opportunity to acquire a working knowledge of the methods that are commonly used by professional engineers.

1. A beam 10 ft long is uniformly loaded at 20# per ft as shown in Fig. 22.20. Plot distance in feet along the X-axis. Draw (1) the integral curve to show the shearing force, and (2) the second integral curve to show the bending moment.

2. A beam 15 ft long and supported at both ends is loaded uniformly at 18# per foot as shown in Fig. 22.21. Plot distance in feet along the X-axis and load along the Y-axis. Draw (1) the integral curve to show the shearing force, and (2) the second integral curve to show the bending moment.

3. Plot the points given in the table and draw a smooth curve. Construct the derivative curve. Write the equation of the derivative curve

x	0	1	2	3	4	5	6	7	8	9	10
y	10	10.5	12	14.5	18	22.5	28	34.5	42	50.5	60

Equation of given curve $y = \frac{1}{2}x^2 + 10$.

4. Construct the distance-time, velocity-time, and acceleration-time curves for an automobile moving as follows: time = 10 sec, acceleration = 5 ft per sec per sec throughout the interval, initial velocity = 0.

5. The passenger train for which derived curves are shown in Fig. 22.19 is brought to a stop with a constant negative acceleration of 1.0 ft per sec per sec. Before applying the brakes the train was traveling with a constant velocity of 55 ft per sec. Construct the curves showing acceleration-time, velocity-time, and distance-time relationships.

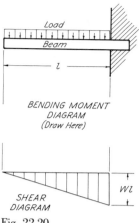

Fig. 22.20

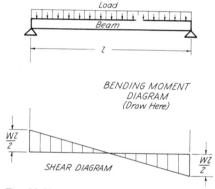

Fig. 22.21

23

NOMOGRAPHY: ALIGNMENT CHARTS

23.1. Alignment charts (nomographs). The purpose of alignment charts is to eliminate many of the laborious calculations necessary to solve formulas containing three or more variables. Such a chart is often complicated and difficult to construct, but if it can be used repeatedly, the labor involved in making it will be justified. In the commercial field, these charts appear in varied forms, which may be very simple or very complicated. Figure 23.1 illustrates an alignment chart consisting of three graduated parallel lines.

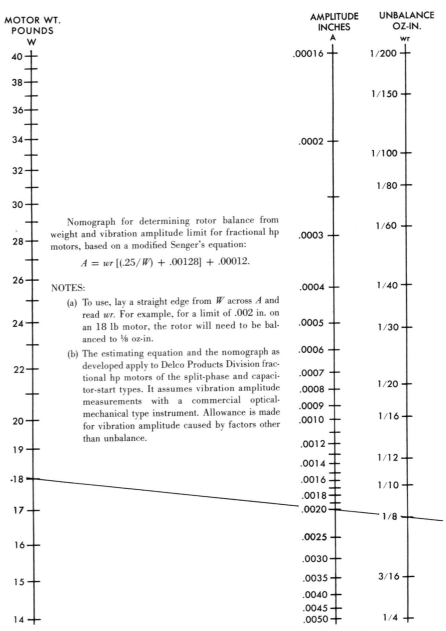

Nomograph for determining rotor balance from weight and vibration amplitude limit for fractional hp motors, based on a modified Senger's equation:

$$A = wr\left[(.25/W) + .00128\right] + .00012.$$

NOTES:

(a) To use, lay a straight edge from W across A and read wr. For example, for a limit of .002 in. on an 18 lb motor, the rotor will need to be balanced to ⅛ oz-in.

(b) The estimating equation and the nomograph as developed apply to Delco Products Division fractional hp motors of the split-phase and capacitor-start types. It assumes vibration amplitude measurements with a commercial optical-mechanical type instrument. Allowance is made for vibration amplitude caused by factors other than unbalance.

Fig. 23.1. An alignment chart (*Courtesy General Motors Corp.*).

Briefly stated, the simplest form of alignment chart consists of a set of three or more inclined or vertical scales so spaced and graduated as to represent graphically the variables in a formula. The scales may be divided into logarithmic units or some other types of functions, depending upon the form of equation. As illustrated in Fig. 23.1, the unknown value may be found by aligning a straight-edge to the points representing known values on two of the scales. With a scale or triangle so placed, the numerical value representing the solution of the equation can be read on the third scale at the point of intersection.

Since alignment charts in varied forms are being used more and more by engineers and scientists, it is desirable that students studying in the fields dealing with the sciences have some knowledge of the fundamental principles underlying their construction. However, in any brief treatment, directed toward a beginner, it is impossible to explain fully the mathematics involved in the construction of the many and varied types. Therefore, our attention here must be directed toward an understanding of a few of the less complicated straight-line forms with the hope that the student will gather sufficient knowledge to construct simple charts for familiar equations.

To satisfy the growing demand for training in the construction of graphical aids for engineering computation, several technical schools have added special courses dealing with alignment charts, special slide rules, and so on.

23.2. Construction of simple alignment charts. In this limited study, the explanation for the constructions will be based on the principles of plane geometry. The two forms to be considered for formulas having no more than three variables are the parallel-scale chart and the Z-chart, also called an N-chart (Fig. 23.2).

Without giving much more than a passing thought at this time to the geometry underlying the construction of alignment charts and to the selection of scales, the methods that might be used to construct simple charts for graphical addition and subtraction and graphical multiplication and division might well be considered [see Fig. 23.2(a) and (b)].

A parallel-scale alignment chart of the type shown in (a), prepared for the purpose of making additions and subtractions, could be constructed as follows:

Step 1. Draw three vertical straight lines spaced an equal distance apart.

Step 2. Draw a horizontal base line. This line will align and establish the origins (0) of the three scales.

Step 3. Using an engineer's decimal scale, mark off a series of

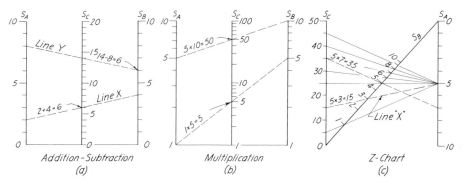

Fig. 23.2. Parallel-scale and Z-charts.

equal lengths on scales S_A and S_B. Start at the base line in each case. Mark the values of the graduations upward on both scales starting with 0 at the base line.

Step 4. Mark off on the S_C scale a series of lengths that are half as long as those on scales S_A and S_B. Number the graduation marks starting at the base line.

In using this chart to add two numbers, say 2 and 4, one may align the ruling edge of a triangle through 2 on the S_A scale and 4 on the S_B scale, then, read their sum at the point where the edge of the triangle crosses the S_C scale (see line X). To subtract one number from another, say 8 from 14, the edge of the triangle should be placed so as to pass through 8 on scale S_A and 14 on S_C. The difference, read on the S_B scale, will be 6 as shown by line Y.

For proof of this construction, it is necessary to turn to this principle of geometry: that the median of a trapezoid (a line parallel to the bases and located equidistant between them) will have a length equal to one-half the sum of the lengths of the two bases. Let it be supposed then that lines X and Y form the sides of such a trapezoid, and the bases are the lines intercepted between X and Y on the scales S_A and S_B. Then, since S_C is equidistant between S_A and S_B, the segment between points 6 and 14 must represent the line located midway between the bases of the trapezoid. With the lengths of the units on S_C equal to one-half the length of those along scales S_A and S_B, the number of units intercepted along S_C must be equal to the sum of the number of units intercepted on the other two scales. The base line and the line X could also be considered to be the sides of the trapezoid. In this case 6 units on S_C equals the sum of the 2 units on S_A and the 4 units on S_B.

If logarithmic scales are used for this form of chart as in (b) instead of natural scales as in (a), a chart for multiplication and division results, for the log of the product of two numbers is equal to the sum of the logs of the factors. Thus, by a method of addition a product can be obtained.

EXAMPLE: $c = a \times b$ and $\log c = \log a + \log b$

To find the product of two numbers, say 5 and 10, one should place the ruling edge of a triangle so that it will pass through 5 on the S_A scale and 10 on the S_B scale. The product may be read on the S_C scale [see (b)].

Necessary information for the construction of logarithmic scales is given in Sec. 23.4.

A Z-chart (also called an N-chart), which will give the product of two numbers, is shown in (c). For example, if line X is assumed to represent the edge of a triangle so placed as to pass through 5 on the S_A scale and 3 on the S_B scale, it can be seen that $3 \times 5 = 15$.

A simple Z-chart that has been prepared solely for straight multiplication will have outside vertical scales of uniform spacing. The length of the scales and the spacing of the graduation marks can be arbitrarily determined as long as the chart will fit on the paper that is available and provided that the graduations cover the desired range in each case. The two vertical scales begin with 0 (zero) value at opposite ends of the diagonal scale so that the values of the graduations read in increasing magnitude upward on one scale and downward on the other.

The steps in constructing a chart of this type are as follows:

Step 1. Lay out the vertical scales using uniform spacing for the graduation marks.

Step 2. Draw the line for the diagonal scale by joining the two zero points.

Step 3. Graduate the diagonal scale. In order to simplify the construction, it is suggested that one convenient value for the factor (say 5) be selected from which to draw construction lines to the graduation marks on the scale giving the product. The points of intersection of these lines with the diagonal line establish the location of the graduation marks for the diagonal scale. For instance, a line drawn from 5 on S_A to 5 on S_C will give the location of the graduation mark for the 1 on scale S_B. Similarly, a line drawn from 5 on S_A to 45 on S_C will locate the graduation mark for the 9 on S_B.

23.3. Definitions. Before starting a discussion on the construction of scales, it is necessary that the student have an understanding of the meaning of the following terms and expressions that are commonly used when constructing alignment charts for solving equations:

Constant—A quantity whose value remains unchanged in an equation.

Variable—A quantity capable of taking different values in an equation. A variable is designated by some letter, usually one of the latter letters of the alphabet.

Function of a variable—A mathematical expression for a combination of terms containing a variable, usually expressed in abbreviated form as $f(x)$ which is understood to mean "function of x." An equation usually contains several functions of different variables, such as $f(r) + f(s) = f(t)$; or $f(u)$. $f(v) = f(w)$.

Functional modulus—A proportionality multiplier that is used to bring a range of values of a particular function within a selected length for a scale. For instance, with the upper and lower limits of a function known and a definite length L chosen for the scale, the value of the functional modulus (m) can be found by dividing L by the amount of the difference between the upper and lower limits of the function. The scale equation for determining m may be written

$$m = \frac{L}{f(u_2) - f(u_1)}$$

where $f(u_2)$ and $f(u_1)$ are the upper and lower limits.

Scale—A graduated line that may be either straight or curved. When the graduation marks are equally spaced, that is, when the distance between marks is the same for equal increments of the variable as the variable increases in magnitude, the scale is known as a uniform scale. When the lengths to the graduation marks are laid off to correspond to scale values of the function of a variable, the scale is called a functional scale.

23.4. Construction of a functional scale. Let it be supposed that it is necessary to construct a functional scale, 5 in. in length, for $f(u) = u^2/2$ with u to range from 0 to 10. It will be found desirable to make the necessary computations by steps and to record the scale data in tabular form (Fig. 23.3).

Step 1. Record the values of u in the table.

Step 2. Compute the values of the function.

Step 3. Determine the functional modulus m.

u	0	1	2	3	4	5	6	7	8	9	10
u^2	0	1	4	9	16	25	36	49	64	81	100
$u^2/2$	0	0.5	2.0	4.5	8.0	12.5	18.0	24.5	32.0	40.5	50.0
$m(u^2/2)$	0	0.05″	0.2″	0.45″	0.80″	1.25″	1.80″	2.45″	3.20″	4.05″	5.00″

Fig. 23.3. Table.

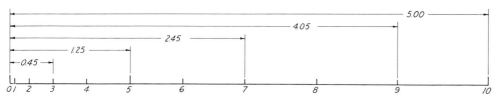

Fig. 23.4. Functional scale for $u^2/2$.

Step 4. Multiply the recorded values of the function by the functional modulus.

In this case and in many other cases, the functional modulus may be chosen by inspection. For this problem, the over-all length (L) of the scale will be 5 in. when $m = 0.10$. If the scale equation is used to determine the functional modulus then

$$m = \frac{L}{f(u_2) - f(u_1)} = \frac{5}{(10^2/2) - 0} = \frac{5}{50} = 0.10$$

All that now remains to be done to construct the scale is to lay off the computed distances along the line for the scale and mark the values at the corresponding interval points (Fig. 23.4).

Although a logarithmic scale might be constructed in this same manner, much time can be saved by using the graphic method shown in Fig. 23.5 for subdividing the scale between its end-points. To apply this method to a scale that has already been laid off to a predetermined length with the end-points of the range (say 1 to 10) marked, the steps of the construction are as follows:

Step 1. Draw a light construction line through point 1 making any convenient angle with the scale line.

Step 2. Using a printed log scale, mark off points on the auxiliary line.

Step 3. Draw a line through the 10 point on the construction line and the 10 point on the scale, then, through the remaining points draw lines parallel to this line through the 10's. These will divide the scale in proportion to the logarithms of numbers from 1 to 10.

23.5. Parallel-scale charts for equations of the form $f(t) + f(u) = f(v)$. An alignment chart that is designed for solving an equation that can be set up to take this form will have three parallel functional scales that may be either uniform or logarithmic depending upon the equation. More information will be presented later concerning parallel-scale charts with logarithmic scales. In this section, attention will be directed to charts having scales with uniform spacing.

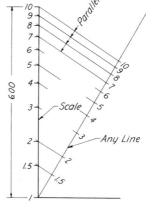

Fig. 23.5. Graduating a log scale.

Before one can start constructing the chart, he must determine by calculation certain necessary information. First, he must determine how the scales are to be graduated, and second, he must calculate the ratio for the scale spacing.

To be competent to design parallel-scale charts, one must have a full understanding of the geometric basis for their construction. The explanation to follow is associated with the line layout in Fig. 23.6. Three parallel scales S_A, S_B, and S_C are shown and the origins t_0, u_0, and v_0 fall on line (isopleth) AB. Line (1) and line (2) are drawn parallel to AB through points v and u respectively. By similar triangles (shown shaded);

$$\frac{L_t - L_v}{a} = \frac{L_v - L_u}{b}$$

Now if

$$m_t = \frac{L_t}{f(t) - f(t_0)}$$

then

$$L_t = m_t[f(t) - f(t_0)]$$

When the function of t_0 is zero, the equation becomes

$$L_t = m_t f(t)$$

Similarly, when v_0 is zero,

$$L_v = m_v f(v)$$

and, when u_0 is zero,

$$L_u = m_u f(u)$$

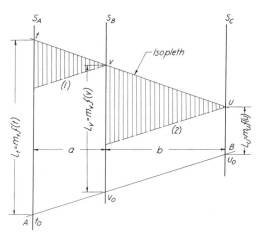

Fig. 23.6. Geometric basis for construction of parallel-scale alignment charts.

Substituting these values;

$$\frac{m_t f(t) - m_v f(v)}{a} = \frac{m_v f(v) - m_u f(u)}{b}$$

Collecting terms,

$$m_t f(t) + \left(\frac{a}{b}\right) m_u f(u) = \left(\frac{a}{b}\right) m_v f(v) + m_v f(v)$$

$$= m_v \left(1 + \frac{a}{b}\right) f(v)$$

But $f(t) + f(u) = f(v)$ only if the coefficient of the three terms are equal, therefore,

$$m_t = \left(\frac{a}{b}\right) m_u = \left(1 + \frac{a}{b}\right) m_v$$

and,

$$\frac{m_t}{m_u} = \frac{a}{b} \qquad\qquad \text{Eq. (1)}$$

Now since

$$m_t = \left(1 + \frac{a}{b}\right) m_v$$

and

$$\frac{a}{b} = \frac{m_t}{m_u}$$

Then,

$$m_t = \left(1 + \frac{m_t}{m_u}\right) m_v$$

$$m_v = \frac{m_t}{\left(1 + \frac{m_t}{m_u}\right)}$$

and finally,

$$m_v = \frac{m_t m_u}{m_t + m_u} \qquad\qquad \text{Eq. (2)}$$

Now suppose that it is desired to construct a chart having the form of $t + u = v$ and that t is to have a range from 0 to 10 and u from 0 to 20 (Fig. 23.7). It has been determined that the scale lengths should be 6 in.

Then

$$m_t = \frac{6}{10.0} = \frac{6}{10} = 0.6; \qquad m_u = \frac{6}{20.0} = \frac{6}{20} = 0.3$$

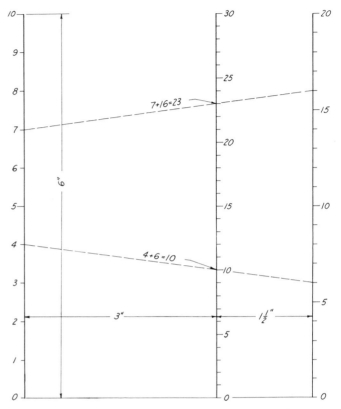

Fig. 23.7. Alignment chart for equation of the form
$f(t) + f(u) = f(v)$.

and,

$$m_v = \frac{m_t m_u}{m_t + m_u} = \frac{0.6 \times 0.3}{0.6 + 0.3} = \frac{0.18}{0.90} = 0.20 \quad \text{Eq. (2)}$$

To determine the ratio of the scale spacing;

$$\frac{m_t}{m_u} = \frac{a}{b} = \frac{0.6}{0.3} = \frac{2}{1} \qquad \text{Eq. (1)}$$

For convenience, distance a between scales can be made 3 in. Distance b must then be 1½ in. to satisfy the proportion of 2 to 1. The total width of the chart will be 4½ in.

Since in this particular case the modulus for each of the scales is in full tenths and the scales are to be uniformly divided, an engineer's scale may be used to mark off the scales of the chart. With other conditions, it would be necessary to prepare either a table such as the one shown in Fig. 23.3 or to divide the line between its end-points using a geometric method.

23.6. Parallel-scale charts for equations of the form $f(t) \cdot f(u) = f(v)$.
Equations of this form may be rewritten so as to take the form $f(t) + f(u) = f(v)$ by using logarithms for both sides of the equation. For example, suppose that it is desirable to prepare a chart for $M = Wl$, a formula commonly used by designers and engineers. In this equation, M is the maximum bending moment at the point of support of a cantilever beam; W is the concentrated load; and l is the distance from the point of support to the load.

Given: $M = Wl$
Rewritten: $\log M = \log W + \log l$

Another example would be the formula for determining the discharge of trapezoidal weirs.

Given: $Q = 3.367Lh^{3/2}$
Rewritten: $\log Q = \log 3.367 + \log L + 1.5 \log h$

In this last equation, Q is discharge in cubic feet per second; L is the length of the crest in feet (width of weir); and h is the observed head (depth of water).

For the purpose of our discussion, the formula $P = I^2R$ will be used where P is power in watts; I is current in amperes; and R is resistance in ohms (Fig. 23.8). It has been determined that I must vary from 1 to 10 amp and R from 1 to 10 ohms. A chart of this type might be used to determine the power loss in inductive windings. The length of the scales is to be 5 in.

The steps for the construction are as follows:

Step 1. Write the equation in standard form.

$$\log P = 2 \log I + \log R$$

Step 2. Determine the moduli m_I and m_R for the outside scales.

$$m_I = \frac{5}{2 \log 10 - 2 \log 1} = \frac{5}{2} = 2.5; \quad L_I = 2.5\,(2 \log I) = 5 \log I$$

$$m_R = \frac{5}{\log 10 - \log 1} = \frac{5}{1} = 5; \quad L_R = 5 \log R$$

Step 3. Determine m_P and L_P for the P-scale.

$$m_P = \frac{2.5 \times 5}{2.5 + 5} = \frac{12.5}{7.5} = \frac{5}{3}; \quad L_P = \frac{5}{3} \log P$$

Step 4. Determine the ratio for the spacing of the scales.

$$\frac{m_I}{m_R} = \frac{2.5}{5} = \frac{1}{2} \text{ (ratio)}$$

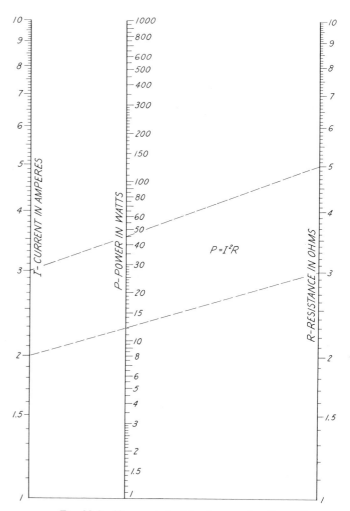

Fig. 23.8. Alignment chart for the equation $P = I^2R$.

Step 5. Draw three vertical lines 1 in. and 2 in. apart and add a horizontal base line. By using these selected values, the ratio for spacing will be maintained and the chart will have good proportion.

Step 6. Graduate the scales for I and R using the method shown in Fig. 23.5. In this particular case, both logarithmic scales will be alike and will range from 1 on the base line upward to 10.

Step 7. Graduate the P-scale. By substituting values in the equation, it will be found that P will range from 1 w to 1000 w; therefore, the scale will be a three-cycle logarithmic scale, and the graphic method may be used for locating the graduation marks.

Figure 23.9 shows another parallel-scale alignment chart. This particular one could be used to determine the volume of a cylindrical tank when the diameter and height are known.

The formula for the volume of a cylinder, as given in the illustration, may be rewritten as

$$\log V = \log (\pi/4) + 2 \log D + \log H$$

Suppose that it has been decided, as in this case, that both the diameter (D) and the height (H) are to vary from 1 ft to 10 ft, and that the length of the two outside scales is to be 6 in. For the moment, the constant term $\log (\pi/4)$ can be ignored, for it can be accounted for at a later time by shifting the V-scale for the volume upward until it is in the position for furnishing a correct reading for a particular value as computed using the formula.

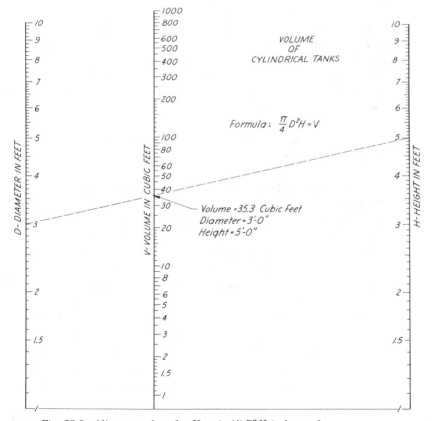

Fig. 23.9. Alignment chart for $V = (\pi/4)D^2H$ (volume of a cylinder).

The moduli can be determined as previously explained.

$$m_D = \frac{6}{2 \log 10 - 2 \log 1} = 3 \quad \text{and} \quad L_D = 3(2 \log D) = 6 \log D$$

$$m_H = \frac{6}{\log 10 - \log 1} = 6 \quad \text{and} \quad L_H = 6 \log H$$

$$m_V = \frac{m_D \times m_H}{m_D + m_H} = \frac{3 \times 6}{3 + 6} = \frac{18}{9} = 2 \quad \text{and} \quad L_V = 2(\log V)$$

Scale spacing ratio;

$$\frac{m_D}{m_H} = \frac{3}{6}$$

For convenience, the scales can be spaced at 2 in. and 4 in., giving a chart that is a square in form.

The scales for D and H may be graduated by using the graphical method illustrated in Fig. 23.5. The scale for V will be a three-cycle scale with a 6-in. range of length between the 1 and 1000 values. Since the value of V at the base line must result from the substitution in the equation of the values of 1 and 1 for the other two scales, the resulting value of 0.7854 cu ft is the volume at the base line. The most convenient procedure to follow in graduating the V-scale is to start with the 0.7854 value at the base line. By so doing, the constant term, $\log \pi/4$, is taken into account. Should one desire to determine the distance to be laid off along the V-scale from the base line to the 1, it will be found to be equal to two times the difference between the logs of the numbers in this particular case, for the value of m_v is 2.

23.7. Three-scale alignment chart—simplified (graphical) construction. After the student has acquired a thorough understanding of the theory of alignment charts, which includes a full knowledge of the geometric basis underlying their construction, he will be in a position to simplify his construction work and make it purely graphical through the use of tie-lines. Of course, this can only be done after the chart form has been identified, the equation converted, and the ranges for the variables (as needed) have been decided upon. The use of tie-lines to locate check points on the third scale of a three-scale alignment chart is shown in Fig. 23.10.

Given: $M = wl^2/12$, the equation for the bending moment (maximum) of a beam, having a uniformly distributed load and fixed at both ends. In this equation, w is the load in pounds per foot of length and l is the span in feet.

It was decided that the alignment chart would fulfill most needs if w had limits from 10 to 200 lb per ft and l had limits from 5 to 25 ft.

Equation rewritten: $\log w + 2 \log l = \log M + \log 12$.

The steps for the construction of the chart, with only minor calculations that may be performed mentally, are as follows:

1. Draw two vertical lines (say 5 in. long) at any convenient distance apart.

2. Graduate the *w*-scale (left-hand line) from the lower point 10 to the uppermost point 200. (In this case, use was made of the method shown in Fig. 23.5 to locate the scale values between 10 and 200.)

3. Graduate the *l*-scale, with the lower point as 5 and the point at the top of the scale as 25. (Scale values located as in Step 2.)

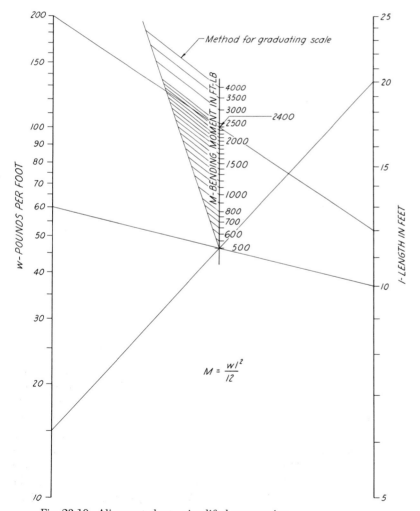

Fig. 23.10. Alignment chart—simplified construction.

4. Using a value of 10 for l and 500 for M yields $w = 60$ for the tie-line from the 60 value on the w-scale to the 10 value on the l-scale. Again, with $l = 20$ and $M = 500$, w is found to be 15 for the second tie-line through $M = 500$. The intersection of these two tie-lines is a check point on the third vertical scale, a point that establishes not only the position of the scale line but the 500 value as well.

5. Locate a second check point on the M-scale by drawing a third tie line. In this case it was found to be convenient to use $w = 200$ and $l = 12$ to yield $M = 2400$.

6. Graduate the M-scale as shown (read Sec. 23.4).

23.8. Graphical construction of a Z-chart. A simplified graphical construction may be employed to construct a Z-chart (N-chart) such as the one shown in Fig. 23.11, for the equation $V = 2.467Dd^2$ which gives the volume of a torus, a solid taking the form illustrated in Fig. 4.63. The given equation was considered to be so arranged that the vertical V- and D-scales would be uniformly graduated. The d-scale on the diagonal representing a variable to a power, is nonuniformly graduated. For this form of chart, one should recall that the vertical scales begin at zero and run in opposite directions (see Sec. 23.2). The diagonal connecting these two zero points completes the usual N-shape.

The steps in making the construction are as follows:

Step 1. Draw the scale lines for the variables V and D at any convenient distance apart, in this case 3.50 in. Then, lay off the D-scale to some selected length, say 6 in., and locate the zero point of V-scale opposite the 10 of the D-scale.

Step 2. Graduate the V-scale uniformly, being certain that the range is sufficient to make possible a full reading when using the maximum values of the other scales.

Step 3. Graduate the D-scale for the selected range of values, in this case from 0 to 10 in.

Step 4. Graduate the d-scale by selecting one convenient value of D and substituting it repeatedly in the original equation, each time with a different value of d which is to be marked on the diagonal scale. In so doing, values of V are found that establish the ends of tie-lines from the pole point (10) selected on the D-scale. For example, when the values 10 and 1 are substituted for D and d, respectively, in the given equation, V is found to be 24.67 cu in. With this known, a tie-line drawn from the pole to 24.67 on the V-scale, will locate $d = 1$ on the diagonal scale. The volumes for a range of d from 1 to 5 in.

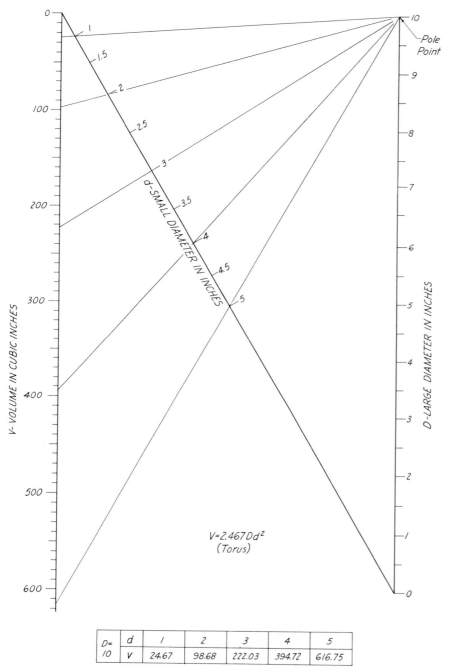

Fig. 23.11. Chart for equation $V = 2.467Dd^2$.

are shown in the table below the illustration. These values were used to draw the tie-lines shown.

23.9. Four-variable relationship—parallel-scale alignment chart.

A four-variable parallel-scale alignment chart may be constructed for an equation of the form $f(t) + f(u) + f(v) = f(w)$ when the equation has been rewritten as follows:

$$f(t) + f(u) = f(k)$$
$$f(k) + f(v) = f(w)$$

When rewritten in this form, the four-variable chart can then be constructed as two three-scale nomographs with the k-scale common to both. The k-scale, which serves as a pivot line in using the chart, need not be graduated but it must be remembered that it does have a modulus and does represent a function in both equations.

In Fig. 23.12, a four-variable alignment chart is shown for the addition of numbers. For this particular construction, it was arbitrarily decided that t should have a range from 0 to 5, u from 0 to 10, and v from 0 to 20. The procedure for the construction of this chart is as follows:

Step 1. Draw the vertical lines (stems) for the t- and u-scales at any convenient distance apart and, by means of the engineer's scale or graphically, graduate t from 0 to 5 and u from 0 to 10.

Step 2. Draw the two intersecting tie-lines between the t and u scales that determine the position of the pivot line k at their point of intersection (7). Intersecting tie-lines could have been drawn from other graduation marks along the t and u scales as long as the sum of the values at the ends of one of the selected tie-lines equals the sum of the values at the ends of the other tie-line intersecting it.

Step 3. Draw a third tie-line to locate another check point along the pivot line k. In this case, the tie-line was drawn from 3 on the t-scale to 10 on the u-scale to locate the mark for 13 on the k-scale.

Step 4. Decide upon the best location for the v-scale, then draw the stem line and graduate it uniformly from 0 to 20.

Step 5. Using the 7 and 13 value marks that have now been established on the k-scale, draw the two tie-lines ($18 + 7 = 25$ and $13 + 12 = 25$) that will determine the location of the w-scale at their point of intersection as well as the position of the 25 graduation mark.

Step 6. Draw the w-scale and graduate it from 0 to 35, the 35 value representing the largest sum obtainable from the use of

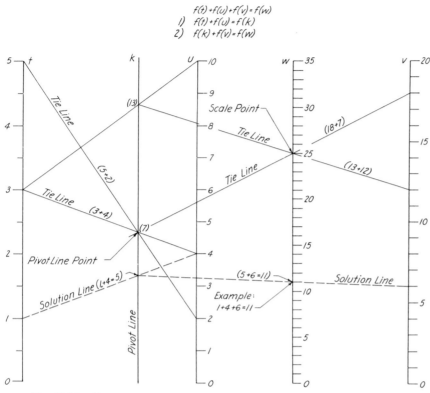

Fig. 23.12. Alignment chart for the equation $f(t) + f(u) + f(v) = f(w)$.

the t-, u-, and v-scales as they have been graduated for this particular chart.

The procedure for finding the sum of the numbers 1, 4, and 6 is illustrated by the broken lines extending between the scales. First, a straightedge can be laid across the t- and u-scales through the 1 and 4 values, as shown, to determine the position on the pivot line (k) that the graduation mark would have that represents their sum, in this case 5. Then the straightedge should be shifted so that its edge will pass through the 5 position on the pivot line and the graduation mark for the 6 value on the v-scale. The sum of the three given numbers can then be read as 11 on the w-scale.

The four-scale alignment chart, shown in Fig. 23.13, for the computation of simple interest, may be easily constructed once the equation $I = PRT$ has first been written in the logarithmic form of

$$\log P + \log R + \log T = \log I,$$

and, then rewritten as

$$\log P + \log R = \log k \qquad (1)$$

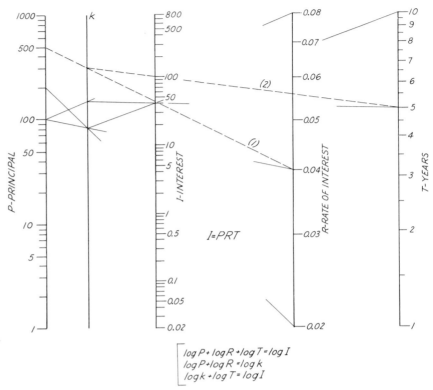

$$\begin{bmatrix} \log P + \log R + \log T = \log I \\ \log P + \log R = \log k \\ \log k + \log T = \log I \end{bmatrix}$$

Fig. 23.13. Alignment chart for the equation $I = PRT$.

and

$$\log k + \log T = \log I \tag{2}$$

The equation as first rewritten is in the form of $f(t) + f(u) + f(v) = f(w)$ and as arranged in (1) and (2) in the form of

$$f(t) + f(u) = f(k)$$
$$f(k) + f(v) = f(w)$$

Now, since equations (1) and (2) have the same form as those for the previous problem, the alignment chart for the equation $I = PRT$ is constructed similarly except that logarithmic scales must be used in this case in place of natural (uniformly divided) scales. As before, tie-lines were used to position the k and I scales and to locate needed check points. The procedure for reading the chart is illustrated by the broken lines, numbered (1) and (2).

The reader is urged to follow through the construction of the alignment chart for the equation $I = PRT$ mentally, step by step. At the start, however, he must recognize that the k-scale belongs first to the PRk chart and then to the kTI three-scale chart that together make the complete chart for the four variables P, R, T, and I.

23.10. Some other forms of alignment charts. Examples of some of the forms that alignment charts may have are shown in outline in Fig. 23.14. Examples of forms of proportional charts are illustrated in (a), (b), and (c). Miscellaneous forms are shown in (d), (e), and (f). One may obtain information needed for the construction of proportional type charts, concurrent scale charts, four-variable N-charts, and charts having a curved scale from any of the several books on nomography that are listed in the bibliography of this text.

PROBLEMS

The following problems have been designed to emphasize the fundamental principles underlying the preparation and use of alignment charts.

1-12. Prepare an alignment chart for the given equation. Chart scales should have a sufficient number of division marks to enable the user to obtain some reasonably accurate results (readings). In each problem the range for two of the variables has been given. The range of the third variable must make possible the use of the full range of each of the other two variables.

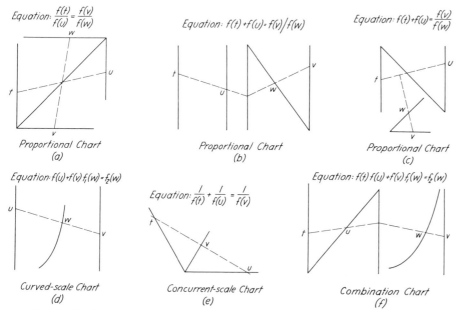

Fig. 23.14. Some common chart forms.

1. Construct an alignment chart for the multiplication of numbers from 1 to 100 (read Sec. 23.2 and study Fig. 23.2).

2. Construct an alignment chart of the form $t + u = v$. Let t vary from 0 to 10 and u from 0 to 15 (read Sec. 23.5 and study Fig. 23.7).

3. Construct an alignment chart for determining the area of a triangle. The student is to determine for himself the range for each of the scales.

4. Construct an alignment chart for determining the volume of a cylinder. The diameter is to range from 1 to 5 in. and the height from 1 to 10 in. The volume is to be in cubic inches (read Sec. 23.6).

5. Make an alignment chart for determining the volume of a paraboloid, $V = 1/8\pi ab^2$, where a is the length (measured along the axis) and b is the diameter of the base. Let a vary from 1 to 20 in. and b from 1 to 10 in.

6. Construct an alignment chart for the maximum bending moment at the point of support of a cantilever beam, formula $M = Wl$. W is the concentrated load at the end of the beam and l is the distance from the point of support to the load (read Sec. 23.6). Let W vary from 100 to 1000 lb and l from 10 to 20 ft. M will be in ft-lb.

7. Make an alignment chart for the discharge of trapezoidal weirs, formula $Q = 3.367Lh^{3/2}$. Q is discharged in cubic feet per second; L is length of crest in feet (width of weir); and, h is the head (depth of water). Let L vary from 1 to 10 ft and h from 0.5 to 2 ft (read Secs. 23.6 and 23.7).

8. Make an alignment chart for the formula $P = I^2R$ as explained in Sec. 23.6. Let I vary from 1 to 20 amp and R from 1 to 10 ohms.

9. Make an alignment chart for the formula $R = E/I$ where E is the electromotive force in volts; I is current in amperes; and, R is resistance in ohms. Let R vary from 1 to 20 ohms and I from 1 to 100 amp (read Secs. 23.6 and 23.7).

10. Make an alignment chart for the formula $I = bd^3/36$ where I is the moment of inertia of a triangular section; b is the length of the base in inches; and d is the depth of the section (altitude of triangle). Let b vary from 1 to 10 in. and d from 1 to 10 in. (read Secs. 23.6 and 23.7).

11. Make an alignment chart for the formula $M = wl^2/8$ where M is the bending moment in foot-pounds, w is the load in pounds per foot, and l the length of span in feet. Let w vary from 10 to 200 lb per ft and l from 5 to 25 ft (see Fig. 23.10).

12. Make an alignment chart (Z-chart) for the equation for the volume of a right circular cylinder, $V = \pi r^2 h/144$, where V is the volume in cubic feet, r is the radius of the base in inches and h is the height in feet. Let r vary from 0 to 20 in. and h from 0 to 20 ft.

APPENDIX

Graphical Symbols for Electrical Diagrams

AMPLIFIER General	**DEVICE, VISUAL SIGNALING** Annunciator	**MICROPHONE**
ANTENNA General	**ELEMENT, THERMAL** Thermal Cutout, Flasher	**PATH, TRANSMISSION** General
Loop	Thermal Relay	Crossing, Not Connected
ARRESTER General Multigap	or	Junction
BATTERY Multicell		Junction, Connected Paths
		Pair
BREAKER, CIRCUIT General	**FUSE** General	Assembled Conductors; Cable Coaxial
CAPACITOR General	Fusible Element	2-Conductor Cable Grouping Leads
COIL Blowout (Broken line not part of symbol) Operating	**GROUND**	or
	HANDSET General	**RECEIVER** General Headset
CONNECTOR Female Contact Male Contact	**INDUCTOR WINDING** General or	**RECTIFIER** General
CONTACT, ELECTRIC Fixed ○ or Locking Nonlocking Rotating Closed or Open or	**LAMP** Ballast Lamp Incandescent	**REPEATER** 1-Way
		RESISTOR General
	MACHINE, ROTATING Basic Generator Motor Wound Rotor Armature Winding Symbols 1-Phase 2-Phase 3-Phase Wye 3-Phase Delta	**SWITCH** General Single Throw Double Throw Knife
CORE Magnetic (General) Magnet or Relay		**THERMOCOUPLE.** Temperature-Measuring
COUPLER, DIRECTIONAL General		**TRANSFORMER** Magnetic Core Shielded

ASA Y32.2–1954.

Graphical Symbols for Heat-Power Apparatus

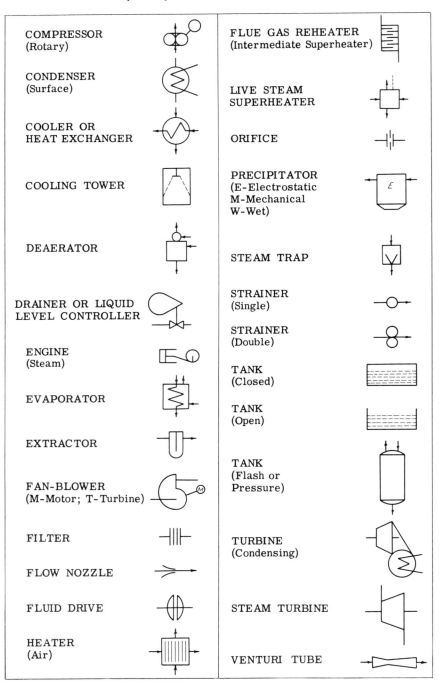

COMPRESSOR (Rotary)		FLUE GAS REHEATER (Intermediate Superheater)
CONDENSER (Surface)		LIVE STEAM SUPERHEATER
COOLER OR HEAT EXCHANGER		ORIFICE
COOLING TOWER		PRECIPITATOR (E-Electrostatic M-Mechanical W-Wet)
DEAERATOR		STEAM TRAP
DRAINER OR LIQUID LEVEL CONTROLLER		STRAINER (Single)
		STRAINER (Double)
ENGINE (Steam)		TANK (Closed)
EVAPORATOR		TANK (Open)
EXTRACTOR		TANK (Flash or Pressure)
FAN-BLOWER (M-Motor; T-Turbine)		
FILTER		TURBINE (Condensing)
FLOW NOZZLE		
FLUID DRIVE		STEAM TURBINE
HEATER (Air)		VENTURI TUBE

ASA Z32.2.6–1950 (R1956).

Graphical Symbols for Pipe Fittings

	FLANGED	SCREWED	BELL & SPIGOT	WELDED	SOLDERED
1) BUSHING					
2) CAP					
3) CROSS-STRAIGHT SIZE					
4) ELBOW — 45 DEGREE					
— 90 DEGREE					
— TURNED DOWN					
— TURNED UP					
5) LATERAL					
6) PLUG					
7) TEE — STRAIGHT SIZE					
— OUTLET UP					
— OUTLET DOWN					
8) UNION					
9) REDUCER — CONCENTRIC					
— ECCENTRIC					
10) CHECK VALVE — STRAIGHT WAY					
11) GATE VALVE					
12) GLOBE VALVE					
13) ANGLE VALVE GLOBE — ELEVATION					
GLOBE — PLAN					

ASA Z32.2.3–1949.

TABLE 1
Standard Conversion Table

4ths	8ths	16ths	32nds	64ths	To 4 places	To 3 places	To 2 places
				1/64 ——	.0156	.016	.02
			1/32		.0312	.031	.03
				3/64 ——	.0469	.047	.05
		1/16			.0625	.062	.06
				5/64 ——	.0781	.078	.08
			3/32		.0938	.094	.09
				7/64 ——	.1094	.109	.11
	1/8				.1250	.125	.12
				9/64 ——	.1406	.141	.14
			5/32		.1562	.156	.16
				11/64 ——	.1719	.172	.17
		3/16			.1875	.188	.19
				13/64 ——	.2031	.203	.20
			7/32		.2188	.219	.22
				15/64 ——	.2344	.234	.23
1/4					.2500	.250	.25
				17/64 ——	.2656	.266	.27
			9/32		.2812	.281	.28
				19/64 ——	.2969	.297	.30
		5/16			.3125	.312	.31
				21/64 ——	.3281	.328	.33
			11/32		.3438	.344	.34
				23/64 ——	.3594	.359	.36
	3/8				.3750	.375	.38
				25/64 ——	.3906	.391	.39
			13/32		.4062	.406	.41
				27/64 ——	.4219	.422	.42
		7/16			.4375	.438	.44
				29/64 ——	.4531	.453	.45
			15/32		.4688	.469	.47
				31/64 ——	.4844	.484	.48
					.5000	.500	.50

TABLE 1 (cont.)
Standard Conversion Table

4ths	8ths	16ths	32nds	64ths	To 4 places	To 3 places	To 2 places
				$33/64$	.5156	.516	.52
			$17/32$		.5312	.531	.53
				$35/64$	.5469	.547	.55
		$9/16$			.5625	.562	.56
				$37/64$	.5781	.578	.58
			$19/32$		.5938	.594	.59
				$39/64$	.6094	.609	.61
	$5/8$				.6250	.625	.62
				$41/64$	.6406	.641	.64
			$21/32$		.6562	.656	.66
				$43/64$	.6719	.672	.67
		$11/16$			.6875	.688	.69
				$45/64$	.7031	.703	.70
			$23/32$		.7188	.719	.72
				$47/64$	.7344	.734	.73
$3/4$					.7500	.750	.75
				$49/64$	.7656	.766	.77
			$25/32$		.7812	.781	.78
				$51/64$	.7969	.797	.80
		$13/16$			.8125	.812	.81
				$53/64$	.8281	.828	.83
			$27/32$		.8438	.844	.84
				$55/64$	.8594	.859	.86
	$7/8$				.8750	.875	.88
				$57/64$	.8906	.891	.89
			$29/32$		.9062	.906	.91
				$59/64$	.9219	.922	.92
		$15/16$			.9375	.938	.94
				$61/64$	.9531	.953	.95
			$31/32$		.9688	.969	.97
				$63/64$	.9844	.984	.98
					1.0000	1.000	1.00

TABLE 2
Unified and American Thread Series*

Nom. diam.	COARSE (NC) (UNC)		FINE (NF) (UNF)		EXTRA FINE (NEF) (UNEF)	
	Threads per inch	*Tap drill†*	*Threads per inch*	*Tap drill†*	*Threads per inch*	*Tap drill†*
0	—	—	80	$\frac{3}{64}$	—	—
1	64	No. 53	72	No. 53	—	—
2	56	No. 50	64	No. 50	—	—
3	48	No. 47	56	No. 45	—	—
4	**40**	No. 43	48	No. 42	—	—
5	40	No. 38	44	No. 37	—	—
6	**32**	No. 36	40	No. 33	—	—
8	32	No. 29	36	No. 29	—	—
10	**24**	No. 25	**32**	No. 21	—	—
12	24	No. 16	28	No. 14	32	—
¼	**20**	No. 7	**28**	No. 3	32	No. 2
⁵⁄₁₆	**18**	F	**24**	I	32	K
⅜	**16**	⁵⁄₁₆	**24**	Q	32	S
⁷⁄₁₆	**14**	U	**20**	$\frac{25}{64}$	**28**	Y
½	**13**	$\frac{27}{64}$	**20**	$\frac{29}{64}$	**28**	$\frac{15}{32}$
⁹⁄₁₆	**12**	$\frac{31}{64}$	**18**	$\frac{33}{64}$	24	$\frac{17}{32}$
⅝	**11**	$\frac{17}{32}$	**18**	$\frac{37}{64}$	24	$\frac{19}{32}$
¾	**10**	$\frac{21}{32}$	**16**	$\frac{11}{16}$	**20**	$\frac{45}{64}$
⅞	**9**	$\frac{49}{64}$	**14**	$\frac{13}{16}$	**20**	$\frac{53}{64}$
1	**8**	⅞	**12**	$\frac{59}{64}$	**20**	$\frac{61}{64}$
1⅛	**7**	$\frac{63}{64}$	**12**	$1\frac{3}{64}$	18	$1\frac{5}{64}$
1¼	**7**	$1\frac{7}{64}$	**12**	$1\frac{11}{64}$	18	$1\frac{13}{64}$
1⅜	**6**	$1\frac{13}{64}$	**12**	$1\frac{19}{64}$	18	—
1½	**6**	$1\frac{21}{64}$	**12**	$1\frac{27}{64}$	18	$1\frac{29}{64}$
1¾	**5**	$1\frac{35}{64}$	—	—	**16**	$1\frac{11}{16}$
2	**4½**	$1\frac{25}{32}$	—	—	**16**	$1\frac{15}{16}$
2¼	**4½**	$2\frac{1}{32}$	—	—	—	—
2½	**4**	2¼	—	—	—	—
2¾	**4**	2½	—	—	—	—
3	**4**	2¾	—	—	—	—
3¼	**4**	3	—	—	—	—
3½	**4**	3¼	—	—	—	—
3¾	**4**	3½	—	—	—	—
4	**4**	3¾	—	—	—	—

* ASA B1.1–1949 (third printing).

Bold type indicates Unified threads. To be designated UNC or UNF for sizes above one-fourth inch. Unified Standard—Classes 1A, 2A, 3A, 1B, 2B, 3B.

For recommended hole size limits before threading see Table 41, ASA B1.1–1949.

† Tap drill for a 75 per cent thread (not Unified—American Standard).

Bold type sizes smaller than one-fourth inch accepted for limited applications by the British, but the symbols NC or NF, as applicable, are retained.

TABLE 3
Unified-American Special Threads* (8 Pitch, 12 Pitch, and 16 Pitch Series)

Nom. diam.	Threads per inch			Nom. diam.	Threads per inch		
1/2	—	12	—	2 3/16	—	—	16
9/16	—	12	—	2 1/4	8	12	16
5/8	—	12	—	2 5/16	—	—	16
11/16	—	12	—	2 3/8	—	12	16
3/4	—	12	16	2 7/16	—	—	16
13/16	—	12	16	2 1/2	8	12	16
7/8	—	12	16	2 5/8	—	12	16
15/16	—	12	16	2 3/4	8	12	16
1	8	12	16	2 7/8	—	12	16
1 1/16	—	12	16	3	8	12	16
1 1/8	8	12	16	3 1/8	—	12	16
1 3/16	—	12	16	3 1/4	8	12	16
1 1/4	8	12	16	3 3/8	—	12	16
1 5/16	—	12	16	3 1/2	8	12	16
1 3/8	8	12	16	3 5/8	—	12	16
1 7/16	—	12	16	3 3/4	8	12	16
1 1/2	8	12	16	3 7/8	—	12	16
1 9/16	—	—	16	4	8	12	16
1 5/8	8	12	16	4 1/4	8	12	16
1 11/16	—	—	16	4 1/2	8	12	16
1 3/4	8	12	16	4 3/4	8	12	16
1 13/16	—	—	16	5	8	12	16
1 7/8	8	12	16	5 1/4	8	12	16
1 15/16	—	—	16	5 1/2	8	12	16
2	8	12	16	5 3/4	8	12	16
2 1/16	—	—	16	6	8	12	16
2 1/8	8	12	16				

* ASA B1.1–1949.
For recommended hole size limits before threading see Table 41, ASA B1.1–1949.
Bold type indicates Unified threads (UN).

TABLE 4
American Standard Acme and Stub Acme Threads

Nom. diam.	Thds. per in.	Nom. diam.	Thds. per in.
1/4	16	1 1/2	4
5/16	14	1 3/4	4
3/8	12	2	4
7/16	12	2 1/4	3
1/2	10	2 1/2	3
5/8	8	2 3/4	3
3/4	6	3	2
7/8	6	3 1/2	2
1	5	4	2
1 1/8	5	4 1/2	2
1 1/4	5	5	2
1 3/8	4		

ASA B1.5 and B1.8–1952.

TABLE 5
American Standard Wrench-Head Bolts and Nuts—Regular Series*

Bolt Diam. Nominal size	Bolt Heads				Nuts				
	Width across flats	Height of head			Width across flats	Thickness			
						Regular		Jam	
	Unfinished and semifinished square and hex.[1]	Unfinished square	Unfinished hexagon	Semifinished hexagon	Unfinished hex. semifinished hex. and hex. jam	Unfinished square and hex.	Semifinished hex. and hex. slotted	Unfinished hexagonal	Semifinished hexagonal
1/4	{ 3/8 sq. 7/16 hex.	11/64	11/64	5/32	7/16	7/32	13/64	5/32	9/64
5/16	1/2	13/64	7/32	13/64	9/16	17/64	1/4	3/16	11/64
3/8	9/16	1/4	1/4	15/64	5/8	21/64	5/16	7/32	13/64
7/16	5/8	19/64	19/64	9/32	3/4	3/8	23/64	1/4	15/64
1/2	3/4	21/64	11/32	5/16	13/16	7/16	27/64	5/16	19/64
9/16	—	—	—	—	7/8	1/2	31/64	11/32	21/64
5/8	15/16	27/64	27/64	25/64	1	35/64	17/32	3/8	23/64
3/4	1 1/8	1/2	1/2	15/32	1 1/8	21/32	41/64	7/16	27/64
7/8	1 5/16	19/32	37/64	35/64	1 5/16	49/64	3/4	1/2	31/64
1	1 1/2	21/32	43/64	39/64	1 1/2	7/8	55/64	9/16	35/64
1 1/8	1 11/16	3/4	3/4	11/16	1 11/16	1	31/32	5/8	39/64
1 1/4	1 7/8	27/32	27/32	25/32	1 7/8	1 3/32	1 1/16	3/4	23/32
1 3/8	2 1/16	29/32	29/32	27/32	2 1/16	1 13/64	1 11/64	13/16	25/32
1 1/2	2 1/4	1	1	15/16	2 1/4	1 5/16	1 9/32	7/8	27/32
1 5/8	2 7/16	1 3/32	—	—	2 7/16	—	1 25/64	—	29/32
1 3/4	2 5/8	—	1 5/32	1 3/32	2 5/8	—	1 1/2	—	31/32
1 7/8	—	—	—	—	2 13/16	—	1 39/64	—	1 1/32
2	3	—	1 11/32	1 7/32	3	—	1 23/32	—	1 3/32
2 1/4	3 3/8	—	1 1/2	1 3/8	3 3/8	—	1 59/64	—	1 13/64
2 1/2	3 3/4	—	1 21/32	1 17/32	3 3/4	—	2 9/64	—	1 23/64
2 3/4	4 1/8	—	1 13/16	1 11/16	4 1/8	—	2 23/64	—	1 37/64
3	4 1/2	—	2	1 7/8	4 1/2	—	2 37/64	—	1 45/64

* ASA B18.2–1955. All dimensions in inches.
Threads-bolts: course thread series, class 2A.
Threads-nuts: unfinished; coarse series, class 2B: semifinished; coarse, fine, or 8-pitch series.
[1] Square bolts in 1/4 to 1 5/8 sizes (nominal) only.

TABLE 6
American Standard Finished Hexagon Castle Nuts*

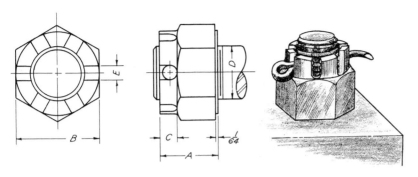

Nominal size	Threads per inch		Thickness	Width across flats	Slot		Diam. of cylindrical part min.
D	UNC	UNF	A	B	Depth C	Width E	
¼	20	28	%32	⁷⁄₁₆	0.094	0.078	0.371
⁵⁄₁₆	18	24	²¹⁄₆₄	½	0.094	0.094	0.425
⅜	16	24	¹³⁄₃₂	⁹⁄₁₆	0.125	0.125	0.478
⁷⁄₁₆	14	20	²⁹⁄₆₄	¹¹⁄₁₆	0.156	0.125	0.582
½	13	20	⁹⁄₁₆	¾	0.156	0.156	0.637
⁹⁄₁₆	12	18	³⁹⁄₆₄	⅞	0.188	0.156	0.744
⅝	11	18	²³⁄₃₂	¹⁵⁄₁₆	0.219	0.188	0.797
¾	10	16	¹³⁄₁₆	1⅛	0.250	0.188	0.941
⅞	9	14	²⁹⁄₃₂	1⁵⁄₁₆	0.250	0.188	1.097
1	8	12	1	1½	0.281	0.250	1.254
1⅛	7	12	1⁵⁄₃₂	1¹¹⁄₁₆	0.344	0.250	1.411

* ASA B18.2–1955.

Thread may be coarse- or fine-thread series, class 2B tolerance; unless otherwise specified fine-thread series shall be furnished.

TABLE 7
American Standard Set Screws

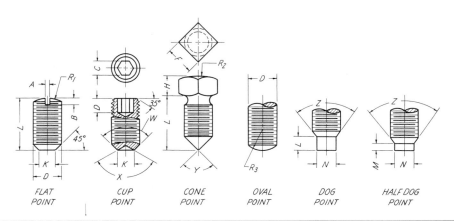

FLAT POINT   CUP POINT   CONE POINT   OVAL POINT   DOG POINT   HALF DOG POINT

Nominal size D	Slotted headless			Hex. socket (min.)		Square head (F-max.)			POINTS Cup and flat (K-max.)			Cone	Oval	Full and half dog (N-max.)			
	A	B	R_1	C	D*	F	H	R_2	K	W	X	Y	R_3	L	M	N	Z
5	.023	.031	.125	1/16	.050	—	—	—	.067				.094	.060	.030	.083	
6	.025	.035	.138	1/16	.050	—	—	—	.074				.109	.070	.035	.092	
8	.029	.041	.164	5/64	.062	—	—	—	.087				.125	.080	.040	.109	
10	.032	.048	.190	3/32	.075	.1875	9/64	15/32	.102				.141	.090	.045	.127	
12	.036	.054	.216	3/32	.075	.216	5/32	35/64	.115				.156	.110	.055	.144	
1/4	.045	.063	.250	1/8	.100	.250	3/16	5/8	.132				.188	.125	.063	.156	
5/16	.051	.078	.313	5/32	.125	.3125	15/64	25/32	.172				.234	.156	.078	.203	
3/8	.064	.094	.375	3/16	.150	.375	9/32	15/16	.212				.281	.188	.094	.250	
7/16	.072	.109	.438	7/32	.175	.4375	21/64	1 3/32	.252				.328	.219	.109	.297	
1/2	.081	.125	.500	1/4	.200	.500	3/8	1 1/4	.291				.375	.250	.125	.344	
9/16	.091	.141	.563	1/4	.200	.5625	27/64	1 13/32	.332				.422	.281	.140	.391	
5/8	.102	.156	.625	5/16	.250	.625	15/32	1 9/16	.371				.469	.313	.156	.469	
3/4	.129	.188	.750	3/8	.300	.750	9/16	1 7/8	.450				.563	.375	.188	.563	
7/8	—	—	—	1/2	.400	.875	21/32	2 3/16	—				—	—	—	—	
1	—	—	—	9/16	.450	1.000	3/4	2 1/2	—				—	—	—	—	
1 1/8	—	—	—	9/16	.450	1.125	27/32	2 13/16	—				—	—	—	—	
1 1/4	—	—	—	5/8	.500	1.250	15/16	3 1/8	—				—	—	—	—	
1 3/8	—	—	—	5/8	.500	1.375	1 1/32	3 7/16	—				—	—	—	—	
1 1/2	—	—	—	3/4	.600	1.500	1 1/8	3 3/4	—				—	—	—	—	

Angle annotations (spanning columns):
- W = 80° to 90° (Draw as 90°)
- X = 118° ± 5°
- Y = 118° ± 2° ; When L equals nominal diameter or less, Y = 118° ± 2° ; When L exceeds nominal diameter, Y = 90° ± 2°
- Z = 100° to 110°

ASA B18.6.2–1956.
ASA B18.3–1954.
* Dimensions apply to cup and flat point screws one diameter in length or longer. For screws shorter than one diameter in length, and for other types of points, socket to be as deep as practicable.

TABLE 8
American Standard Machine Screws

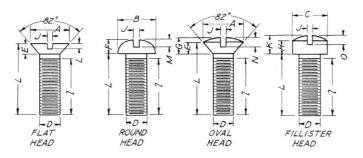

FLAT HEAD   ROUND HEAD   OVAL HEAD   FILLISTER HEAD

Size (number) and Threads per Inch			American Standard Dimensions (max.)													
Nominal size	Diameter D	Thread		Head diameter			Height dimensions					Slot width	Slot depth			
		Coarse	Fine	A	B	C	E	F	G	H	K	J	L	M	N	O
0	.060	—	80	.119	.113	.096	.035	.053	.056	.045	.059	.023	.015	.039	.030	.025
1	.073	64	72	.146	.138	.118	.043	.061	.068	.053	.071	.026	.019	.044	.038	.031
2	.086	56	64	.172	.162	.140	.051	.069	.080	.062	.083	.031	.023	.048	.045	.037
3	.099	48	56	.199	.187	.161	.059	.078	.092	.070	.095	.035	.027	.053	.052	.043
4	.112	40	48	.225	.211	.183	.067	.086	.104	.079	.107	.039	.030	.058	.059	.048
5	.125	40	44	.252	.236	.205	.075	.095	.116	.088	.120	.043	.034	.063	.067	.054
6	.138	32	40	.279	.260	.226	.083	.103	.128	.096	.132	.048	.038	.068	.074	.060
8	.164	32	36	.332	.309	.270	.100	.120	.152	.113	.156	.054	.045	.077	.088	.071
10	.190	24	32	.385	.359	.313	.116	.137	.176	.130	.180	.060	.053	.087	.103	.083
12	.216	24	28	.438	.408	.357	.132	.153	.200	.148	.205	.067	.060	.096	.117	.094
¼	.250	20	28	.507	.472	.414	.153	.175	.232	.170	.237	.075	.070	.109	.136	.109
5⁄16	.3125	18	24	.635	.590	.518	.191	.216	.290	.211	.295	.084	.088	.132	.171	.137
⅜	.375	16	24	.762	.708	.622	.230	.256	.347	.253	.355	.094	.106	.155	.206	.164
7⁄16	.4375	14	20	.812	.750	.625	.223	.328	.345	.265	.368	.094	.103	.196	.210	.170
½	.500	13	20	.875	.813	.750	.223	.355	.354	.297	.412	.106	.103	.211	.216	.190
9⁄16	.5625	12	18	1.000	.938	.812	.260	.410	.410	.336	.466	.118	.120	.242	.250	.214
⅝	.625	11	18	1.125	1.000	.875	.298	.438	.467	.375	.521	.133	.137	.258	.285	.240
¾	.750	10	16	1.375	1.250	1.000	.372	.547	.578	.441	.612	.149	.171	.320	.353	.281

ASA B18.6–1947.

Thread length—screws 2 in. in length or less are threaded as close to the head as practicable. Screws longer than 2 in. should have a minimum thread length of 1¾ in.

TABLE 9
American Standard Cap Screws

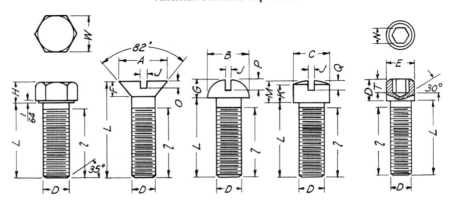

Nominal size (diam.)	AMERICAN STANDARD DIMENSIONS (MAX.)															
	Head diameter					Height dimensions					Slot width	Slot depth			Socket dimensions	
	A	B	C	E	W	F ave.	G	H nom.	K	M	J	O	P	Q	N min.	T min.
¼	.500	.437	.375	⅜	⁷⁄₁₆	.140	.191	⁵⁄₃₂	.172	.216	.075	.068	.117	.097	³⁄₁₆	.120
⁵⁄₁₆	.625	.562	.437	⁷⁄₁₆	½	.177	.245	¹³⁄₆₄	.203	.253	.084	.086	.151	.115	⁷⁄₃₂	.151
⅜	.750	.625	.562	⁹⁄₁₆	⁹⁄₁₆	.210	.273	¹⁵⁄₆₄	.250	.314	.094	.103	.168	.142	⁵⁄₁₆	.182
⁷⁄₁₆	.8125	.750	.625	⅝	⅝	.210	.328	⁹⁄₃₂	.297	.368	.094	.103	.202	.168	⁵⁄₁₆	.213
½	.875	.812	.750	¾	¾	.210	.354	⁵⁄₁₆	.328	.413	.106	.103	.218	.193	⅜	.245
⁹⁄₁₆	1.000	.937	.812	¹³⁄₁₆	¹³⁄₁₆	.244	.409	²³⁄₆₄	.375	.467	.118	.120	.252	.213	⅜	.276
⅝	1.125	1.000	.875	⅞	¹⁵⁄₁₆	.281	.437	²⁵⁄₆₄	.422	.521	.133	.137	.270	.239	½	.307
¾	1.375	1.250	1.000	1	1⅛	.352	.546	¹⁵⁄₃₂	.500	.612	.149	.171	.338	.283	⁹⁄₁₆	.370
⅞	1.625	—	1.125	1⅛	1⁵⁄₁₆	.423	—	³⁵⁄₆₄	.594	.720	.167	.206	—	.334	⁹⁄₁₆	.432
1	1.875	—	1.312	1⁵⁄₁₆	1½	.494	—	³⁹⁄₆₄	.656	.803	.188	.240	—	.371	⅝	.495
1⅛	2.062	—	—	1½	1¹¹⁄₁₆	.529	—	¹¹⁄₁₆	—	—	.196	.257	—	—	¾	.557
1¼	2.312	—	—	1¾	1⅞	.600	—	²⁵⁄₃₂	—	—	.211	.291	—	—	¾	.620
1⅜	2.562	—	—	1⅞	2¹⁄₁₆	.665	—	²⁷⁄₃₂	—	—	.226	.326	—	—	¾	.682
1½	2.812	—	—	2	2¼	.742	—	¹⁵⁄₁₆	—	—	.258	.360	—	—	1	.745

ASA B18.3–1954.
ASA B18.6.2–1956.
Bold type indicates products unified dimensionally with British and Canadian standards.
Minimum thread length shall be twice the diameter plus one-fourth in. for lengths up to and including 6 in.
Threads shall be coarse, fine, or 8-thread series, class 2A for plain (unplated) cap screws.

TABLE 10
American Standard Washers

Nominal size	Plain Washers[1]					
	LIGHT			MEDIUM		
	A ID	B OD	H Thickness	A ID	B OD	H Thickness
¼	9⁄32	⅝	0.065	5⁄16	¾	0.065
5⁄16	11⁄32	11⁄16	0.065	⅜	¾	0.065
⅜	13⁄32	13⁄16	0.065	7⁄16	⅞	0.083
7⁄16	15⁄32	59⁄64	0.065	½	1⅛	0.083
½	17⁄32	1 1⁄16	0.095	9⁄16	1¼	0.109
9⁄16	19⁄32	1 3⁄16	0.095	⅝	1⅜	0.109
⅝	21⁄32	1 5⁄16	0.095	11⁄16	1½	0.134
¾	13⁄16	1½	0.134	13⁄16	1¾	0.148
⅞	15⁄16	1¾	0.134	15⁄16	2	0.165
1	1 1⁄16	2	0.134	1 1⁄16	2¼	0.165
1⅛	—	—	—	1 3⁄16	2½	0.165
1¼	—	—	—	1 5⁄16	2¾	0.165
1⅜	—	—	—	1 7⁄16	3	0.180
1½	—	—	—	1 9⁄16	3¼	0.180

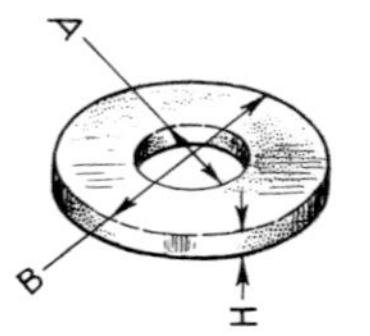

Nominal size	Lock Washers[2]					
	LIGHT			MEDIUM		
	C ID	D OD (max.)	T Thickness (min.)	C ID	D OD (max.)	T Thickness (min.)
¼	0.255	0.489	0.047		0.493	0.062
5⁄16	0.319	0.575	0.056		0.591	0.078
⅜	0.382	0.678	0.070		0.688	0.094
7⁄16	0.446	0.780	0.085		0.784	0.109
½	0.509	0.877	0.099		0.879	0.125
9⁄16	0.573	0.975	0.113	Same	0.979	0.141
⅝	0.636	1.082	0.126	as for	1.086	0.156
11⁄16	0.700	1.178	0.138	light	1.184	0.172
¾	0.763	1.277	0.153	lock	1.279	0.188
⅞	0.890	1.470	0.179	washers	1.474	0.219
1	1.017	1.656	0.202		1.672	0.250
1⅛	1.144	1.837	0.224		1.865	0.281
1¼	1.271	2.012	0.244		2.058	0.312
1⅜	1.398	2.183	0.264		2.253	0.344
1½	1.525	2.352	0.282		2.446	0.375

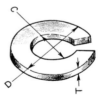

[1] ASA B27.2–1953. All dimensions in inches.
[2] ASA B27.1–1950. All dimensions in inches.
Dimensions for heavy and extra heavy washers may be found in the standards listed above.

TABLE 11
Cotter Pins

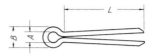

Bolt and rod diam. (NC)	Cotter diam.	A	B	Drill no.	Length Short	Length Long
¼	1/16	3/32	5/32	48	½	5/8
5/16	1/16	3/32	5/32	48	5/8	¾
3/8	3/32	1/8	7/32	36	¾	7/8
7/16	3/32	1/8	7/32	36	¾	1
½	3/32	1/8	7/32	36	7/8	1⅛
9/16	1/8	5/32	9/32	28	1	1¼
5/8	1/8	5/32	9/32	28	1⅛	1⅜
¾	1/8	5/32	9/32	28	1¼	1½
7/8	1/8	5/32	9/32	28	1⅜	1¾
1	1/8	5/32	9/32	28	1⅝	2

TABLE 12
American Standard Machine Screw and Stove Bolt Nuts

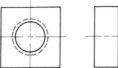

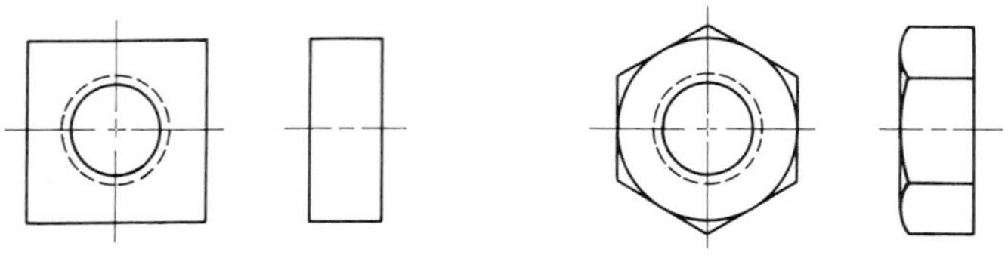

Diameter		0	1	2	3	4	5	6	8	10	12	¼	5/16	3/8
Across flats (nom.)		5/32	5/32	3/16	3/16	¼	5/16	5/16	11/32	3/8	7/16	7/16	9/16	5/8
Across corners (min.)	Hex.	.171	.171	.205	.205	.275	.344	.344	.378	.413	.482	.482	.621	.692
	Square	.206	.206	.247	.247	.331	.415	.415	.456	.497	.581	.581	.748	.833
Thickness (nom.)		3/64	3/64	1/16	1/16	3/32	7/64	7/64	1/8	1/8	5/32	3/16	7/32	¼

Nominal size (column header spanning 0 through 3/8)

ASA B18.2–1955.
Dimensions in inches.

TABLE 13
American Standard Small Rivets

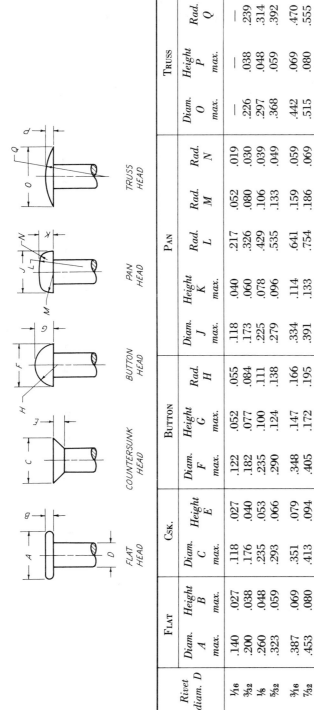

FLAT HEAD COUNTERSUNK HEAD BUTTON HEAD PAN HEAD TRUSS HEAD

Rivet diam. D	FLAT		CSK.		BUTTON			PAN					TRUSS		
	Diam. A max.	Height B max.	Diam. C max.	Height E	Diam. F max.	Height G max.	Rad. H	Diam. J max.	Height K max.	Rad. L	Rad. M	Rad. N	Diam. O max.	Height P max.	Rad. Q
1/16	.140	.027	.118	.027	.122	.052	.055	.118	.040	.217	.052	.019	—	—	—
3/32	.200	.038	.176	.040	.182	.077	.084	.173	.060	.326	.080	.030	.226	.038	.239
1/8	.260	.048	.235	.053	.235	.100	.111	.225	.078	.429	.106	.039	.297	.048	.314
5/32	.323	.059	.293	.066	.290	.124	.138	.279	.096	.535	.133	.049	.368	.059	.392
3/16	.387	.069	.351	.079	.348	.147	.166	.334	.114	.641	.159	.059	.442	.069	.470
7/32	.453	.080	.413	.094	.405	.172	.195	.391	.133	.754	.186	.069	.515	.080	.555
1/4	.515	.091	.469	.106	.460	.196	.221	.444	.151	.858	.213	.079	.590	.091	.628
9/32	.579	.103	.528	.119	.518	.220	.249	.499	.170	.963	.239	.088	.661	.103	.706
5/16	.641	.113	.588	.133	.572	.243	.276	.552	.187	1.070	.266	.098	.732	.113	.784
11/32	.705	.124	.646	.146	.630	.267	.304	.608	.206	1.176	.292	.108	.806	.124	.862
3/8	.769	.135	.704	.159	.684	.291	.332	.663	.225	1.286	.319	.118	.878	.135	.942
13/32	.834	.146	.763	.172	.743	.316	.358	.719	.243	1.392	.345	.127	.949	.145	1.028
7/16	.896	.157	.823	.186	.798	.339	.387	.772	.261	1.500	.372	.137	1.020	.157	1.098

ASA B18.1–1955.

The length of a rivet is measured from the under side (bearing surface) of the head to the end of the shank except in the case of a rivet with a countersunk head. The length of a countersunk head rivet is measured from the top of the head to the end of the shank.

TABLE 14
American Standard Square and Flat Keys

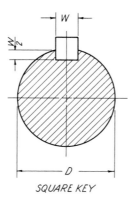

SQUARE KEY

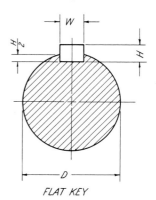

FLAT KEY

Shaft diameter	Square stock key W	Flat stock key W × H	Shaft diameter	Square stock key W	Flat stock key W × H
½–⁹⁄₁₆	⅛	⅛ × ³⁄₃₂	2⁵⁄₁₆–2¾	⅝	⅝ × ⁷⁄₁₆
⅝–⅞	³⁄₁₆	³⁄₁₆ × ⅛	2⅞–3¼	¾	¾ × ½
1⁵⁄₁₆–1¼	¼	¼ × ³⁄₁₆	3⅜–3¾	⅞	⅞ × ⅝
1⁵⁄₁₆–1⅜	⁵⁄₁₆	⁵⁄₁₆ × ¼	3⅞–4½	1	1 × ¾
1⁷⁄₁₆–1¾	⅜	⅜ × ¼	4¾–5½	1¼	1¼ × ⅞
1¹³⁄₁₆–2¼	½	½ × ⅜	5¾–6	1½	1½ × 1

ASA B17.1–1943.
All dimensions in inches.

TABLE 15
American Standard Plain Taper and Gib Head Keys

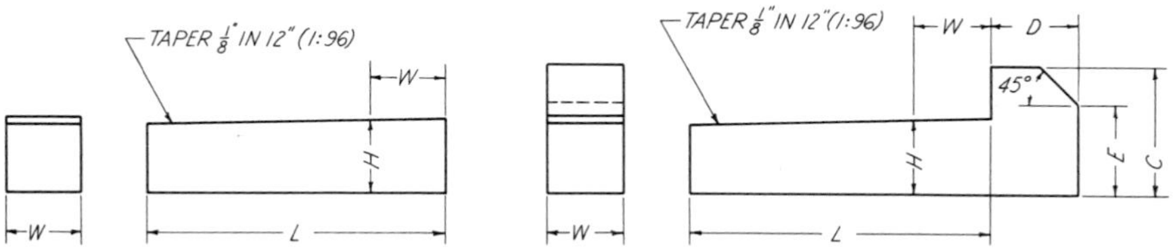

Plain Taper and Gib Head Keys (Square and Flat)			Gib Head					
			Square			*Flat*		
Diameter of shaft	*Square type*	*Flat type*	*Height of head*	*Length*	*Height to chamfer*	*Height of head*	*Length*	*Height to chamfer*
D	$W = H$	$W \times H$	*C*	*D*	*E*	*C*	*D*	*E*
1/2–9/16	1/8	1/8 × 3/32	1/4	7/32	5/32	3/16	1/8	1/8
5/8–7/8	3/16	3/16 × 1/8	5/16	9/32	7/32	1/4	3/16	5/32
15/16–1 1/4	1/4	1/4 × 3/16	7/16	11/32	11/32	5/16	1/4	3/16
1 5/16–1 3/8	5/16	5/16 × 1/4	9/16	13/32	13/32	3/8	5/16	1/4
1 7/16–1 3/4	3/8	3/8 × 1/4	11/16	15/32	15/32	7/16	3/8	5/16
1 13/16–2 1/4	1/2	1/2 × 3/8	7/8	19/32	5/8	5/8	1/2	7/16
2 5/16–2 3/4	5/8	5/8 × 7/16	1 1/16	23/32	3/4	3/4	5/8	1/2
2 7/8–3 1/4	3/4	3/4 × 1/2	1 1/4	7/8	7/8	7/8	3/4	5/8
3 3/8–3 3/4	7/8	7/8 × 5/8	1 1/2	1	1	1 1/16	7/8	3/4
3 7/8–4 1/2	1	1 × 3/4	1 3/4	1 3/16	1 3/16	1 1/4	1	13/16
4 3/4–5 1/2	1 1/4	1 1/4 × 7/8	2	1 7/16	1 7/16	1 1/2	1 1/4	1
5 3/4–6	1 1/2	1 1/2 × 1	2 1/2	1 3/4	1 3/4	1 3/4	1 1/2	1 1/4

ASA B17.1–1943.
All dimensions in inches. Minimum length = 4*W*. Maximum length = 16*W*.

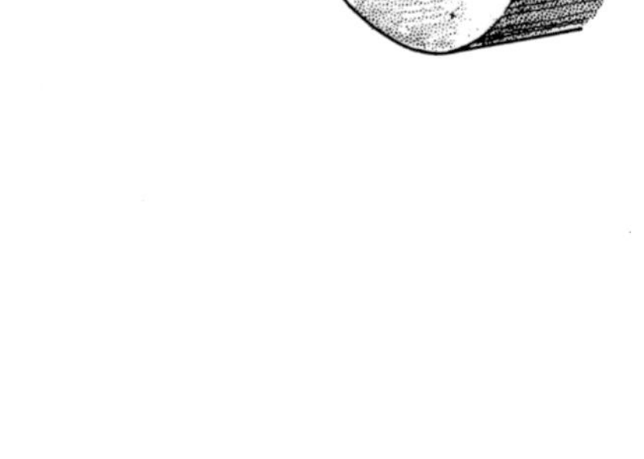

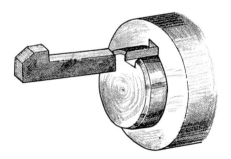

TABLE 16
American Standard Woodruff Keys

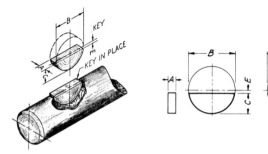

Key[1] number	Nominal size $A \times B$	Height of Key		Distance above center E	Depth of key slot in shaft
		$C_{max.}$	$D_{max.}$		
204	1/16 × 1/2	0.203	.194	3/64	.1718
304	3/32 × 1/2	.203	.194	3/64	.1561
305	3/32 × 5/8	.250	.240	1/16	.2031
404	1/8 × 1/2	.203	.194	3/64	.1405
405	1/8 × 5/8	.250	.240	1/16	.1875
406	1/8 × 3/4	.313	.303	1/16	.2505
505	5/32 × 5/8	.250	.240	1/16	.1719
506	5/32 × 3/4	.313	.303	1/16	.2349
507	5/32 × 7/8	.375	.365	1/16	.2969
606	3/16 × 3/4	.313	.303	1/16	.2193
607	3/16 × 7/8	.375	.365	1/16	.2813
608	3/16 × 1	.438	.428	1/16	.3443
609	3/16 × 1 1/8	.484	.475	5/64	.3903
807	1/4 × 7/8	.375	.365	1/16	.2500
808	1/4 × 1	.438	.428	1/16	.3130
809	1/4 × 1 1/8	.484	.475	5/64	.3590
810	1/4 × 1 1/4	.547	.537	5/64	.4220
811	1/4 × 1 3/8	.594	.584	3/32	.4690
812	1/4 × 1 1/2	.641	.631	7/64	.5160
1008	5/16 × 1	.438	.428	1/16	.2818
1009	5/16 × 1 1/8	.484	.475	5/64	.3278
1010	5/16 × 1 1/4	.547	.537	5/64	.3908
1011	5/16 × 1 3/8	.594	.584	3/32	.4378
1012	5/16 × 1 1/2	.641	.631	7/64	.4848
1210	3/8 × 1 1/4	.547	.537	5/64	.3595
1211	3/8 × 1 3/8	.594	.584	3/32	.4065
1212	3/8 × 1 1/2	.641	.631	7/64	.4535

ASA B17f–1930 (R1955).

[1] All dimensions in inches. Key numbers indicate the nominal key dimensions. The last two digits give the nominal diameter in eighths of an inch and the digits preceding the last two give the nominal width in thirty-seconds of an inch.

TABLE 17
Pratt and Whitney Keys

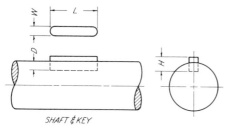

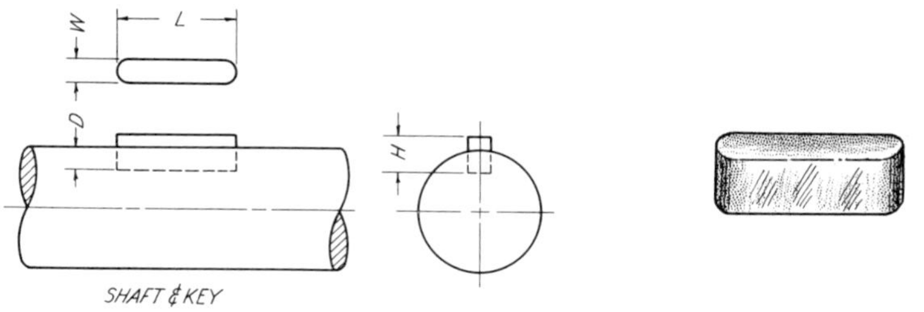

SHAFT & KEY

Key no.	L	W	H	D	Key no.	L	W	H	D
1	½	¹⁄₁₆	³⁄₃₂	¹⁄₁₆	22	1⅜	¼	⅜	¼
2	½	³⁄₃₂	⁹⁄₆₄	³⁄₃₂	23	1⅜	⁵⁄₁₆	¹⁵⁄₃₂	⁵⁄₁₆
3	½	⅛	³⁄₁₆	⅛	F	1⅜	⅜	⁹⁄₁₆	⅜
4	⅝	³⁄₃₂	⁹⁄₆₄	³⁄₃₂	24	1½	¼	⅜	¼
5	⅝	⅛	³⁄₁₆	⅛	25	1½	⁵⁄₁₆	¹⁵⁄₃₂	⁵⁄₁₆
6	⅝	⁵⁄₃₂	¹⁵⁄₆₄	⁵⁄₃₂	G	1½	⅜	⁹⁄₁₆	⅜
7	¾	⅛	³⁄₁₆	⅛	51	1¾	¼	⅜	¼
8	¾	⁵⁄₃₂	¹⁵⁄₆₄	⁵⁄₃₂	52	1¾	⁵⁄₁₆	¹⁵⁄₃₂	⁵⁄₁₆
9	¾	³⁄₁₆	⁹⁄₃₂	³⁄₁₆	53	1¾	⅜	⁹⁄₁₆	⅜
10	⅞	⁵⁄₃₂	¹⁵⁄₆₄	⁵⁄₃₂	26	2	³⁄₁₆	⁹⁄₃₂	³⁄₁₆
11	⅞	³⁄₁₆	⁹⁄₃₂	³⁄₁₆	27	2	¼	⅜	¼
12	⅞	⁷⁄₃₂	²¹⁄₆₄	⁷⁄₃₂	28	2	⁵⁄₁₆	¹⁵⁄₃₂	⁵⁄₁₆
A	⅞	¼	⅜	¼	29	2	⅜	⁹⁄₁₆	⅜
13	1	³⁄₁₆	⁹⁄₃₂	³⁄₁₆	54	2¼	¼	⅜	¼
14	1	⁷⁄₃₂	²¹⁄₆₄	⁷⁄₃₂	55	2¼	⁵⁄₁₆	¹⁵⁄₃₂	⁵⁄₁₆
15	1	¼	⅜	¼	56	2¼	⅜	⁹⁄₁₆	⅜
B	1	⁵⁄₁₆	¹⁵⁄₃₂	⁵⁄₁₆	57	2¼	⁷⁄₁₆	²¹⁄₃₂	⁷⁄₁₆
16	1⅛	³⁄₁₆	⁹⁄₃₂	³⁄₁₆	58	2½	⁵⁄₁₆	¹⁵⁄₃₂	⁵⁄₁₆
17	1⅛	⁷⁄₃₂	²¹⁄₆₄	⁷⁄₃₂	59	2½	⅜	⁹⁄₁₆	⅜
18	1⅛	¼	⅜	¼	60	2½	⁷⁄₁₆	²¹⁄₃₂	⁷⁄₁₆
C	1⅛	⁵⁄₁₆	¹⁵⁄₃₂	⁵⁄₁₆	61	2½	½	¾	½
19	1¼	³⁄₁₆	⁹⁄₃₂	³⁄₁₆	30	3	⅜	⁹⁄₁₆	⅜
20	1¼	⁷⁄₃₂	²¹⁄₆₄	⁷⁄₃₂	31	3	⁷⁄₁₆	²¹⁄₃₂	⁷⁄₁₆
21	1¼	¼	⅜	¼	32	3	½	¾	½
D	1¼	⁵⁄₁₆	¹⁵⁄₃₂	⁵⁄₁₆	33	3	⁹⁄₁₆	²⁷⁄₃₂	⁹⁄₁₆
E	1¼	⅜	⁹⁄₁₆	⅜	34	3	⅝	¹⁵⁄₁₆	⅝

The length L may vary but should always be at least $2W$.

TABLE 18
Standard Taper Pins

No. of pin	DIAMETER AT LARGE END		MAX. LENGTH
	D	D	L
00000	.094	3/32	3/4
0000	.109	7/64	7/8
000	.125	1/8	1
00	.141	9/64	1⅛
0	.156	5/32	1¼
1	.172	11/64	1¼
2	.193	3/16	1½
3	.219	7/32	1¾
4	.250	¼	2
5	.289	19/64	2¼
6	.341	11/32	3
7	.409	13/32	3¾
8	.492	½	4½
9	.591	19/32	5¼
10	.706	23/32	6
11	.860	55/64	7¼
12	1.032	1 1/32	9
13	1.241	1 15/64	11
14	1.523	1 33/64	13

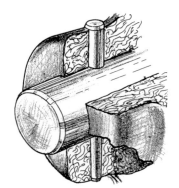

Standard Taper Pins—Diameters at Small End

Length	Number of pin										
	0	1	2	3	4	5	6	7	8	9	10
3/4	.140	.156	.177	.203	.235	.273	.325				
1	.135	.151	.172	.198	.230	.268	.320	.388			
1¼		.146	.167	.193	.224	.263	.315	.383	.466		
1½			.162	.188	.219	.258	.310	.378	.461	.560	.675
1¾				.182	.214	.252	.304	.372	.455	.554	.669
2					.209	.247	.299	.367	.450	.549	.664
2¼						.242	.294	.362	.445	.544	.659
2½							.289	.357	.440	.539	.654
2¾							.284	.352	.435	.534	.649
3							.279	.346	.429	.528	.643

TABLE 19
American Standard Wrought-Iron and Steel Pipe

Standard Weight							Heavy			
Nominal size	*Outside diameter (all weights)*	*Threads per inch*	*Tap drill sizes*[1]	*Distance pipe enters fitting*	*Nominal wall thickness*		*Nominal wall thickness*			
							Extra heavy		*Double extra heavy*	
					Wrought iron	*Steel*	*Wrought iron*	*Steel*	*Wrought iron*	*Steel*
1/8	.405	72	11/32	5/16	.069	.068	.099	.095	—	—
1/4	.540	18	7/16	7/16	.090	.088	.122	.119	—	—
3/8	.675	18	19/32	7/16	.093	.091	.129	.126	—	—
1/2	.840	14	23/32	9/16	.111	.109	.151	.147	.307	.294
3/4	1.050	14	15/16	9/16	.115	.113	.157	.154	.318	.308
1	1.315	11½	1 5/32	11/16	.136	.133	.183	.179	.369	.358
1¼	1.660	11½	1½	11/16	.143	.140	.195	.191	.393	.382
1½	1.900	11½	1 23/32	11/16	.148	.145	.204	.200	.411	.400
2	2.375	11½	2 3/16	3/4	.158	.154	.223	.218	.447	.436
2½	2.875	8	2 5/8	1 1/16	.208	.203	.282	.276	.567	.552
3	3.500	8	3¼	1 1/8	.221	.216	.306	.300	.615	.600
3½	4.000	8	3¾	1 3/16	.231	.226	.325	.318	—	—
4	4.500	8	4¼	1 3/16	.242	.237	.344	.337	.690	.674
5	5.563	8	5 5/16	1 5/16	.263	.258	.383	.375	.768	.750
6	6.625	8	6 3/8	1 3/8	.286	.280	.441	.432	.884	.864
8	8.625	8	—	—	.329	.322	.510	.500	.895	.875

ASA B36.10–1950.
ASA B2.1–1945.
All dimensions in inches.
[1] Not American Standard.
See ASA B36.10–1950 for sizes larger than 8 in.

TABLE 20
American Standard Malleable-Iron Screwed Fittings
For use under maximum working steam pressures of 150 lb per sq in.

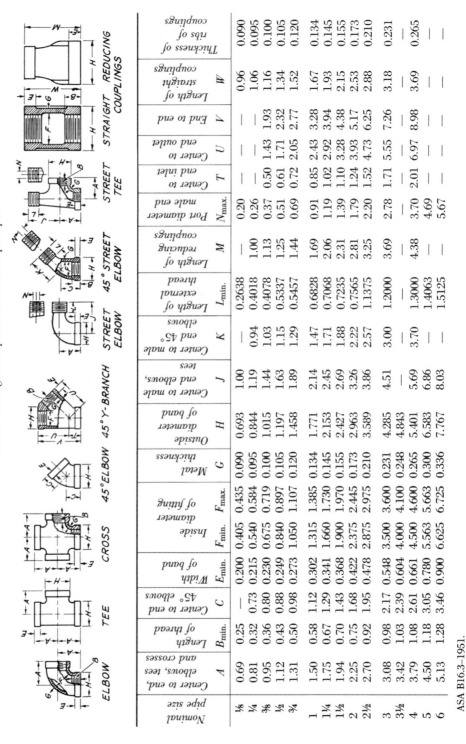

ELBOW   TEE   CROSS   45° ELBOW   45° Y-BRANCH   STREET ELBOW   45° STREET ELBOW   STREET TEE   STRAIGHT REDUCING COUPLINGS

Nominal pipe size	Center to end, elbows, tees and crosses A	Length of thread $B_{min.}$	Center to end 45° elbows C	Width of band $E_{min.}$	Inside diameter of fitting $F_{min.}$	$F_{max.}$	Metal thickness G	Outside diameter of band H	Center to male end elbows, tees J	Center to male end 45° elbows K	Length of external thread $L_{min.}$	Length of reducing couplings M	Port diameter male end $N_{max.}$	Center to end inlet T	Center to end outlet U	End to end V	Length of straight couplings W	Thickness of ribs of couplings
⅛	0.69	0.25	—	0.200	0.405	0.435	0.090	0.693	1.00	—	0.2638	—	0.20	—	—	—	0.96	0.090
¼	0.81	0.32	0.73	0.215	0.540	0.584	0.095	0.844	1.19	0.94	0.4018	1.00	0.26	—	—	—	1.06	0.095
⅜	0.95	0.36	0.80	0.230	0.675	0.719	0.100	1.015	1.44	1.03	0.4078	1.13	0.37	0.50	1.43	1.93	1.16	0.100
½	1.12	0.43	0.88	0.249	0.840	0.897	0.105	1.197	1.63	1.15	0.5337	1.25	0.51	0.61	1.71	2.32	1.34	0.105
¾	1.31	0.50	0.98	0.273	1.050	1.107	0.120	1.458	1.89	1.29	0.5457	1.44	0.69	0.72	2.05	2.77	1.52	0.120
1	1.50	0.58	1.12	0.302	1.315	1.385	0.134	1.771	2.14	1.47	0.6828	1.69	0.91	0.85	2.43	3.28	1.67	0.134
1¼	1.75	0.67	1.29	0.341	1.660	1.730	0.145	2.153	2.45	1.71	0.7068	2.06	1.19	1.02	2.92	3.94	1.93	0.145
1½	1.94	0.70	1.43	0.368	1.900	1.970	0.155	2.427	2.69	1.88	0.7235	2.31	1.39	1.10	3.28	4.38	2.15	0.155
2	2.25	0.75	1.68	0.422	2.375	2.445	0.173	2.963	3.26	2.22	0.7565	2.81	1.79	1.24	3.93	5.17	2.53	0.173
2½	2.70	0.92	1.95	0.478	2.875	2.975	0.210	3.589	3.86	2.57	1.1375	3.25	2.20	1.52	4.73	6.25	2.88	0.210
3	3.08	0.98	2.17	0.548	3.500	3.600	0.231	4.285	4.51	3.00	1.2000	3.69	2.78	1.71	5.55	7.26	3.18	0.231
3½	3.42	1.03	2.39	0.604	4.000	4.100	0.248	4.843	—	—	—	—	—	—	—	—	—	—
4	3.79	1.08	2.61	0.661	4.500	4.600	0.265	5.401	5.69	3.70	1.3000	4.38	3.70	2.01	6.97	8.98	3.69	0.265
5	4.50	1.18	3.05	0.780	5.563	5.663	0.300	6.583	6.86	—	1.4063	—	4.69	—	—	—	—	—
6	5.13	1.28	3.46	0.900	6.625	6.725	0.336	7.767	8.03	—	1.5125	—	5.67	—	—	—	—	—

ASA B16.3–1951.

TABLE 21
125 lb American Standard Cast-Iron Screwed Fittings

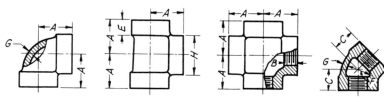

Nominal pipe size	Center to end, elbows, tees, and crosses	Length of thread	Center to end, 45° elbows	Width of band	Inside diameter of fitting		Metal thickness	Outside diameter of band
	A	$B_{min.}$	C	$E_{min.}$	$F_{min.}$	$F_{max.}$	$G_{min.}$	$H_{min.}$
¼	0.81	0.32	0.73	0.38	0.540	0.584	0.110	0.93
⅜	0.95	0.36	0.80	0.44	0.675	0.719	0.120	1.12
½	1.12	0.43	0.88	0.50	0.840	0.897	0.130	1.34
¾	1.31	0.50	0.98	0.56	1.050	1.107	0.155	1.63
1	1.50	0.58	1.12	0.62	1.315	1.385	0.170	1.95
1¼	1.75	0.67	1.29	0.69	1.660	1.730	0.185	2.39
1½	1.94	0.70	1.43	0.75	1.900	1.970	0.200	2.68
2	2.25	0.75	1.68	0.84	2.375	2.445	0.220	3.28
2½	2.70	0.92	1.95	0.94	2.875	2.975	0.240	3.86
3	3.08	0.98	2.17	1.00	3.500	3.600	0.260	4.62
3½	3.42	1.03	2.39	1.06	4.000	4.100	0.280	5.20
4	3.79	1.08	2.61	1.12	4.500	4.600	0.310	5.79
5	4.50	1.18	3.05	1.18	5.563	5.663	0.380	7.05
6	5.13	1.28	3.46	1.28	6.625	6.725	0.430	8.28
8	6.56	1.47	4.28	1.47	8.625	8.725	0.550	10.63
10	8.08	1.68	5.16	1.68	10.750	10.850	0.690	13.12
12	9.50	1.88	5.97	1.88	12.750	12.850	0.800	15.47

ASA B16.4–1949 (R1953).
All dimensions in inches.

TABLE 22
American Standard Pipe Plugs and Caps

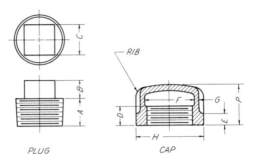

PLUG   CAP

Nominal pipe size	Plug			Cap*						
	Length of thread	Height of square	Width across flats	Length of thread	Width of band	Inside diameter of fitting	Metal thickness	Outside diameter of band	Height	Thickness of ribs
	$A_{min.}$	$B_{min.}$	$C_{nom.}$	$D_{min.}$	$E_{min.}$	$F_{max.}$	G	$H_{min.}$	$P_{min.}$	
⅛	.37	.24	9⁄32	.25	.200	.435	.090	.693	.53	—
¼	.44	.28	⅜	.32	.215	.584	.095	.844	.63	—
⅜	.48	.31	7⁄16	.36	.230	.719	.100	1.015	.74	—
½	.56	.38	9⁄16	.43	.249	.897	.105	1.197	.87	.105
¾	.63	.44	⅝	.50	.273	1.107	.120	1.458	.97	.120
1	.75	.50	13⁄16	.58	.302	1.385	.134	1.771	1.16	.134
1¼	.80	.56	15⁄16	.67	.341	1.730	.145	2.153	1.28	.145
1½	.83	.62	1⅛	.70	.368	1.970	.155	2.427	1.33	.155
2	.88	.68	1 5⁄16	.75	.422	2.445	.173	2.963	1.45	.173
2½	1.07	.74	1½	.92	.478	2.975	.210	3.589	1.70	.210
3	1.13	.80	1 11⁄16	.98	.548	3.600	.231	4.285	1.80	.231
3½	1.18	.86	1⅞	1.03	.604	4.100	.248	4.843	1.90	.248
4	—	—	—	1.08	.661	4.600	.265	5.401	2.08	.265
5	—	—	—	1.18	.780	5.663	.300	6.583	2.32	.300
6	—	—	—	1.28	.900	6.725	.336	7.767	2.55	.336

* ASA B16.3–1951.
The outside radius of top of cap is equal to $3 \times F$.

TABLE 23

American Standard Cast-Iron Pipe Flanges and Flanged Fittings

For use under maximum working pressures of 125 lb per sq in.

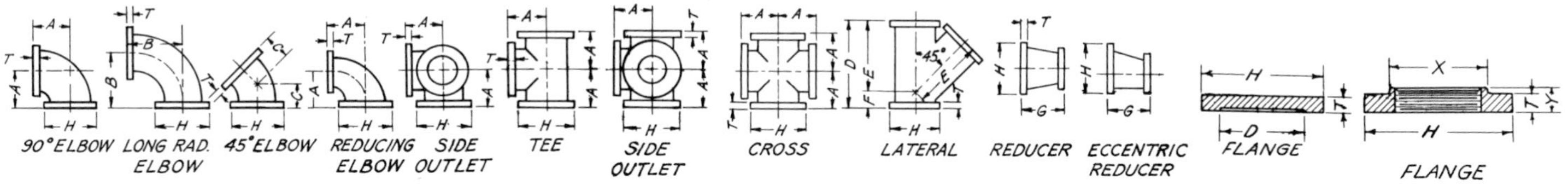
90°ELBOW
LONG RAD. ELBOW
45°ELBOW
REDUCING ELBOW
SIDE OUTLET
TEE
SIDE OUTLET
CROSS
LATERAL
REDUCER
ECCENTRIC REDUCER
FLANGE
FLANGE

Nominal pipe size D	Center to face, elbow tees, etc. A	Center to face, long radius elbow B	Center to face, 45° elbow C	Face to face, lateral D	Center to face, lateral E	Center to face, "Y" and lateral F	Face to face reducer G	Diameter of flange H	Thickness of flange T	Diameter of hub X	Length of hub Y	Diameter of holes in flanges	Number of bolts for flanges	Diameter of bolts for flanges	Length of bolts for flanges	Diameter of bolt circle
1	3½	5	1¾	7½	5¾	1¾	—	4¼	7/16	1 15/16	11/16	⅝	4	½	1¾	3⅛
1¼	3¾	5½	2	8	6¼	1¾	—	4⅝	½	2 5/16	13/16	⅝	4	½	2	3½
1½	4	6	2¼	9	7	2	—	5	9/16	2 9/16	⅞	⅝	4	½	2	3⅞
2	4½	6½	2½	10½	8	2½	5	6	⅝	3 1/16	1	¾	4	⅝	2¼	4¾
2½	5	7	3	12	9½	2½	5½	7	11/16	3 9/16	1⅛	¾	4	⅝	2½	5½
3	5½	7¾	3	13	10	3	6	7½	¾	4¼	1 3/16	¾	4	⅝	2½	6
3½	6	8½	3½	14½	11½	3	6½	8½	13/16	4 13/16	1¼	¾	8	⅝	2¾	7
4	6½	9	4	15	12	3	7	9	15/16	5 5/16	1 5/16	¾	8	⅝	3	7½
5	7½	10¼	4½	17	13½	3½	8	10	15/16	6 7/16	1 7/16	⅞	8	¾	3	8½
6	8	11½	5	18	14½	3½	9	11	1	7 9/16	1 9/16	⅞	8	¾	3¼	9½
8	9	14	5½	22	17½	4½	11	13½	1⅛	9 11/16	1¾	⅞	8	¾	3½	11¾
10	11	16½	6½	25½	20½	5	12	16	1 3/16	11 15/16	1 15/16	1	12	⅞	3¾	14¼
12	12	19	7½	30	24½	5½	14	19	1¼	14 1/16	2 3/16	1	12	⅞	3¾	17

ASA B16.1–1948 (R1953).

TABLE 24A
Running and Sliding Fits[1]

Limits are in thousandths of an inch. Limits for hole and shaft are applied algebraically to the basic size to obtain the limits of size for the parts. Symbols $H5$, $g5$, etc., are Hole and Shaft designations used in ABC System.[2]

Nominal size range inches Over To	Class RC 1 Limits of clearance	Class RC 1 Standard limits Hole $H5$	Class RC 1 Standard limits Shaft $g4$	Class RC 2 Limits of clearance	Class RC 2 Standard limits Hole $H6$	Class RC 2 Standard limits Shaft $g5$	Class RC 3 Limits of clearance	Class RC 3 Standard limits Hole $H6$	Class RC 3 Standard limits Shaft $f6$	Class RC 4 Limits of clearance	Class RC 4 Standard limits Hole $H7$	Class RC 4 Standard limits Shaft $f7$
0.04–0.12	0.1	+0.2	−0.1	0.1	+0.25	−0.1	0.3	+0.25	−0.3	0.3	+0.4	−0.3
	0.45	0	−0.25	0.55	0	−0.3	0.8	0	−0.55	1.1	0	−0.7
0.12–0.24	0.15	+0.2	−0.15	0.15	+0.3	−0.15	0.4	+0.3	−0.4	0.4	+0.5	−0.4
	0.5	0	−0.3	0.65	0	−0.35	1.0	0	−0.7	1.4	0	−0.9
0.24–0.40	0.2	+0.25	−0.2	0.2	+0.4	−0.2	0.5	+0.4	−0.5	0.5	+0.6	−0.5
	0.6	0	−0.35	0.85	0	−0.45	1.3	0	−0.9	1.7	0	−1.1
0.40–0.71	0.25	+0.3	−0.25	0.25	+0.4	−0.25	0.6	+0.4	−0.6	0.6	+0.7	−0.6
	0.75	0	−0.45	0.95	0	−0.55	1.4	0	−1.0	2.0	0	−1.3
0.71–1.19	0.3	+0.4	−0.3	0.3	+0.5	−0.3	0.8	+0.5	−0.8	0.8	+0.8	−0.8
	0.95	0	−0.55	1.2	0	−0.7	1.8	0	−1.3	2.4	0	−1.6
1.19–1.97	0.4	+0.4	−0.4	0.4	+0.6	−0.4	1.0	+0.6	−1.0	1.0	+1.0	−1.0
	1.1	0	−0.7	1.4	0	−0.8	2.2	0	−1.6	3.0	0	−2.0
1.97–3.15	0.4	+0.5	−0.4	0.4	+0.7	−0.4	1.2	+0.7	−1.2	1.2	+1.2	−1.2
	1.2	0	−0.7	1.6	0	−0.9	2.6	0	−1.9	3.6	0	−2.4
3.15–4.73	0.5	+0.6	−0.5	0.5	+0.9	−0.5	1.4	+0.9	−1.4	1.4	+1.4	−1.4
	1.5	0	−0.9	2.0	0	−1.1	3.2	0	−2.3	4.2	0	−2.8
4.73–7.09	0.6	+0.7	−0.6	0.6	+1.0	−0.6	1.6	+1.0	−1.6	1.6	+1.6	−1.6
	1.8	0	−1.1	2.3	0	−1.3	3.6	0	−2.6	4.8	0	−3.2
7.09–9.85	0.6	+0.8	−0.6	0.6	+1.2	−0.6	2.0	+1.2	−2.0	2.0	+1.8	−2.0
	2.0	0	−1.2	2.6	0	−1.4	4.4	0	−3.2	5.6	0	−3.8

[1] Extracted from ASA B4.1–1955 (Table 1).
[2] Data are in accordance with ABC agreements.
For diameters greater than 9.85 in. see standard.

TABLE 24A (cont.)
Running and Sliding Fits

Limits are in thousandths of an inch. Limits for hole and shaft are applied algebraically to the basic size to obtain the limits of size for the parts. Symbols H7, e7, etc., are Hole and Shaft designations used in ABC System.

Nominal size range inches Over — To	Class RC 5			Class RC 6			Class RC 7			Class RC 8			Class RC 9		
	Limits of clearance	Hole H7	Shaft e7	Limits of clearance	Hole H8	Shaft e8	Limits of clearance	Hole H9	Shaft d8	Limits of clearance	Hole H10	Shaft c9	Limits of clearance	Hole H11	Shaft
0.04–0.12	0.6	+0.4	−0.6	0.6	+0.6	−0.6	1.0	+1.0	−1.0	2.5	+1.6	−2.5	4.0	+2.5	−4.0
	1.4	0	−1.0	1.8	0	−1.2	2.6	0	−1.6	5.1	0	−3.5	8.1	0	−5.6
0.12–0.24	0.8	+0.5	−0.8	0.8	+0.7	−0.8	1.2	+1.2	−1.2	2.8	+1.8	−2.8	4.5	+3.0	−4.5
	1.8	0	−1.3	2.2	0	−1.5	3.1	0	−1.9	5.8	0	−4.0	9.3	0	−6.0
0.24–0.40	1.0	+0.6	−1.0	1.0	+0.9	−1.0	1.6	+1.4	−1.6	3.0	+2.2	−3.0	5.0	+3.5	−5.0
	2.2	0	−1.6	2.8	0	−1.9	3.9	0	−2.5	6.6	0	−4.4	10.7	0	−7.2
0.40–0.71	1.2	+0.7	−1.2	1.2	+1.0	−1.2	2.0	+1.6	−2.0	3.5	+2.8	−3.5	6.0	+4.0	−6.0
	2.6	0	−1.9	3.2	0	−2.2	4.6	0	−3.0	7.9	0	−5.1	12.8	0	−8.8
0.71–1.19	1.6	+0.8	−1.6	1.6	+1.2	−1.6	2.5	+2.0	−2.5	4.5	+3.5	−4.5	7.0	+5.0	−7.0
	3.2	0	−2.4	4.0	0	−2.8	5.7	0	−3.7	10.0	0	−6.5	15.5	0	−10.5
1.19–1.97	2.0	+1.0	−2.0	2.0	+1.6	−2.0	3.0	+2.5	−3.0	5.0	+4.0	−5.0	8.0	+6.0	−8.0
	4.0	0	−3.0	5.2	0	−3.6	7.1	0	−4.6	11.5	0	−7.5	18.0	0	−12.0
1.97–3.15	2.5	+1.2	−2.5	2.5	+1.8	−2.5	4.0	+3.0	−4.0	6.0	+4.5	−6.0	9.0	+7.0	−9.0
	4.9	0	−3.7	6.1	0	−4.3	8.8	0	−5.8	13.5	0	−9.0	20.5	0	−13.5
3.15–4.73	3.0	+1.4	−3.0	3.0	+2.2	−3.0	5.0	+3.5	−5.0	7.0	+5.0	−7.0	10.0	+9.0	−10.0
	5.8	0	−4.4	7.4	0	−5.2	10.7	0	−7.2	15.5	0	−10.5	24.0	0	−15.0
4.73–7.09	3.5	+1.6	−3.5	3.5	+2.5	−3.5	6.0	+4.0	−6.0	8.0	+6.0	−8.0	12.0	+10.0	−12.0
	6.7	0	−5.1	8.5	0	−6.0	12.5	0	−8.5	18.0	0	−12.0	28.0	0	−18.0
7.09–9.85	4.0	+1.8	−4.0	4.0	+2.8	−4.0	7.0	+4.5	−7.0	10.0	+7.0	−10.0	15.0	+12.0	−15.0
	7.6	0	−5.8	9.6	0	−6.8	14.3	0	−9.8	21.5	0	−14.5	34.0	0	−22.0

TABLE 24B
Clearance Locational Fits[1]

Limits are in thousandths of an inch. Limits for hole and shaft are applied algebraically to the basic size to obtain the limits of size for the parts. Symbols *H6*, *h5*, etc., are Hole and Shaft designations used in ABC System.[2]

Nominal size range inches Over / To	Class LC 1 Limits of clearance	Class LC 1 Hole H6	Class LC 1 Shaft h5	Class LC 2 Limits of clearance	Class LC 2 Hole H7	Class LC 2 Shaft h6	Class LC 3 Limits of clearance	Class LC 3 Hole H8	Class LC 3 Shaft h7	Class LC 4 Limits of clearance	Class LC 4 Hole H9	Class LC 4 Shaft h9	Class LC 5 Limits of clearance	Class LC 5 Hole H7	Class LC 5 Shaft g6
0.04–0.12	0 / 0.45	+0.25 / −0	+0 / −0.2	0 / 0.65	+0.4 / −0	+0 / −0.25	0 / 1	+0.6 / −0	+0 / −0.4	0 / 2.0	+1.0 / −0	+0 / −1.0	0.1 / 0.75	+0.4 / −0	−0.1 / −0.35
0.12–0.24	0 / 0.5	+0.3 / −0	+0 / −0.2	0 / 0.8	+0.5 / −0	+0 / −0.3	0 / 1.2	+0.7 / −0	+0 / −0.5	0 / 2.4	+1.2 / −0	+0 / −1.2	0.15 / 0.95	+0.5 / −0	−0.15 / −0.45
0.24–0.40	0 / 0.65	+0.4 / −0	+0 / −0.25	0 / 1.0	+0.6 / −0	+0 / −0.4	0 / 1.5	+0.9 / −0	+0 / −0.6	0 / 2.8	+1.4 / −0	+0 / −1.4	0.2 / 1.2	+0.6 / −0	−0.2 / −0.6
0.40–0.71	0 / 0.7	+0.4 / −0	+0 / −0.3	0 / 1.1	+0.7 / −0	+0 / −0.4	0 / 1.7	+1.0 / −0	+0 / −0.7	0 / 3.2	+1.6 / −0	+0 / −1.6	0.25 / 1.35	+0.7 / −0	−0.25 / −0.65
0.71–1.19	0 / 0.9	+0.5 / −0	+0 / −0.4	0 / 1.3	+0.8 / −0	+0 / −0.5	0 / 2	+1.2 / −0	+0 / −0.8	0 / 4	+2.0 / −0	+0 / −2.0	0.3 / 1.6	+0.8 / −0	−0.3 / −0.8
1.19–1.97	0 / 1.0	+0.6 / −0	+0 / −0.4	0 / 1.6	+1.0 / −0	+0 / −0.6	0 / 2.6	+1.6 / −0	+0 / −1	0 / 5	+2.5 / −0	+0 / −2.5	0.4 / 2.0	+1.0 / −0	−0.4 / −1.0
1.97–3.15	0 / 1.2	+0.7 / −0	+0 / −0.5	0 / 1.9	+1.2 / −0	+0 / −0.7	0 / 3	+1.8 / −0	+0 / −1.2	0 / 6	+3 / −0	+0 / −3	0.4 / 2.3	+1.2 / −0	−0.4 / −1.1
3.15–4.73	0 / 1.5	+0.9 / −0	+0 / −0.6	0 / 2.3	+1.4 / −0	+0 / −0.9	0 / 3.6	+2.2 / −0	+0 / −1.4	0 / 7	+3.5 / −0	+0 / −3.5	0.5 / 2.8	+1.4 / −0	−0.5 / −1.4
4.73–7.09	0 / 1.7	+1.0 / −0	+0 / −0.7	0 / 2.6	+1.6 / −0	+0 / −1.0	0 / 4.1	+2.5 / −0	+0 / −1.6	0 / 8	+4 / −0	+0 / −4	0.6 / 3.2	+1.6 / −0	−0.6 / −1.6
7.09–9.85	0 / 2.0	+1.2 / −0	+0 / −0.8	0 / 3.0	+1.8 / −0	+0 / −1.2	0 / 4.6	+2.8 / −0	+0 / −1.8	0 / 9	+4.5 / −0	+0 / −4.5	0.6 / 3.6	+1.8 / −0	−0.6 / −1.8

[1] Extracted from ASA B4.1–1955 (Table 2).
[2] Data are in accordance with ABC agreements.
For diameters greater than 9.85 in. see standard.

TABLE 24B (cont.)
Clearance Locational Fits

Limits are in thousandths of an inch. Limits for hole and shaft are applied algebraically to the basic size to obtain the limits of size for the parts. Symbols H8, f8, etc., are Hole and Shaft designations used in ABC System.

Nominal size range inches Over–To	LC 6 Limits of clearance	LC 6 Hole H8	LC 6 Shaft f8	LC 7 Limits of clearance	LC 7 Hole H9	LC 7 Shaft e9	LC 8 Limits of clearance	LC 8 Hole H10	LC 8 Shaft d9	LC 9 Limits of clearance	LC 9 Hole H11	LC 9 Shaft c11	LC 10 Limits of clearance	LC 10 Hole H12	LC 10 Shaft	LC 11 Limits of clearance	LC 11 Hole H13	LC 11 Shaft
0.04–0.12	0.3 / 1.5	+0.6 / −0	−0.3 / −0.9	0.6 / 2.6	+1.0 / −0	−0.6 / −1.6	1.0 / 2.0	+1.6 / −0	−1.0 / −2.0	2.5 / 7.5	+2.5 / −0	−2.5 / −5.0	4 / 12	+4 / −0	−4 / −8	5 / 17	+6 / −0	−5 / −11
0.12–0.24	0.4 / 1.8	+0.7 / −0	−0.4 / −1.1	0.8 / 3.2	+1.2 / −0	−0.8 / −2.0	1.2 / 4.2	+1.8 / −0	−1.2 / −2.4	2.8 / 8.8	+3.0 / −0	−2.8 / −5.8	4.5 / 14.5	+5 / −0	−4.5 / −9.5	6 / 20	+7 / −0	−6 / −13
0.24–0.40	0.5 / 2.3	+0.9 / −0	−0.5 / −1.4	1.0 / 3.8	+1.4 / −0	−1.0 / −2.4	1.6 / 5.2	+2.2 / −0	−1.6 / −3.0	3.0 / 10.0	+3.5 / −0	−3.0 / −6.5	5 / 17	+6 / −0	−5 / −11	7 / 25	+9 / −0	−7 / −16
0.40–0.71	0.6 / 2.6	+1.0 / −0	−0.6 / −1.6	1.2 / 4.4	+1.6 / −0	−1.2 / −2.8	2.0 / 6.4	+2.8 / −0	−2.0 / −3.6	3.5 / 11.5	+4.0 / −0	−3.5 / −7.5	6 / 20	+7 / −0	−6 / −13	8 / 28	+10 / −0	−8 / −18
0.71–1.19	0.8 / 3.2	+1.2 / −0	−0.8 / −2.0	1.6 / 5.6	+2.0 / −0	−1.6 / −3.6	2.5 / 8.0	+3.5 / −0	−2.5 / −4.5	4.5 / 14.5	+5.0 / −0	−4.5 / −9.5	7 / 23	+8 / −0	−7 / −15	10 / 34	+12 / −0	−10 / −22
1.19–1.97	1.0 / 4.2	+1.6 / −0	−1.0 / −2.6	2.0 / 7.0	+2.5 / −0	−2.0 / −4.5	3.6 / 9.5	+4.0 / −0	−3.0 / −5.5	5 / 17	+6 / −0	−5 / −11	8 / 28	+10 / −0	−8 / −18	12 / 44	+16 / −0	−12 / −28
1.97–3.15	1.2 / 4.8	+1.8 / −0	−1.0 / −3.0	2.5 / 8.5	+3.0 / −0	−2.5 / −5.5	4.0 / 11.5	+4.5 / −0	−4.0 / −7.0	6 / 20	+7 / −0	−6 / −13	10 / 34	+12 / −0	−10 / −22	14 / 50	+18 / −0	−14 / −32
3.15–4.73	1.4 / 5.8	+2.2 / −0	−1.4 / −3.6	3.0 / 10.0	+3.5 / −0	−3.0 / −6.5	5.0 / 13.5	+5.0 / −0	−5.0 / −8.5	7 / 25	+9 / −0	−7 / −16	11 / 39	+14 / −0	−11 / −25	16 / 60	+22 / −0	−16 / −38
4.73–7.09	1.6 / 6.6	+2.5 / −0	−1.6 / −4.1	3.5 / 11.5	+4.0 / −0	−3.5 / −7.5	6 / 16	+6 / −0	−6 / −10	8 / 28	+10 / −0	−8 / −18	12 / 44	+16 / −0	−12 / −28	18 / 68	+25 / −0	−18 / −43
7.09–9.85	2.0 / 7.6	+2.8 / −0	−2.0 / −4.8	4.0 / 13.0	+4.5 / −0	−4.0 / −8.5	7 / 18.5	+7 / −0	−7 / −11.5	10 / 34	+12 / −0	−10 / −22	16 / 52	+18 / −0	−16 / −34	22 / 78	+28 / −0	−22 / −50

TABLE 24C
Transition Locational Fits[1]

Limits are in thousandths of an inch. Limits for hole and shaft are applied algebraically to the basic size to obtain the limits of size for the mating parts. "Fit" represents the maximum interference (minus values) and the maximum clearance (plus values). Symbols H8, j6, etc., are Hole and Shaft designations used in ABC System.[2]

Nominal size range inches (Over–To)	LT 1 Fit	LT 1 Hole H7	LT 1 Shaft j6	LT 2 Fit	LT 2 Hole H8	LT 2 Shaft j7	LT 3 Fit	LT 3 Hole H7	LT 3 Shaft k6	LT 4 Fit	LT 4 Hole H8	LT 4 Shaft k7	LT 6 Fit	LT 6 Hole H8	LT 6 Shaft m7	LT 7 Fit	LT 7 Hole H7	LT 7 Shaft h6
0.04–0.12	−0.15	+0.4	+0.15	−0.3	+0.6	+0.3							−0.55	+0.6	+0.55	−0.5	+0.4	+0.5
	+0.5	−0	−0.1	+0.7	−0	−0.1							+0.45	−0	+0.15	+0.15	−0	+0.25
0.12–0.24	−0.2	+0.5	+0.2	−0.4	+0.7	+0.4							−0.7	+0.7	+0.7	−0.6	+0.5	+0.6
	+0.6	−0	−0.1	+0.8	−0	−0.1							+0.5	−0	+0.2	+0.2	−0	+0.3
0.24–0.40	−0.3	+0.6	+0.3	−0.4	+0.9	+0.4	−0.5	+0.6	+0.5	−0.7	+0.9	+0.7	−0.8	+0.9	+0.8	−0.8	+0.6	+0.8
	+0.7	−0	−0.1	+1.1	−0	−0.2	+0.5	−0	+0.1	+0.8	−0	+0.1	+0.7	−0	+0.2	+0.2	−0	+0.4
0.40–0.71	−0.3	+0.7	+0.3	−0.5	+1.0	+0.5	−0.5	+0.7	+0.5	−0.8	+1.0	+0.8	−1.0	+1.0	+1.0	−0.9	+0.7	+0.9
	+0.8	−0	−0.1	+1.2	−0	−0.2	+0.6	−0	+0.1	+0.9	−0	+0.1	+0.7	−0	+0.3	+0.2	−0	+0.5
0.71–1.19	−0.3	+0.8	+0.3	−0.5	+1.2	+0.5	−0.6	+0.8	+0.6	−0.9	+1.2	+0.9	−1.1	+1.2	+1.1	−1.1	+0.8	+1.1
	+1.0	−0	−0.2	+1.5	−0	−0.3	+0.7	−0	+0.1	+1.1	−0	+0.1	+0.9	−0	+0.3	+0.2	−0	+0.6
1.19–1.97	−0.4	+1.0	+0.4	−0.6	+1.6	+0.6	−0.7	+1.0	+0.7	−1.1	+1.6	+1.1	−1.4	+1.6	+1.4	−1.3	+1.0	+1.3
	+1.2	−0	−0.2	+2.0	−0	−0.4	+0.9	−0	+0.1	+1.5	−0	+0.1	+1.2	−0	+0.4	+0.3	−0	+0.7
1.97–3.15	−0.4	+1.2	+0.4	−0.7	+1.8	+0.7	−0.8	+1.2	+0.8	−1.3	+1.8	+1.3	−1.7	+1.8	+1.7	−1.5	+1.2	+1.5
	+1.5	−0	−0.3	+2.3	−0	−0.5	+1.1	−0	+0.1	+1.7	−0	+0.1	+1.3	−0	+0.5	+0.4	−0	+0.8
3.15–4.73	−0.5	+1.4	+0.5	−0.8	+2.2	+0.8	−1.0	+1.4	+1.0	−1.5	+2.2	+1.5	−1.9	+2.2	+1.9	−1.9	+1.4	+1.9
	+1.8	−0	−0.4	+2.8	−0	−0.6	+1.3	−0	+0.1	+2.1	−0	+0.1	+1.7	−0	+0.5	+0.4	−0	+1.0
4.73–7.09	−0.6	+1.6	+0.6	−0.9	+2.5	+0.9	−1.1	+1.6	+1.1	−1.7	+2.5	+1.7	−2.2	+2.5	+2.2	−2.2	+1.6	+2.2
	+2.0	−0	−0.4	+3.2	−0	−0.7	+1.5	−0	+0.1	+2.4	−0	+0.1	+1.9	−0	+0.6	+0.4	−0	+1.2
7.09–9.85	−0.7	+1.8	+0.7	−1.0	+2.8	+1.0	−1.4	+1.8	+1.4	−2.0	+2.8	+2.0	−2.4	+2.8	+2.4	−2.6	+1.8	+2.6
	+2.3	−0	−0.5	+3.6	−0	−0.8	+1.6	−0	+0.2	+2.6	−0	+0.2	+2.2	−0	+0.6	+0.4	−0	+1.4

[1] Extracted from ASA B4.1–1955 (Table 3).
[2] Data are in accordance with ABC agreements.
For diameters greater than 9.85 in. see standard.

TABLE 24D
Interference Locational Fits[1]

Limits are in thousandths of an inch. Limits for hole and shaft are applied algebraically to the basic size to obtain the limits of size for the parts. Symbols *H7*, *p*6, etc., are Hole and Shaft designations used in ABC System.[2]

Nominal size range inches Over To	Class LN 2			Class LN 3		
	Limits of interference	*Standard limits*		*Limits of interference*	*Standard limits*	
		Hole H7	*Shaft p*6		*Hole H7*	*Shaft r*6
0.04–0.12	0	+0.4	+0.65	0.1	+0.4	+0.75
	0.65	−0	+0.4	0.75	−0	+0.5
0.12–0.24	0	+0.5	+0.8	0.1	+0.5	+0.9
	0.8	−0	+0.5	0.9	−0	+0.6
0.24–0.40	0	+0.6	+1.0	0.2	+0.6	+1.2
	1.0	−0	+0.6	1.2	−0	+0.8
0.40–0.71	0	+0.7	+1.1	0.3	+0.7	+1.4
	1.1	−0	+0.7	1.4	−0	+1.0
0.71–1.19	0	+0.8	+1.3	0.4	+0.8	+1.7
	1.3	−0	+0.8	1.7	−0	+1.2
1.19–1.97	0	+1.0	+1.6	0.4	+1.0	+2.0
	1.6	−0	+1.0	2.0	−0	+1.4
1.97–3.15	0.2	+1.2	+2.1	0.4	+1.2	+2.3
	2.1	−0	+1.4	2.3	−0	+1.6
3.15–4.73	0.2	+1.4	+2.5	0.6	+1.4	+2.9
	2.5	−0	+1.6	2.9	−0	+2.0
4.73–7.09	0.2	+1.6	+2.8	0.9	+1.6	+3.5
	2.8	−0	+1.8	3.5	−0	+2.5
7.09–9.85	0.2	+1.8	+3.2	1.2	+1.8	+4.2
	3.2	−0	+2.0	4.2	−0	+3.0

[1] Extracted from ASA B4.1–1955 (Table 4).
[2] Data are in accordance with ABC agreements.
For diameters greater than 9.85 in. see standard.

TABLE 24E
Force and Shrink Fits[1]

Limits are in thousandths of an inch. Limits for hole and shaft are applied algebraically to the basic size to obtain the limits of size for the parts. Symbols *H7*, *s6*, etc., are Hole and Shaft designations used in ABC System.[2]

Nominal size range inches Over – To	Class FN 1 Limits of interference	Class FN 1 Hole H6	Class FN 1 Shaft	Class FN 2 Limits of interference	Class FN 2 Hole H7	Class FN 2 Shaft s6	Class FN 3 Limits of interference	Class FN 3 Hole H7	Class FN 3 Shaft t6	Class FN 4 Limits of interference	Class FN 4 Hole H7	Class FN 4 Shaft u6	Class FN 5 Limits of interference	Class FN 5 Hole H7	Class FN 5 Shaft x7
0.04–0.12	0.05	+0.25	+0.5	0.2	+0.4	+0.85				0.3	+0.4	+0.95	0.5	+0.4	+1.3
	0.5	−0	+0.3	0.85	−0	+0.6				0.95	−0	+0.7	1.3	−0	+0.9
0.12–0.24	0.1	+0.3	+0.6	0.2	+0.5	+1.0				0.4	+0.5	+1.2	0.7	+0.5	+1.7
	0.6	−0	+0.4	1.0	−0	+0.7				1.2	−0	+0.9	1.7	−0	+1.2
0.24–0.40	0.1	+0.4	+0.75	0.4	+0.6	+1.4				0.6	+0.6	+1.6	0.8	+0.6	+2.0
	0.75	−0	+0.5	1.4	−0	+1.0				1.6	−0	+1.2	2.0	−0	+1.4
0.40–0.56	0.1	+0.4	+0.8	0.5	+0.7	+1.6				0.7	+0.7	+1.8	0.9	+0.7	+2.3
	0.8	−0	+0.5	1.6	−0	+1.2				1.8	−0	+1.4	2.3	−0	+1.6
0.56–0.71	0.2	+0.4	+0.9	0.5	+0.7	+1.6				0.7	+0.7	+1.8	1.1	+0.7	+2.5
	0.9	−0	+0.6	1.6	−0	+1.2				1.8	−0	+1.4	2.5	−0	+1.8
0.71–0.95	0.2	+0.5	+1.1	0.6	+0.8	+1.9				0.8	+0.8	+2.1	1.4	+0.8	+3.0
	1.1	−0	+0.7	1.9	−0	+1.4				2.1	−0	+1.6	3.0	−0	+2.2
0.95–1.19	0.3	+0.5	+1.2	0.6	+0.8	+1.9	0.8	+0.8	+2.1	1.0	+0.8	+2.3	1.7	+0.8	+3.3
	1.2	−0	+0.8	1.9	−0	+1.4	2.1	−0	+1.6	2.3	−0	+1.8	3.3	−0	+2.5
1.19–1.58	0.3	+0.6	+1.3	0.8	+1.0	+2.4	0.8	+1.0	+2.6	1.5	+1.0	+3.1	2.0	+1.0	+4.0
	1.3	−0	+0.9	2.4	−0	+1.8	2.4	−0	+2.0	3.1	−0	+2.5	4.0	−0	+3.0
1.58–1.97	0.4	+0.6	+1.4	0.8	+1.0	+2.4	1.2	+1.0	+2.8	1.8	+1.0	+3.4	3.0	+1.0	+5.0
	1.4	−0	+1.0	2.4	−0	+1.8	2.8	−0	+2.2	3.4	−0	+2.8	5.0	−0	+4.0
1.97–2.56	0.6	+0.7	+1.8	0.8	+1.2	+2.7	1.3	+1.2	+3.2	2.3	+1.2	+4.2	3.8	+1.2	+6.2
	1.8	−0	+1.3	2.7	−0	+2.0	3.2	−0	+2.5	4.2	−0	+3.5	6.2	−0	+5.0
2.56–3.15	0.7	+0.7	+1.9	1.0	+1.2	+2.9	1.8	+1.2	+3.7	2.8	+1.2	+4.7	4.8	+1.2	+7.2
	1.9	−0	+1.4	2.9	−0	+2.2	3.7	−0	+3.0	4.7	−0	+4.0	7.2	−0	+6.0

[1] Extracted from ASA B4.1–1955 (Table 5).
[2] Data are in accordance with ABC agreements.
For diameters greater than 3.15 in. see standard.

TABLE 25
Twist Drill Sizes*

NUMBER SIZES				LETTER SIZES	
No. size	*Decimal equivalent*	*No. size*	*Decimal equivalent*	*Size letter*	*Decimal equivalent*
1	.2280	41	.0960	A	.234
2	.2210	42	.0935	B	.238
3	.2130	43	.0890	C	.242
4	.2090	44	.0860	D	.246
5	.2055	45	.0820	E	.250
6	.2040	46	.0810	F	.257
7	.2010	47	.0785	G	.261
8	.1990	48	.0760	H	.266
9	.1960	49	.0730	I	.272
10	.1935	50	.0700	J	.277
11	.1910	51	.0670	K	.281
12	.1890	52	.0635	L	.290
13	.1850	53	.0595	M	.295
14	.1820	54	.0550	N	.302
15	.1800	55	.0520	O	.316
16	.1770	56	.0465	P	.323
17	.1730	57	.0430	Q	.332
18	.1695	58	.0420	R	.339
19	.1660	59	.0410	S	.348
20	.1610	60	.0400	T	.358
21	.1590	61	.0390	U	.368
22	.1570	62	.0380	V	.377
23	.1540	63	.0370	W	.386
24	.1520	64	.0360	X	.397
25	.1495	65	.0350	Y	.404
26	.1470	66	.0330	Z	.413
27	.1440	67	.0320		
28	.1405	68	.0310		
29	.1360	69	.0292		
30	.1285	70	.0280		
31	.1200	71	.0260		
32	.1160	72	.0250		
33	.1130	73	.0240		
34	.1110	74	.0225		
35	.1100	75	.0210		
36	.1065	76	.0200		
37	.1040	77	.0180		
38	.1015	78	.0160		
39	.0995	79	.0145		
40	.0980	80	.0135		

* Fraction size drills range in size from one-sixteenth–4 inches and over in diameter—by 64ths.

TABLE 26
Standard Wire and Sheet-Metal Gages

(Dimensions in decimal parts of an inch)

Gage number	(A) Brown & Sharpe or American	(B) American Steel & Wire Co.	(C) Piano wire	(E) U.S. St'd.	Gage number
0000000	.6513	.4900	—	.5000	0000000
000000	.5800	.4615	.004	.4688	000000
00000	.5165	.4305	.005	.4375	00000
0000	.4600	.3938	.006	.4063	0000
000	.4096	.3625	.007	.3750	000
00	.3648	.3310	.008	.3438	00
0	.3249	.3065	.009	.3125	0
1	.2893	.2830	.010	.2813	1
2	.2576	.2625	.011	.2656	2
3	.2294	.2437	.012	.2500	3
4	.2043	.2253	.013	.2344	4
5	.1819	.2070	.014	.2188	5
6	.1620	.1920	.016	.2031	6
7	.1443	.1770	.018	.1875	7
8	.1285	.1620	.020	.1719	8
9	.1144	.1483	.022	.1563	9
10	.1019	.1350	.024	.1406	10
11	.0907	.1205	.026	.1250	11
12	.0808	.1055	.029	.1094	12
13	.0720	.0915	.031	.0938	13
14	.0641	.0800	.033	.0781	14
15	.0571	.0720	.035	.0703	15
16	.0508	.0625	.037	.0625	16
17	.0453	.0540	.039	.0563	17
18	.0403	.0475	.041	.0500	18
19	.0359	.0410	.043	.0438	19
20	.0320	.0348	.045	.0375	20
21	.0285	.0317	.047	.0344	21
22	.0253	.0286	.049	.0313	22
23	.0226	.0258	.051	.0281	23
24	.0201	.0230	.055	.0250	24
25	.0179	.0204	.059	.0219	25
26	.0159	.0181	.063	.0188	26
27	.0142	.0173	.067	.0172	27
28	.0126	.0162	.071	.0156	28
29	.0113	.0150	.075	.0141	29
30	.0100	.0140	.080	.0125	30
31	.0089	.0132	.085	.0109	31
32	.0080	.0128	.090	.0102	32
33	.0071	.0118	.095	.0094	33
34	.0063	.0104	.100	.0086	34
35	.0056	.0095	.106	.0078	35
36	.0050	.0090	.112	.0070	36
37	.0045	.0085	.118	.0066	37
38	.0040	.0080	.124	.0063	38
39	.0035	.0075	.130	—	39
40	.0031	.0070	.138	—	40

(A) Standard in U.S. for sheet metal and wire (except steel & iron).
(B) Standard for iron and steel wire (U.S. Steel Wire Gage).
(C) American Steel and Wire Company's music (or piano) wire gage sizes. Recognized by U.S. Bureau of Standards.
(E) U.S. Standard for iron and steel plate. However, plate is now generally specified by its thickness in decimals of an inch.

TABLE 27
Trigonometric Functions

Angle	Sine	Cosine	Tan	Co-Tan	Angle
0°	0.0000	1.0000	0.0000	∞	90°
1°	0.0175	0.9998	0.0175	57.290	89°
2°	.0349	.9994	.0349	28.636	88°
3°	.0523	.9986	.0524	19.081	87°
4°	.0698	.9976	.0699	14.301	86°
5°	.0872	.9962	.0875	11.430	85°
6°	.1045	.9945	.1051	9.5144	84°
7°	.1219	.9925	.1228	8.1443	83°
8°	.1392	.9903	.1405	7.1154	82°
9°	.1564	.9877	.1584	6.3138	81°
10°	.1736	.9848	.1763	5.6713	80°
11°	.1908	.9816	.1944	5.1446	79°
12°	.2079	.9781	.2126	4.7046	78°
13°	.2250	.9744	.2309	4.3315	77°
14°	.2419	.9703	.2493	4.0108	76°
15°	.2588	.9659	.2679	3.7321	75°
16°	.2756	.9613	.2867	3.4874	74°
17°	.2924	.9563	.3057	3.2709	73°
18°	.3090	.9511	.3249	3.0777	72°
19°	.3256	.9455	.3443	2.9042	71°
20°	.3420	.9397	.3640	2.7475	70°
21°	.3584	.9336	.3839	2.6051	69°
22°	.3746	.9272	.4040	2.4751	68°
23°	.3907	.9205	.4245	2.3559	67°
24°	.4067	.9135	.4452	2.2460	66°
25°	.4226	.9063	.4663	2.1445	65°
26°	.4384	.8988	.4877	2.0503	64°
27°	.4540	.8910	.5095	1.9626	63°
28°	.4695	.8829	.5317	1.8807	62°
29°	.4848	.8746	.5543	1.8040	61°
30°	.5000	.8660	.5774	1.7321	60°
31°	.5150	.8572	.6009	1.6643	59°
32°	.5299	.8480	.6249	1.6003	58°
33°	.5446	.8387	.6494	1.5399	57°
34°	.5592	.8290	.6745	1.4826	56°
35°	.5736	.8192	.7002	1.4281	55°
36°	.5878	.8090	.7265	1.3764	54°
37°	.6018	.7986	.7536	1.3270	53°
38°	.6157	.7880	.7813	1.2799	52°
39°	.6293	.7771	.8098	1.2349	51°
40°	.6428	.7660	.8391	1.1918	50°
41°	.6561	.7547	.8693	1.1504	49°
42°	.6691	.7431	.9004	1.1106	48°
43°	.6820	.7314	.9325	1.0724	47°
44°	.6947	.7193	.9657	1.0355	46°
45°	.7071	.7071	1.0000	1.0000	45°
Angle	Cosine	Sine	Co-Tan	Tan	Angle

TABLE 28
Logarithms of Numbers

	0	1	2	3	4	5	6	7	8	9	1	2	3	4	5	6	7	8	9
10	0000	0043	0086	0128	0170	0212	0253	0294	0334	0374	4	8	12	17	21	25	29	33	37
11	0414	0453	0492	0531	0569	0607	0645	0682	0719	0755	4	8	11	15	19	23	26	30	34
12	0792	0828	0864	0899	0934	0969	1004	1038	1072	1106	3	7	10	14	17	21	24	28	31
13	1139	1173	1206	1239	1271	1303	1335	1367	1399	1430	3	6	10	13	16	19	23	26	29
14	1461	1492	1523	1553	1584	1614	1644	1673	1703	1732	3	6	9	12	15	18	21	24	27
15	1761	1790	1818	1847	1875	1903	1931	1959	1987	2014	3	6	8	11	14	17	20	22	25
16	2041	2068	2095	2122	2148	2175	2201	2227	2253	2279	3	5	8	11	13	16	18	21	24
17	2304	2330	2355	2380	2405	2430	2455	2480	2504	2529	2	5	7	10	12	15	17	20	22
18	2553	2577	2601	2625	2648	2672	2695	2718	2742	2765	2	5	7	9	12	14	16	19	21
19	2788	2810	2833	2856	2878	2900	2923	2945	2967	2989	2	4	7	9	11	13	16	18	20
20	3010	3032	3054	3075	3096	3118	3139	3160	3181	3201	2	4	6	8	11	13	15	17	19
21	3222	3243	3263	3284	3304	3324	3345	3365	3385	3404	2	4	6	8	10	12	14	16	18
22	3424	3444	3464	3483	3502	3522	3541	3560	3579	3598	2	4	6	8	10	12	14	15	17
23	3617	3636	3655	3674	3692	3711	3729	3747	3766	3784	2	4	6	7	9	11	13	15	17
24	3802	3820	3838	3856	3874	3892	3909	3927	3945	3962	2	4	5	7	9	11	12	14	16
25	3979	3997	4014	4031	4048	4065	4082	4099	4116	4133	2	3	5	7	9	10	12	14	15
26	4150	4166	4183	4200	4216	4232	4249	4265	4281	4298	2	3	5	7	8	10	11	13	15
27	4314	4330	4346	4362	4378	4393	4409	4425	4440	4456	2	3	5	6	8	9	11	13	14
28	4472	4487	4502	4518	4533	4548	4564	4579	4594	4609	2	3	5	6	8	9	11	12	14
29	4624	4639	4654	4669	4683	4698	4713	4728	4742	4757	1	3	4	6	7	9	10	12	13
30	4771	4786	4800	4814	4829	4843	4857	4871	4886	4900	1	3	4	6	7	9	10	11	13
31	4914	4928	4942	4955	4969	4983	4997	5011	5024	5038	1	3	4	6	7	8	10	11	12
32	5051	5065	5079	5092	5105	5119	5132	5145	5159	5172	1	3	4	5	7	8	9	11	12
33	5185	5198	5211	5224	5237	5250	5263	5276	5289	5302	1	3	4	5	6	8	9	10	12
34	5315	5328	5340	5353	5366	5378	5391	5403	5416	5428	1	3	4	5	6	8	9	10	11
35	5441	5453	5465	5478	5490	5502	5514	5527	5539	5551	1	2	4	5	6	7	9	10	11
36	5563	5575	5587	5599	5611	5623	5635	5647	5658	5670	1	2	4	5	6	7	8	10	11
37	5682	5694	5705	5717	5729	5740	5752	5763	5775	5786	1	2	3	5	6	7	8	9	10
38	5798	5809	5821	5832	5843	5855	5866	5877	5888	5899	1	2	3	5	6	7	8	9	10
39	5911	5922	5933	5944	5955	5966	5977	5988	5999	6010	1	2	3	4	5	7	8	9	10
40	6021	6031	6042	6053	6064	6075	6085	6096	6107	6117	1	2	3	4	5	6	8	9	10
41	6128	6138	6149	6160	6170	6180	6191	6201	6212	6222	1	2	3	4	5	6	7	8	9
42	6232	6243	6253	6263	6274	6284	6294	6304	6314	6325	1	2	3	4	5	6	7	8	9
43	6335	6345	6355	6365	6375	6385	6395	6405	6415	6425	1	2	3	4	5	6	7	8	9
44	6435	6444	6454	6464	6474	6484	6493	6503	6513	6522	1	2	3	4	5	6	7	8	9
45	6532	6542	6551	6561	6571	6580	6590	6599	6609	6618	1	2	3	4	5	6	7	8	9
46	6628	6637	6646	6656	6665	6675	6684	6693	6702	6712	1	2	3	4	5	6	7	7	8
47	6721	6730	6739	6749	6758	6767	6776	6785	6794	6803	1	2	3	4	5	5	6	7	8
48	6812	6821	6830	6839	6848	6857	6866	6875	6884	6893	1	2	3	4	4	5	6	7	8
49	6902	6911	6920	6928	6937	6946	6955	6964	6972	6981	1	2	3	4	4	5	6	7	8
50	6990	6998	7007	7016	7024	7033	7042	7050	7059	7067	1	2	3	3	4	5	6	7	8
51	7076	7084	7093	7101	7110	7118	7126	7135	7143	7152	1	2	3	3	4	5	6	7	8
52	7160	7168	7177	7185	7193	7202	7210	7218	7226	7235	1	2	2	3	4	5	6	7	7
53	7243	7251	7259	7267	7275	7284	7292	7300	7308	7316	1	2	2	3	4	5	6	6	7
54	7324	7332	7340	7348	7356	7364	7372	7380	7388	7396	1	2	2	3	4	5	6	6	7

TABLE 28 (cont.)
Logarithms of Numbers

	0	1	2	3	4	5	6	7	8	9	1	2	3	4	5	6	7	8	9
55	7404	7412	7419	7427	7435	7443	7451	7459	7466	7474	1	2	2	3	4	5	5	6	7
56	7482	7490	7497	7505	7513	7520	7528	7536	7543	7551	1	2	2	3	4	5	5	6	7
57	7559	7566	7574	7582	7589	7597	7604	7612	7619	7627	1	2	2	3	4	5	5	6	7
58	7634	7642	7649	7657	7664	7672	7679	7686	7694	7701	1	1	2	3	4	4	5	6	7
59	7709	7716	7723	7731	7738	7745	7752	7760	7767	7774	1	1	2	3	4	4	5	6	7
60	7782	7789	7796	7803	7810	7818	7825	7832	7839	7846	1	1	2	3	4	4	5	6	6
61	7853	7860	7868	7875	7882	7889	7896	7903	7910	7917	1	1	2	3	4	4	5	6	6
62	7924	7931	7938	7945	7952	7959	7966	7973	7980	7987	1	1	2	3	3	4	5	6	6
63	7993	8000	8007	8014	8021	8028	8035	8041	8048	8055	1	1	2	3	3	4	5	5	6
64	8062	8069	8075	8082	8089	8096	8102	8109	8116	8122	1	1	2	3	3	4	5	5	6
65	8129	8136	8142	8149	8156	8162	8169	8176	8182	8189	1	1	2	3	3	4	5	5	6
66	8195	8202	8209	8215	8222	8228	8235	8241	8248	8254	1	1	2	3	3	4	5	5	6
67	8261	8267	8274	8280	8287	8293	8299	8306	8312	8319	1	1	2	3	3	4	5	5	6
68	8325	8331	8338	8344	8351	8357	8363	8370	8376	8382	1	1	2	3	3	4	4	5	6
69	8388	8395	8401	8407	8414	8420	8426	8432	8439	8445	1	1	2	2	3	4	4	5	6
70	8451	8457	8463	8470	8476	8482	8488	8494	8500	8506	1	1	2	2	3	4	4	5	6
71	8513	8519	8525	8531	8537	8543	8549	8555	8561	8567	1	1	2	2	3	4	4	5	5
72	8573	8579	8585	8591	8597	8603	8609	8615	8621	8627	1	1	2	2	3	4	4	5	5
73	8633	8639	8645	8651	8657	8663	8669	8675	8681	8686	1	1	2	2	3	4	4	5	5
74	8692	8698	8704	8710	8716	8722	8727	8733	8739	8745	1	1	2	2	3	4	4	5	5
75	8751	8756	8762	8768	8774	8779	8785	8791	8797	8802	1	1	2	2	3	3	4	5	5
76	8808	8814	8820	8825	8831	8837	8842	8848	8854	8859	1	1	2	2	3	3	4	5	5
77	8865	8871	8876	8882	8887	8893	8899	8904	8910	8915	1	1	2	2	3	3	4	4	5
78	8921	8927	8932	8938	8943	8949	8954	8960	8965	8971	1	1	2	2	3	3	4	4	5
79	8976	8982	8987	8993	8998	9004	9009	9015	9020	9025	1	1	2	2	3	3	4	4	5
80	9031	9036	9042	9047	9053	9058	9063	9069	9074	9079	1	1	2	2	3	3	4	4	5
81	9085	9090	9096	9101	9106	9112	9117	9122	9128	9133	1	1	2	2	3	3	4	4	5
82	9138	9143	9149	9154	9159	9165	9170	9175	9180	9186	1	1	2	2	3	3	4	4	5
83	9191	9196	9201	9206	9212	9217	9222	9227	9232	9238	1	1	2	2	3	3	4	4	5
84	9243	9248	9253	9258	9263	9269	9274	9279	9284	9289	1	1	2	2	3	3	4	4	5
85	9294	9299	9304	9309	9315	9320	9325	9330	9335	9340	1	1	2	2	3	3	4	4	5
86	9345	9350	9355	9360	9365	9370	9375	9380	9385	9390	1	1	2	2	3	3	4	4	5
87	9395	9400	9405	9410	9415	9420	9425	9430	9435	9440	0	1	1	2	2	3	3	4	4
88	9445	9450	9455	9460	9465	9469	9474	9479	9484	9489	0	1	1	2	2	3	3	4	4
89	9494	9499	9504	9509	9513	9518	9523	9528	9533	9538	0	1	1	2	2	3	3	4	4
90	9542	9547	9552	9557	9562	9566	9571	9576	9581	9586	0	1	1	2	2	3	3	4	4
91	9590	9595	9600	9605	9609	9614	9619	9624	9628	9633	0	1	1	2	2	3	3	4	4
92	9638	9643	9647	9652	9657	9661	9666	9671	9675	9680	0	1	1	2	2	3	3	4	4
93	9685	9689	9694	9699	9703	9708	9713	9717	9722	9727	0	1	1	2	2	3	3	4	4
94	9731	9736	9741	9745	9750	9754	9759	9763	9768	9773	0	1	1	2	2	3	3	4	4
95	9777	9782	9786	9791	9795	9800	9805	9809	9814	9818	0	1	1	2	2	3	3	4	4
96	9823	9827	9832	9836	9841	9845	9850	9854	9859	9863	0	1	1	2	2	3	3	4	4
97	9868	9872	9877	9881	9886	9890	9894	9899	9903	9908	0	1	1	2	2	3	3	4	4
98	9912	9917	9921	9926	9930	9934	9939	9943	9948	9952	0	1	1	2	2	3	3	4	4
99	9956	9961	9965	9969	9974	9978	9983	9987	9991	9996	0	1	1	2	2	3	3	3	4

TABLE 29
Table of Chords

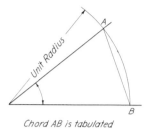

Chord AB is tabulated

Tabulated values are chord lengths of arcs of unit radius subtending the specified angles. Use multiples for accuracy.

Degrees	0′	10′	20′	30′	40′	50′
0	.0000	.0029	.0058	.0087	.0116	.0145
1	.0174	.0204	.0233	.0202	.0291	.0320
2	.0349	.0378	.0407	.0436	.0465	.0494
3	.0523	.0553	.0582	.0611	.0640	.0669
4	.0698	.0727	.0756	.0785	.0814	.0843
5	.0872	.0901	.0930	.0959	.0988	.1017
6	.1047	.1076	.1105	.1134	.1163	.1192
7	.1221	.1250	.1279	.1308	.1337	.1366
8	.1395	.1424	.1453	.1482	.1511	.1540
9	.1569	.1598	.1627	.1656	.1685	.1714
10	.1743	.1772	.1801	.1830	.1859	.1888
11	.1917	.1946	.1975	.2004	.2033	.2062
12	.2090	.2119	.2148	.2177	.2206	.2235
13	.2264	.2293	.2322	.2351	.2380	.2409
14	.2437	.2466	.2495	.2524	.2553	.2582
15	.2610	.2639	.2668	.2697	.2726	.2755
16	.2783	.2812	.2841	.2870	.2899	.2927
17	.2956	.2985	.3014	.3042	.3071	.3100
18	.3129	.3157	.3186	.3215	.3243	.3272
19	.3301	.3330	.3358	.3387	.3416	.3444
20	.3473	.3502	.3530	.3559	.3587	.3616
21	.3645	.3673	.3702	.3730	.3759	.3788
22	.3816	.3845	.3873	.3902	.3930	.3959
23	.3987	.4016	.4044	.4073	.4101	.4130
24	.4158	.4187	.4215	.4243	.4272	.4300
25	.4329	.4357	.4385	.4414	.4442	.4471
26	.4499	.4527	.4556	.4584	.4612	.4641
27	.4669	.4697	.4725	.4754	.4782	.4810
28	.4838	.4867	.4895	.4923	.4951	.4979
29	.5008	.5036	.5064	.5092	.5120	.5148
30	.5176	.5204	.5232	.5261	.5289	.5317
31	.5345	.5373	.5401	.5429	.5457	.5485
32	.5513	.5541	.5569	.5596	.5624	.5652
33	.5680	.5708	.5736	.5764	.5792	.5820
34	.5847	.5875	.5903	.5931	.5959	.5986
35	.6014	.6042	.6069	.6097	.6125	.6153
36	.6180	.6208	.6236	.6263	.6291	.6318
37	.6346	.6374	.6401	.6429	.6456	.6484
38	.6511	.6539	.6566	.6594	.6621	.6649
39	.6676	.6703	.6731	.6758	.6786	.6813
40	.6840	.6868	.6895	.6922	.6950	.6977
41	.7004	.7031	.7059	.7086	.7113	.7140
42	.7167	.7194	.7222	.7249	.7276	.7303
43	.7330	.7357	.7384	.7411	.7438	.7465
44	.7492	.7519	.7546	.7573	.7600	.7627
45	.7654	.7680	.7707	.7734	.7761	.7788

Abbreviations and Symbols

alternating current . . . . a-c
aluminum . . . . Al
American Standard . . . . Am. Std.
approved . . . . App.
average . . . . avg.
ball bearing . . . . bb
Brown & Sharpe . . . . B & S
Babbitt . . . . Bab.
brass . . . . Br.
bronze . . . . Bro.
Brinell hardness number . . . . Bhn.
cast iron . . . . C.I.
center line . . . . CL or ℄
center to center . . . . c to c.
centimeter . . . . cm.
chemical . . . . chem.
circular . . . . cir.
circular pitch . . . . CP
copper . . . . Cop.
cold-rolled steel . . . . C.R.S.
counterbore . . . . c'bore
countersink . . . . c's'k
cubic . . . . cu
cubic inch . . . . cu in.
cubic foot . . . . cu ft
cubic yard . . . . cu yd
cylinder . . . . cyl.
degree . . . . deg. or °
diameter . . . . D., Dia., or Diam.
direct current . . . . d-c
diagonal . . . . diag.
diametral pitch . . . . DP
drawing . . . . Dwg.
drawn . . . . Dr.
detail drawing . . . . Dtl. dwg.
efficiency . . . . eff.
electric . . . . elec.
engineer . . . . engr.
external . . . . ext.
fabricate . . . . fab.
fillister . . . . fil.
finish . . . . fin.
foot . . . . ft or '
gallon . . . . gal.
galvanized iron . . . . G.I.
grind . . . . G or gr.
harden . . . . hdn.
hexagonal . . . . hex.
horsepower . . . . hp
hour . . . . hr
impregnate . . . . impreg.
inch . . . . in. or "
inside diameter . . . . I.D.
internal . . . . int.
left hand . . . . L.H.

lateral . . . . lat.
long . . . . lg.
longitudinal . . . . long.
linear foot . . . . lin. ft
machine . . . . mach.
malleable iron . . . . Mal. I.
material . . . . mat.
maximum . . . . max.
meter . . . . m
mile . . . . mi
millimeter . . . . mm
miles per hour . . . . mph
minimum . . . . min.
minute (angular measure) . . . . '
minute (time) . . . . min
outside diameter . . . . O.D.
pattern . . . . patt.
phosphor bronze . . . . Phos. Bro.
piece . . . . pc.
pitch . . . . P
pitch diameter . . . . P.D.
plate . . . . pl.
pound . . . . # or lb
pounds per square foot . . . . lb per sq ft
pounds per square inch . . . . . . lb per sq in.
Pratt & Whitney . . . . P & W.
quantity . . . . quan.
radius . . . . R or Rad.
required . . . . req. or req'd.
revolution per minute . . . . rpm
right hand . . . . R.H.
round . . . . rd.
round bar . . . . φ
screw . . . . sc.
second (time) . . . . sec
second (angular measure) . . . . "
section . . . . sec.
Society of Automotive Engineers . . . . . SAE
square . . . . sq
square inch . . . . sq in.
square foot . . . . sq ft
standard . . . . std.
steel . . . . Stl.
steel casting . . . . Stl. C.
thousand . . . . M
ton . . . . ton
thread . . . . thd.
traced . . . . Tr.
volt v
watt . . . . w
weight . . . . wt.
Woodruff key . . . . Wdrf. key
wrought iron . . . . W.I.
yard . . . . yd
year . . . . yr

694 APPENDIX

ASA Standards

A few of the more than 500 standards approved by the American Standards Association are listed below. Copies may be obtained from the Association's Sales Department at 70 East 45th Street, New York 17, N.Y.

A13.1–1956	Identification of Piping Systems, Scheme for
B1.1–1949	Unified and American Screw Threads for Screws, Bolts, Nuts, and Other Threaded Parts
B1.2–1951	Screw Thread Gages and Gaging
B1.5–1952	Acme Screw Threads
B2.1–1945	Pipe Threads
B4.1–1955	Preferred Limits and Fits for Cylindrical Parts
B5.6–1941	Jig Bushings
B5.10–1953	Machine Tapers, Self-holding and Steep Taper Series
B5.15–1950	Involute Splines, Side Bearing
B5.20–1954	Machine Pins
B6.1–1932	Spur Gear Tooth Form
B16.1–1948	Cast-Iron Pipe Flanges and Flanged Fittings, Class 125
B16b–1944 (R1953)	Cast-Iron Pipe Flanges and Flanged Fittings for Maximum WSP of 250 lb
B16b2–1931	Cast-Iron Pipe Flanges and Flanged Fittings for Maximum WSP of 25 lb
B16.3–1951	Malleable-Iron Screwed Fittings, 150 lb
B16.4–1949	Cast-Iron Screwed Fittings for Maximum WSP of 125 and 250 lb
B16.5–1953	Steel Pipe Flanges and Flanged Fittings
B16.9–1951	Steel Butt-Welding Fittings
B16.10–1957	Face-to-Face and End-to-End Dimensions of Ferrous Valves
B17f–1930	Woodruff Keys, Keyslots, and Cutters
B17.1–1943	Shafting and Stock Keys
B18.1–1955	Small Solid Rivets
B18.2–1955	Square and Hexagon Bolts and Nuts
B18.3–1954	Socket Set Screws and Socket Head Cap Screws
B18.4–1950	Large Rivets
B18.5–1952	Round Head Bolts
B18.6.2–1956	Hexagon Head Cap Screws, Slotted Head Cap Screws, Square Head Set Screws, and Slotted Headless Set Screws
B36.1–1956	Welded and Seamless Steel Pipe (ASTM A53-44)
B36.2–1956	Welded Wrought-Iron Pipe
B36.10–1950	Wrought-Iron and Wrought-Steel Pipe
B45.1–1932	Foundry Patterns of Wood (CS 19-32)
B48.1–1933	Inch-Millimeter Conversion for Industrial Use
Y14.1–1957	Size and Format
Y14.2–1957	Line Conventions, Sectioning and Lettering
Y14.3–1957	Projections
Y14.4–1957	Pictorial Drawing
Y14.5–1957	Dimensioning and Notes
Y14.6–1957	Screw Threads
Y14.7–1958	Gears, Splines and Serrations
Y14.8– —	Castings (In preparation)
Y14.9–1958	Forgings
Y14.10–1959	Metal-Stampings
Y14.11–1958	Plastics
Y14.12– —	Die Castings
Y14.13– —	Springs, Helical and Flat } (In preparation)
Y14.14– —	Mechanical Assemblies
Y14.15–1960	Electrical Diagrams
Y14.16– —	Tools, Dies and Gages (In preparation)
Y14.17–1959	Fluid Power Diagrams

Y32.2–1954	Graphical Symbols for Electrical Diagrams
Z10.1–1941	Abbreviations for Scientific Engineering Terms*
Z10.5–1949	Electrical Quantities, Letter Symbols for*
Z15.1–1932	Engineering and Scientific Charts for Lantern Slides*
Z15.2–1938	Time-Series Charts, Manual of Design and Construction*
Z15.3–1943	Engineering and Scientific Graphs for Publications*
Z32.2.1–1949 (R1953)	Welding Symbols and Instructions for Their Use*
Z32.3–1946	Graphical Symbols for Power Control and Measurement*
Z32.5–1944	Symbols for Telephone, Telegraph, and Radio Use*

* Y is the new letter assigned to standards for abbreviations, charts and graphs, drawings, graphical symbols, and letter symbols. The Z will be changed to Y as the standards are revised and reaffirmed.

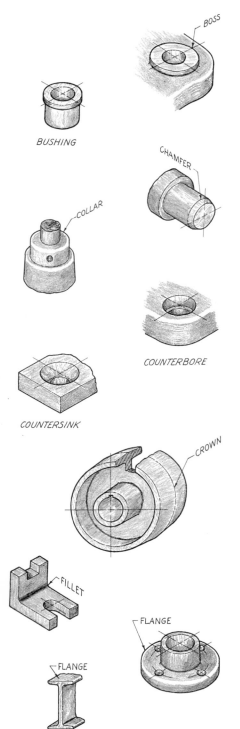

BUSHING

COLLAR

BOSS

CHAMFER

COUNTERBORE

COUNTERSINK

CROWN

FILLET

FLANGE

FLANGE

Glossary of Common Shop Terms

ANNEAL (*v*). To heat a piece of metal to a particular temperature and then allow it to cool slowly for the purpose of removing internal stresses.

BORE (*v*). To enlarge a hole using a boring bar in order to make it smooth, round, and co-axial. Boring is usually done on a lathe or boring mill.

BOSS (*n*). A circular projection which is raised above a principal surface of a casting or forging.

BRAZE (*v*). To join two pieces of metal by the use of hard solder. The solder is usually a copper-zinc alloy.

BROACH (*v*). To machine a hole to a desired shape, usually other than round. The cutting tool, known as a broach, is pushed or pulled through the rough finished hole. It has transverse cutting edges.

BURNISH (*v*). To smooth or apply a brilliant finish.

BUSHING (*n*). A removable cylindrical sleeve which is used to provide a bearing surface.

CARBURIZE (*v*). To harden the surface of a piece of low-grade steel by heating in a carbonizing material to increase the carbon content and then quenching.

CASE-HARDEN (*v*). To harden a surface as described above or through the use of potassium cyanide.

CHAMFER (*v*). To bevel an external edge or corner.

CHASE (*v*). To cut screw threads on a lathe using a chaser, a tool shaped to the profile of a thread.

CHILL (*v*). To cool the surface of a casting suddenly so that the surface will be white and hard.

CHIP (*v*). To cut away or remove surface defects with a chisel.

COLLAR (*n*). A cylindrical part fitted on a shaft to prevent a sliding movement.

COLOR-HARDEN (*v*). (See CASE-HARDEN.) A piece is color-hardened mainly for the sake of appearance.

CORE (*v*). To form a hole or hollow cavity in a casting through the use of a core.

COUNTERBORE (*v*). To enlarge the end of a cylindrical hole to a certain depth, as is often done to accommodate the head of a fillister head screw. (*n*) The name of the tool used to produce the enlargement.

COUNTERSINK (*v*). To form a conical enlargement at the end of a cylindrical hole to accommodate the head of a screw or rivet. (*n*) The name of the tool used to form a conical shaped enlargement.

CROWN (*n*). The angular or curved contour of the outer surface of a part such as on a pulley.

DIE (*n*). A metal block used for forming or stamping operations. A thread-cutting tool for producing external threads.

DIE CASTING (*n*). A casting which has been produced by forcing a molten alloy having an aluminum, copper, zinc, tin, or lead base into a metal mold composed of two halves.

DIE STAMPING (*n*). A piece which has been cut or formed from sheet metal through the use of a die.

DRAW (*v*). To form metal, which may be either cold or hot, by a distorting or stretching process. To temper steel by gradual or intermittent quenching.

DRILL (*v*). To form a cylindrical hole in metal. (*n*) A revolving cutting tool designed for cutting at the point.

DROP FORGING (*n*). A piece formed while hot between two dies under a drop hammer.

FACE (*v*). To machine on a lathe a flat face which is perpendicular to the axis of rotation of the piece.

FEATHER (*n*). A rectangular sliding key which permits a pulley to move along the shaft parallel to its axis.

FILE (*v*). To shape, finish, or trim with a fine-toothed metal cutting tool which is used with the hands.

FILLET (*n*). A rounded filling which increases the strength at the junction of two surfaces which form an internal angle.

FIT (*n*). The tightness of adjustment between the contacting surfaces of mating parts.

FLANGE (*n*). The top and bottom member of a beam. A projecting rim added on the end of a pipe or fitting for making a connection.

FORGE (*v*). To shape hot metals by hammering, using a hand-hammer or machine.

GALVANIZE (*v*). To coat steel or iron by immersion in a bath of zinc.

GRADUATE (*v*). To mark off or divide a scale into intervals.

GRIND (*v*). To finish a surface through the action of a revolving abrasive wheel.

KERF (*n*). A groove or channel cut by a saw or some other tool.

KEY (*n*). A piece used between a shaft and a hub to prevent the movement of one relative to the other.

KEYWAY or KEYSEAT (*n*). A longitudinal groove cut in a shaft or a hub to receive a key. A key rests in a keyseat and slides in a keyway.

KNURL (*v*). To roughen a cylindrical surface to produce a better grip for the fingers.

LAP (*v*). To finish or polish with a piece of soft metal, wood, or leather impregnated with an abrasive.

LUG (*n*). A projection or ear which has been cast or forged as a portion of a piece to provide a support or to allow the attachment of another part.

MALLEABLE CASTING (*n*). A casting which has been annealed to toughen it.

MILL (*v*). To machine a piece on a milling machine by means of a rotating toothed cutter.

NECK (*v*). To cut a circumferential groove around a shaft.

PACK-HARDEN (*v*). To case-carburize and harden.

PAD (*n*). A low projecting surface, usually rectangular.

PEEN (*v*). To stretch or bend over metal using the peen end (ball end) of a hammer.

PICKLE (*v*). To remove scale and rust from a casting or forging by immersing it in an acid bath.

PLANE (*v*). To machine a flat surface on a planer, a machine having a fixed tool and a reciprocating bed.

POLISH (*v*). To make a surface smooth and lustrous through the use of a fine abrasive.

PUNCH (*v*). To perforate a thin piece of metal by shearing out a circular wad with a nonrotating tool under pressure.

REAM (*v*). To finish a hole to an exact size using a rotating fluted cutting tool known as a reamer.

RIB (*n*). A thin component of a part that acts as a brace or support.

RIVET (*n*). A headed shank which more or less permanently unites two pieces. (*v*) To fasten steel plates with rivets.

ROUND (*n*). A rounded external corner on a casting.

SANDBLAST (*v*). To clean the surface of castings or forgings by means of sand forced from a nozzle at a high velocity.

SHEAR (*v*). To cut off sheet or bar metal through the shearing action of two blades.

SHIM (*n*). A thin metal plate which is inserted between two surfaces for the purpose of adjustment.

SPLINE (*n*). A keyway, usually for a feather key. (See FEATHER.)

SPOTFACE (*v*). To finish a round spot on the rough surface of a casting at a drilled hole for the purpose of providing a smooth seat for a bolt or screw head.

SPOT WELD (*v*). To weld two overlapping metal sheets in spots by means of the heat of resistance to an electric current between a pair of electrodes.

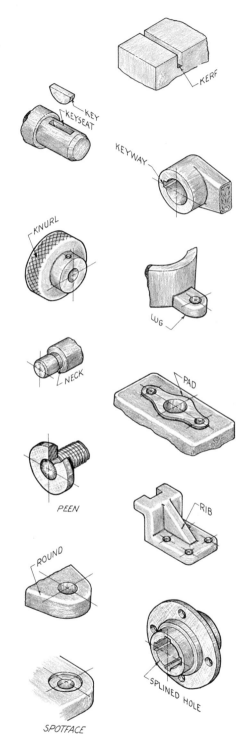

STEEL CASTING (*n*). A casting made of cast iron to which scrap steel has been added.

SWAGE (*v*). To form metal with a "swage block," a tool so constructed that through hammering or pressure the work may be made to take a desired shape.

SWEAT (*v*). To solder together by clamping the pieces in contact with soft solder between and then heating.

TACK WELD (*n*). A weld of short intermittent sections.

TAP (*v*). To cut an internal thread, by hand or with power, by screwing into the hole a fluted tapered tool having thread-cutting edges.

TEMPER (*v*). To reduce the hardness of a piece of hardened steel through reheating and sudden quenching.

TEMPLATE (*n*). A pattern cut to a desired shape which is used in layout work to establish shearing lines, to locate holes, etc.

TUMBLE (*v*). To clean and smooth castings and forgings through contact in a revolving barrel. To further the results, small pieces of scrap are added.

TURN (*v*). To turn-down or machine a cylindrical surface on a lathe.

UNDERCUT (*n*). A recessed cut.

UPSET (*v*). To increase the diameter or form a shoulder on a piece during forging.

WELD (*v*). To join two pieces of metal by pressure or hammering after heating to the fusion point.

UNDERCUT

Bibliography of Engineering Drawing and Allied Subjects

AERONAUTICAL DRAFTING AND ENGINEERING

Anderson, N. H., *Aircraft Layout and Detail Design*, 2nd ed. McGraw-Hill.
Katz, H. H., *Aircraft Drafting*. Macmillan.
LeMaster, C. A., *Aircraft Sheet Metal Work*. American Technical Society.
Svensen, C. L., *A Manual of Aircraft Drafting*. Van Nostrand.

ARCHITECTURAL DRAWING

Hornung, W. J., *Architectural Drafting*. Prentice-Hall.
Crane, T., *Architectural Construction*. Wiley.
Ramsey, C. G., and H. R. Sleeper, *Architectural Graphic Standards*. Wiley.

CASTINGS

Campbell, H. I., *Metal Castings*. Wiley.
Morris, J. L., *Metal Castings*. Prentice-Hall.

CATALOGS (Instruments)

Alteneder, Theo., and Sons, Philadelphia, Pa.
Boston Gear Works, Inc., Chicago, Ill. (Gears, etc.)
Crane Co., Chicago, Ill. (Pipe Fittings.)
Elliott, B. K., Co., Pittsburgh, Pa.
Eugene Dietzgen Co., Chicago, Ill.
Frederic Post Co., Chicago, Ill.
Keuffel & Esser Co., Hoboken, N. J.
New Departure, Bristol, Conn. (Ball-Bearing Handbook.)
Timken Roller Bearing Co., Canton, Ohio. (Roller Bearings.)
U.S. Blue Co., Chicago, Ill.

DESCRIPTIVE GEOMETRY

Grant, H. E., *Practical Descriptive Geometry*. McGraw-Hill.
Hood, G. J., and A. S. Palmerlee, *Geometry of Engineering Drawing*, 4th ed. McGraw-Hill.
Johnson, L. O., and I. Wladaver, *Elements of Descriptive Geometry*. Prentice-Hall.
Paré, E. G., R. O. Loving, and I. L. Hill, *Descriptive Geometry*. Macmillan.
Street, W. E., *Technical Descriptive Geometry*. Van Nostrand.
Warner, F. M., and M. McNeary, *Applied Descriptive Geometry*, 5th ed. McGraw-Hill.
Watts, E. F., and J. T. Rule, *Descriptive Geometry*. Prentice-Hall.
Wellman, B. L., *Technical Descriptive Geometry*, 2nd ed. McGraw-Hill.

DESCRIPTIVE GEOMETRY PROBLEMS

Hood, G. J., and A. S. Palmerlee, *Problem Sheets*. McGraw-Hill.
Paré, E. G., and others, *Descriptive Geometry Worksheets*. Macmillan.
Wiedhaas, E. R., *Applied Descriptive Geometry Problems*. McGraw-Hill.

ELECTRICAL DRAWING

Baer, C. J., *Electrical and Electronic Drawing*. McGraw-Hill.

ENGINEERING DRAWING

Arnold, J. N., *Introductory Graphics.* McGraw-Hill.
Black, E. D., *Graphical Communication.* McGraw-Hill.
French, T. E., and C. J. Vierck, *Engineering Drawing*, 9th ed. McGraw-Hill.
Giesecke, F. E., and others, *Technical Drawing*, 4th ed. Macmillan.
Hoelscher, R. P., and others, *Industrial Production Illustration*, 2nd ed. McGraw-Hill.
Hoelscher, R. P., and C. H. Springer, *Engineering Drawing and Geometry*, 2nd ed. Wiley.
Hornung, W. J., *Mechanical Drafting.* Prentice-Hall.
Levens, A. S., *Graphics in Engineering and Science.* Wiley.
Luzadder, W. J., *Fundamentals of Engineering Drawing*, 4th ed. Prentice-Hall.
————, *Fundamentos de Dibujo Para Ingenieros*, 2nd ed. Compañia Editorial Continental.
————, *Technical Drafting Essentials*, 2nd ed. Prentice-Hall.
Mochel, M. G., *Fundamentals of Engineering Graphics.* Prentice-Hall.
Svensen, C. L., *Drafting for Engineers*, 2nd ed. Van Nostrand.
————, *Essentials of Drafting*, 3rd ed. Van Nostrand.
Turner, W. W., and others, *Basic Engineering Drawing.* Ronald.
Zozzoro, F., *Engineering Drawing*, 2nd ed. McGraw-Hill.

ENGINEERING DRAWING PROBLEMS

Giesecke, F. E., and others, *Technical Drawing Problems*, 3rd ed. Macmillan.
Grant, H. E., *Engineering Drawing Problems.* McGraw-Hill.
Higbee, F. G., and J. M. Russ, *Engineering Drawing Problems.* Johnsen.
Johnson, L. O., and I. Wladaver, *Engineering Drawing Problems.* Prentice-Hall.
Levens, A. S., and A. E. Edstrom, *Problems in Mechanical Drawing.* McGraw-Hill.
Luzadder, W. J., J. N. Arnold, and F. H. Thompson, *Problems in Engineering Drawing*, 4th ed. Prentice-Hall.
————, R. H. Hammond, C. J. Rogers, and C. T. Seeley, *Problems for Engineering Graphics.* Prentice-Hall.
————, and R. E. Bolles, *Problems in Drafting Fundamentals.* Prentice-Hall.
Spencer, H. C., and I. L. Hill, *Technical Drawing Problems.* Macmillan.
Turner, W. W., *Basic Problems in Engineering Drawing.* Ronald.
Vierck, C. J., and R. I. Hang, *Engineering Drawing Problems.* McGraw-Hill.

GRAPHICAL REPRESENTATION AND COMPUTATION

Adams, D. P., *Index of Nomograms.* Wiley.
Davis, D. S., *Empirical Equations and Nomography.* McGraw-Hill.
Douglass, R. D., and D. P. Adams, *Elements of Nomography.* McGraw-Hill.
Hoelscher, R. P., J. N. Arnold, and S. H. Pierce, *Graphic Aids in Engineering Computation.* McGraw-Hill.
Levens, A. S., *Nomography*, 2nd ed. Wiley.
————, *Graphics in Engineering and Science.* Wiley.
Lipka, J., *Graphical and Mechanical Computation.* Wiley.
Robinson, A. H., *Elements of Cartography.* Wiley.

HANDBOOKS

American Institute of Steel Construction, *Steel Construction.* New York.
Crocker, S., *Piping Handbook*, 4th ed. McGraw-Hill.
Kent, W., *Mechanical Engineer's* Handbook, 12th ed. Wiley.
Knowlton, A. E., *Standard Handbook for Electrical Engineers*, 9th ed. McGraw-Hill.
Le Grand, R., Ed., *New American Machinist's Handbook.* McGraw-Hill.
Marks, L. S., *Mechanical Engineers' Handbook*, 6th ed. McGraw-Hill.

McNeese, D. C., and A. L. Hoag, *Engineering and Technical Handbook.* Prentice-Hall.
Oberg, E., and F. D. Jones, *Machinery's Handbook,* 16th ed. Industrial Press.
O'Rourke, C. E., *General Engineering Handbook,* 2nd ed. McGraw-Hill.
Perry, J. H., *Chemical Engineers' Handbook,* 3rd ed. McGraw-Hill.
Wilson, F. W., Ed., *Tool Engineers' Handbook,* 2nd ed. McGraw-Hill.

JIG AND FIXTURE DESIGN

Colvin, F. H., and L. L. Haas, *Jigs and Fixtures,* 5th ed. McGraw-Hill.
Hinman, C. W., *Die Engineering Layouts and Formulas.* McGraw-Hill.
Jones, F. D., *Jig and Fixture Design.* Industrial Press.

KINEMATICS—MACHINE DESIGN

Faires, V. M., *Design of Machine Elements,* 3rd ed. Macmillan.
Hinkle, R. T., *Kinematics of Machines.* Prentice-Hall.
Lent, D., *Analysis and Design of Mechanisms.* Prentice-Hall.
Maleev, V. L., *Machine Design,* 3rd ed. International.
Norman, C. A., E. S. Ault, and I. F. Zarobsky, *Fundamentals of Machine Design.* Macmillan.
Sahag, L. M., *Kinematics of Machines,* rev. ed. Ronald.
Spotts, M. F., *Design of Machine Elements,* 2nd ed. Prentice-Hall.

LETTERING

De Garmo, E. P., and F. Jonassen, *Technical Lettering.* Macmillan.
French, T. E., and W. D. Turnbill, *Lessons in Lettering,* 3rd ed. Vols. 1 and 2. McGraw-Hill.

MACHINE DRAWING

Svensen, C. L., *Machine Drawing,* 3rd ed. Van Nostrand.

MAP AND TOPOGRAPHIC DRAWING

Sloane, R. C., and I. M. Montz, *Elements of Topographic Drawing,* 2nd ed. McGraw-Hill.

PERSPECTIVE

Lawson, P. J., *Practical Perspective Drawing.* McGraw-Hill.
Turner, W. W., *Simplified Perspective.* Ronald.

PIPE

Crocker, S., *Piping Hand Book,* 4th ed. McGraw-Hill.
Day, L. J., *Standard Plumbing Details.* Wiley.
Thompson, C. H., *Fundamentals of Pipe Drafting.* Wiley.

SHOP PRACTICE

Begeman, M. L., *Manufacturing Processes,* 4th ed. Wiley.
Boston, O. W., *Metal Processing,* 2nd ed. Wiley.
Doyle, L. E., *Metal Machining.* Prentice-Hall.
———, J. L. Leach, J. L. Morris, and G. F. Schrader, *Manufacturing Processes and Materials for Engineers.* Prentice-Hall.
Marek, C. T., *Fundamentals in the Production and Design of Castings.* Wiley.
Stieri, E., *Fundamentals of Machine Shop Practice.* Prentice-Hall.
Young, J. F., *Materials and Processes,* 2nd ed. Wiley.

SKETCHING

Katz, H., *Technical Sketching and Visualization for Engineers.* Macmillan.
Turner, W. W., *Freehand Sketching for Engineers.* Ronald.
Zipprich, A. E., *Freehand Drafting for Technical Sketching,* 3rd ed. Van Nostrand.

SLIDE RULE

Arnold, J. N., *The Slide Rule.* Prentice-Hall.
Machovina, P. E., *A Manual for the Slide Rule.* McGraw-Hill.

STRUCTURAL DRAFTING

American Institute of Steel Construction, *Structural Shop Drafting* (Vols. 1–3). New York.
Bishop, C. T., *Structural Drafting.* Wiley.
Lothers, S. E., *Design in Structural Steel.* Prentice-Hall.

TECHNICAL DICTIONARY

Tweney, C. F., and L. E. C. Hughes, *Chamber's Technical Dictionary,* 3rd rev. ed. Macmillan.

TECHNICAL ILLUSTRATION

Gibby, J. C., *Technical Illustration.* American Technical Society.
Thomas, T. A., *Technical Illustration.* McGraw-Hill.

TOOL DESIGN

Cole, C. B., *Tool Design.* American Technical Society.
Donaldson, C., and G. H. LeCain, *Tool Design,* 2nd ed. Harper.
Doyle, L. E., *Tool Engineering, Analysis and Procedure.* Prentice-Hall.
Jeffries, W. R., *Tool Design.* Prentice-Hall.

WELDING

Lincoln Electric Co., *Simple Blueprint Reading.* Cleveland.
————, *Procedure Handbook of Arc Welding Design and Practice.* Cleveland.
Morris, J. L., *Welding Processes and Procedures.* Prentice-Hall.
————, *Welding Principles for Engineers.* Prentice-Hall.

TEXT FILMS

"Engineering Drawing." 7 films, 6 strips. McGraw-Hill.
"Engineering Drawing." 16 films. Purdue University.

703

704

708

709

713